Spreadsheet Modeling & Decision Analysis

Revised 5th Edition

Cliff Ragsdale

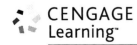

CENGAGE
Learning™

Australia • Brazil • Japan • Korea • Mexico • Singapore • Spain • United Kingdom • United States

**Spreadsheet Modeling & Decision Analysis:
Revised 5th Edition**

Cliff Ragsdale

Executive Editors:
Michele Baird

Maureen Staudt

Michael Stranz

Project Development Manager:
Linda deStefano

Senior Marketing Coordinators:
Sara Mercurio

Lindsay Shapiro

Senior Production / Manufacturing Manager:
Donna M. Brown

PreMedia Services Supervisor:
Rebecca A. Walker

Rights & Permissions Specialist:
Kalina Hintz

Cover Image:
Getty Images*

© 2008, Cengage Learning

For product information and technology assistance, contact us at
Cengage Learning Customer & Sales Support, 1-800-354-9706

For permission to use material from this text or product,
submit all requests online at **cengage.com/permissions**
Further permissions questions can be emailed to
permissionrequest@cengage.com

ISBN-13: 978-0-324-61414-5

ISBN-10: 0-324-61414-4

Cengage Learning
5191 Natorp Boulevard
Mason, Ohio 45040
USA

Cengage Learning is a leading provider of customized learning solutions with office locations around the globe, including Singapore, the United Kingdom, Australia, Mexico, Brazil, and Japan. Locate your local office at:
international.cengage.com/region

Cengage Learning products are represented in Canada by Nelson Education, Ltd.

For your lifelong learning solutions, visit **custom.cengage.com**

Visit our corporate website at **cengage.com**

Printed in the United States of America

Contents

Chapter 1

Introduction to Modeling and Decision Analysis

1.0 Introduction

This book is titled *Spreadsheet Modeling and Decision Analysis: A Practical Introduction to Management Science*, so let's begin by discussing exactly what this title means. By the very nature of life, all of us must continually make decisions that we hope will solve problems and lead to increased opportunities for ourselves or the organizations for which we work. But making good decisions is rarely an easy task. The problems faced by decision makers in today's competitive, fast-paced business environment are often extremely complex and can be addressed by numerous possible courses of action. Evaluating these alternatives and choosing the best course of action represents the essence of decision analysis.

During the past decade, millions of business people discovered that one of the most effective ways to analyze and evaluate decision alternatives involves using electronic spreadsheets to build computer models of the decision problems they face. A **computer model** is a set of mathematical relationships and logical assumptions implemented in a computer as a representation of some real-world decision problem or phenomenon. Today, electronic spreadsheets provide the most convenient and useful way for business people to implement and analyze computer models. Indeed, most business people probably would rate the electronic spreadsheet as their most important analytical tool apart from their brain! Using a **spreadsheet model** (a computer model implemented via a spreadsheet), a business person can analyze decision alternatives before having to choose a specific plan for implementation.

This book introduces you to a variety of techniques from the field of management science that can be applied in spreadsheet models to assist in the decision-analysis process. For our purposes, we will define **management science** as a field of study that uses computers, statistics, and mathematics to solve business problems. It involves applying the methods and tools of science to management and decision making. It is the science of making better decisions. Management science is also sometimes referred to as operations research or decision science. See Figure 1.1 for a summary of how management science has been applied successfully in several real-world situations.

In the not too distant past, management science was a highly specialized field that generally could be practiced only by those who had access to mainframe computers and who possessed an advanced knowledge of mathematics and computer programming languages. However, the proliferation of powerful personal computers (PCs) and the development of easy-to-use electronic spreadsheets have made the tools of management science far more practical and available to a much larger audience. Virtually

Home Runs in Management Science

Over the past decade, scores of operations research and management science projects saved companies millions of dollars. Each year, the Institute For Operations Research and the Management Sciences (INFORMS) sponsors the Franz Edelman Awards competition to recognize some of the most outstanding OR/MS projects during the past year. Here are some of the "home runs" from the 2004 Edelman Awards (described in *Interfaces*, Vol. 31, No. 1, January–February, 2005).

- At the turn of the century, **Motorola** faced a crisis due to economic conditions in its marketplaces; the company needed to reduce costs dramatically and quickly. A natural target was its purchases of goods and services, as these expenses account for more than half of Motorola's costs. Motorola decided to create an Internet-based system to conduct multi-step negotiations and auctions for supplier negotiation. The system can handle complex bids and constraints, such as bundled bids, volume-based discounts, and capacity limits. In addition, it can optimize multi-product, multi-vendor awards subject to these constraints and nonlinear price schedules. **Benefits:** In 2003, Motorola used this system to source 56 percent of its total spending, with 600 users and a total savings exceeding $600 million.

- **Waste Management** is the leading company in North America in the waste-collection industry. The company has a fleet of over 26,000 vehicles for collecting waste from nearly 20 million residential customers, plus another two million commercial customers. To improve trash collection and make its operations more efficient, Waste Management implemented a vehicle-routing application to optimize its collection routes. **Benefits:** The successful deployment of this system brought benefits including the elimination of nearly 1,000 routes within one year of implementation and an estimated annual savings of $44 million.

- Hong Kong has the world's busiest port. Its largest terminal operator, **Hong Kong International Terminals** (HIT), has the busiest container terminal in the world serving over 125 ships per week, with 10 berths at which container ships dock, and 122 yard cranes to move containers around the 227 acres of storage yard. Thousands of trucks move containers into and out of the storage yard each day. HIT implemented a decision-support system (with several embedded decision models and algorithms) to guide its operational decisions concerning the number and deployment of trucks for moving containers, the assignment of yard cranes, and the storage locations for containers. **Benefits:** The cumulative effect of this system has led to a 35 percent reduction in container handling costs, a 50 percent increase in throughput, and a 30 percent improvement in vessel turnaround time.

- The **John Deere Company** sells lawn equipment, residential and commercial mowers, and utility tractors through a network of 2,500 dealers, supported by five Deere warehouses. Each dealer stocks about 100 products, leading to approximately 250,000 product-stocking locations. Furthermore, demand is quite seasonal and stochastic. Deere implemented a system designed to optimize large-scale multi-echelon, non-stationary stochastic inventory systems. Deere runs the system each week to obtain recommended stocking levels for each product for each stocking location for each week over a 26-week planning horizon. **Benefits:** The impact of the application has been remarkable, leading to an inventory reduction of nearly one billion dollars and improving customer-service levels.

everyone who uses a spreadsheet today for model building and decision making is a practitioner of management science—whether they realize it or not.

1.1 The Modeling Approach to Decision Making

The idea of using models in problem solving and decision analysis is really not new, and certainly is not tied to the use of computers. At some point, all of us have used a modeling approach to make a decision. For example, if you ever have moved into a dormitory, apartment, or house, you undoubtedly faced a decision about how to arrange the furniture in your new dwelling. There probably were several different arrangements to consider. One arrangement might give you the most open space but require that you build a loft. Another might give you less space but allow you to avoid the hassle and expense of building a loft. To analyze these different arrangements and make a decision, you did not build the loft. You more likely built a **mental model** of the two arrangements, picturing what each looked like in your mind's eye. Thus, a simple mental model is sometimes all that is required to analyze a problem and make a decision.

For more complex decision problems, a mental model might be impossible or insufficient, and other types of models might be required. For example, a set of drawings or blueprints for a house or building provides a **visual model** of the real-world structure. These drawings help illustrate how the various parts of the structure will fit together when it is completed. A road map is another type of visual model because it assists a driver in analyzing the various routes from one location to another.

You probably also have seen car commercials on television showing automotive engineers using **physical models** or **scale models** to study the aerodynamics of various car designs, to find the shape that creates the least wind resistance and maximizes fuel economy. Similarly, aeronautical engineers use scale models of airplanes to study the flight characteristics of various fuselage and wing designs. And civil engineers might use scale models of buildings and bridges to study the strengths of different construction techniques.

Another common type of model is a **mathematical model**, which uses mathematical relationships to describe or represent an object or decision problem. Throughout this book we will study how various mathematical models can be implemented and analyzed on computers using spreadsheet software. But before we move to an in-depth discussion of spreadsheet models, let's look at some of the more general characteristics and benefits of modeling.

1.2 Characteristics and Benefits of Modeling

Although this book focuses on mathematical models implemented in computers via spreadsheets, the examples of non-mathematical models given earlier are worth discussing a bit more because they help illustrate several important characteristics and benefits of modeling in general. First, the models mentioned earlier are usually simplified versions of the object or decision problem they represent. To study the aerodynamics of a car design, we do not need to build the entire car complete with engine and stereo. Such components have little or no effect on aerodynamics. So, although a model is often a simplified representation of reality, the model is useful as long as it is valid. A **valid** model is one that accurately represents the relevant characteristics of the object or decision problem being studied.

Second, it is often less expensive to analyze decision problems using a model. This is especially easy to understand with respect to scale models of big-ticket items such as cars and planes. Besides the lower financial cost of building a model, the analysis of a model can help avoid costly mistakes that might result from poor decision making. For example, it is far less costly to discover a flawed wing design using a scale model of an aircraft than after the crash of a fully loaded jetliner.

Frank Brock, former executive vice president of the Brock Candy Company, related the following story about blueprints his company prepared for a new production facility. After months of careful design work he proudly showed the plans to several of his production workers. When he asked for their comments, one worker responded, "It's a fine looking building, Mr. Brock, but that sugar valve looks like it's about twenty feet away from the steam valve." "What's wrong with that?" asked Brock. "Well, nothing," said the worker, "except that I have to have my hands on both valves at the same time!"[1] Needless to say, it was far less expensive to discover and correct this "little" problem using a visual model before pouring the concrete and laying the pipes as originally planned.

Third, models often deliver needed information on a more timely basis. Again, it is relatively easy to see that scale models of cars or airplanes can be created and analyzed more quickly than their real-world counterparts. Timeliness is also an issue when vital data will not become available until later. In these cases, we might create a model to help predict the missing data to assist in current decision making.

Fourth, models are frequently helpful in examining things that would be impossible to do in reality. For example, human models (crash dummies) are used in crash tests to see what might happen to an actual person if a car were to hit a brick wall at a high speed. Likewise, models of DNA can be used to visualize how molecules fit together. Both of these are difficult, if not impossible, to do without the use of models.

Finally, and probably most important, models allow us to gain insight and understanding about the object or decision problem under investigation. The ultimate purpose of using models is to improve decision making. As you will see, the process of building a model can shed important light and understanding on a problem. In some cases, a decision might be made while building the model as a previously misunderstood element of the problem is discovered or eliminated. In other cases, a careful analysis of a completed model might be required to "get a handle" on a problem and gain the insights needed to make a decision. In any event, the insight gained from the modeling process ultimately leads to better decision making.

1.3 Mathematical Models

As mentioned earlier, the modeling techniques in this book differ quite a bit from scale models of cars and planes, or visual models of production plants. The models we will build use mathematics to describe a decision problem. We use the term "mathematics" in its broadest sense, encompassing not only the most familiar elements of math, such as algebra, but also the related topic of logic.

---

[1] Colson, Charles and Jack Eckerd, *Why America Doesn't Work* (Denver, Colorado: Word Publishing, 1991), 146–147.

Now, let's consider a simple example of a mathematical model:

$$\text{PROFIT} = \text{REVENUE} - \text{EXPENSES} \qquad\qquad \textbf{1.1}$$

Equation 1.1 describes a simple relationship between revenue, expenses, and profit. It is a mathematical relationship that describes the operation of determining profit—or a mathematical model of profit. Of course, not all models are this simple, but taken piece by piece, the models we will discuss are not much more complex than this one.

Frequently, mathematical models describe functional relationships. For example, the mathematical model in equation 1.1 describes a functional relationship between revenue, expenses, and profit. Using the symbols of mathematics, this functional relationship is represented as:

$$\text{PROFIT} = f(\text{REVENUE, EXPENSES}) \qquad\qquad \textbf{1.2}$$

In words, the previous expression means "profit is a function of revenue and expenses." We also could say that profit *depends* on (or is *dependent* on) revenue and expenses. Thus, the term PROFIT in equation 1.2 represents a **dependent** variable, whereas REVENUE and EXPENSES are **independent** variables. Frequently, compact symbols (such as A, B, and C) are used to represent variables in an equation such as 1.2. For instance, if we let Y, X_1, and X_2 represent PROFIT, REVENUE, and EXPENSES, respectively, we could rewrite equation 1.2 as follows:

$$Y = f(X_1, X_2) \qquad\qquad \textbf{1.3}$$

The notation $f(\bullet)$ represents the function that defines the relationship between the dependent variable Y and the independent variables X_1 and X_2. In the case of determining PROFIT from REVENUE and EXPENSES, the mathematical form of the function $f(\bullet)$ is quite simple: $f(X_1, X_2) = X_1 - X_2$. However, in many other situations we will model, the form of $f(\bullet)$ is quite complex and might involve many independent variables. But regardless of the complexity of $f(\bullet)$ or the number of independent variables involved, many of the decision problems encountered in business can be represented by models that assume the general form,

$$Y = f(X_1, X_2, \ldots, X_k) \qquad\qquad \textbf{1.4}$$

In equation 1.4, the dependent variable Y represents some bottom-line performance measure of the problem we are modeling. The terms $X_1, X_2, \ldots, X_k$ represent the different independent variables that play some role or have some effect in determining the value of Y. Again, $f(\bullet)$ is the function (possibly quite complex) that specifies or describes the relationship between the dependent and independent variables.

The relationship expressed in equation 1.4 is very similar to what occurs in most spreadsheet models. Consider a simple spreadsheet model to calculate the monthly payment for a car loan, as shown in Figure 1.2.

The spreadsheet in Figure 1.2 contains a variety of **input** cells (for example, purchase price, down payment, trade-in, term of loan, annual interest rate) that correspond conceptually to the independent variables $X_1, X_2, \ldots, X_k$ in equation 1.4. Similarly, a variety of mathematical operations are performed using these input cells in a manner analogous to the function $f(\bullet)$ in equation 1.4. The results of these mathematical operations determine the value of some **output** cell in the spreadsheet (for example, monthly payment) that corresponds to the dependent variable Y in equation 1.4. Thus, there is a direct correspondence between equation 1.4 and the spreadsheet in Figure 1.2. This type of correspondence exists for most of the spreadsheet models in this book.

FIGURE 1.2

Example of a simple spreadsheet model

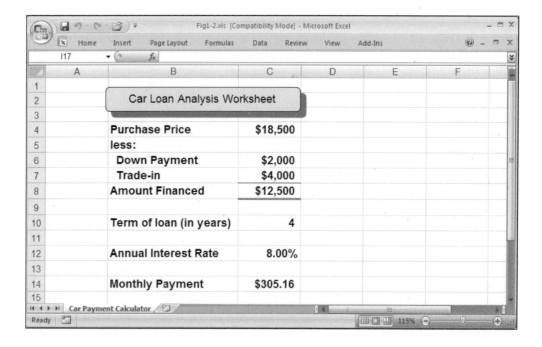

1.4 Categories of Mathematical Models

Not only does equation 1.4 describe the major elements of mathematical or spreadsheet models, but it also provides a convenient means for comparing and contrasting the three categories of modeling techniques presented in this book—Prescriptive Models, Predictive Models, and Descriptive Models. Figure 1.3 summarizes the characteristics and techniques associated with each of these categories.

In some situations, a manager might face a decision problem involving a very precise, well-defined functional relationship $f(\cdot)$ between the independent variables $X_1, X_2, \ldots, X_k$ and the dependent variable Y. If the values for the independent variables are under

FIGURE 1.3

Categories and characteristics of management science modeling techniques

	Model Characteristics		
Category	**Form of $f(\cdot)$**	**Values of Independent Variables**	**Management Science Techniques**
Prescriptive Models	known, well-defined	known or under decision maker's control	Linear Programming, Networks, Integer Programming, CPM, Goal Programming, EOQ, Nonlinear Programming
Predictive Models	unknown, ill-defined	known or under decision maker's control	Regression Analysis, Time Series Analysis, Discriminant Analysis
Descriptive Models	known, well-defined	unknown or uncertain	Simulation, Queuing, PERT, Inventory Models

the decision maker's control, the decision problem in these types of situations boils down to determining the values of the independent variables $X_1, X_2, \ldots, X_k$ that produce the best possible value for the dependent variable Y. These types of models are called **Prescriptive Models** because their solutions tell the decision maker what actions to take. For example, you might be interested in determining how a given sum of money should be allocated to different investments (represented by the independent variables) to maximize the return on a portfolio without exceeding a certain level of risk.

A second category of decision problems is one in which the objective is to predict or estimate what value the dependent variable Y will take on when the independent variables $X_1, X_2, \ldots, X_k$ take on specific values. If the function $f(\cdot)$ relating the dependent and independent variables is known, this is a very simple task—simply enter the specified values for $X_1, X_2, \ldots, X_k$ into the function $f(\cdot)$ and compute Y. In some cases, however, the functional form of $f(\cdot)$ might be unknown and must be estimated for the decision maker to make predictions about the dependent variable Y. These types of models are called **Predictive Models**. For example, a real estate appraiser might know that the value of a commercial property (Y) is influenced by its total square footage (X_1) and age (X_2), among other things. However, the functional relationship $f(\cdot)$ that relates these variables to one another might be unknown. By analyzing the relationship between the selling price, total square footage, and age of other commercial properties, the appraiser might be able to identify a function $f(\cdot)$ that relates these two variables in a reasonably accurate manner.

The third category of models you are likely to encounter in the business world is called **Descriptive Models**. In these situations, a manager might face a decision problem that has a very precise, well-defined functional relationship $f(\cdot)$ between the independent variables $X_1, X_2, \ldots, X_k$ and the dependent variable Y. However, there might be great uncertainty as to the exact values that will be assumed by one or more of the independent variables $X_1, X_2, \ldots, X_k$. In these types of problems, the objective is to describe the outcome or behavior of a given operation or system. For example, suppose a company is building a new manufacturing facility and has several choices about the type of machines to put in the new plant, and also various options for arranging the machines. Management might be interested in studying how the various plant configurations would affect on-time shipments of orders (Y), given the uncertain number of orders that might be received (X_1) and the uncertain due dates (X_2) that might be required by these orders.

1.5 The Problem-Solving Process

Throughout our discussion, we have said that the ultimate goal in building models is to help managers make decisions that solve problems. The modeling techniques we will study represent a small but important part of the total problem-solving process. To become an effective modeler, it is important to understand how modeling fits into the entire problem-solving process.

Because a model can be used to represent a decision problem or phenomenon, we might be able to create a visual model of the phenomenon that occurs when people solve problems—what we call the problem-solving process. Although a variety of models could be equally valid, the one in Figure 1.4 summarizes the key elements of the problem-solving process and is sufficient for our purposes.

The first step of the problem-solving process, identifying the problem, is also the most important. If we do not identify the correct problem, all the work that follows will amount to nothing more than wasted effort, time, and money. Unfortunately, identifying

FIGURE 1.4

*A visual model of
the problem-
solving process*

the problem to solve is often not as easy as it seems. We know that a problem exists when there is a gap or disparity between the present situation and some desired state of affairs. However, we usually are not faced with a neat, well-defined problem. Instead, we often find ourselves facing a "mess"![2] Identifying the real problem involves gathering a lot of information and talking with many people to increase our understanding of the mess. We must then sift through all this information and try to identify the root problem or problems causing the mess. Thus, identifying the real problem (and not just the symptoms of the problem) requires insight, some imagination, time, and a good bit of detective work.

The end result of the problem-identification step is a well-defined statement of the problem. Simply defining a problem well will often make it much easier to solve. Having identified the problem, we turn our attention to creating or formulating a model of the problem. Depending on the nature of the problem, we might use a mental model, a visual model, a scale model, or a mathematical model. Although this book focuses on mathematical models, this does not mean that mathematical models are always applicable or best. In most situations, the best model is the simplest model that accurately reflects the relevant characteristic or essence of the problem being studied.

We will discuss several different management science modeling techniques in this book. It is important that you not develop too strong a preference for any one technique. Some people have a tendency to want to formulate every problem they face as a model that can be solved by their favorite management science technique. This simply will not work.

As indicated in Figure 1.3, there are fundamental differences in the types of problems a manager might face. Sometimes, the values of the independent variables affecting a problem are under the manager's control; sometimes they are not. Sometimes, the form of the functional relationship $f(\cdot)$ relating the dependent and independent variables is well-defined, and sometimes it is not. These fundamental characteristics of the problem should guide your selection of an appropriate management science modeling technique. Your goal at the model-formulation stage is to select a modeling technique that fits your problem, rather than trying to fit your problem into the required format of a pre-selected modeling technique.

After you select an appropriate representation or formulation of your problem, the next step is to implement this formulation as a spreadsheet model. We will not dwell on the implementation process now because that is the focus of the remainder of this book. After you verify that your spreadsheet model has been implemented accurately, the next step in the problem-solving process is to use the model to analyze the problem it represents. The main focus of this step is to generate and evaluate alternatives that might lead to a solution. This often involves playing out a number of scenarios or asking several "What if?" questions. Spreadsheets are particularly helpful in analyzing mathematical models in this manner. In a well-designed spreadsheet model, it should be fairly simple to change some of the assumptions in the model to see what might happen in different

---

[2] This characterization is borrowed from Chapter 5, James R. Evans, *Creative Thinking in the Decision and Management Sciences* (Cincinnati, Ohio: South-Western Publishing, 1991), 89–115.

situations. As we proceed, we will highlight some techniques for designing spreadsheet models that facilitate this type of "what if?" analysis. "What if?" analysis is also very appropriate and useful when working with nonmathematical models.

The end result of analyzing a model does not always provide a solution to the actual problem being studied. As we analyze a model by asking various "What if?" questions, it is important to test the feasibility and quality of each potential solution. The blueprints that Frank Brock showed to his production employees represented the end result of his analysis of the problem he faced. He wisely tested the feasibility and quality of this alternative before implementing it, and discovered an important flaw in his plans. Thus, the testing process can give important new insights into the nature of a problem. The testing process is also important because it provides the opportunity to double-check the validity of the model. At times, we might discover an alternative that appears to be too good to be true. This could lead us to find that some important assumption has been left out of the model. Testing the results of the model against known results (and simple common sense) helps ensure the structural integrity and validity of the model. After analyzing the model, we might discover that we need to go back and modify the model.

The last step of the problem-solving process, implementation, is often the most difficult. By their very nature, solutions to problems involve people and change. For better or for worse, most people resist change. However, there are ways to minimize the seemingly inevitable resistance to change. For example, it is wise, if possible, to involve anyone who will be affected by the decision in all steps of the problem-solving process. This not only helps develop a sense of ownership and understanding of the ultimate solution, but it also can be the source of important information throughout the problem-solving process. As the Brock Candy story illustrates, even if it is impossible to include those affected by the solution in all steps, their input should be solicited and considered before a solution is accepted for implementation. Resistance to change and new systems also can be eased by creating flexible, user-friendly interfaces for the mathematical models that often are developed in the problem-solving process.

Throughout this book, we focus mostly on the model formulation, implementation, analysis, and testing steps of the problem-solving process, summarized in Figure 1.4. Again, this does not imply that these steps are more important than the others. If we do not identify the correct problem, the best we can hope for from our modeling effort is "the right answer to the wrong question," which does not solve the real problem. Similarly, even if we do identify the problem correctly and design a model that leads to a perfect solution, if we cannot implement the solution, then we still have not solved the problem. Developing the interpersonal and investigative skills required to work with people in defining the problem and implementing the solution are as important as the mathematical modeling skills you will develop by working through this book.

1.6 Anchoring and Framing Effects

At this point, some of you reading this book are probably thinking it is better to rely on subjective judgment and intuition rather than models when making decisions. Indeed, most nontrivial decision problems involve some issues that are difficult or impossible to structure and analyze in the form of a mathematical model. These unstructurable aspects of a decision problem might require the use of judgment and intuition. However, it is important to realize that human cognition is often flawed and can lead to incorrect judgments and irrational decisions. Errors in human judgment often arise because of what psychologists term **anchoring** and **framing** effects associated with decision problems.

Anchoring effects arise when a seemingly trivial factor serves as a starting point (or anchor) for estimations in a decision-making problem. Decision makers adjust their estimates from this anchor but nevertheless remain too close to the anchor and usually under-adjust. In a classic psychological study on this issue, one group of subjects were asked to individually estimate the value of $1 \times 2 \times 3 \times 4 \times 5 \times 6 \times 7 \times 8$ (without using a calculator). Another group of subjects were each asked to estimate the value of $8 \times 7 \times 6 \times 5 \times 4 \times 3 \times 2 \times 1$. The researchers hypothesized that the first number presented (or perhaps the product of the first three or four numbers) would serve as a mental anchor. The results supported the hypothesis. The median estimate of subjects shown the numbers in ascending sequence $(1 \times 2 \times 3 \ldots)$ was 512, whereas the median estimate of subjects shown the sequence in descending order $(8 \times 7 \times 6 \ldots)$ was 2,250. Of course, the order of multiplication for these numbers is irrelevant and the product of both series is the same: 40,320.

Framing effects refer to how a decision maker views or perceives the alternatives in a decision problem—often involving a win/loss perspective. The way a problem is framed often influences the choices made by a decision maker and can lead to irrational behavior. For example, suppose you have just been given $1,000 but must choose one of the following alternatives: (A_1) Receive an additional $500 with certainty, or ($B_1$) Flip a fair coin and receive an additional $1,000 if heads occurs or $0 additional is tails occurs. Here, alternative A_1 is a "sure win" and is the alternative most people prefer. Now suppose you have been given $2,000 and must choose one of the following alternatives: (A_2) Give back $500 immediately, or ($B_2$) Flip a fair coin and give back $0 if heads occurs or $1,000 if tails occurs. When the problem is framed this way, alternative A_2 is a "sure loss" and many people who previously preferred alternative A_1 now opt for alternative B_2 (because it holds a chance of avoiding a loss). However, Figure 1.5 shows a single decision tree for these two scenarios making it clear that, in both cases, the "A" alternative guarantees a total payoff of $1,500, whereas the "B" alternative offers a 50% chance of a $2,000 total payoff and a 50% chance of a $1,000 total payoff. (Decision trees will be covered in greater detail in a later chapter.) A purely rational decision maker should focus on the consequences of his or her choices and consistently select the same alternative, regardless of how the problem is framed.

Whether we want to admit it or not, we are all prone to make errors in estimation due to anchoring effects and may exhibit irrationality in decision making due to framing effects. As a result, it is best to use computer models to do what they are best at (i.e., modeling structurable portions of a decision problem) and let the human brain do what it is best at (i.e., dealing with the unstructurable portion of a decision problem).

FIGURE 1.5

Decision tree for framing effects

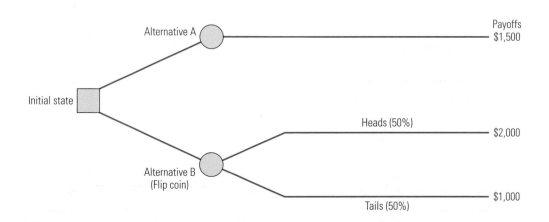

1.7 Good Decisions vs. Good Outcomes

The goal of the modeling approach to problem solving is to help individuals make good decisions. But good decisions do not always result in good outcomes. For example, suppose the weather report on the evening news predicts a warm, dry, sunny day tomorrow. When you get up and look out the window tomorrow morning, suppose there is not a cloud in sight. If you decide to leave your umbrella at home and subsequently get soaked in an unexpected afternoon thundershower, did you make a bad decision? Certainly not. Unforeseeable circumstances beyond your control caused you to experience a bad outcome, but it would be unfair to say that you made a bad decision. Good decisions sometimes result in bad outcomes. See Figure 1.6 for the story of another good decision having a bad outcome.

The modeling techniques presented in this book can help you make good decisions, but cannot guarantee that good outcomes will always occur as a result of those decisions. Even when a good decision is made, luck often plays a role in determining whether a good or bad outcome occurs. However, using a structured, modeling approach to decision making should produce good outcomes more frequently than making decisions in a more haphazard manner.

1.8 Summary

This book introduces you to a variety of techniques from the field of management science that can be applied in spreadsheet models to assist in decision analysis and problem solving. This chapter discussed how spreadsheet models of decision problems can be used to analyze the consequences of possible courses of action before a particular alternative is selected for implementation. It described how models of decision problems differ in several important characteristics and how you should select a modeling technique that is most appropriate for the type of problem being faced. Finally, it discussed how spreadsheet modeling and analysis fit into the problem-solving process.

FIGURE 1.6

A good decision with a bad outcome

Andre-Francois Raffray thought he had a great deal in 1965 when he agreed to pay a 90-year-old woman named Jeanne Calment $500 a month until she died to acquire her grand apartment in Arles, northwest of Marseilles in the south of France—a town Vincent Van Gogh once roamed. Buying apartments "for life" is common in France. The elderly owner gets to enjoy a monthly income from the buyer who gambles on getting a real estate bargain—betting the owner doesn't live too long. Upon the owner's death, the buyer inherits the apartment regardless of how much was paid. But in December of 1995, Raffray died at age 77, having paid more than $180,000 for an apartment he never got to live in.

On the same day, Calment, then the world's oldest living person at 120, dined on foie gras, duck thighs, cheese, and chocolate cake at her nursing home near the sought-after apartment. And she does not need to worry about losing her $500 monthly income. Although the amount Raffray already paid is twice the apartment's current market value, his widow is obligated to keep sending the monthly check to Calment. If Calment also outlives her, then the Raffray children will have to pay. "In life, one sometimes makes bad deals," said Calment of the outcome of Raffray's decision. (Source: *The Savannah Morning News*, 12/29/95.)

1.9 References

Edwards, J., P. Finlay, and J. Wilson. "The role of the OR specialist in 'do it yourself' spreadsheet development." *European Journal of Operational Research*, vol. 127, no. 1, 2000.

Forgione, G. "Corporate MS Activities: An Update." *Interfaces*, vol. 13, no. 1, 1983.

Hall, R. "What's So Scientific about MS/OR?" *Interfaces*, vol. 15, 1985.

Hastie, R. and R. M. Dawes. *Rational Choice in an Uncertain World*, Sage Publications, 2001.

Schrage, M. *Serious Play*, Harvard Business School Press, 2000.

Sonntag, C. and Grossman, T. "End-User Modeling Improves R&D Management at AgrEvo Canada, Inc." *Interfaces*, vol. 29, no. 5, 1999.

THE WORLD OF MANAGEMENT SCIENCE

"Business Analysts Trained in Management Science Can Be a Secret Weapon in a CIO's Quest for Bottom-Line Results."

Efficiency nuts. These are the people you see at cocktail parties explaining how the host could disperse that crowd around the popular shrimp dip if he would divide it into three bowls and place them around the room. As she draws the improved traffic flow on a paper napkin, you notice that her favorite word is "optimize"—a tell-tale sign that she has studied the field of "operations research" or "management science" (also known as OR/MS).

OR/MS professionals are driven to solve logistics problems. This trait might not make them the most popular people at parties, but it is exactly what today's information systems (IS) departments need to deliver more business value. Experts say that smart IS executives will learn to exploit the talents of these mathematical wizards in their quest to boost a company's bottom line.

According to Ron J. Ponder, chief information officer (CIO) at Sprint Corp. in Kansas City, Mo., and former CIO at Federal Express Corp., "If IS departments had more participation from operations research analysts, they would be building much better, richer IS solutions." As someone who has a Ph.D. in operations research and who built the renowned package-tracking systems at Federal Express, Ponder is a true believer in OR/MS. Ponder and others say analysts trained in OR/MS can turn ordinary information systems into money-saving, decision-support systems, and are ideally suited to be members of the business process reengineering team. "I've always had an operations research department reporting to me, and it's been invaluable. Now I'm building one at Sprint," says Ponder.

The Beginnings

OR/MS got its start in World War II, when the military had to make important decisions about allocating scarce resources to various military operations. One of the first business applications for computers in the 1950s was to solve operations research problems for the petroleum industry. A technique called linear programming was used to figure out how to blend gasoline for the right flash point, viscosity, and octane in the most economical way. Since then, OR/MS has spread throughout business and government, from designing efficient drive-thru window operations for Burger King Corp. to creating ultrasophisticated computerized stock trading systems.

A classic OR/MS example is the crew scheduling problem faced by all major airlines. How do you plan the itineraries of 8,000 pilots and 17,000 flight attendants when there is an astronomical number of combinations of planes, crews, and cities? The OR/MS analysts at United Airlines came up with a scheduling system called Paragon that attempts to minimize the amount of paid time that crews spend waiting for flights. Their model factors in constraints such as labor agreement provisions and Federal Aviation Administration regulations, and is projected to save the airline at least $1 million a year.

OR/MS and IS

Somewhere in the 1970s, the OR/MS and IS disciplines went in separate directions. "The IS profession has had less and less contact with the operations research folks . . . and IS lost a powerful intellectual driver," says Peter G. W. Keen, executive director of the International Center for Information Technologies in Washington, D.C. However, many feel that now is an ideal time for the two disciplines to rebuild some bridges.

Today's OR/MS professionals are involved in a variety of IS-related fields, including inventory management, electronic data interchange, supply chain management, IT security, computer-integrated manufacturing, network management, and practical applications of artificial intelligence. Furthermore, each side needs something the other side has: OR/MS analysts need corporate data to plug into their models, and the IS folks need to plug the OR/MS models into their strategic information systems. At the same time, CIOs need intelligent applications that enhance the bottom line and make them heroes with the chief executive officer.

OR/MS analysts can develop a model of how a business process works now and simulate how it could work more efficiently in the future. Therefore, it makes sense to have an OR/MS analyst on the interdisciplinary team that tackles business process reengineering projects. In essence, OR/MS professionals add more value to the IS infrastructure by building "tools that really help decision makers analyze complex situations," says Andrew B. Whinston, director of the Center for Information Systems Management at the University of Texas at Austin.

Although IS departments typically believe their job is done if they deliver accurate and timely information, Thomas M. Cook, president of American Airlines Decision Technologies, Inc. says that adding OR/MS skills to the team can produce intelligent systems that actually recommend solutions to business problems. One of the big success stories at Cook's operations research shop is a "yield management" system that decides how much to overbook and how to set prices for each seat so that a plane is filled up and profits are maximized. The yield management system deals with more than 250 decision variables and accounts for a significant amount of American Airlines' revenue.

Where to Start

So how can the CIO start down the road toward collaboration with OR/MS analysts? If the company already has a group of OR/MS professionals, the IS department can draw on their expertise as internal consultants. Otherwise, the CIO can simply hire a few OR/MS wizards, throw a problem at them, and see what happens. The payback may come surprisingly quickly. As one former OR/MS professional put it: "If I couldn't save my employer the equivalent of my own salary in the first month of the year, then I wouldn't feel like I was doing my job."

Adapted from: Mitch Betts, "Efficiency Einsteins," *ComputerWorld*, March 22, 1993, p. 64.

Questions and Problems

1. What is meant by the term decision analysis?
2. Define the term computer model.
3. What is the difference between a spreadsheet model and a computer model?
4. Define the term management science.
5. What is the relationship between management science and spreadsheet modeling?
6. What kinds of spreadsheet applications would not be considered management science?
7. In what ways do spreadsheet models facilitate the decision-making process?
8. What are the benefits of using a modeling approach to decision making?
9. What is a dependent variable?
10. What is an independent variable?
11. Can a model have more than one dependent variable?
12. Can a decision problem have more than one dependent variable?
13. In what ways are prescriptive models different from descriptive models?
14. In what ways are prescriptive models different from predictive models?
15. In what ways are descriptive models different from predictive models?
16. How would you define the words description, prediction, and prescription? Carefully consider what is unique about the meaning of each word.
17. Identify one or more mental models you have used. Can any of them be expressed mathematically? If so, identify the dependent and independent variables in your model.
18. Consider the spreadsheet model shown in Figure 1.2. Is this model descriptive, predictive, or prescriptive in nature, or does it not fall into any of these categories?
19. What are the steps in the problem-solving process?
20. Which step in the problem-solving process do you think is most important? Why?
21. Must a model accurately represent every detail of a decision situation to be useful? Why or why not?
22. If you were presented with several different models of a given decision problem, which would you be most inclined to use? Why?
23. Describe an example in which business or political organizations may use anchoring effects to influence decision making.
24. Describe an example in which business or political organizations may use framing effects to influence decision making.
25. Suppose sharks have been spotted along the beach where you are vacationing with a friend. You and your friend have been informed of the shark sightings and are aware of the damage a shark attack can inflict on human flesh. You both decide (individually) to go swimming anyway. You are promptly attacked by a shark while your friend has a nice time body surfing in the waves. Did you make a good or bad decision? Did your friend make a good or bad decision? Explain your answer.
26. Describe an example in which a well-known business, political, or military leader made a good decision that resulted in a bad outcome, or a bad decision that resulted in a good outcome.

CASE 1.1   # Patrick's Paradox

Patrick's luck had changed overnight—but not his skill at mathematical reasoning. The day after graduating from college he used the $20 that his grandmother had given him as a graduation gift to buy a lottery ticket. He knew that his chances of winning the lottery were extremely low and it probably was not a good way to spend this money. But he also remembered from the class he took in management science that bad decisions sometimes result in good outcomes. So he said to himself, "What the heck? Maybe this bad decision will be the one with a good outcome." And with that thought, he bought his lottery ticket.

The next day Patrick pulled the crumpled lottery ticket out of the back pocket of his blue jeans and tried to compare his numbers to the winning numbers printed in the paper. When his eyes finally came into focus on the numbers they also just about popped out of his head. He had a winning ticket! In the ensuing days he learned that his share of the jackpot would give him a lump sum payout of about $500,000 after taxes. He knew what he was going to do with part of the money: buy a new car, pay off his college loans, and send his grandmother on an all-expenses-paid trip to Hawaii. But he also knew that he couldn't continue to hope for good outcomes to arise from more bad decisions. So he decided to take half of his winnings and invest it for his retirement.

A few days later, Patrick was sitting around with two of his fraternity buddies, Josh and Peyton, trying to figure out how much money his new retirement fund might be worth in 30 years. They were all business majors in college and remembered from their finance class that if you invest p dollars for n years at an annual interest rate of i percent then in n years you would have $p(1 + i)^n$ dollars. So they figure that if Patrick invested $250,000 for 30 years in an investment with a 10% annual return then in 30 years he would have $4,362,351 (that is, $250,000(1 + 0.10)^{30}$).

But after thinking about it a little more, they all agreed that it would be unlikely for Patrick to find an investment that would produce a return of exactly 10% each and every year for the next 30 years. If any of this money is invested in stocks then some years the return might be higher than 10% and some years it would probably be lower. So to help account for the potential variability in the investment returns Patrick and his friends came up with a plan; they would assume he could find an investment that would produce an annual return of 17.5% seventy percent of the time and a return (or actually a loss) of -7.5% thirty percent of the time. Such an investment should produce an average annual return of $0.7(17.5\%) + 0.3(-7.5\%) = 10\%$. Josh felt certain that this meant Patrick could still expect his $250,000 investment to grow to $4,362,351 in 30 years (because $250,000(1 + 0.10)^{30} = \$4,362,351$).

After sitting quietly and thinking about it for a while, Peyton said that he thought Josh was wrong. The way Peyton looked at it, Patrick should see a 17.5% return in 70% of the 30 years (or $0.7(30) = 21$ years) and a -7.5% return in 30% of the 30 years (or $0.3(30) = 9$ years). So, according to Peyton, that would mean Patrick should have $250,000(1 + 0.175)^{21}(1 - 0.075)^9 = \$3,664,467$ after 30 years. But that's $697,884 less than what Josh says Patrick should have.

After listening to Peyton's argument, Josh said he thought Peyton was wrong because his calculation assumes that the "good" return of 17.5% would occur in each of the first 21 years and the "bad" return of -7.5% would occur in each of the last 9 years. But Peyton countered this argument by saying that the order of good and bad returns does not matter. The commutative law of arithmetic says that when you add or multiply numbers, the order doesn't matter (that is, $X + Y = Y + X$ and $X \times Y = Y \times X$). So Peyton says that because Patrick can expect 21 "good" returns and 9 "bad" returns and it doesn't matter in what order they occur, then the expected outcome of the investment should be $3,664,467 after 30 years.

Patrick is now really confused. Both of his friends' arguments seem to make perfect sense logically—but they lead to such different answers, and they can't both be right. What really worries Patrick is that he is starting his new job as a business analyst in a couple of weeks. And if he can't reason his way to the right answer in a relatively simple problem like this, what is he going to do when he encounters the more difficult problems awaiting him the business world? Now he really wishes he had paid more attention in his management sciences class.

So what do you think? Who is right, Josh or Peyton? And more important, why?

Chapter 2

Introduction to Optimization and Linear Programming

2.0 Introduction

Our world is filled with limited resources. The amount of oil we can pump out of the earth is limited. The amount of land available for garbage dumps and hazardous waste is limited and, in many areas, diminishing rapidly. On a more personal level, each of us has a limited amount of time in which to accomplish or enjoy the activities we schedule each day. Most of us have a limited amount of money to spend while pursuing these activities. Businesses also have limited resources. A manufacturing organization employs a limited number of workers. A restaurant has a limited amount of space available for seating.

Deciding how best to use the limited resources available to an individual or a business is a universal problem. In today's competitive business environment, it is increasingly important to make sure that a company's limited resources are used in the most efficient manner possible. Typically, this involves determining how to allocate the resources in such a way as to maximize profits or minimize costs. **Mathematical programming** (MP) is a field of management science that finds the optimal, or most efficient, way of using limited resources to achieve the objectives of an individual or a business. For this reason, mathematical programming often is referred to as **optimization**.

2.1 Applications of Mathematical Optimization

To help you understand the purpose of optimization and the types of problems for which it can be used, let's consider several examples of decision-making situations in which MP techniques have been applied.

Determining Product Mix. Most manufacturing companies can make a variety of products. However, each product usually requires different amounts of raw materials and labor. Similarly, the amount of profit generated by the products varies. The manager of such a company must decide how many of each product to produce to maximize profits or to satisfy demand at minimum cost.

Manufacturing. Printed circuit boards, like those used in most computers, often have hundreds or thousands of holes drilled in them to accommodate the different electrical components that must be plugged into them. To manufacture these boards, a computer-controlled drilling machine must be programmed to drill in a given location, then move the drill bit to the next location and drill again. This process is repeated hundreds or thousands of times to complete all the holes on a circuit board. Manufacturers of these boards would benefit from determining the drilling order that minimizes the total distance the drill bit must be moved.

Routing and Logistics. Many retail companies have warehouses around the country that are responsible for keeping stores supplied with merchandise to sell. The amount of merchandise available at the warehouses and the amount needed at each store tends to fluctuate, as does the cost of shipping or delivering merchandise from the warehouses to the retail locations. Large amounts of money can be saved by determining the least costly method of transferring merchandise from the warehouses to the stores.

Financial Planning. The federal government requires individuals to begin withdrawing money from individual retirement accounts (IRAs) and other tax-sheltered retirement programs no later than age 70.5. There are various rules that must be followed to avoid paying penalty taxes on these withdrawals. Most individuals want to withdraw their money in a manner that minimizes the amount of taxes they must pay while still obeying the tax laws.

Optimization Is Everywhere

Going to Disney World this summer? Optimization will be your ubiquitous companion, scheduling the crews and planes, pricing the airline tickets and hotel rooms, even helping to set capacities on the theme park rides. If you use Orbitz to book your flights, an optimization engine sifts through millions of options to find the cheapest fares. If you get directions to your hotel from MapQuest, another optimization engine figures out the most direct route. If you ship souvenirs home, an optimization engine tells UPS which truck to put the packages on, exactly where on the truck the packages should go to make them fastest to load and unload, and what route the driver should follow to make his deliveries most efficiently.

(Adapted from: V. Postrel, "Operation Everything," *The Boston Globe*, June 27, 2004.)

2.2 Characteristics of Optimization Problems

These examples represent just a few areas in which MP has been used successfully. We will consider many other examples throughout this book. However, these examples give you some idea of the issues involved in optimization. For instance, each example involves one or more *decisions* that must be made: How many of each product should be produced? Which hole should be drilled next? How much of each product should be shipped from each warehouse to the various retail locations? How much money should an individual withdraw each year from various retirement accounts?

Also, in each example, restrictions, or *constraints*, are likely to be placed on the alternatives available to the decision maker. In the first example, when determining the number of products to manufacture, a production manager probably is faced with a limited amount of raw materials and a limited amount of labor. In the second example, the drill never should return to a position where a hole has already been drilled. In the third example, there is a physical limitation on the amount of merchandise a truck can carry from one warehouse to the stores on its route. In the fourth example, laws determine the minimum and maximum amounts that can be withdrawn from retirement accounts without incurring a penalty. There might be many other constraints for these examples. Indeed, it is not unusual for real-world optimization problems to have hundreds or thousands of constraints.

A final common element in each of the examples is the existence of some goal or *objective* that the decision maker considers when deciding which course of action is best. In the first example, the production manager can decide to produce several different product mixes given the available resources, but the manager probably will choose the mix of products that maximizes profits. In the second example, a large number of possible drilling patterns can be used, but the ideal pattern probably will involve moving the drill bit the shortest total distance. In the third example, there are numerous ways merchandise can be shipped from the warehouses to supply the stores, but the company probably will want to identify the routing that minimizes the total transportation cost. Finally, in the fourth example, individuals can withdraw money from their retirement accounts in many ways without violating the tax laws, but they probably want to find the method that minimizes their tax liability.

2.3 Expressing Optimization Problems Mathematically

From the preceding discussion, we know that optimization problems involve three elements: decisions, constraints, and an objective. If we intend to build a mathematical model of an optimization problem, we will need mathematical terms or symbols to represent each of these three elements.

2.3.1 DECISIONS

The decisions in an optimization problem often are represented in a mathematical model by the symbols $X_1, X_2, \ldots, X_n$. We will refer to $X_1, X_2, \ldots, X_n$ as the **decision variables** (or simply the variables) in the model. These variables might represent the quantities of different products the production manager can choose to produce. They might represent the amount of different pieces of merchandise to ship from a warehouse to a certain store. They might represent the amount of money to be withdrawn from different retirement accounts.

The exact symbols used to represent the decision variables are not particularly important. You could use $Z_1, Z_2, \ldots, Z_n$ or symbols like Dog, Cat, and Monkey to represent the decision variables in the model. The choice of which symbols to use is largely a matter of personal preference and might vary from one problem to the next.

2.3.2 CONSTRAINTS

The constraints in an optimization problem can be represented in a mathematical model in several ways. Three general ways of expressing the possible constraint relationships in an optimization problem are:

A "less than or equal to" constraint: $\quad f(X_1, X_2, \ldots, X_n) \leq b$

A "greater than or equal to" constraint: $\quad f(X_1, X_2, \ldots, X_n) \geq b$

An "equal to" constraint: $\quad f(X_1, X_2, \ldots, X_n) = b$

In each case, the **constraint** is some function of the decision variables that must be less than or equal to, greater than or equal to, or equal to some specific value (represented above by the letter b). We will refer to $f(X_1, X_2, \ldots, X_n)$ as the left-hand-side (LHS) of the constraint and to b as the right-hand-side (RHS) value of the constraint.

For example, we might use a "less than or equal to" constraint to ensure that the total labor used in producing a given number of products does not exceed the amount of available labor. We might use a "greater than or equal to" constraint to ensure that the total amount of money withdrawn from a person's retirement accounts is at least the minimum amount required by the IRS. You can use any number of these constraints to represent a given optimization problem depending on the requirements of the situation.

2.3.3 OBJECTIVE

The objective in an optimization problem is represented mathematically by an objective function in the general format:

$$\text{MAX (or MIN):} \quad f(X_1, X_2, \ldots, X_n)$$

The **objective function** identifies some function of the decision variables that the decision maker wants to either MAXimize or MINimize. In our earlier examples, this function might be used to describe the total profit associated with a product mix, the total distance the drill bit must be moved, the total cost of transporting merchandise, or a retiree's total tax liability.

The mathematical formulation of an optimization problem can be described in the general format:

$$\text{MAX (or MIN):} \quad f_0(X_1, X_2, \ldots, X_n) \tag{2.1}$$
$$\text{Subject to:} \quad f_1(X_1, X_2, \ldots, X_n) \leq b_1 \tag{2.2}$$
$$\vdots$$
$$f_k(X_1, X_2, \ldots, X_n) \geq b_k \tag{2.3}$$
$$\vdots$$
$$f_m(X_1, X_2, \ldots, X_n) = b_m \tag{2.4}$$

This representation identifies the objective function (equation 2.1) that will be maximized (or minimized) and the constraints that must be satisfied (equations 2.2 through 2.4). Subscripts added to the f and b in each equation emphasize that the functions describing the objective and constraints can all be different. The goal in optimization is to find the values of the decision variables that maximize (or minimize) the objective function without violating any of the constraints.

2.4 Mathematical Programming Techniques

Our general representation of an MP model is just that—general. You can use many kinds of functions to represent the objective function and the constraints in an MP model. Of course, you always should use functions that accurately describe the objective and constraints of the problem you are trying to solve. Sometimes, the functions in a model are linear in nature (that is, they form straight lines or flat surfaces); other times, they are nonlinear (that is, they form curved lines or curved surfaces). Sometimes, the optimal values of the decision variables in a model must take on integer values (whole numbers); other times, the decision variables can assume fractional values.

Given the diversity of MP problems that can be encountered, many techniques have been developed to solve different types of MP problems. In the next several chapters, we will look at these MP techniques and develop an understanding of how they differ and when each should be used. We will begin by examining a technique called **linear programming** (LP), which involves creating and solving optimization problems with linear objective functions and linear constraints. LP is a very powerful tool that can be applied in many business situations. It also forms a basis for several other techniques discussed later and is, therefore, a good starting point for our investigation into the field of optimization.

2.5 An Example LP Problem

We will begin our study of LP by considering a simple example. You should not interpret this to mean that LP cannot solve more complex or realistic problems. LP has been used to solve extremely complicated problems, saving companies millions of dollars. However, jumping directly into one of these complicated problems would be like starting a marathon without ever having gone out for a jog—you would get winded and could be left behind very quickly. So we'll start with something simple.

> Blue Ridge Hot Tubs manufactures and sells two models of hot tubs: the Aqua-Spa and the Hydro-Lux. Howie Jones, the owner and manager of the company, needs to decide how many of each type of hot tub to produce during his next production cycle. Howie buys prefabricated fiberglass hot tub shells from a local supplier and adds the pump and tubing to the shells to create his hot tubs. (This supplier has the capacity to deliver as many hot tub shells as Howie needs.) Howie installs the same type of pump into both hot tubs. He will have only 200 pumps available during his next production cycle. From a manufacturing standpoint, the main difference between the two models of hot tubs is the amount of tubing and labor required. Each Aqua-Spa requires 9 hours of labor and 12 feet of tubing. Each Hydro-Lux requires 6 hours of labor and 16 feet of tubing. Howie expects to have 1,566 production labor hours and 2,880 feet of tubing available during the next production cycle. Howie earns a profit of $350 on each Aqua-Spa he sells and $300 on each Hydro-Lux he sells. He is confident that he can sell all the hot tubs he produces. The question is, how many Aqua-Spas and Hydro-Luxes should Howie produce if he wants to maximize his profits during the next production cycle?

2.6 Formulating LP Models

The process of taking a practical problem—such as determining how many Aqua-Spas and Hydro-Luxes Howie should produce—and expressing it algebraically in the form of an LP model is known as **formulating** the model. Throughout the next several chapters, you will see that formulating an LP model is as much an art as a science.

2.6.1 STEPS IN FORMULATING AN LP MODEL

There are some general steps you can follow to help make sure your formulation of a particular problem is accurate. We will walk through these steps using the hot tub example.

1. **Understand the problem.** This step appears to be so obvious that it hardly seems worth mentioning. However, many people have a tendency to jump into a problem and start writing the objective function and constraints before they really understand the problem. If you do not fully understand the problem you face, it is unlikely that your formulation of the problem will be correct.

    The problem in our example is fairly easy to understand: How many Aqua-Spas and Hydro-Luxes should Howie produce to maximize his profit, while using no more than 200 pumps, 1,566 labor hours, and 2,880 feet of tubing?

2. **Identify the decision variables.** After you are sure you understand the problem, you need to identify the decision variables. That is, what are the fundamental decisions that must be made to solve the problem? The answers to this question often will help you identify appropriate decision variables for your model. Identifying the decision variables means determining what the symbols $X_1, X_2, \ldots, X_n$ represent in your model.

    In our example, the fundamental decision Howie faces is this: How many Aqua-Spas and Hydro-Luxes should be produced? In this problem, we will let X_1 represent the number of Aqua-Spas to produce and X_2 represent the number of Hydro-Luxes to produce.

3. **State the objective function as a linear combination of the decision variables.** After determining the decision variables you will use, the next step is to create the objective function for the model. This function expresses the mathematical relationship between the decision variables in the model to be maximized or minimized.

    In our example, Howie earns a profit of \$350 on each Aqua-Spa (X_1) he sells and \$300 on each Hydro-Lux (X_2) he sells. Thus, Howie's objective of maximizing the profit he earns is stated mathematically as:

$$\text{MAX:} \quad 350X_1 + 300X_2$$

    For whatever values might be assigned to X_1 and X_2, the previous function calculates the associated total profit that Howie would earn. Obviously, Howie wants to maximize this value.

4. **State the constraints as linear combinations of the decision variables.** As mentioned earlier, there are usually some limitations on the values that can be assumed by the decision variables in an LP model. These restrictions must be identified and stated in the form of constraints.

    In our example, Howie faces three major constraints. Because only 200 pumps are available and each hot tub requires one pump, Howie cannot produce more than a total of 200 hot tubs. This restriction is stated mathematically as:

$$1X_1 + 1X_2 \le 200$$

    This constraint indicates that each unit of X_1 produced (that is, each Aqua-Spa built) will use one of the 200 pumps available—as will each unit of X_2 produced (that is, each Hydro-Lux built). The total number of pumps used (represented by $1X_1 + 1X_2$) must be less than or equal to 200.

    Another restriction Howie faces is that he has only 1,566 labor hours available during the next production cycle. Because each Aqua-Spa he builds (each unit of X_1) requires 9 labor hours and each Hydro-Lux (each unit of X_2) requires 6 labor hours, the constraint on the number of labor hours is stated as:

$$9X_1 + 6X_2 \le 1{,}566$$

The total number of labor hours used (represented by $9X_1 + 6X_2$) must be less than or equal to the total labor hours available, which is 1,566.

The final constraint specifies that only 2,880 feet of tubing is available for the next production cycle. Each Aqua-Spa produced (each unit of X_1) requires 12 feet of tubing, and each Hydro-Lux produced (each unit of X_2) requires 16 feet of tubing. The following constraint is necessary to ensure that Howie's production plan does not use more tubing than is available:

$$12X_1 + 16X_2 \leq 2,880$$

The total number of feet of tubing used (represented by $12X_1 + 16X_2$) must be less than or equal to the total number of feet of tubing available, which is 2,880.

5. **Identify any upper or lower bounds on the decision variables.** Often, simple upper or lower bounds apply to the decision variables. You can view upper and lower bounds as additional constraints in the problem.

In our example, there are simple lower bounds of zero on the variables X_1 and X_2 because it is impossible to produce a negative number of hot tubs. Therefore, the following two constraints also apply to this problem:

$$X_1 \geq 0$$
$$X_2 \geq 0$$

Constraints like these are often referred to as nonnegativity conditions and are quite common in LP problems.

2.7 Summary of the LP Model for the Example Problem

The complete LP model for Howie's decision problem can be stated as:

MAX:	$350X_1 + 300X_2$	**2.5**
Subject to:	$1X_1 + 1X_2 \leq 200$	**2.6**
	$9X_1 + 6X_2 \leq 1,566$	**2.7**
	$12X_1 + 16X_2 \leq 2,880$	**2.8**
	$1X_1 \geq 0$	**2.9**
	$1X_2 \geq 0$	**2.10**

In this model, the decision variables X_1 and X_2 represent the number of Aqua-Spas and Hydro-Luxes to produce, respectively. Our goal is to determine the values for X_1 and X_2 that maximize the objective in equation 2.5 while simultaneously satisfying all the constraints in equations 2.6 through 2.10.

2.8 The General Form of an LP Model

The technique of linear programming is so named because the MP problems to which it applies are linear in nature. That is, it must be possible to express all the functions in an

LP model as some weighted sum (or linear combination) of the decision variables. So, an LP model takes on the general form:

$$\text{MAX (or MIN):} \qquad c_1X_1 + c_2X_2 + \cdots + c_nX_n \qquad\qquad \textbf{2.11}$$

$$\text{Subject to:} \qquad a_{11}X_1 + a_{12}X_2 + \cdots + a_{1n}X_n \leq b_1 \qquad\qquad \textbf{2.12}$$

$$\vdots$$

$$a_{k1}X_1 + a_{k2}X_2 + \cdots + a_{kn}X_n \geq b_k \qquad\qquad \textbf{2.13}$$

$$\vdots$$

$$a_{m1}X_1 + a_{m2}X_2 + \cdots + a_{mn}X_n = b_m \qquad\qquad \textbf{2.14}$$

Up to this point, we have suggested that the constraints in an LP model represent some type of limited resource. Although this is frequently the case, in later chapters you will see examples of LP models in which the constraints represent things other than limited resources. The important point here is that *any* problem that can be formulated in the above fashion is an LP problem.

The symbols $c_1, c_2, \ldots, c_n$ in equation 2.11 are called **objective function coefficients** and might represent the marginal profits (or costs) associated with the decision variables $X_1, X_2, \ldots, X_n$, respectively. The symbol a_{ij} found throughout equations 2.12 through 2.14 represents the numeric coefficient in the ith constraint for variable X_j. The objective function and constraints of an LP problem represent different weighted sums of the decision variables. The b_i symbols in the constraints, once again, represent values that the corresponding linear combination of the decision variables must be less than or equal to, greater than or equal to, or equal to.

You should now see a direct connection between the LP model we formulated for Blue Ridge Hot Tubs in equations 2.5 through 2.10 and the general definition of an LP model given in equations 2.11 through 2.14. In particular, note that the various symbols used in equations 2.11 through 2.14 to represent numeric constants (that is, the c_j, a_{ij}, and b_i) were replaced by actual numeric values in equations 2.5 through 2.10. Also, note that our formulation of the LP model for Blue Ridge Hot Tubs did not require the use of "equal to" constraints. Different problems require different types of constraints, and you should use whatever types of constraints are necessary for the problem at hand.

2.9 Solving LP Problems: An Intuitive Approach

After an LP model has been formulated, our interest naturally turns to solving it. But before we actually solve our example problem for Blue Ridge Hot Tubs, what do you think is the optimal solution to the problem? Just by looking at the model, what values for X_1 and X_2 do you think would give Howie the largest profit?

Following one line of reasoning, it might seem that Howie should produce as many units of X_1 (Aqua-Spas) as possible because each of these generates a profit of $350, whereas each unit of X_2 (Hydro-Luxes) generates a profit of only $300. But what is the maximum number of Aqua-Spas that Howie could produce?

Howie can produce the maximum number of units of X_1 by making no units of X_2 and devoting all his resources to the production of X_1. Suppose we let $X_2 = 0$ in the model in equations 2.5 through 2.10 to indicate that no Hydro-Luxes will be produced.

What then is the largest possible value of X_1? If $X_2 = 0$, then the inequality in equation 2.6 tells us:

$$X_1 \leq 200 \qquad\qquad\qquad\qquad\qquad \textbf{2.15}$$

So we know that X_1 cannot be any greater than 200 if $X_2 = 0$. However, we also have to consider the constraints in equations 2.7 and 2.8. If $X_2 = 0$, then the inequality in equation 2.7 reduces to:

$$9X_1 \leq 1{,}566 \qquad\qquad\qquad\qquad\qquad \textbf{2.16}$$

If we divide both sides of this inequality by 9, we find that the previous constraint is equivalent to:

$$X_1 \leq 174 \qquad\qquad\qquad\qquad\qquad \textbf{2.17}$$

Now consider the constraint in equation 2.8. If $X_2 = 0$, then the inequality in equation 2.8 reduces to:

$$12X_1 \leq 2{,}880 \qquad\qquad\qquad\qquad\qquad \textbf{2.18}$$

Again, if we divide both sides of this inequality by 12, we find that the previous constraint is equivalent to:

$$X_1 \leq 240 \qquad\qquad\qquad\qquad\qquad \textbf{2.19}$$

So, if $X_2 = 0$, the three constraints in our model imposing upper limits on the value of X_1 reduce to the values shown in equations 2.15, 2.17, and 2.19. The most restrictive of these constraints is equation 2.17. Therefore, the maximum number of units of X_1 that can be produced is 174. In other words, 174 is the largest value X_1 can take on and still satisfy all the constraints in the model.

If Howie builds 174 units of X_1 (Aqua-Spas) and 0 units of X_2 (Hydro-Luxes), he will have used all of the labor that is available for production ($9X_1 = 1{,}566$ if $X_1 = 174$). However, he will have 26 pumps remaining ($200 - X_1 = 26$ if $X_1 = 174$) and 792 feet of tubing remaining ($2{,}880 - 12X_1 = 792$ if $X_1 = 174$). Also, notice that the objective function value (or total profit) associated with this solution is:

$$\$350X_1 + \$300X_2 = \$350 \times 174 + \$300 \times 0 = \$60{,}900$$

From this analysis, we see that the solution $X_1 = 174$, $X_2 = 0$ is a *feasible solution* to the problem because it satisfies all the constraints of the model. But is it the *optimal solution*? In other words, is there any other possible set of values for X_1 and X_2 that also satisfies all the constraints *and* results in a higher objective function value? As you will see, the intuitive approach to solving LP problems that we have taken here cannot be trusted because there actually is a *better* solution to Howie's problem.

2.10 Solving LP Problems: A Graphical Approach

The constraints of an LP model define the set of feasible solutions—or the **feasible region**—for the problem. The difficulty in LP is determining which point or points in the feasible region correspond to the best possible value of the objective function. For simple problems with only two decision variables, it is fairly easy to sketch the feasible region for the LP model and locate the optimal feasible point graphically. Because the graphical approach can be used only if there are two decision variables, it has limited practical use. However, it is an extremely good way to develop a basic understanding of the strategy involved in solving LP problems. Therefore, we will use the graphical approach to solve the simple problem faced by Blue Ridge Hot Tubs. Chapter 3 shows how to solve this and other LP problems using a spreadsheet.

To solve an LP problem graphically, first you must plot the constraints for the problem and identify its feasible region. This is done by plotting the *boundary lines* of the constraints and identifying the points that will satisfy all the constraints. So, how do we do this for our example problem (repeated below)?

$$\text{MAX:} \qquad 350X_1 + 300X_2 \qquad\qquad\qquad\qquad \textbf{2.20}$$
$$\text{Subject to:} \qquad 1X_1 + 1X_2 \leq 200 \qquad\qquad\qquad \textbf{2.21}$$
$$9X_1 + 6X_2 \leq 1{,}566 \qquad\qquad\qquad \textbf{2.22}$$
$$12X_1 + 16X_2 \leq 2{,}880 \qquad\qquad\qquad \textbf{2.23}$$
$$1X_1 \qquad\quad \geq 0 \qquad\qquad\qquad\qquad \textbf{2.24}$$
$$1X_2 \geq 0 \qquad\qquad\qquad\qquad \textbf{2.25}$$

2.10.1 PLOTTING THE FIRST CONSTRAINT

The boundary of the first constraint in our model, which specifies that no more than 200 pumps can be used, is represented by the straight line defined by the equation:

$$X_1 + X_2 = 200 \qquad\qquad\qquad\qquad \textbf{2.26}$$

If we can find any two points on this line, the entire line can be plotted easily by drawing a straight line through these points. If $X_2 = 0$, we can see from equation 2.26 that $X_1 = 200$. Thus, the point $(X_1, X_2) = (200, 0)$ must fall on this line. If we let $X_1 = 0$, from equation 2.26, it is easy to see that $X_2 = 200$. So, the point $(X_1, X_2) = (0, 200)$ also must fall on this line. These two points are plotted on the graph in Figure 2.1 and connected to form the straight line representing equation 2.26.

Note that the graph of the line associated with equation 2.26 actually extends beyond the X_1 and X_2 axes shown in Figure 2.1. However, we can disregard the points beyond these axes because the values assumed by X_1 and X_2 cannot be negative (because we also have the constraints given by $X_1 \geq 0$ and $X_2 \geq 0$).

The line connecting the points (0, 200) and (200, 0) in Figure 2.1 identifies the points (X_1, X_2) that satisfy the equality $X_1 + X_2 = 200$. But recall that the first constraint in the LP model is the inequality $X_1 + X_2 \leq 200$. Thus, after plotting the boundary line of a constraint, we must determine which area on the graph corresponds to feasible solutions for the original constraint. This can be done easily by picking an arbitrary point on either side of (*i.e.*, not on) the boundary line and checking whether it satisfies the original constraint. For example, the point $(X_1, X_2) = (0, 0)$ is not on the boundary line of the first constraint and also satisfies the first constraint. Therefore, the area of the graph on the same side of the boundary line as the point (0, 0) corresponds to the feasible solutions of our first constraint. This area of feasible solutions is shaded in Figure 2.1.

2.10.2 PLOTTING THE SECOND CONSTRAINT

Some of the feasible solutions to one constraint in an LP model usually will not satisfy one or more of the other constraints in the model. For example, the point $(X_1, X_2) = (200, 0)$ satisfies the first constraint in our model, but it does not satisfy the second constraint, which requires that no more than 1,566 labor hours be used (because $9 \times 200 + 6 \times 0 = 1{,}800$). So, what values for X_1 and X_2 will satisfy both of these

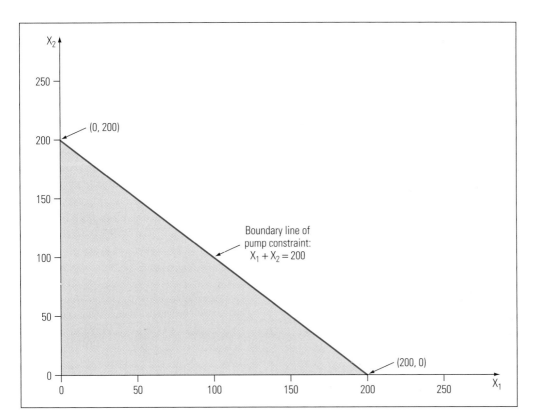

FIGURE 2.1

Graphical representation of the pump constraint

constraints simultaneously? To answer this question, we also need to plot the second constraint on the graph. This is done in the same manner as before—by locating two points on the boundary line of the constraint and connecting these points with a straight line.

The boundary line for the second constraint in our model is given by:

$$9X_1 + 6X_2 = 1,566 \qquad \textbf{2.27}$$

If $X_1 = 0$ in equation 2.27, then $X_2 = 1,566/6 = 261$. So, the point $(0, 261)$ must fall on the line defined by equation 2.27. Similarly, if $X_2 = 0$ in equation 2.27, then $X_1 = 1,566/9 = 174$. So, the point $(174, 0)$ also must fall on this line. These two points are plotted on the graph and connected with a straight line representing equation 2.27, as shown in Figure 2.2.

The line drawn in Figure 2.2 representing equation 2.27 is the boundary line for our second constraint. To determine the area on the graph that corresponds to feasible solutions to the second constraint, we again need to test a point on either side of this line to see if it is feasible. The point $(X_1, X_2) = (0, 0)$ satisfies $9X_1 + 6X_2 \leq 1,566$. Therefore, all points on the same side of the boundary line satisfy this constraint.

2.10.3 PLOTTING THE THIRD CONSTRAINT

To find the set of values for X_1 and X_2 that satisfies all the constraints in the model, we need to plot the third constraint. This constraint requires that no more than 2,880 feet of tubing be used in producing the hot tubs. Again, we will find two points on the graph that fall on the boundary line for this constraint and connect them with a straight line.

FIGURE 2.2

Graphical representation of the pump and labor constraints

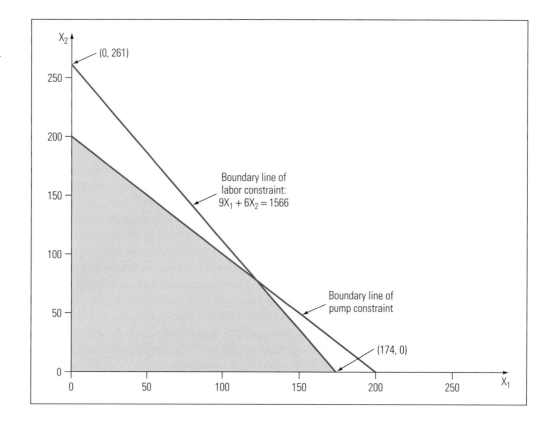

The boundary line for the third constraint in our model is:

$$12X_1 + 16X_2 = 2{,}880 \qquad\qquad \textbf{2.28}$$

If $X_1 = 0$ in equation 2.28, then $X_2 = 2{,}880/16 = 180$. So, the point $(0, 180)$ must fall on the line defined by equation 2.28. Similarly, if $X_2 = 0$ in equation 2.28, then $X_1 = 2{,}880/12 = 240$. So, the point $(240, 0)$ also must fall on this line. These two points are plotted on the graph and connected with a straight line representing equation 2.28, as shown in Figure 2.3.

Again, the line drawn in Figure 2.3 representing equation 2.28 is the boundary line for our third constraint. To determine the area on the graph that corresponds to feasible solutions to this constraint, we need to test a point on either side of this line to see if it is feasible. The point $(X_1, X_2) = (0, 0)$ satisfies $12X_1 + 16X_2 \leq 2{,}880$. Therefore, all points on the same side of the boundary line satisfy this constraint.

2.10.4 THE FEASIBLE REGION

It is now easy to see which points satisfy all the constraints in our model. These points correspond to the shaded area in Figure 2.3, labeled "Feasible Region." The **feasible region** is the set of points or values that the decision variables can assume and simultaneously satisfy all the constraints in the problem. Take a moment now to carefully compare the graphs in Figures 2.1, 2.2, and 2.3. In particular, notice that when we added the second constraint in Figure 2.2, some of the feasible solutions associated with the first constraint were eliminated because these solutions did not satisfy the second constraint. Similarly, when we added the third constraint in Figure 2.3, another portion of the feasible solutions for the first constraint was eliminated.

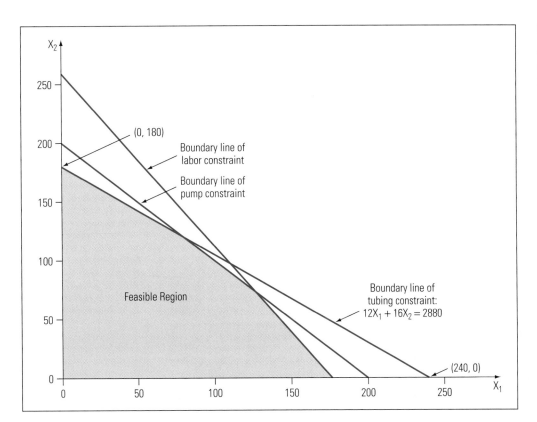

FIGURE 2.3

*Graphical
representation of
the feasible region*

2.10.5 PLOTTING THE OBJECTIVE FUNCTION

Now that we have isolated the set of feasible solutions to our LP problem, we need to determine which of these solutions is best. That is, we must determine which point in the feasible region will maximize the value of the objective function in our model. At first glance, it might seem that trying to locate this point is like searching for a needle in a haystack. After all, as shown by the shaded region in Figure 2.3, there are an *infinite* number of feasible solutions to this problem. Fortunately, it is easy to eliminate most of the feasible solutions in an LP problem from consideration. It can be shown that if an LP problem has an optimal solution with a finite objective function value, this solution always will occur at a point in the feasible region where two or more of the boundary lines of the constraints intersect. These points of intersection are sometimes called **corner points** or **extreme points** of the feasible region.

To see why the finite optimal solution to an LP problem occurs at an extreme point of the feasible region, consider the relationship between the objective function and the feasible region of our example LP model. Suppose we are interested in finding the values of X_1 and X_2 associated with a given level of profit, such as $35,000. Then, mathematically, we are interested in finding the points (X_1, X_2) for which our objective function equals $35,000, or where:

$$\$350X_1 + \$300X_2 = \$35,000 \qquad \qquad \textbf{2.29}$$

This equation defines a straight line, which we can plot on our graph. Specifically, if $X_1 = 0$ then, from equation 2.29, $X_2 = 116.67$. Similarly, if $X_2 = 0$ in equation 2.29, then $X_1 = 100$. So, the points $(X_1, X_2) = (0, 116.67)$ and $(X_1, X_2) = (100, 0)$ both fall on the line defining a profit level of $35,000. (Note that all the points on this line produce a profit level of $35,000.) This line is shown in Figure 2.4.

FIGURE 2.4

Graph showing values of X₁ and X₂ that produce an objective function value of $35,000

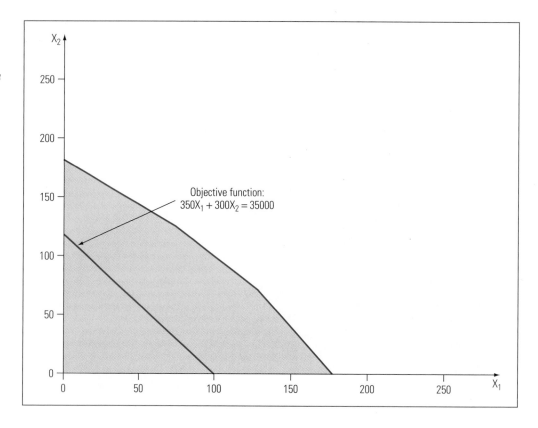

Now, suppose we are interested in finding the values of X_1 and X_2 that produce some higher level of profit, such as $52,500. Then, mathematically, we are interested in finding the points (X_1, X_2) for which our objective function equals $52,500, or where:

$$\$350X_1 + \$300X_2 = \$52,500 \qquad \textbf{2.30}$$

This equation also defines a straight line, which we could plot on our graph. If we do this, we'll find that the points $(X_1, X_2) = (0, 175)$ and $(X_1, X_2) = (150, 0)$ both fall on this line, as shown in Figure 2.5.

2.10.6 FINDING THE OPTIMAL SOLUTION USING LEVEL CURVES

The lines in Figure 2.5 representing the two objective function values are sometimes referred to as **level curves** because they represent different levels or values of the objective. Note that the two level curves in Figure 2.5 are *parallel* to one another. If we repeat this process of drawing lines associated with larger and larger values of our objective function, we will continue to observe a series of parallel lines shifting away from the origin—that is, away from the point $(0, 0)$. The very last level curve we can draw that still intersects the feasible region will determine the maximum profit we can achieve. This point of intersection, shown in Figure 2.6, represents the optimal feasible solution to the problem.

As shown in Figure 2.6, the optimal solution to our example problem occurs at the point where the largest possible level curve intersects the feasible region at a single point. This is the feasible point that produces the largest profit for Blue Ridge Hot Tubs. But how do we figure out exactly what point this is and how much profit it provides?

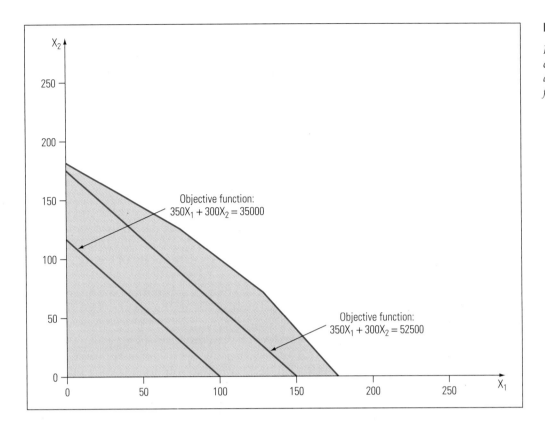

FIGURE 2.5

Parallel level curves for two different objective function values

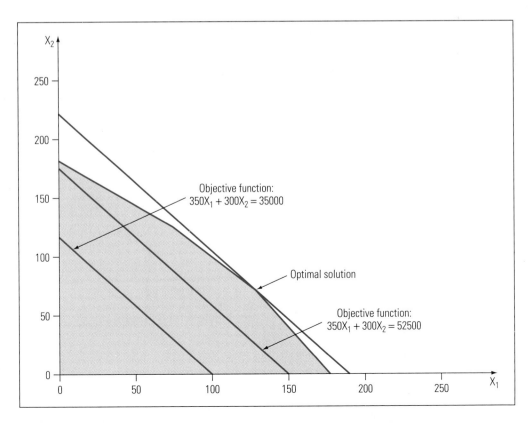

FIGURE 2.6

Graph showing optimal solution where the level curve is tangent to the feasible region

If you compare Figure 2.6 to Figure 2.3, you see that the optimal solution occurs where the boundary lines of the pump and labor constraints intersect (or are equal). Thus, the optimal solution is defined by the point (X_1, X_2) that simultaneously satisfies equations 2.26 and 2.27, which are repeated below:

$$X_1 + X_2 = 200$$
$$9X_1 + 6X_2 = 1{,}566$$

From the first equation, we easily conclude that $X_2 = 200 - X_1$. If we substitute this definition of X_2 into the second equation we obtain:

$$9X_1 + 6(200 - X_1) = 1{,}566$$

Using simple algebra, we can solve this equation to find that $X_1 = 122$. And because $X_2 = 200 - X_1$, we can conclude that $X_2 = 78$. Therefore, we have determined that the optimal solution to our example problem occurs at the point $(X_1, X_2) = (122, 78)$. This point satisfies all the constraints in our model and corresponds to the point in Figure 2.6 identified as the optimal solution.

The total profit associated with this solution is found by substituting the optimal values of $X_1 = 122$ and $X_2 = 78$ into the objective function. Thus, Blue Ridge Hot Tubs can realize a profit of $66,100 if it produces 122 Aqua-Spas and 78 Hydro-Luxes ($350 × 122 + $300 × 78 = $66,100). Any other production plan results in a lower total profit. In particular, note that the solution we found earlier using the intuitive approach (which produced a total profit of $60,900) is inferior to the optimal solution identified here.

2.10.7 FINDING THE OPTIMAL SOLUTION BY ENUMERATING THE CORNER POINTS

Earlier, we indicated that if an LP problem has a finite optimal solution, this solution always will occur at some corner point of the feasible region. So, another way of solving an LP problem is to identify all the corner points, or extreme points, of the feasible region and calculate the value of the objective function at each of these points. The corner point with the largest objective function value is the optimal solution to the problem.

This approach is illustrated in Figure 2.7, where the X_1 and X_2 coordinates for each of the extreme points are identified along with the associated objective function values. As expected, this analysis also indicates that the point $(X_1, X_2) = (122, 78)$ is optimal.

Enumerating the corner points to identify the optimal solution is often more difficult than the level curve approach because it requires that you identify the coordinates for *all* the extreme points of the feasible region. If there are many intersecting constraints, the number of extreme points can become rather large, making this procedure very tedious. Also, a special condition exists for which this procedure will not work. This condition, known as an unbounded solution, is described shortly.

2.10.8 SUMMARY OF GRAPHICAL SOLUTION TO LP PROBLEMS

To summarize this section, a two-variable LP problem is solved graphically by performing these steps:

1. Plot the boundary line of each constraint in the model.
2. Identify the feasible region, that is, the set of points on the graph that simultaneously satisfies all the constraints.

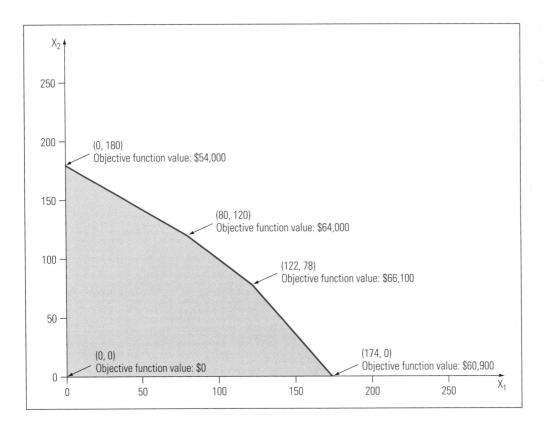

FIGURE 2.7

Objective function values at each extreme point of the feasible region

3. Locate the optimal solution by one of the following methods:
   a. Plot one or more level curves for the objective function and determine the direction in which parallel shifts in this line produce improved objective function values. Shift the level curve in a parallel manner in the improving direction until it intersects the feasible region at a single point. Then find the coordinates for this point. This is the optimal solution.
   b. Identify the coordinates of all the extreme points of the feasible region and calculate the objective function values associated with each point. If the feasible region is bounded, the point with the best objective function value is the optimal solution.

2.10.9 UNDERSTANDING HOW THINGS CHANGE

It is important to realize that if changes occur in any of the coefficients in the objective function or constraints of this problem, then the level curve, feasible region, and optimal solution to this problem also might change. To be an effective LP modeler, it is important for you to develop some intuition about how changes in various coefficients in the model will affect the solution to the problem. We will study this in greater detail in Chapter 4 when discussing sensitivity analysis. However, the spreadsheet shown in Figure 2.8 (and in the file named Fig2-8.xls on your data disk) allows you to change any of the coefficients in this problem and, instantly, see its effect. You are encouraged to experiment with this file to make sure that you understand the relationships between various model coefficients and their impact on this LP problem. (Case 2-1 at the end of this chapter asks some specific questions that can be answered using the spreadsheet shown in Figure 2.8.)

FIGURE 2.8

Interactive spreadsheet for the Blue Ridge Hot Tubs LP problem

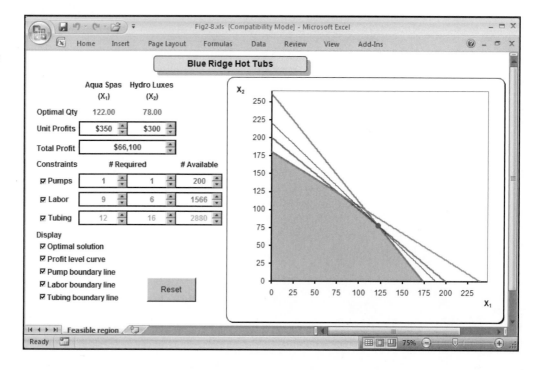

2.11 Special Conditions in LP Models

Several special conditions can arise in LP modeling: *alternate optimal solutions, redundant constraints, unbounded solutions*, and *infeasibility*. The first two conditions do not prevent you from solving an LP model and are not really problems—they are just anomalies that sometimes occur. On the other hand, the last two conditions represent real problems that prevent us from solving an LP model.

2.11.1 ALTERNATE OPTIMAL SOLUTIONS

Some LP models can have more than one optimal solution, or **alternate optimal solutions**. That is, there can be more than one feasible point that maximizes (or minimizes) the value of the objective function.

For example, suppose Howie can increase the price of Aqua-Spas to the point at which each unit sold generates a profit of $450 rather than $350. The revised LP model for this problem is:

$$\text{MAX:} \qquad 450X_1 + 300X_2$$
$$\text{Subject to:} \qquad 1X_1 + 1X_2 \leq 200$$
$$9X_1 + 6X_2 \leq 1{,}566$$
$$12X_1 + 16X_2 \leq 2{,}880$$
$$1X_1 \qquad\qquad \geq 0$$
$$1X_2 \geq 0$$

Because none of the constraints changed, the feasible region for this model is the same as for the earlier example. The only difference in this model is the objective function. Therefore, the level curves for the objective function are different from what we observed earlier. Several level curves for this model are plotted with its feasible region in Figure 2.9.

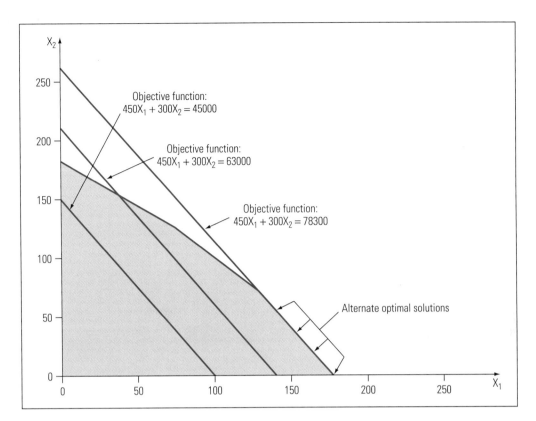

FIGURE 2.9

Example of an LP problem with an infinite number of alternate optimal solutions

Notice that the final level curve in Figure 2.9 intersects the feasible region along an *edge* of the feasible region rather than at a single point. All the points on the line segment joining the corner point at (122, 78) to the corner point at (174, 0) produce the same optimal objective function value of $78,300 for this problem. Thus, all these points are alternate optimal solutions to the problem. If we used a computer to solve this problem, it would identify only one of the corner points of this edge as the optimal solution.

The fact that alternate optimal solutions sometimes occur is really not a problem because this anomaly does not prevent us from finding an optimal solution to the problem. In fact, in Chapter 7, "Goal Programming and Multiple Objective Optimization," you will see that alternate optimal solutions are sometimes very desirable.

2.11.2 REDUNDANT CONSTRAINTS

Redundant constraints present another special condition that sometimes occurs in an LP model. A **redundant constraint** is a constraint that plays no role in determining the feasible region of the problem. For example, in the hot tub example, suppose that 225 hot tub pumps are available instead of 200. The earlier LP model can be modified as follows to reflect this change:

$$
\begin{array}{lrcl}
\text{MAX:} & 350X_1 + 300X_2 & & \\
\text{Subject to:} & 1X_1 + 1X_2 & \leq & 225 \\
& 9X_1 + 6X_2 & \leq & 1{,}566 \\
& 12X_1 + 16X_2 & \leq & 2{,}880 \\
& 1X_1 & \geq & 0 \\
& 1X_2 & \geq & 0
\end{array}
$$

FIGURE 2.10

Example of a redundant constraint

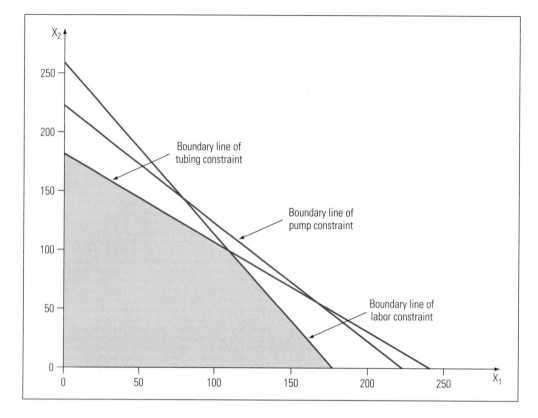

This model is identical to the original model we formulated for this problem *except* for the new upper limit on the first constraint (representing the number of pumps that can be used). The constraints and feasible region for this revised model are shown in Figure 2.10.

Notice that the pump constraint in this model no longer plays any role in defining the feasible region of the problem. That is, as long as the tubing constraint and labor constraints are satisfied (which is always the case for any feasible solution), then the pump constraint will also be satisfied. Therefore, we can remove the pump constraint from the model without changing the feasible region of the problem—the constraint is simply redundant.

The fact that the pump constraint does not play a role in defining the feasible region in Figure 2.10 implies that there will always be an excess number of pumps available. Because none of the feasible solutions identified in Figure 2.10 fall on the boundary line of the pump constraint, this constraint will always be satisfied as a strict inequality ($1X_1 + 1X_2 < 225$) and never as a strict equality ($1X_1 + 1X_2 = 225$).

Again, redundant constraints are not really a problem. They do not prevent us (or the computer) from finding the optimal solution to an LP problem. However, they do represent "excess baggage" for the computer; so if you know that a constraint is redundant, eliminating it saves the computer this excess work. On the other hand, if the model you are working with will be modified and used repeatedly, it might be best to leave any redundant constraints in the model because they might not be redundant in the future. For example, from Figure 2.3, we know that if the availability of pumps is returned to 200, then the pump constraint again plays an important role in defining the feasible region (and optimal solution) of the problem.

2.11.3 UNBOUNDED SOLUTIONS

When attempting to solve some LP problems, you might encounter situations in which the objective function can be made infinitely large (in the case of a maximization problem) or infinitely small (in the case of a minimization problem). As an example, consider this LP problem:

$$
\begin{array}{llrcl}
\text{MAX:} & & X_1 + X_2 & & \\
\text{Subject to:} & & X_1 + X_2 & \geq & 400 \\
& & -X_1 + 2X_2 & \leq & 400 \\
& & X_1 & \geq & 0 \\
& & X_2 & \geq & 0
\end{array}
$$

The feasible region and some level curves for this problem are shown in Figure 2.11. From this graph, you can see that as the level curves shift farther and farther away from the origin, the objective function increases. Because the feasible region is not bounded in this direction, you can continue shifting the level curve by an infinite amount and make the objective function infinitely large.

Although it is not unusual to encounter an **unbounded** solution when solving an LP model, such a solution indicates that there is something wrong with the formulation—for example, one or more constraints were omitted from the formulation, or a "less than" constraint was entered erroneously as a "greater than" constraint.

While describing how to find the optimal solution to an LP model by enumerating corner points, we noted that this procedure will not always work if the feasible region for the problem is unbounded. Figure 2.11 provides an example of such a situation. The only extreme points for the feasible region in Figure 2.11 occur at the points (400, 0) and

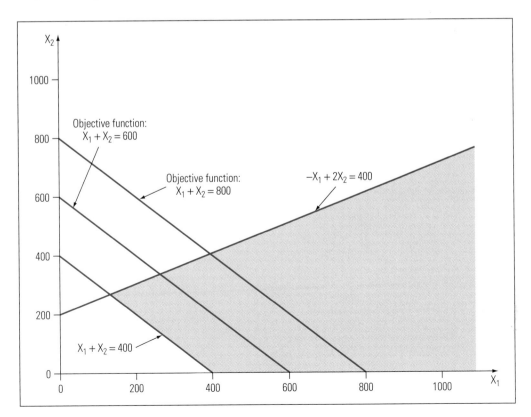

FIGURE 2.11

Example of an LP problem with an unbounded solution

$(133.\overline{3}, 266.\overline{6})$. The objective function value at both of these points (and at any point on the line segment joining them) is 400. By enumerating the extreme points for this problem, we might erroneously conclude that alternate optimal solutions to this problem exist that produce an optimal objective function value of 400. This is true if the problem involved *minimizing* the objective function. However, the goal here is to *maximize* the objective function value, which, as we have seen, can be done without limit. So, when trying to solve an LP problem by enumerating the extreme points of an unbounded feasible region, you also must check whether or not the objective function is unbounded.

2.11.4 INFEASIBILITY

An LP problem is **infeasible** if there is no way to satisfy all the constraints in the problem simultaneously. As an example, consider the LP model:

$$
\begin{array}{llrl}
\text{MAX:} & & X_1 + X_2 & \\
\text{Subject to:} & & X_1 + X_2 & \leq 150 \\
& & X_1 + X_2 & \geq 200 \\
& & X_1 & \geq 0 \\
& & X_2 & \geq 0
\end{array}
$$

The feasible solutions for the first two constraints in this model are shown in Figure 2.12. Notice that the feasible solutions to the first constraint fall on the left side of its boundary line, whereas the feasible solutions to the second constraint fall on the right side of its boundary line. Therefore, no possible values for X_1 and X_2 exist that satisfy both constraints in the model simultaneously. In such a case, there are no feasible solutions to the problem.

FIGURE 2.12

Example of an LP problem with no feasible solution

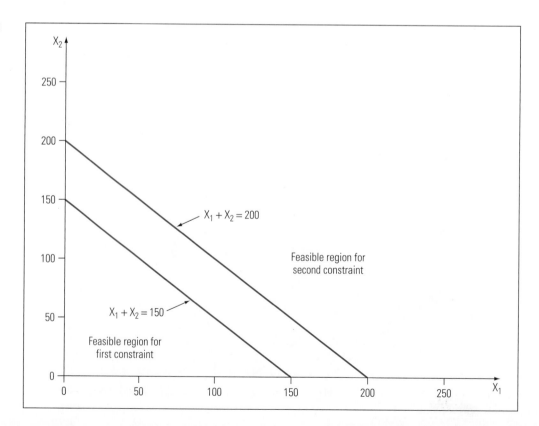

Infeasibility can occur in LP problems, perhaps because of an error in the formulation of the model—such as unintentionally making a "less than or equal to" constraint a "greater than or equal to" constraint. Or there just might not be a way to satisfy all the constraints in the model. In this case, constraints would have to be eliminated or loosened to obtain a feasible region (and feasible solution) for the problem.

Loosening constraints involves increasing the upper limits (or reducing the lower limits) to expand the range of feasible solutions. For example, if we loosen the first constraint in the previous model by changing the upper limit from 150 to 250, there is a feasible region for the problem. Of course, loosening constraints should not be done arbitrarily. In a real model, the value 150 would represent some actual characteristic of the decision problem (such as the number of pumps available to make hot tubs). We obviously cannot change this value to 250 unless it is appropriate to do so—that is, unless we know another 100 pumps can be obtained.

2.12 Summary

This chapter provided an introduction to an area of management science known as mathematical programming (MP), or optimization. Optimization covers a broad range of problems that share a common goal—determining the values for the decision variables in a problem that will maximize (or minimize) some objective function while satisfying various constraints. Constraints impose restrictions on the values that can be assumed by the decision variables and define the set of feasible options (or the feasible region) for the problem.

Linear programming (LP) problems represent a special category of MP problems in which the objective function and all the constraints can be expressed as linear combinations of the decision variables. Simple, two-variable LP problems can be solved graphically by identifying the feasible region and plotting level curves for the objective function. An optimal solution to an LP problem always occurs at a corner point of its feasible region (unless the objective function is unbounded).

Some anomalies can occur in optimization problems; these include alternate optimal solutions, redundant constraints, unbounded solutions, and infeasibility.

2.13 References

Bazaraa, M. and J. Jarvis. *Linear Programming and Network Flows*. New York: Wiley, 1990.

Dantzig, G. *Linear Programming and Extensions*. Princeton, NJ: Princeton University Press, 1963.

Eppen, G., F. Gould, and C. Schmidt, *Introduction to Management Science*. Englewood Cliffs, NJ: Prentice Hall, 1993.

Shogan, A. *Management Science*. Englewood Cliffs, NJ: Prentice Hall, 1988.

Winston, W. *Operations Research: Applications and Algorithms*. Belmont, CA: Duxbury Press, 1997.

Questions and Problems

1. An LP model can have more than one optimal solution. Is it possible for an LP model to have exactly two optimal solutions? Why or why not?
2. In the solution to the Blue Ridge Hot Tubs problem, the optimal values for X_1 and X_2 turned out to be integers (whole numbers). Is this a general property of the solutions to LP problems? In other words, will the solution to an LP problem always consist of integers? Why or why not?

3. To determine the feasible region associated with "less than or equal to" constraints or "greater than or equal to" constraints, we graphed these constraints as if they were "equal to" constraints. Why is this possible?

4. Are the following objective functions for an LP model equivalent? That is, if they are both used, one at a time, to solve a problem with exactly the same constraints, will the optimal values for X_1 and X_2 be the same in both cases? Why or why not?

$$\text{MAX:} \qquad 2X_1 + 3X_2$$
$$\text{MIN:} \qquad -2X_1 - 3X_2$$

5. Which of the following constraints are not linear or cannot be included as a constraint in a linear programming problem?
   a. $2X_1 + X_2 - 3X_3 \geq 50$
   b. $2X_1 + \sqrt{X_2} \geq 60$
   c. $4X_1 - \frac{1}{3}X_2 = 75$
   d. $\dfrac{3X_1 + 2X_2 - 3X_3}{X_1 + X_2 + X_3} \leq 0.9$
   e. $3X_1^2 + 7X_2 \leq 45$

6. Solve the following LP problem graphically by enumerating the corner points.

$$\text{MAX:} \qquad 3X_1 + 4X_2$$
$$\text{Subject to:} \qquad X_1 \qquad\qquad \leq 12$$
$$X_2 \leq 10$$
$$4X_1 + 6X_2 \leq 72$$
$$X_1, X_2 \geq 0$$

7. Solve the following LP problem graphically using level curves.

$$\text{MIN:} \qquad 2X_1 + 3X_2$$
$$\text{Subject to:} \qquad 2X_1 + 1X_2 \geq 3$$
$$4X_1 + 5X_2 \geq 20$$
$$2X_1 + 8X_2 \geq 16$$
$$5X_1 + 6X_2 \leq 60$$
$$X_1, X_2 \geq 0$$

8. Solve the following LP problem graphically using level curves.

$$\text{MAX:} \qquad 2X_1 + 5X_2$$
$$\text{Subject to:} \qquad 6X_1 + 5X_2 \leq 60$$
$$2X_1 + 3X_2 \leq 24$$
$$3X_1 + 6X_2 \leq 48$$
$$X_1, X_2 \geq 0$$

9. Solve the following LP problem graphically by enumerating the corner points.

$$\text{MIN:} \qquad 5X_1 + 20X_2$$
$$\text{Subject to:} \qquad X_1 + X_2 \geq 12$$
$$2X_1 + 5X_2 \geq 40$$
$$X_1 + X_2 \leq 15$$
$$X_1, X_2 \geq 0$$

10. Consider the following LP problem.

$$\text{MAX:} \qquad 3X_1 + 2X_2$$
$$\text{Subject to:} \qquad 3X_1 + 3X_2 \leq 300$$
$$6X_1 + 3X_2 \leq 480$$
$$3X_1 + 3X_2 \leq 480$$
$$X_1, X_2 \geq 0$$

 a. Sketch the feasible region for this model.
 b. What is the optimal solution?
 c. Identify any redundant constraints in this model.
11. Solve the following LP problem graphically by enumerating the corner points.

$$\text{MAX:} \qquad 10X_1 + 12X_2$$
$$\text{Subject to:} \qquad 8X_1 + 6X_2 \leq 98$$
$$6X_1 + 8X_2 \leq 98$$
$$X_1 + X_2 \geq 14$$
$$X_1, X_2 \geq 0$$

12. Solve the following LP problem using level curves.

$$\text{MAX:} \qquad 4X_1 + 5X_2$$
$$\text{Subject to:} \qquad 2X_1 + 3X_2 \leq 120$$
$$4X_1 + 3X_2 \leq 140$$
$$X_1 + X_2 \geq 80$$
$$X_1, X_2 \geq 0$$

13. The marketing manager for Mountain Mist soda needs to decide how many TV spots and magazine ads to run during the next quarter. Each TV spot costs $5,000 and is expected to increase sales by 300,000 cans. Each magazine ad costs $2,000 and is expected to increase sales by 500,000 cans. A total of $100,000 may be spent on TV and magazine ads; however, Mountain Mist wants to spend no more than $70,000 on TV spots and no more than $50,000 on magazine ads. Mountain Mist earns a profit of $0.05 on each can it sells.
 a. Formulate an LP model for this problem.
 b. Sketch the feasible region for this model.
 c. Find the optimal solution to the problem using level curves.
14. Blacktop Refining extracts minerals from ore mined at two different sites in Montana. Each ton of ore type 1 contains 20% copper, 20% zinc and 15% magnesium. Each ton of ore type 2 contains 30% copper, 25% zinc and 10% magnesium. Ore type 1 costs $90 per ton and ore type 2 costs $120 per ton. Blacktop would like to buy enough ore to extract at least 8 tons of copper, 6 tons of zinc, and 5 tons of magnesium in the least costly manner.
 a. Formulate an LP model for this problem.
 b. Sketch the feasible region for this problem.
 c. Find the optimal solution.
15. The Electrotech Corporation manufactures two industrial-sized electrical devices: generators and alternators. Both of these products require wiring and testing during the assembly process. Each generator requires 2 hours of wiring and 1 hour of testing and can be sold for a $250 profit. Each alternator requires 3 hours of wiring and 2 hours of testing and can be sold for a $150 profit. There are 260 hours of wiring

time and 140 hours of testing time available in the next production period and Electrotech wants to maximize profit.

   a. Formulate an LP model for this problem.

   b. Sketch the feasible region for this problem.

   c. Determine the optimal solution to this problem using level curves.

16. Refer to the previous question. Suppose that Electrotech's management decides that they need to make at least 20 generators and at least 20 alternators.

   a. Reformulate your LP model to account for this change.

   b. Sketch the feasible region for this problem.

   c. Determine the optimal solution to this problem by enumerating the corner points.

   d. Suppose that Electrotech can acquire additional wiring time at a very favorable cost. Should it do so? Why or why not?

17. Bill's Grill is a popular college restaurant that is famous for its hamburgers. The owner of the restaurant, Bill, mixes fresh ground beef and pork with a secret ingredient to make delicious quarter-pound hamburgers that are advertised as having no more than 25% fat. Bill can buy beef containing 80% meat and 20% fat at $0.85 per pound. He can buy pork containing 70% meat and 30% fat at $0.65 per pound. Bill wants to determine the minimum cost way to blend the beef and pork to make hamburgers that have no more than 25% fat.

   a. Formulate an LP model for this problem. (*Hint*: The decision variables for this problem represent the percentage of beef and the percentage of pork to combine.)

   b. Sketch the feasible region for this problem.

   c. Determine the optimal solution to this problem by enumerating the corner points.

18. Zippy motorcycle manufacturing produces two popular pocket bikes (miniature motorcycles with 49cc engines): the Razor and the Zoomer. In the coming week, the manufacturer wants to produce a total of up to 700 bikes and wants to ensure that the number of Razors produced does not exceed the number of Zoomers by more than 300. Each Razor produced and sold results in a profit of $70, and each Zoomer results in a profit of $40. The bikes are identical mechanically and differ only in the appearance of the polymer-based trim around the fuel tank and seat. Each Razor's trim requires 2 pounds of polymer and 3 hours of production time, and each Zoomer requires 1 pound of polymer and 4 hours of production time. Assume that 900 pounds of polymer and 2400 labor hours are available for production of these items in the coming week.

   a. Formulate an LP model for this problem.

   b. Sketch the feasible region for this problem.

   c. What is the optimal solution?

19. The Quality Desk Company makes two types of computer desks from laminated particle board. The Presidential model requires 30 square feet of particle board, 1 keyboard sliding mechanism, and 5 hours of labor to fabricate. It sells for $149. The Senator model requires 24 square feet of particle board, 1 keyboard sliding mechanism, and 3 hours of labor to fabricate. It sells for $135. In the coming week, the company can buy up to 15,000 square feet of particle board at $1.35 per square foot and up to 600 keyboard sliding mechanisms at a cost of $4.75 each. The company views manufacturing labor as a fixed cost and has 3000 labor hours available in the coming week for the fabrication of these desks.

   a. Formulate an LP model for this problem.

   b. Sketch the feasible region for this problem.

   c. What is the optimal solution?

20. A farmer in Georgia has a 100-acre farm on which to plant watermelons and cantaloupes. Every acre planted with watermelons requires 50 gallons of water per day and must be prepared for planting with 20 pounds of fertilizer. Every acre planted

with cantaloupes requires 75 gallons of water per day and must be prepared for planting with 15 pounds of fertilizer. The farmer estimates that it will take 2 hours of labor to harvest each acre planted with watermelons and 2.5 hours to harvest each acre planted with cantaloupes. He believes that watermelons will sell for about $3 each, and cantaloupes will sell for about $1 each. Every acre planted with watermelons is expected to yield 90 salable units. Every acre planted with cantaloupes is expected to yield 300 salable units. The farmer can pump about 6,000 gallons of water per day for irrigation purposes from a shallow well. He can buy as much fertilizer as he needs at a cost of $10 per 50-pound bag. Finally, the farmer can hire laborers to harvest the fields at a rate of $5 per hour. If the farmer sells all the watermelons and cantaloupes he produces, how many acres of each crop should the farmer plant to maximize profits?

a. Formulate an LP model for this problem.
b. Sketch the feasible region for this model.
c. Find the optimal solution to the problem using level curves.

21. Sanderson Manufacturing produces ornate, decorative wood frame doors and windows. Each item produced goes through 3 manufacturing processes: cutting, sanding, and finishing. Each door produced requires 1 hour in cutting, 30 minutes in sanding, and 30 minutes in finishing. Each window requires 30 minutes in cutting, 45 minutes in sanding, and 1 hour in finishing. In the coming week Sanderson has 40 hours of cutting capacity available, 40 hours of sanding capacity, and 60 hours of finishing capacity. Assume that all doors produced can be sold for a profit of $500 and all windows can be sold for a profit of $400.

a. Formulate an LP model for this problem.
b. Sketch the feasible region.
c. What is the optimal solution?

22. PC-Express is a computer retail store that sells two kinds of microcomputers: desktops and laptops. The company earns $600 on each desktop computer it sells and $900 on each laptop. The microcomputers PC-Express sells are manufactured by another company. This manufacturer has a special order to fill for another customer and cannot ship more than 80 desktop computers and 75 laptops to PC-Express next month. The employees at PC-Express must spend about 2 hours installing software and checking each desktop computer they sell. They spend roughly 3 hours to complete this process for laptop computers. They expect to have about 300 hours available for this purpose during the next month. The store's management is fairly certain that they can sell all the computers they order, but are unsure how many desktops and laptops they should order to maximize profits.

a. Formulate an LP model for this problem.
b. Sketch the feasible region for this model.
c. Find the optimal solution to the problem by enumerating the corner points.

23. American Auto is evaluating their marketing plan for the sedans, SUVs, and trucks they produce. A TV ad featuring this SUV has been developed. The company estimates that each showing of this commercial will cost $500,000 and increase sales of SUVs by 3%, but reduce sales of trucks by 1%, and have no effect of the sales of sedans. The company also has a print ad campaign developed that it can run in various nationally distributed magazines at a cost of $750,000 per title. It is estimated that each magazine title the ad runs in will increase the sales of sedans, SUVs, and trucks by 2%, 1%, and 4%, respectively. The company desires to increase sales of sedans, SUVs, and trucks by at least 3%, 14%, and 4%, respectively, in the least costly manner.

a. Formulate an LP model for this problem.
b. Sketch the feasible region.
c. What is the optimal solution?

For the Lines They Are A-Changin' (with apologies to Bob Dylan)

CASE 2.1

The owner of Blue Ridge Hot Tubs, Howie Jones, has asked for your assistance in analyzing how the feasible region and solution to his production problem might change in response to changes in various parameters in the LP model. He is hoping that this might further his understanding of LP and how the constraints, objective function, and optimal solution interrelate. To assist in this process, he asked a consulting firm to develop the spreadsheet shown earlier in Figure 2.8 (and the file Fig. 2-8.xls on your data disk) that dynamically updates the feasible region and optimal solution and the various parameters in the model change. Unfortunately, Howie has not had much time to play around with this spreadsheet, so he has left it in your hands and asked you to use it to answer the following questions. (Click the Reset button in file Fig. 2-8.xls before answering each of the following questions.)

Note: The file Fig2-8.xls contains a macro that must be enabled for the workbook to operate correctly. To allow this (and other) macros to run in Excel click: Office button, Excel options, Trust Center, Trust Center Settings, Macro Settings, select "Disable all macros with notification", click OK. Then when Excel opens a workbook containing macros it will display a security warning indicating some active content has been disabled and will give you the opportunity to enable this content, which you should do for the Excel files accompanying this book.

a. In the optimal solution to this problem, how many pumps, hours of labor, and feet of tubing are being used?

b. If the company could increase the number of pumps available, should they? Why or why not? And if so, what is the maximum number of additional pumps that they should consider acquiring, and by how much would this increase profit?

c. If the company could acquire more labor hours, should they? Why or why not? If so, how much additional labor should they consider acquiring and by how much would this increase profit?

d. If the company could acquire more tubing, should they? Why or why not? If so, how additional tubing should they consider acquiring and how much would this increase profit?

e. By how much would profit increase if the company could reduce the labor required to produce Aqua-Spas from 9 to 8 hours? And from 8 to 7 hours? And from 7 to 6 hours?

f. By how much would profit increase if the company could reduce the labor required to produce Hydro-Luxes from 6 to 5 hours? And from 5 to 4 hours? And from 4 to 3 hours?

g. By how much would profit increase if the company could reduce the amount of tubing required to produce Aqua-Spas from 12 to 11 feet? And from 11 to 10 feet? And from 10 to 9 feet?

h. By how much would profit increase if the company could reduce the amount of tubing required to produce Hydro-Luxes from 16 to 15 feet? And from 15 to 14 feet? And from 14 to 13 feet?

i. By how much would the unit profit on Aqua-Spas have to change before the optimal product mix changes?

j. By how much would the unit profit on Hydro-Luxes have to change before the optimal product mix changes?

Chapter 3

Modeling and Solving
LP Problems in a Spreadsheet

3.0 Introduction

Chapter 2 discussed how to formulate linear programming (LP) problems and how to solve simple, two-variable LP problems graphically. As you might expect, very few real-world LP problems involve only two decision variables. So, the graphical solution approach is of limited value in solving LP problems. However, the discussion of two-variable problems provides a basis for understanding the issues involved in all LP problems and the general strategies for solving them.

For example, every solvable LP problem has a feasible region, and an optimal solution to the problem can be found at some extreme point of this region (assuming the problem is not unbounded). This is true of all LP problems regardless of the number of decision variables. Although it is fairly easy to graph the feasible region for a two-variable LP problem, it is difficult to visualize or graph the feasible region of an LP problem with three variables because such a graph is three-dimensional. If there are more than three variables, it is virtually impossible to visualize or graph the feasible region for an LP problem because such a graph involves more than three dimensions.

Fortunately, several mathematical techniques exist to solve LP problems involving almost any number of variables without visualizing or graphing their feasible regions. These techniques are now built into spreadsheet packages in a way that makes solving LP problems a fairly simple task. So, using the appropriate computer software, you can solve almost any LP problem easily. The main challenge is ensuring that you formulate the LP problem correctly and communicate this formulation to the computer accurately. This chapter shows you how to do this using spreadsheets.

3.1 Spreadsheet Solvers

Excel, Quattro Pro, and Lotus 1-2-3 all come with built-in spreadsheet optimization tools called **solvers**. Their inclusion in these applications demonstrates the importance of LP (and optimization in general). This book uses Excel to illustrate how spreadsheet solvers can solve optimization problems. However, the same concepts and techniques presented here apply to other spreadsheet packages, although certain details of implementation may differ.

You can also solve optimization problems without using a spreadsheet by using a specialized mathematical programming package. A partial list of these packages includes: LINDO, MPSX, CPLEX, and MathPro. Typically, these packages are used by researchers and businesses interested in solving extremely large problems that do not fit conveniently in a spreadsheet.

The Spreadsheet Solver Company

Frontline Systems, Inc. created the solvers in Microsoft Excel, Lotus 1-2-3, and Corel Quattro Pro. Frontline markets enhanced versions of these spreadsheet solvers that offer greater capacity, faster speed, and several ease-of-use features. You can find out more about Frontline Systems and their products by visiting their Web site at http://www.solver.com.

3.2 Solving LP Problems in a Spreadsheet

We will demonstrate the mechanics of using the Solver in Excel by solving the problem faced by Howie Jones, described in Chapter 2. Recall that Howie owns and operates Blue Ridge Hot Tubs, a company that sells two models of hot tubs: the Aqua-Spa and the Hydro-Lux. Howie purchases prefabricated fiberglass hot tub shells and installs a common water pump and the appropriate amount of tubing into each hot tub. Every Aqua-Spa requires 9 hours of labor and 12 feet of tubing; every Hydro-Lux requires 6 hours of labor and 16 feet of tubing. Demand for these products is such that each Aqua-Spa produced can be sold to generate a profit of $350, and each Hydro-Lux produced can be sold to generate a profit of $300. The company expects to have 200 pumps, 1,566 hours of labor, and 2,880 feet of tubing available during the next production cycle. The problem is to determine the optimal number of Aqua-Spas and Hydro-Luxes to produce to maximize profits.

Chapter 2 developed the following LP formulation for the problem Howie faces. In this model, X_1 represents the number of Aqua-Spas to be produced, and X_2 represents the number of Hydro-Luxes to be produced.

$$
\begin{aligned}
\text{MAX:} \quad & 350X_1 + 300X_2 && \} \text{ profit} \\
\text{Subject to:} \quad & 1X_1 + 1X_2 \leq 200 && \} \text{ pump constraint} \\
& 9X_1 + 6X_2 \leq 1{,}566 && \} \text{ labor constraint} \\
& 12X_1 + 16X_2 \leq 2{,}880 && \} \text{ tubing constraint} \\
& 1X_1 \geq 0 && \} \text{ simple lower bound} \\
& 1X_2 \geq 0 && \} \text{ simple lower bound}
\end{aligned}
$$

So, how do you solve this problem in a spreadsheet? First, you must implement, or build, this model in the spreadsheet.

3.3 The Steps in Implementing an LP Model in a Spreadsheet

The following four steps summarize what must be done to implement any LP problem in a spreadsheet.

1. **Organize the data for the model on the spreadsheet**. The data for the model consist of the coefficients in the objective function, the various coefficients in the

constraints, and the right-hand-side (RHS) values for the constraints. There is usually more than one way to organize the data for a particular problem on a spreadsheet, but you should keep in mind some general guidelines. First, the goal is to organize the data so their purpose and meaning are as clear as possible. Think of your spreadsheet as a management report that needs to communicate clearly the important factors of the problem being solved. To this end, you should spend some time organizing the data for the problem in your mind's eye—visualizing how the data can be laid out logically—before you start typing values in the spreadsheet. Descriptive labels should be placed in the spreadsheet to clearly identify the various data elements. Often, row and column structures of the data in the model can be used in the spreadsheet to facilitate model implementation. (Note that some or all of the coefficients and values for an LP model might be calculated from other data, often referred to as the primary data. It is best to maintain primary data in the spreadsheet and use appropriate formulas to calculate the coefficients and values that are needed for the LP formulation. Then, if the primary data change, appropriate changes will be made automatically in the coefficients for the LP model.)

2. **Reserve separate cells in the spreadsheet to represent each decision variable in the algebraic model.** Although you can use any empty cells in a spreadsheet to represent the decision variables, it is usually best to arrange the cells representing the decision variables in a way that parallels the structure of the data. This is often helpful in setting up formulas for the objective function and constraints. When possible, it is also a good idea to keep the cells representing decision variables in the same area of the spreadsheet. In addition, you should use descriptive labels to clearly identify the meaning of these cells.

3. **Create a formula in a cell in the spreadsheet that corresponds to the objective function in the algebraic model.** The spreadsheet formula corresponding to the objective function is created by referring to the data cells where the objective function coefficients have been entered (or calculated) and to the corresponding cells representing the decision variables.

4. **For each constraint, create a formula in a separate cell in the spreadsheet that corresponds to the left-hand-side (LHS) of the constraint.** The formula corresponding to the LHS of each constraint is created by referring to the data cells where the coefficients for these constraints have been entered (or calculated) and to the appropriate decision variable cells. Many of the constraint formulas have a similar structure. Thus, when possible, you should create constraint formulas that can be copied to implement other constraint formulas. This not only reduces the effort required to implement a model, but also helps avoid hard-to-detect typing errors.

Although each of the previous steps must be performed to implement an LP model in a spreadsheet, they do not have to be performed in the order indicated. It is usually wise to perform step 1 first, followed by step 2. But the order in which steps 3 and 4 are performed often varies from problem to problem.

Also, it is often wise to use shading, background colors, and/or borders to identify the cells representing decision variables, constraints, and the objective function in a model. This allows the user of a spreadsheet to distinguish more readily between cells representing raw data (that can be changed) and other elements of the model. We have more to say about how to design and implement effective spreadsheet models for LP problems. But first, let's see how to use the previous steps to implement a spreadsheet model using our example problem.

3.4 A Spreadsheet Model for the Blue Ridge Hot Tubs Problem

One possible spreadsheet representation for our example problem is given in Figure 3.1 (and in the file named Fig3-1.xls on your data disk). Let's walk through the creation of this model step-by-step so you can see how it relates to the algebraic formulation of the model.

A Note About Macros

In most of the spreadsheet examples accompanying this book, you can click on the blue title bars at the top of the spreadsheet to toggle on and off a note that provides additional documentation about the spreadsheet model. This documentation feature is enabled through the use of macros. To allow this (and other) macros to run in Excel, click: Office button, Excel options, Trust Center, Trust Center Settings, Macro Settings, select "Disable all macros with notification," click OK. If you then open a file containing macros, Excel displays a security warning indicating some active content has been disabled and will give you the opportunity to enable this content, which you should do to make use of the macro features in the spreadsheet files accompanying this book.

FIGURE 3.1

A spreadsheet model for the Blue Ridge Hot Tub production problem

X_1

X_2

Objective Function = $B6 \times B5 + C6 \times C5$

LHS of 1st constraint = $B9 \times B5 + C9 \times C5$

LHS of 2nd constraint = $B10 \times B5 + C10 \times C5$

LHS of 3rd constraint = $B11 \times B5 + C11 \times C5$

3.4.1 ORGANIZING THE DATA

One of the first steps in building any spreadsheet model for an LP problem is to organize the data for the model on the spreadsheet. In Figure 3.1, we enter the data for the unit profits for Aqua-Spas and Hydro-Luxes in cells B6 and C6, respectively. Next, we enter the number of pumps, labor hours, and feet of tubing required to produce each type of hot tub, in cells B9 through C11. The values in cells B9 and C9 indicate that one pump is required to produce each type of hot tub. The values in cells B10 and C10 show that each Aqua-Spa produced requires 9 hours of labor, and each Hydro-Lux requires 6 hours. Cells B11 and C11 indicate that each Aqua-Spa produced requires 12 feet of tubing, and each Hydro-Lux requires 16 feet. The available number of pumps, labor hours, and feet of tubing are entered in cells E9 through E11. Notice that appropriate labels also are entered to identify all the data elements for the problem.

3.4.2 REPRESENTING THE DECISION VARIABLES

As indicated in Figure 3.1, cells B5 and C5 represent the decision variables X_1 and X_2 in our algebraic model. These cells are shaded and outlined with dashed borders to distinguish them visually from other elements of the model. Values of zero were placed in cells B5 and C5 because we do not know how many Aqua-Spas and Hydro-Luxes should be produced. Shortly, we will use Solver to determine the optimal values for these cells. Figure 3.2 summarizes the relationship between the decision variables in the algebraic model and the corresponding cells in the spreadsheet.

Decision Variables:	X_1	X_2
	↓	↓
Spreadsheet Cells:	B5	C5

FIGURE 3.2

Summary of the relationship between the decision variables and corresponding spreadsheet cells

3.4.3 REPRESENTING THE OBJECTIVE FUNCTION

The next step in implementing our LP problem is to create a formula in a cell of the spreadsheet to represent the objective function. We can accomplish this in many ways. Because the objective function is $350X_1 + 300X_2$, you might be tempted to enter the formula =350*B5+300*C5 in the spreadsheet. However, if you wanted to change the coefficients in the objective function, you would have to go back and edit this formula to reflect the changes. Because the objective function coefficients are entered in cells B6 and C6, a better way of implementing the objective function is to refer to the values in cells B6 and C6 rather than entering numeric constants in the formula. The formula for the objective function is entered in cell D6 as:

$$\text{Formula for cell D6:} \qquad \text{=B6*B5+C6*C5}$$

As shown in Figure 3.1, cell D6 initially returns the value 0 because cells B5 and C5 both contain zeros. Figure 3.3 summarizes the relationship between the algebraic objective function and the formula entered in cell D6. By implementing the objective function in this manner, if the profits earned on the hot tubs ever change, the spreadsheet model can be changed easily and the problem can be re-solved to determine the effect of this change on the optimal solution. Note that cell D6 has been shaded and outlined with a double border to distinguish it from other elements of the model.

FIGURE 3.3

Summary of the relationship between the decision variables and corresponding spreadsheet cells

3.4.4 REPRESENTING THE CONSTRAINTS

The next step in building the spreadsheet model involves implementing the constraints of the LP model. Earlier we said that for each constraint in the algebraic model, you must create a formula in a cell of the spreadsheet that corresponds to the LHS of the constraint. The LHS of each constraint in our model is:

LHS of the pump constraint

$$\boxed{1X_1 + 1X_2} \leq 200$$

LHS of the labor constraint

$$\boxed{9X_1 + 6X_2} \leq 1{,}566$$

LHS of the tubing constraint

$$\boxed{12X_1 + 16X_2} \leq 2{,}880$$

We need to set up three cells in the spreadsheet to represent the LHS formulas of the three constraints. Again, we do this by referring to the data cells containing the coefficients for these constraints and to the cells representing the decision variables. The LHS of the first constraint is entered in cell D9 as:

Formula for cell D9:   =B9*B5+C9*C5

Similarly, the LHS of the second and third constraints are entered in cells D10 and D11 as:

Formula for cell D10:   =B10*B5+C10*C5
Formula for cell D11:   =B11*B5+C11*C5

These formulas calculate the number of pumps, hours of labor, and feet of tubing required to manufacture the number of hot tubs represented in cells B5 and C5. Note that cells D9 through D11 were shaded and outlined with solid borders to distinguish them from the other elements of the model.

Figure 3.4 summarizes the relationship between the LHS formulas of the constraints in the algebraic formulation of our model and their spreadsheet representations.

We know that Blue Ridge Hot Tubs has 200 pumps, 1,566 labor hours, and 2,880 feet of tubing available during its next production run. In our algebraic formulation of the LP model, these values represent the RHS values for the three constraints. Therefore, we entered the available number of pumps, hours of labor, and feet of tubing in cells E9, E10, and E11, respectively. These terms indicate the upper limits on the values that cells D9, D10, and D11 can assume.

3.4.5 REPRESENTING THE BOUNDS ON THE DECISION VARIABLES

Now, what about the simple lower bounds on our decision variables represented by $X_1 \geq 0$ and $X_2 \geq 0$? These conditions are quite common in LP problems and are referred

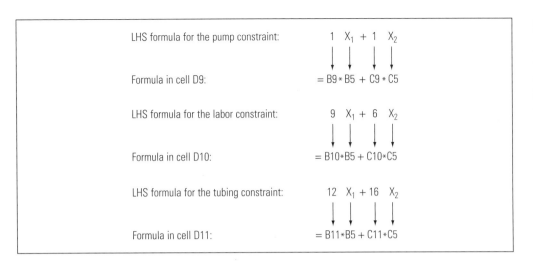

FIGURE 3.4

Summary of the relationship between the LHS formulas of the constraints and their spreadsheet representations

to as **nonnegativity conditions** because they indicate that the decision variables can assume only nonnegative values. These conditions might seem like constraints and can, in fact, be implemented like the other constraints. However, Solver allows you to specify simple upper and lower bounds for the decision variables by referring directly to the cells representing the decision variables. Thus, at this point, we have taken no specific action to implement these bounds in our spreadsheet.

3.5 How Solver Views the Model

After implementing our model in the spreadsheet, we can use Solver to find the optimal solution to the problem. But first, we need to define the following three components of our spreadsheet model for Solver:

1. **Set (or Target) cell.** The cell in the spreadsheet that represents the *objective function* in the model (and whether its value should be maximized or minimized).
2. **Variable (or Changing) cells.** The cells in the spreadsheet that represent the *decision variables* in the model.
3. **Constraint cells.** The cells in the spreadsheet that represent the *LHS formulas* of the constraints in the model (and any upper and lower bounds that apply to these formulas).

These components correspond directly to the cells in the spreadsheet that we established when implementing the LP model. For example, in the spreadsheet for our example problem, the set (or target) cell is represented by cell D6, the variable (or changing) cells are represented by cells B5 and C5, and the constraint cells are represented by cells D9, D10, and D11. Figure 3.5 shows these relationships. Figure 3.5 also shows a cell note documenting the purpose of cell D6. Cell notes can be a very effective way of describing details about the purpose or meaning of various cells in a model.

By comparing Figure 3.1 with Figure 3.5, you can see the direct connection between the way we formulate LP models algebraically and how Solver views the spreadsheet implementation of the model. The decision variables in the algebraic model correspond to the variable (or changing) cells for Solver. The LHS formulas for the different

FIGURE 3.5

Summary of Solver's view of the model

Variable (or Changing) Cells

Set (or Target) Cell

Constraint Cells

constraints in the algebraic model correspond to the constraint cells for Solver. Finally, the objective function in the algebraic model corresponds to the set (or target) cell for Solver. So, although the terminology Solver uses to describe spreadsheet LP models is somewhat different from the terminology we use to describe LP models algebraically, the concepts are the same. Figure 3.6 summarizes these differences in terminology.

Note that some versions of Solver refer to the cells containing the objective function as the "target" cell, whereas other versions of Solver refer to it simply as the "set" cell. Similarly, some versions of Solver refer to the cells representing the decision variables as "changing" cells, whereas other versions refer to them as "variable" cells. As a result, we may use the terms "target" cell and "set" cell interchangeably in this book to refer to the cell containing the objective function. Similarly, we may use the terms "changing" cells and "variable" cells interchangeably to refer to cells representing decision variables.

FIGURE 3.6

Summary of Solver terminology

Terms used to describe LP models algebraically	Corresponding terms used by solver to describe spreadsheet LP models
objective function	set (or target) cell
decision variables	variable (or changing) cells
LHS formulas of constraints	constraint cells

A Note About Creating
Cell Comments...

It is easy to create cell comments like the one shown for cell D6 in Figure 3.5. To create a comment for a cell:

1. Click the cell to select it.
2. Choose Review, New Comment (or press the Shift key and function key F2 simultaneously).
3. Type the comment for the cell, and then select another cell.

The display of cell comments can be turned on or off as follows:

1. Choose Review.
2. Select the appropriate option in the Comments section.
3. Click the OK button.

To copy a cell comment from one cell to a series of other cells:

1. Click the cell containing the comment you want to copy.
2. Choose the Copy command on the Home, Clipboard ribbon (or press the Ctrl and C keys simultaneously).
3. Select the cells you want to copy the comment to.
4. Select the Paste Special command on the Home, Clipboard, Paste ribbon (or click the right mouse button and select Paste Special).
5. Select the Comments option button.
6. Click the OK button.

Installing Premium Solver
for Education

This book comes with Premium Solver for Education—an upgraded version of the standard Solver that ships with Excel. If you have not already done so, install Premium Solver for Education now by running the program called PremSolv.exe found on the CD-ROM that accompanies this book. To do this, use Windows Explorer to locate the file named PremSolv.exe and then double-click the file name. (If you are running Excel in a networked environment, consult with your network administrator.) Although most of the examples in this book also work with the standard Solver that comes with Excel, Premium Solver for Education includes several helpful features that are discussed throughout this book.

3.6 Using Solver

After implementing an LP model in a spreadsheet, we still need to solve the model. To do this, we must first indicate to Solver which cells in the spreadsheet represent the objective function, the decision variables, and the constraints. To invoke Solver in Excel,

FIGURE 3.7

Command for invoking Solver

choose the Solver command from the Add-Ins menu, as shown in Figure 3.7. This should display the first Solver Parameters dialog box shown in Figure 3.8.

A different "standard" version of Solver ships with Excel and is normally found under Excel's Data, Analysis command. The interface of the standard Solver is the second dialog shown in Figure 3.8. Premium Solver is more powerful than the standard Solver and, as a result, we will be using it throughout this book. However, you might sometimes encounter standard Solver on different computers.

Premium Solver for Education provides three different algorithms for solving optimization problems: Standard GRG Nonlinear, Standard Simplex LP, and Standard Evolutionary. If the problem you are trying to solve is an LP problem (that is, an optimization problem with a linear objective function and linear constraints), Solver can use a special algorithm known as the *simplex method* to solve the problem. The simplex method provides an efficient way of solving LP problems and, therefore, requires less solution time. Furthermore, using the simplex method allows for expanded sensitivity information about the solution obtained. (Chapter 4 discusses this in detail.) In any event, when using Solver to solve an LP problem, it is a good idea to select the Standard Simplex LP option, as indicated in Figure 3.8.

3.6.1 DEFINING THE SET (OR TARGET) CELL

In the Solver Parameters dialog box, specify the location of the cell that represents the objective function by entering it in the Set Cell box, as shown in Figure 3.9.

Notice that cell D6 contains a formula representing the objective function for our problem and that we instructed Solver to try to maximize this value, as specified by the Max button. Select the Min button when you want Solver to find a solution that minimizes the value of the objective. The Value button may be used to find a solution for which the objective function takes on a specific value.

FIGURE 3.8

The Solver Parameters dialog box

An Evolutionary Force
in Spreadsheets

Dan Fylstra is the president of Frontline Systems, the company that created Solver. He was also one of the instrumental people behind the release of the first spreadsheet program, VisiCalc. Dan received his bachelor's degree at MIT in 1975 and went on to get his master's of business from Harvard Business School in 1978. A Harvard professor introduced Fylstra to another Harvard student named Dan Bricklin, who had an idea for a software program that would let users enter numbers in an electronic spreadsheet, automatically calculating the results on-screen. Bricklin was the idea man and his friend, Bob Frankston, would write the program. Fylstra loaned Bricklin the Apple computer to write the program in 1978. Source: www.smartcomputing.com, *May 2002 • Vol. 6 Issue 5*

FIGURE 3.9

Specifying the set (or target) cell

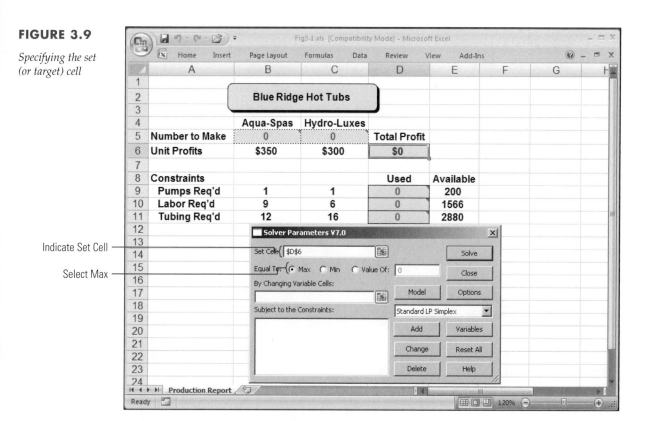

3.6.2 DEFINING THE VARIABLE CELLS

To solve our LP problem, we also need to indicate which cells represent the decision variables in the model. Again, Solver refers to these cells as variable cells. The variable cells for our example problem are specified as shown in Figure 3.10.

Cells B5 and C5 represent the decision variables for the model. Solver will determine the optimal values for these cells. If the decision variables were not in a contiguous range, we would have to list the individual decision variable cells separated by commas in the By Changing Variable Cells box. Whenever possible, it is best to use contiguous cells to represent the decision variables.

3.6.3 DEFINING THE CONSTRAINT CELLS

Next, we must define the constraint cells in the spreadsheet and the restrictions that apply to these cells. As mentioned earlier, the constraint cells are the cells in which we implemented the LHS formulas for each constraint in our model. To define the constraint cells, click the Add button shown in Figure 3.10, and then complete the Add Constraint dialog box shown in Figure 3.11. In the Add Constraint dialog box, click the Add button again to define additional constraints. Click the OK button when you have finished defining constraints.

Cells D9 through D11 represent constraint cells whose values must be less than or equal to the values in cells E9 through E11, respectively. If the constraint cells were not in contiguous cells in the spreadsheet, we would have to define the constraint cells repeatedly. As with the variable cells, it usually is best to choose contiguous cells in your spreadsheet to implement the LHS formulas of the constraints in a model.

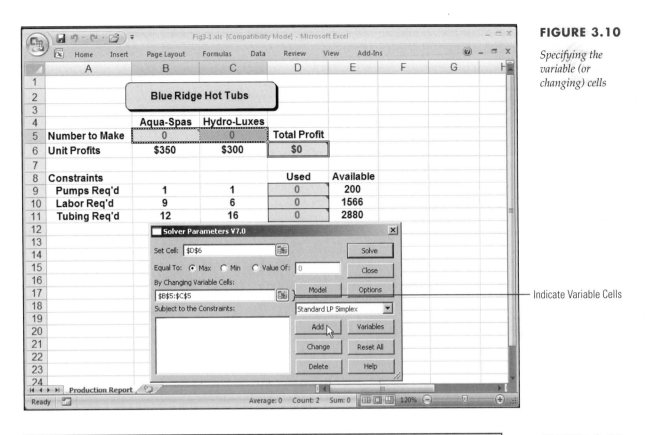

FIGURE 3.10

Specifying the variable (or changing) cells

Indicate Variable Cells

FIGURE 3.11

Specifying the constraint cells

Indicate RHS Formula Cells

Indicate LHS Formula Cells

If you want to define more than one constraint at the same time, as in Figure 3.11, all the constraint cells you select must be the same type (that is, they must all be $\leq$, $\geq$, or $=$). Therefore, it is a good idea to keep constraints of a given type grouped in contiguous cells so that you can select them at the same time. For example, in our case, the three constraint cells we selected are all "less than or equal to" ($\leq$) constraints. However, this consideration should not take precedence over setting up the spreadsheet in the way that communicates its purpose most clearly.

3.6.4 DEFINING THE NONNEGATIVITY CONDITIONS

One final specification we need to make for our model is that the decision variables must be greater than or equal to zero. As mentioned earlier, we can impose these conditions as constraints by placing appropriate restrictions on the values that can be assigned to the cells representing the decision variables (in this case, cells B5 and C5). To do this, we simply add another set of constraints to the model, as shown in Figure 3.12.

Figure 3.12 indicates that cells B5 and C5, which represent the decision variables in our model, must be greater than or equal to zero. Notice that the RHS value of this constraint is a numeric constant that is entered manually. The same type of constraints also could be used if we placed some strictly positive lower bounds on these variables (for example, if we wanted to produce at least 10 Aqua-Spas and at least 10 Hydro-Luxes). However, in that case, it probably would be best to place the minimum required production amounts on the spreadsheet so that these restrictions are displayed clearly. We can then refer to those cells in the spreadsheet when specifying the RHS values for these constraints.

FIGURE 3.12

Adding the nonnegativity conditions for the problem

Important Software Note

There is another way to impose nonnegativity conditions—just check the Assume Non-Negative check box in the Solver Options dialog box (shown in Figure 3.14.) Checking this box tells Solver to assume that all the variables (or variable cells) in your model that have not been assigned explicit lower bounds should have lower bounds of zero.

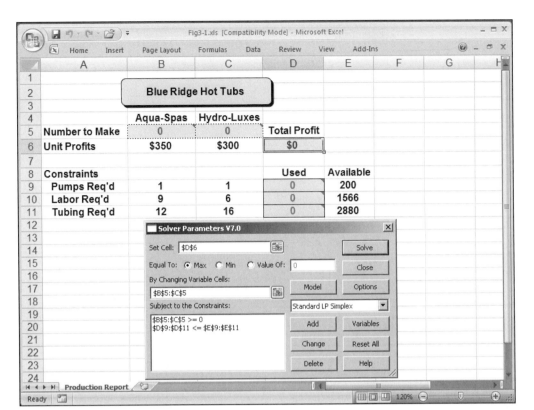

FIGURE 3.13

Summary of how Solver views the model

3.6.5 REVIEWING THE MODEL

After specifying all the constraints for our model, the final Solver Parameters dialog box appears, as shown in Figure 3.13. This dialog box provides a summary of how Solver views our model. It is a good idea to review this information before solving the model to make sure that you entered all the parameters accurately, and to correct any errors before proceeding.

3.6.6 OPTIONS

Solver provides several options that affect how it solves a problem. These options are available in the Solver Options dialog box, which you display by clicking the Options button in the Solver Parameters dialog box. Figure 3.14 shows the Solver Options dialog box for the Standard Simplex LP solution algorithm. We will discuss the meanings of several of these options as we proceed. You also can find out more about these options by clicking the Help button in the Solver Options dialog box.

3.6.7 SOLVING THE MODEL

After entering all the appropriate parameters and choosing any necessary options for our model, the next step is to solve the problem. Click the Solve button in the Solver Parameters dialog box to solve the problem. When Solver finds the optimal solution, it displays the Solver Results dialog box shown in Figure 3.15. If the values on your screen do not match those in Figure 3.15, click the Restore Original Values option button, click OK, and try again.

This dialog box provides options for keeping the solution found by Solver or restoring the spreadsheet to its original condition. Most often, you will want to keep Solver's solution unless there is an obvious problem with it. Notice that the Solver Results dialog

FIGURE 3.14

*The Solver
Options dialog box*

FIGURE 3.15

*Optimal solution
for the Blue Ridge
Hot Tubs problem*

box also provides options for generating Answer, Sensitivity, and Limits reports. Chapter 4 discusses these options.

As shown in Figure 3.15, Solver determined that the optimal value for cell B5 is 122 and the optimal value for cell C5 is 78. These values correspond to the optimal values for X_1 and X_2 that we determined graphically in Chapter 2. The value of the set cell (D6) now indicates that if Blue Ridge Hot Tubs produces and sells 122 Aqua-Spas and 78 Hydro-Luxes, the company will earn a profit of $66,100. Cells D9, D10, and D11 indicate that this solution uses all the 200 available pumps, all the 1,566 available labor hours, and 2,712 of the 2,880 feet of available tubing.

3.7 Goals and Guidelines for Spreadsheet Design

Now that you have a basic idea of how Solver works and how to set up an LP model in a spreadsheet, we'll walk through several more examples of formulating LP models and solving them with Solver. These problems highlight the wide variety of business problems in which LP can be applied and also will show you some helpful "tricks of the trade" that should help you solve the problems at the end of this chapter. When you work through the end-of-the-chapter problems, you will better appreciate how much thought is required to find a good way to implement a given model.

As we proceed, keep in mind that you can set up these problems more than one way. Creating spreadsheet models that communicate their purpose effectively is very much an art—or at least an acquired skill. Spreadsheets are inherently free-form and impose no particular structure on the way we model problems. As a result, there is no one "right" way to model a problem in a spreadsheet; however some ways certainly are better (or more logical) than others. To achieve the end result of a logical spreadsheet design, your modeling efforts should be directed toward the following goals:

- **Communication.** A spreadsheet's primary business purpose is that of communicating information to managers. As such, the primary design objective in most spreadsheet modeling tasks is to communicate the relevant aspects of the problem at hand in as clear and intuitively appealing a manner as possible.
- **Reliability.** The output that a spreadsheet generates should be correct and consistent. This has an obvious impact on the degree of confidence a manager places in the results of the modeling effort.
- **Auditability.** A manager should be able to retrace the steps followed to generate the different outputs from the model, to understand the model and to verify results. Models that are set up in an intuitively appealing, logical layout tend to be the most auditable.
- **Modifiability.** The data and assumptions upon which we build spreadsheet models can change frequently. A well-designed spreadsheet should be easy to change or enhance to meet changing user requirements.

In most cases, the spreadsheet design that communicates its purpose most clearly also will be the most reliable, auditable, and modifiable design. As you consider different ways of implementing a spreadsheet model for a particular problem, consider how well the modeling alternatives compare in terms of these goals. Some practical suggestions and guidelines for creating effective spreadsheet models are given in Figure 3.16.

Spreadsheet Design Guidelines

- **Organize the data, then build the model around the data.** After the data is arranged in a visually appealing manner, logical locations for decision variables, constraints, and the objective function tend to naturally suggest themselves. This also tends to enhance the reliability, auditability, and maintainability of the model.
- **Do not embed numeric constants in formulas.** Numeric constants should be placed in individual cells and labeled appropriately. This enhances the reliability and modifiability of the model.
- **Things which are logically related (for example, LHS and RHS of constraints) should be arranged in close physical proximity to one another and in the same columnar or row orientation.** This enhances reliability and auditability of the model.

(Continued)

FIGURE 3.16

Guidelines for effective spreadsheet design

- **A design that results in formulas that can be copied is probably better than one that does not.** A model with formulas that can copied to complete a series of calculations in a range is less prone to error (more reliable) and tends to be more understandable (auditable). Once users understand the first formula in a range, they understand all the formulas in a range.
- **Column or row totals should be in close proximity to the columns or rows being totaled.** Spreadsheet users often expect numbers at the end of a column or row to represent a total or some other summary measure involving the data in the column or row. Numbers at the ends of columns or rows that do not represent totals can be misinterpreted easily (reducing auditability).
- **The English-reading human eye scans left to right, top to bottom.** This fact should be considered and reflected in the spreadsheet design to enhance the auditability of the model.
- **Use color, shading, borders, and protection to distinguish changeable parameters from other elements of the model.** This enhances the reliability and modifiability of the model.
- **Use text boxes and cell comments to document various elements of the model.** These devices can be used to provide greater detail about a model or particular cells in a model than labels on a spreadsheet might allow.

Spreadsheet-Based LP Solvers Create New Applications for Linear Programming

In 1987, *The Wall Street Journal* reported on an exciting new trend in business—the availability of solvers for personal computers that allowed many businesses to transfer LP models from mainframe computers. Newfoundland Energy Ltd., for example, had evaluated its mix of crude oils to purchase with LP on a mainframe for 25 years. Since it began using a personal computer for this application, the company has saved thousands of dollars per year in mainframe access time charges.

The expansion of access to LP also spawned new applications. Therese Fitzpatrick, a nursing administrator at Grant Hospital in Chicago, used spreadsheet optimization to create a staff scheduling model that was projected to save the hospital $80,000 per month in overtime and temporary hiring costs. The task of scheduling 300 nurses so that those with appropriate skills were in the right place at the right time required 20 hours per month. The LP model enabled Therese to do the job in four hours, even with such complicating factors as leaves, vacations, and variations in staffing requirements at different times and days of the week.

Hawley Fuel Corp., a New York wholesaler of coal, found that it could minimize its cost of purchases while still meeting customers' requirements for sulfur and ash content by optimizing a spreadsheet LP model. Charles Howard of Victoria, British Columbia, developed an LP model to increase electricity generation from a dam just by opening and closing the outlet valves at the right time.

(Source: Bulkely, William M., "The Right Mix: New Software Makes the Choice Much Easier," *The Wall Street Journal*, March 27, 1987, p. 17.)

3.8 Make vs. Buy Decisions

As mentioned at the beginning of Chapter 2, LP is particularly well-suited to problems where scarce or limited resources must be allocated or used in an optimal manner. Numerous examples of these types of problems occur in manufacturing organizations. For example, LP might be used to determine how the various components of a job should be assigned to multipurpose machines to minimize the time it takes to complete the job. As another example, a company might receive an order for several items that it cannot fill entirely with its own production capacity. In such a case, the company must determine which items to produce and which items to subcontract (or buy) from an outside supplier. The following is an example of this type of make vs. buy decision.

> The Electro-Poly Corporation is the world's leading manufacturer of slip rings. A slip ring is an electrical coupling device that allows current to pass through a spinning or rotating connection—such as a gun turret on a ship, aircraft, or tank. The company recently received a $750,000 order for various quantities of three types of slip rings. Each slip ring requires a certain amount of time to wire and harness. The following table summarizes the requirements for the three models of slip rings.

	Model 1	Model 2	Model 3
Number Ordered	3,000	2,000	900
Hours of Wiring Required per Unit	2	1.5	3
Hours of Harnessing Required per Unit	1	2	1

> Unfortunately, Electro-Poly does not have enough wiring and harnessing capacity to fill the order by its due date. The company has only 10,000 hours of wiring capacity and 5,000 hours of harnessing capacity available to devote to this order. However, the company can subcontract any portion of this order to one of its competitors. The unit costs of producing each model in-house and buying the finished products from a competitor are summarized below.

	Model 1	Model 2	Model 3
Cost to Make	$50	$83	$130
Cost to Buy	$61	$97	$145

> Electro-Poly wants to determine the number of slip rings to make and the number to buy to fill the customer order at the least possible cost.

3.8.1 DEFINING THE DECISION VARIABLES

To solve the Electro-Poly problem, we need six decision variables to represent the alternatives under consideration. The six variables are:

M_1 = number of model 1 slip rings to make in-house

M_2 = number of model 2 slip rings to make in-house

M_3 = number of model 3 slip rings to make in-house

B_1 = number of model 1 slip rings to buy from competitor

B_2 = number of model 2 slip rings to buy from competitor

B_3 = number of model 3 slip rings to buy from competitor

As mentioned in Chapter 2, we do not have to use the symbols $X_1, X_2, \ldots, X_n$ for the decision variables. If other symbols better clarify the model, you are certainly free to use them. In this case, the symbols M_i and B_i help distinguish the **M**ake in-house variables from the **B**uy from competitor variables.

3.8.2 DEFINING THE OBJECTIVE FUNCTION

The objective in this problem is to minimize the total cost of filling the order. Recall that each model 1 slip ring made in-house (each unit of M_1) costs \$50; each model 2 slip ring made in-house (each unit of M_2) costs \$83; and each model 3 slip ring (each unit of M_3) costs \$130. Each model 1 slip ring bought from the competitor (each unit of B_1) costs \$61; each model 2 slip ring bought from the competitor (each unit of B_2) costs \$97; and each model 3 slip ring bought from the competitor (each unit of B_3) costs \$145. Thus, the objective is stated mathematically as:

$$\text{MIN:} \qquad 50M_1 + 83M_2 + 130M_3 + 61B_1 + 97B_2 + 145B_3$$

3.8.3 DEFINING THE CONSTRAINTS

Several constraints affect this problem. Two constraints are needed to ensure that the number of slip rings made in-house does not exceed the available capacity for wiring and harnessing. These constraints are stated as:

$$2M_1 + 1.5M_2 + 3M_3 \leq 10{,}000 \qquad \} \text{ wiring constraint}$$
$$1M_1 + 2M_2 + 1M_3 \leq 5{,}000 \qquad \} \text{ harnessing constraint}$$

Three additional constraints ensure that 3,000 model 1 slip rings, 2,000 model 2 slip rings, and 900 model 3 slip rings are available to fill the order. These constraints are stated as:

$$M_1 + B_1 = 3{,}000 \qquad \} \text{ demand for model 1}$$
$$M_2 + B_2 = 2{,}000 \qquad \} \text{ demand for model 2}$$
$$M_3 + B_3 = 900 \qquad \} \text{ demand for model 3}$$

Finally, because none of the variables in the model can assume a value of less than zero, we also need the following nonnegativity condition:

$$M_1, M_2, M_3, B_1, B_2, B_3 \geq 0$$

3.8.4 IMPLEMENTING THE MODEL

The LP model for Electro-Poly's make vs. buy problem is summarized as:

MIN: $50M_1 + 83M_2 + 130M_3 + 61B_1 + 97B_2 + 145B_3$ } total cost
Subject to: $M_1 + B_1 = 3{,}000$ } demand for model 1
             $M_2 + B_2 = 2{,}000$ } demand for model 2
             $M_3 + B_3 = 900$ } demand for model 3
             $2M_1 + 1.5M_2 + 3M_3 \leq 10{,}000$ } wiring constraint
             $1M_1 + 2M_2 + 1M_3 \leq 5{,}000$ } harnessing constraint
             $M_1, M_2, M_3, B_1, B_2, B_3 \geq 0$ } nonnegativity condition

The data for this model are implemented in the spreadsheet shown in Figure 3.17 (and in the file Fig3-17.xls on your data disk). The coefficients that appear in the objective function are entered in the range B10 through D11. The coefficients for the LHS

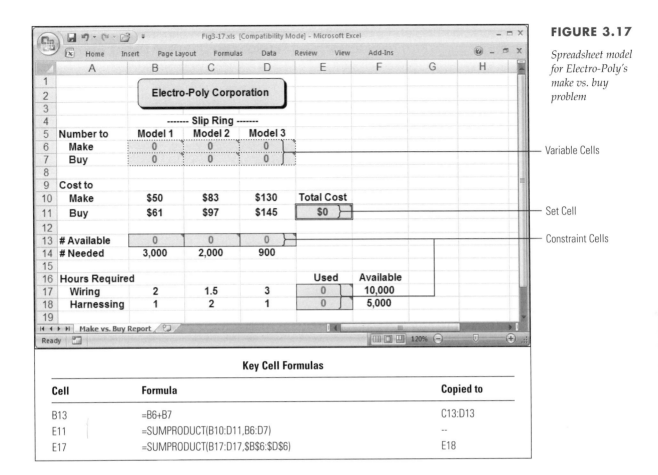

FIGURE 3.17

Spreadsheet model for Electro-Poly's make vs. buy problem

Key Cell Formulas

Cell	Formula	Copied to
B13	=B6+B7	C13:D13
E11	=SUMPRODUCT(B10:D11,B6:D7)	--
E17	=SUMPRODUCT(B17:D17,$B$6:$D$6)	E18

formulas for the wiring and harnessing constraints are entered in cells B17 through D18, and the corresponding RHS values are entered in cells F17 and F18. Because the LHS formulas for the demand constraints involve simply summing the decision variables, we do not need to list the coefficients for these constraints in the spreadsheet. The RHS values for the demand constraints are entered in cells B14 through D14.

Cells B6 through D7 are reserved to represent the six variables in our algebraic model. So, the objective function could be entered in cell E11 as:

Formula for cell E11: $= B10{*}B6 + C10{*}C6 + D10{*}D6 + B11{*}B7 + C11{*}C7 + D11{*}D7$

In this formula, the values in the range B6 through D7 are multiplied by the corresponding values in the range B10 through D11; these individual products are then added together. Therefore, the formula is simply the sum of a collection of products—or a *sum of products*. It turns out that this formula can be implemented in an equivalent (and easier) way as:

Equivalent formula for cell E11:   =SUMPRODUCT(B10:D11,B6:D7)

The preceding formula takes the values in the range B10 through D11, multiplies them by the corresponding values in the range B6 through D7, and adds (or sums) these products. The SUMPRODUCT( ) function greatly simplifies the implementation of many formulas required in optimization problems and will be used extensively throughout this book.

Because the LHS of the demand constraint for model 1 slip rings involves adding variables M_1 and B_1, this constraint is implemented in cell B13 by adding the two cells in the spreadsheet that correspond to these variables—cells B6 and B7:

Formula for cell B13:   =B6+B7

(Copy to C13 through D13.)

The formula in cell B13 is then copied to cells C13 and D13 to implement the LHS formulas for the constraints for model 2 and model 3 slip rings.

The coefficients for the wiring and harnessing constraints are entered in cells B17 through D18. The LHS formula for the wiring constraint is implemented in cell E17 as:

Formula for cell E17:   =SUMPRODUCT(B17:D17,$B$6:$D$6)

(Copy to cell E18.)

This formula is then copied to cell E18 to implement the LHS formula for the harnessing constraint. (In the preceding formula, the dollar signs denote absolute cell references. An **absolute cell reference** will not change if the formula containing the reference is copied to another location.)

3.8.5 SOLVING THE MODEL

To solve this model, we need to specify the set cell, variable cells, and constraint cells identified in Figure 3.17, just as we did earlier in the Blue Ridge Hot Tubs example. Figure 3.18 shows the Solver parameters required to solve Electro-Poly's make vs. buy problem.

After we click the Solve button in the Solver Parameters dialog box, Solver finds the optimal solution shown in Figure 3.19.

3.8.6 ANALYZING THE SOLUTION

The optimal solution shown in Figure 3.19 indicates that Electro-Poly should make (in-house) 3,000 model 1 slip rings, 550 model 2 slip rings, and 900 model 3 slip rings (that is, $M_1 = 3,000$, $M_2 = 550$, $M_3 = 900$). Additionally, it should buy 1,450 model 2 slip rings from its competitor (that is, $B_1 = 0$, $B_2 = 1,450$, $B_3 = 0$). This solution allows Electro-Poly

FIGURE 3.18

Solver parameters for the make vs. buy problem

FIGURE 3.19

Optimal solution to Electro-Poly's make vs. buy problem

to fill the customer order at a minimum cost of $453,300. This solution uses 9,525 of the 10,000 hours of available wiring capacity and all 5,000 hours of the harnessing capacity.

At first glance, this solution might seem a bit surprising. Electro-Poly has to pay $97 for each model 2 slip ring that it purchases from its competitor. This represents a $14 premium over its in-house cost of $83. On the other hand, Electro-Poly has to pay a premium of $11 over its in-house cost to purchase model 1 slip rings from its competitor. It seems as if the optimal solution would be to purchase model 1 slip rings from its competitor rather than model 2 slip rings because the additional cost premium for model 1 slip rings is smaller. However, this argument fails to consider the fact that each model 2 slip ring produced in-house uses twice as much of the company's harnessing capacity as does each model 1 slip ring. Making more model 2 slip rings in-house would deplete the company's harnessing capacity more quickly, and would require buying an excessive number of model 1 slip rings from the competitor. Fortunately, the LP technique automatically considers such trade-offs in determining the optimal solution to the problem.

3.9 An Investment Problem

There are numerous problems in the area of finance to which we can apply various optimization techniques. These problems often involve attempting to maximize the return on an investment while meeting certain cash flow requirements and risk constraints. Alternatively, we might want to minimize the risk on an investment while maintaining a certain level of return. We'll consider one such problem here and discuss several other financial engineering problems throughout this text.

Brian Givens is a financial analyst for Retirement Planning Services, Inc. who specializes in designing retirement income portfolios for retirees using corporate bonds. He has just completed a consultation with a client who expects to have

$750,000 in liquid assets to invest when she retires next month. Brian and his client agreed to consider upcoming bond issues from the following six companies:

Company	Return	Years to Maturity	Rating
Acme Chemical	8.65%	11	1-Excellent
DynaStar	9.50%	10	3-Good
Eagle Vision	10.00%	6	4-Fair
MicroModeling	8.75%	10	1-Excellent
OptiPro	9.25%	7	3-Good
Sabre Systems	9.00%	13	2-Very Good

The column labeled "Return" in this table represents the expected annual yield on each bond, the column labeled "Years to Maturity" indicates the length of time over which the bonds will be payable, and the column labeled "Rating" indicates an independent underwriter's assessment of the quality or risk associated with each issue.

Brian believes that all of the companies are relatively safe investments. However, to protect his client's income, Brian and his client agreed that no more than 25% of her money should be invested in any one investment and at least half of her money should be invested in long-term bonds that mature in ten or more years. Also, even though DynaStar, Eagle Vision, and OptiPro offer the highest returns, it was agreed that no more than 35% of the money should be invested in these bonds because they also represent the highest risks (i.e., they were rated lower than "very good").

Brian needs to determine how to allocate his client's investments to maximize her income while meeting their agreed-upon investment restrictions.

3.9.1 DEFINING THE DECISION VARIABLES

In this problem, Brian must decide how much money to invest in each type of bond. Because there are six different investment alternatives, we need the following six decision variables:

$$X_1 = \text{amount of money to invest in Acme Chemical}$$
$$X_2 = \text{amount of money to invest in DynaStar}$$
$$X_3 = \text{amount of money to invest in Eagle Vision}$$
$$X_4 = \text{amount of money to invest in MicroModeling}$$
$$X_5 = \text{amount of money to invest in OptiPro}$$
$$X_6 = \text{amount of money to invest in Sabre Systems}$$

3.9.2 DEFINING THE OBJECTIVE FUNCTION

The objective in this problem is to maximize the investment income for Brian's client. Because each dollar invested in Acme Chemical (X_1) earns 8.65% annually, each dollar invested in DynaStar (X_2) earns 9.50%, and so on, the objective function for the problem is expressed as:

MAX: $.0865X_1 + .095X_2 + .10X_3 + .0875X_4 + .0925X_5 + .09X_6$ } total annual return

3.9.3 DEFINING THE CONSTRAINTS

Again, there are several constraints that apply to this problem. First, we must ensure that exactly $750,000 is invested. This is accomplished by the following constraint:

$$X_1 + X_2 + X_3 + X_4 + X_5 + X_6 = 750,000$$

Next, we must ensure that no more than 25% of the total is invested in any one investment. Twenty-five percent of $750,000 is $187,500. Therefore, Brian can put no more than $187,500 into any one investment. The following constraints enforce this restriction:

$$X_1 \leq 187,500$$
$$X_2 \leq 187,500$$
$$X_3 \leq 187,500$$
$$X_4 \leq 187,500$$
$$X_5 \leq 187,500$$
$$X_6 \leq 187,500$$

Because the bonds for Eagle Vision (X_3) and OptiPro (X_5) are the only ones that mature in fewer than 10 years, the following constraint ensures that at least half the money ($375,000) is placed in investments maturing in ten or more years:

$$X_1 + X_2 + X_4 + X_6 \geq 375,000$$

Similarly, the following constraint ensures that no more than 35% of the money ($262,500) is placed in the bonds for DynaStar (X_2), Eagle Vision (X_3), and OptiPro (X_5):

$$X_2 + X_3 + X_5 \leq 262,500$$

Finally, because none of the variables in the model can assume a value of less than zero, we also need the following nonnegativity condition:

$$X_1, X_2, X_3, X_4, X_5, X_6 \geq 0$$

3.9.4 IMPLEMENTING THE MODEL

The LP model for the Retirement Planning Services, Inc. investment problem is summarized as:

MAX: $.0865X_1 + .095X_2 + .10X_3 + .0875X_4 + .0925X_5 + .09X_6$ } total annual return

Subject to:

$X_1 \leq 187,500$	} 25% restriction per investment
$X_2 \leq 187,500$	} 25% restriction per investment
$X_3 \leq 187,500$	} 25% restriction per investment
$X_4 \leq 187,500$	} 25% restriction per investment
$X_5 \leq 187,500$	} 25% restriction per investment
$X_6 \leq 187,500$	} 25% restriction per investment
$X_1 + X_2 + X_3 + X_4 + X_5 + X_6 = 750,000$	} total amount invested
$X_1 + X_2 + X_4 + X_6 \geq 375,000$	} long-term investment
$X_2 + X_3 + X_5 \leq 262,500$	} higher-risk investment
$X_1, X_2, X_3, X_4, X_5, X_6 \geq 0$	} nonnegativity conditions

FIGURE 3.20

Spreadsheet model for Retirement Planning Services, Inc. bond selection problem

Key Cell Formulas

Cell	Formula	Copied to
C12	=SUM(C6:C11)	--
E12	=SUMPRODUCT(E6:E11,$C$6:$C$11)	G12 and I12

A convenient way of implementing this model is shown in Figure 3.20 (file Fig3-20.xls on your data disk). Each row in this spreadsheet corresponds to one of the investment alternatives. Cells C6 through C11 correspond to the decision variables for the problem ($X_1, \ldots, X_6$). The maximum value that each of these cells can take on is listed in cells D6 through D11. These values correspond to the RHS values for the first six constraints. The sum of cells C6 through C11 is computed in cell C12 as follows, and will be restricted to equal the value shown in cell C13:

$$\text{Formula for cell C12: } =\text{SUM(C6:C11)}$$

The annual returns for each investment are listed in cells E6 through E11. The objective function is then implemented conveniently in cell E12 as follows:

$$\text{Formula for cell E12: } =\text{SUMPRODUCT(E6:E11,\$C\$6:\$C\$11)}$$

The values in cells G6 through G11 indicate which of these rows correspond to "long-term" investments. Note that the use of ones and zeros in this column makes it convenient to compute the sum of the cells C6, C7, C9, and C11 (representing $X_1, X_2, X_4,$ and X_6) representing the LHS of the "long-term" investment constraint. This is done in cell G12 as follows:

$$\text{Formula for cell G12: } =\text{SUMPRODUCT(G6:G11,\$C\$6:\$C\$11)}$$

Similarly, the zeros and ones in cells I6 through I11 indicate the higher-risk investments and allow us to implement the LHS of the "higher-risk investment" constraint as follows:

$$\text{Formula for cell I12: } =\text{SUMPRODUCT(I6:I11,\$C\$6:\$C\$11)}$$

Note that the use of zeros and ones in columns G and I to compute the sums of selected decision variables is a very useful modeling technique that makes it easy for the user to change the variables being included in the sums. Also note that the formula for the objective in cell E12 could be copied to cells G12 and I12 to implement LHS formulas for these constraint cells.

3.9.5 SOLVING THE MODEL

To solve this model, we need to specify the set cell, variable cells, and constraint cells identified in Figure 3.20. Figure 3.21 shows the Solver parameters required to solve this problem. After we click the Solve button in the Solver Parameters dialog box, Solver finds the optimal solution shown in Figure 3.22.

FIGURE 3.21

Solver parameters for the bond selection problem

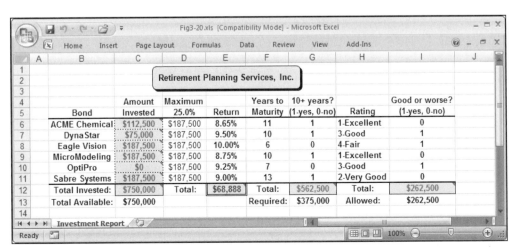

FIGURE 3.22

Optimal solution to the bond selection problem

3.9.6 ANALYZING THE SOLUTION

The solution shown in Figure 3.22 indicates that the optimal investment plan places $112,500 in Acme Chemical (X_1), $75,000 in DynaStar ($X_2$), $187,500 in Eagle Vision (X_3), $187,500 in MicroModeling (X_4), $0 in OptiPro ($X_5$), and $187,500 in Sabre Systems (X_6). It is interesting to note that more money is being invested in Acme Chemical than DynaStar and OptiPro even though the return on Acme Chemical is lower than on the returns for DynaStar and OptiPro. This is because DynaStar and OptiPro are both "higher-risk" investments and the 35% limit on "higher-risk" investments is a binding constraint (or is met as a strict equality in the optimal solution). Thus, the optimal solution could be improved if we could put more than 35% of the money into the higher-risk investments.

3.10 A Transportation Problem

Many transportation and logistics problems businesses face fall into a category of problems known as network flow problems. We will consider one such example here and study this area in more detail in Chapter 5.

> Tropicsun is a leading grower and distributor of fresh citrus products with three large citrus groves scattered around central Florida in the cities of Mt. Dora, Eustis, and Clermont. Tropicsun currently has 275,000 bushels of citrus at the grove in Mt. Dora, 400,000 bushels at the grove in Eustis, and 300,000 bushels at the grove in Clermont. Tropicsun has citrus processing plants in Ocala, Orlando, and Leesburg with processing capacities to handle 200,000, 600,000, and 225,000 bushels, respectively. Tropicsun contracts with a local trucking company to transport its fruit from the groves to the processing plants. The trucking company charges a flat rate for every mile that each bushel of fruit must be transported. Each mile a bushel of fruit travels is known as a bushel-mile. The following table summarizes the distances (in miles) between the groves and processing plants:

Grove	Distances (in miles) Between Groves and Plants		
	Ocala	Orlando	Leesburg
Mt. Dora	21	50	40
Eustis	35	30	22
Clermont	55	20	25

> Tropicsun wants to determine how many bushels to ship from each grove to each processing plant to minimize the total number of bushel-miles the fruit must be shipped.

3.10.1 DEFINING THE DECISION VARIABLES

In this situation, the problem is to determine how many bushels of fruit should be shipped from each grove to each processing plant. The problem is summarized graphically in Figure 3.23.

The circles (or nodes) in Figure 3.23 correspond to the different groves and processing plants in the problem. Note that a number has been assigned to each node. The arrows (or arcs) connecting the various groves and processing plants represent different shipping routes. The decision problem faced by Tropicsun is to determine how many bushels of fruit to ship on each of these routes. Thus, one decision variable is associated with each of the arcs in Figure 3.23. We can define these variables in general as:

X_{ij} = number of bushels to ship from node i to node j

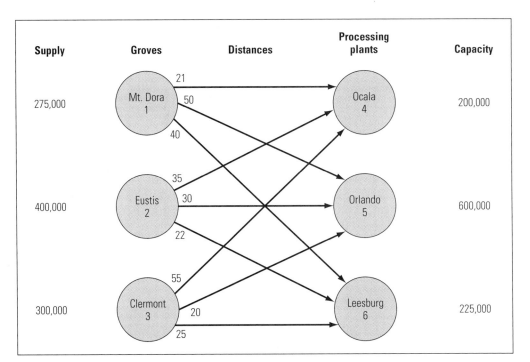

FIGURE 3.23

Diagram for the Tropicsun transportation problem

Specifically, the nine decision variables are:

X_{14} = number of bushels to ship from Mt. Dora (node 1) to Ocala (node 4)

X_{15} = number of bushels to ship from Mt. Dora (node 1) to Orlando (node 5)

X_{16} = number of bushels to ship from Mt. Dora (node 1) to Leesburg (node 6)

X_{24} = number of bushels to ship from Eustis (node 2) to Ocala (node 4)

X_{25} = number of bushels to ship from Eustis (node 2) to Orlando (node 5)

X_{26} = number of bushels to ship from Eustis (node 2) to Leesburg (node 6)

X_{34} = number of bushels to ship from Clermont (node 3) to Ocala (node 4)

X_{35} = number of bushels to ship from Clermont (node 3) to Orlando (node 5)

X_{36} = number of bushels to ship from Clermont (node 3) to Leesburg (node 6)

3.10.2 DEFINING THE OBJECTIVE FUNCTION

The goal in this problem is to determine how many bushels to ship from each grove to each processing plant while minimizing the total distance (or total number of bushel-miles) the fruit must travel. The objective function for this problem is represented by:

MIN: $21X_{14} + 50X_{15} + 40X_{16} + 35X_{24} + 30X_{25} + 22X_{26} + 55X_{34} + 20X_{35} + 25X_{36}$

The term $21X_{14}$ in this function reflects the fact that each bushel shipped from Mt. Dora (node 1) to Ocala (node 4) must travel 21 miles. The remaining terms in the function express similar relationships for the other shipping routes.

3.10.3 DEFINING THE CONSTRAINTS

Two physical constraints apply to this problem. First, there is a limit on the amount of fruit that can be shipped to each processing plant. Tropicsun can ship no more than

200,000, 600,000, and 225,000 bushels to Ocala, Orlando, and Leesburg, respectively. These restrictions are reflected by the following constraints:

$$X_{14} + X_{24} + X_{34} \leq 200{,}000 \qquad \} \text{ capacity restriction for Ocala}$$
$$X_{15} + X_{25} + X_{35} \leq 600{,}000 \qquad \} \text{ capacity restriction for Orlando}$$
$$X_{16} + X_{26} + X_{36} \leq 225{,}000 \qquad \} \text{ capacity restriction for Leesburg}$$

The first constraint indicates that the total bushels shipped to Ocala (node 4) from Mt. Dora (node 1), Eustis (node 2), and Clermont (node 3) must be less than or equal to Ocala's capacity of 200,000 bushels. The other two constraints have similar interpretations for Orlando and Leesburg. Notice that the total processing capacity at the plants (1,025,000 bushels) exceeds the total supply of fruit at the groves (975,000 bushels). Therefore, these constraints are "less than or equal to" constraints because not all the available capacity will be used.

The second set of constraints ensures that the supply of fruit at each grove is shipped to a processing plant. That is, all of the 275,000, 400,000, and 300,000 bushels at Mt. Dora, Eustis, and Clermont, respectively, must be processed somewhere. This is accomplished by the following constraints:

$$X_{14} + X_{15} + X_{16} = 275{,}000 \qquad \} \text{ supply available at Mt. Dora}$$
$$X_{24} + X_{25} + X_{26} = 400{,}000 \qquad \} \text{ supply available at Eustis}$$
$$X_{34} + X_{35} + X_{36} = 300{,}000 \qquad \} \text{ supply available at Clermont}$$

The first constraint indicates that the total amount shipped from Mt. Dora (node 1) to the plants in Ocala (node 4), Orlando (node 5), and Leesburg (node 6) must equal the total amount available at Mt. Dora. This constraint indicates that all the fruit available at Mt. Dora must be shipped somewhere. The other two constraints play similar roles for Eustis and Clermont.

3.10. 4 IMPLEMENTING THE MODEL

The LP model for Tropicsun's fruit transportation problem is summarized as:

MIN: $21X_{14} + 50X_{15} + 40X_{16} +$
         $35X_{24} + 30X_{25} + 22X_{26} +$ $\left.\begin{array}{c} \\ \\ \\ \end{array}\right\}$ total distance fruit is shipped
         $55X_{34} + 20X_{35} + 25X_{36}$ (in bushel-miles)

Subject to: $X_{14} + X_{24} + X_{34} \leq 200{,}000$ } capacity restriction for Ocala
         $X_{15} + X_{25} + X_{35} \leq 600{,}000$ } capacity restriction for Orlando
         $X_{16} + X_{26} + X_{36} \leq 225{,}000$ } capacity restriction for Leesburg
         $X_{14} + X_{15} + X_{16} = 275{,}000$ } supply available at Mt. Dora
         $X_{24} + X_{25} + X_{26} = 400{,}000$ } supply available at Eustis
         $X_{34} + X_{35} + X_{36} = 300{,}000$ } supply available at Clermont
         $X_{ij} \geq 0$, for all i and j } nonnegativity conditions

The last constraint, as in previous models, indicates that all the decision variables must be nonnegative.

A convenient way to implement this model is shown in Figure 3.24 (and in the file Fig3-24.xls on your data disk). In this spreadsheet, the distances between each grove and plant are summarized in a tabular format in cells C7 through E9. Cells C14 through E16 are reserved for representing the number of bushels of fruit to ship from each grove to each processing plant. Notice that these nine cells correspond directly to the nine decision variables in the algebraic formulation of the model.

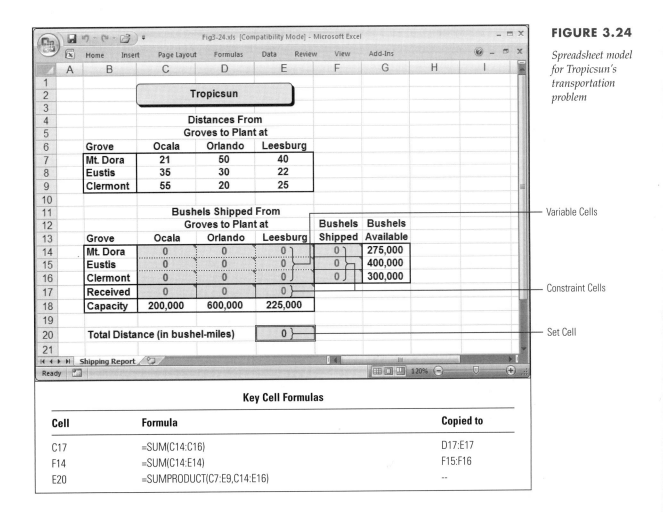

FIGURE 3.24

Spreadsheet model for Tropicsun's transportation problem

The LHS formulas for the three capacity constraints in the model are implemented in cells C17, D17, and E17 in the spreadsheet. To do this, the following formula is entered in cell C17 and copied to cells D17 and E17:

Formula for cell C17:   =SUM(C14:C16)
(Copy to D17 and E17.)

These cells represent the total bushels of fruit being shipped to the plants in Ocala, Orlando, and Leesburg, respectively. Cells C18 through E18 contain the RHS values for these constraint cells.

The LHS formulas for the three supply constraints in the model are implemented in cells F14, F15, and F16 as:

Formula for cell F14:   =SUM(C14:E14)
(Copy to F15 and F16.)

These cells represent the total bushels of fruit being shipped from the groves at Mt. Dora, Eustis, and Clermont, respectively. Cells G14 through G16 contain the RHS values for these constraint cells.

Finally, the objective function for this model is entered in cell E20 as:

Formula for cell E20:   =SUMPRODUCT(C7:E9,C14:E16)

The SUMPRODUCT( ) function multiplies each element in the range C7 through E9 by the corresponding element in the range C14 through E16 and then sums the individual products.

3.10.5 HEURISTIC SOLUTION FOR THE MODEL

To appreciate what Solver is accomplishing, let's consider how we might try to solve this problem manually using a heuristic. A **heuristic** is a rule of thumb for making decisions that might work well in some instances, but is not guaranteed to produce optimal solutions or decisions. One heuristic we can apply to solve Tropicsun's problem is to always ship as much as possible along the next available path with the shortest distance (or least cost). Using this heuristic, we solve the problem as follows:

1. Because the shortest available path between any grove and processing plant is between Clermont and Orlando (20 miles), we first ship as much as possible through this route. The maximum we can ship through this route is the smaller of the supply at Clermont (300,000 bushels) or the capacity at Orlando (600,000 bushels). So we would ship 300,000 bushels from Clermont to Orlando. This depletes the supply at Clermont.
2. The next shortest available route occurs between Mt. Dora and Ocala (21 miles). The maximum we can ship through this route is the smaller of the supply at Mt. Dora (275,000 bushels) or the capacity at Ocala (200,000 bushels). So we would ship 200,000 bushels from Mt. Dora to Ocala. This depletes the capacity at Ocala.
3. The next shortest available route occurs between Eustis and Leesburg (22 miles). The maximum we can ship through this route is the smaller of the supply at Eustis (400,000 bushels) or the capacity at Leesburg (225,000 bushels). So we would ship 225,000 bushels from Eustis to Leesburg. This depletes the capacity at Leesburg.
4. The next shortest available route occurs between Eustis and Orlando (30 miles). The maximum we can ship through this route is the smaller of the remaining supply at Eustis (175,000 bushels) or the remaining capacity at Orlando (300,000 bushels). So we would ship 175,000 bushels from Eustis to Orlando. This depletes the supply at Eustis.
5. The only remaining route occurs between Mt. Dora and Orlando (because the processing capacities at Ocala and Leesburg have both been depleted). This distance is 50 miles. The maximum we can ship through this route is the smaller of the remaining supply at Mt. Dora (75,000 bushels) and the remaining capacity at Orlando (125,000 bushels). So we would ship the final 75,000 bushels at Mt. Dora to Orlando. This depletes the supply at Mt. Dora.

As shown in Figure 3.25, the solution identified with this heuristic involves shipping the fruit a total of 24,150,000 bushel-miles. All the bushels available at each grove have been shipped to the processing plants and none of the capacities at the processing plants have been exceeded. Therefore, this is a *feasible* solution to the problem. And the logic used to find this solution might lead us to believe it is a reasonably good solution—but is it the *optimal* solution? Is there no other feasible solution to this problem that can make the total distance the fruit has to travel less than 24,150,000 bushel-miles?

3.10.6 SOLVING THE MODEL

To find the optimal solution to this model, we must indicate to Solver the set cell, variable cells, and constraint cells identified in Figure 3.24. Figure 3.26 shows the Solver parameters required to solve this problem. The optimal solution is shown in Figure 3.27.

FIGURE 3.25

A heuristic solution to the transportation problem

FIGURE 3.26

Solver parameters for the transportation problem

3.10.7 ANALYZING THE SOLUTION

The optimal solution in Figure 3.27 indicates that 200,000 bushels should be shipped from Mt. Dora to Ocala ($X_{14} = 200{,}000$) and 75,000 bushels should be shipped from Mt. Dora to Leesburg ($X_{16} = 75{,}000$). Of the 400,000 bushels available at the grove in Eustis, 250,000 bushels should be shipped to Orlando for processing ($X_{25} = 250{,}000$) and

FIGURE 3.27

Optimal solution to Tropicsun's transportation problem

150,000 bushels should be shipped to Leesburg ($X_{26} = 150,000$). Finally, all 300,000 bushels available in Clermont should be shipped to Orlando ($X_{35} = 300,000$). None of the other possible shipping routes will be used.

The solution shown in Figure 3.27 satisfies all the constraints in the model and results in a minimum shipping distance of 24,000,000 bushel-miles, which is better than the heuristic solution identified earlier. Therefore, simple heuristics can solve LP problems sometimes, but as this example illustrates, there is no guarantee that a heuristic solution is the best possible solution.

3.11 A Blending Problem

Many business problems involve determining an optimal mix of ingredients. For example, major oil companies must determine the least costly mix of different crude oils and other chemicals to blend together to produce a certain grade of gasoline. Lawn care companies must determine the least costly mix of chemicals and other products to blend together to produce different types of fertilizer. The following is another example of a common blending problem faced in the U.S. agricultural industry, which annually produces goods valued at approximately $200 billion.

Agri-Pro is a company that sells agricultural products to farmers in several states. One service it provides to customers is custom feed mixing, whereby a farmer can order a specific amount of livestock feed and specify the amount of corn, grain, and minerals the feed should contain. This is an important service because the proper feed for various farm animals changes regularly depending on the weather, pasture conditions, and so on.

Agri-Pro stocks bulk amounts of four types of feeds that it can mix to meet a given customer's specifications. The following table summarizes the four feeds, their composition of corn, grain, and minerals, and the cost per pound for each type.

| | Percent of Nutrient in | | | |
Nutrient	Feed 1	Feed 2	Feed 3	Feed 4
Corn	30%	5%	20%	10%
Grain	10%	30%	15%	10%
Minerals	20%	20%	20%	30%
Cost per Pound	$0.25	$0.30	$0.32	$0.15

On average, U.S. citizens consume almost 70 pounds of poultry per year. To remain competitive, chicken growers must ensure that they feed the required nutrients to their flocks in the most cost-effective manner. Agri-Pro has just received an order from a local chicken farmer for 8,000 pounds of feed. The farmer wants this feed to contain at least 20% corn, 15% grain, and 15% minerals. What should Agri-Pro do to fill this order at minimum cost?

3.11.1 DEFINING THE DECISION VARIABLES

In this problem, Agri-Pro must determine how much of the various feeds to blend together to meet the customer's requirements at minimum cost. An algebraic formulation of this problem might use the following four decision variables:

$$X_1 = \text{pounds of feed 1 to use in the mix}$$
$$X_2 = \text{pounds of feed 2 to use in the mix}$$
$$X_3 = \text{pounds of feed 3 to use in the mix}$$
$$X_4 = \text{pounds of feed 4 to use in the mix}$$

3.11.2 DEFINING THE OBJECTIVE FUNCTION

The objective in this problem is to fill the customer's order at the lowest possible cost. Because each pound of feed 1, 2, 3, and 4 costs $0.25, $0.30, $0.32, and $0.15, respectively, the objective function is represented by:

$$\text{MIN:} \quad .25X_1 + .30X_2 + .32X_3 + .15X_4$$

3.11.3 DEFINING THE CONSTRAINTS

Four constraints must be met to fulfill the customer's requirements. First, the customer wants a total of 8,000 pounds of feed. This is expressed by the constraint:

$$X_1 + X_2 + X_3 + X_4 = 8,000$$

The customer also wants the order to consist of at least 20% corn. Because each pound of feed 1, 2, 3, and 4 consists of 30%, 5%, 20%, and 10% corn, respectively, the total amount of corn in the mix is represented by:

$$.30X_1 + .05X_2 + .20X_3 + .10X_4$$

To ensure that *corn* constitutes at least 20% of the 8,000 pounds of feed, we set up the following constraint:

$$\frac{.30X_1 + .05X_2 + .20X_3 + .10X_4}{8,000} \geq .20$$

Similarly, to ensure that *grain* constitutes at least 15% of the 8,000 pounds of feed, we use the constraint:

$$\frac{.10X_1 + .30X_2 + .15X_3 + .10X_4}{8,000} \geq .15$$

Finally, to ensure that *minerals* constitute at least 15% of the 8,000 pounds of feed, we use the constraint:

$$\frac{.20X_1 + .20X_2 + .20X_3 + .30X_4}{8,000} \geq .15$$

3.11.4 SOME OBSERVATIONS ABOUT CONSTRAINTS, REPORTING, AND SCALING

We need to make some important observations about the constraints for this model. First, these constraints look somewhat different from the usual linear sum of products. However, these constraints are equivalent to a sum of products. For example, the constraint for the required percentage of corn can be expressed as:

$$\frac{.30X_1 + .05X_2 + .20X_3 + .10X_4}{8000} \geq .20$$

or as:

$$\frac{.30X_1}{8,000} + \frac{5.0X_2}{8,000} + \frac{.20X_3}{8,000} + \frac{.10X_4}{8,000} \geq .20$$

or, if you multiply both sides of the inequality by 8,000, as:

$$.30X_1 + .05X_2 + .20X_3 + .10X_4 \geq 1,600$$

All these constraints define exactly the same set of feasible values for $X_1, \ldots, X_4$. Theoretically, we should be able to implement and use *any* of these constraints to solve the problem. However, we need to consider a number of practical issues in determining which form of the constraint to implement.

Notice that the LHS formulas for the first and second versions of the constraint represent the *proportion* of corn in the 8,000 pound order, whereas the LHS in the third version of the constraint represents the *total pounds* of corn in the 8,000 pound order. Because we must implement the LHS formula of one of these constraints in the spreadsheet, we need to decide which number to display in the spreadsheet—the *proportion* (or percentage) of corn in the order, or the *total pounds of corn* in the order. If we know one of these values, we can easily set up a formula to calculate the other value. But, when more than one way to implement a constraint exists (as is usually the case), we need to consider what the value of the LHS portion of the constraint means to the user of the spreadsheet so that the results of the model can be reported as clearly as possible.

Another issue to consider involves *scaling* the model so that it can be solved accurately. For example, suppose we decide to implement the LHS formula for the first or second version of the corn constraint given earlier so that the *proportion* of corn in the 8,000 pound feed order appears in the spreadsheet. The coefficients for the variables in these constraints are *very* small values. In either case, the coefficient for X_2 is 0.05/8,000 or 0.000006250.

As Solver tries to solve an LP problem, it must perform intermediate calculations that make the various coefficients in the model larger or smaller. As numbers become extremely large or small, computers often run into storage or representation problems that force them to use approximations of the actual numbers. This opens the door for problems to occur in the accuracy of the results and, in some cases, can prevent the computer from solving the problem at all. So, if some coefficients in the initial model are extremely large or extremely small, it is a good idea to rescale the problem so that all the coefficients are of similar magnitudes.

3.11.5 RESCALING THE MODEL

To illustrate how a problem is rescaled, consider the following equivalent formulation of the Agri-Pro problem:

X_1 = amount of feed 1 *in thousands of pounds* to use in the mix
X_2 = amount of feed 2 *in thousands of pounds* to use in the mix
X_3 = amount of feed 3 *in thousands of pounds* to use in the mix
X_4 = amount of feed 4 *in thousands of pounds* to use in the mix

The objective function and constraints are represented by:

MIN: $250X_1 + 300X_2 + 320X_3 + 150X_4$ } total cost

Subject to: $X_1 + X_2 + X_3 + X_4 = \quad 8$ } pounds of feed required

$$\frac{.30X_1 + .05X_2 + .20X_3 + .10X_4}{8} \geq 0.20 \quad \} \text{ min \% of corn required}$$

$$\frac{.10X_1 + .30X_2 + .15X_3 + .10X_4}{8} \geq 0.15 \quad \} \text{ min \% of grain required}$$

$$\frac{.20X_1 + .20X_2 + .20X_3 + .30X_4}{8} \geq 0.15 \quad \} \text{ min \% of minerals required}$$

$X_1, X_2, X_3, X_4 \geq \quad 0$ } nonnegativity conditions

Each unit of X_1, X_2, X_3, and X_4 now represents 1,000 pounds of feed 1, 2, 3, and 4, respectively. So the objective now reflects the fact that each unit (or each 1,000 pounds) of X_1, X_2, X_3, and X_4 costs $250, $300, $320, and $150, respectively. The constraints have also been adjusted to reflect the fact that the variables now represent thousands of pounds of the different feeds. Notice that the smallest coefficient in the constraints is now $0.05/8 = 0.00625$ and the largest coefficient is 8 (that is, the RHS value for the first constraint). In our original formulation, the smallest coefficient was 0.00000625 and the largest coefficient was 8,000. By rescaling the problem, we dramatically reduced the range between the smallest and largest coefficients in the model.

Automatic Scaling

In solving some earlier problems in this chapter, you might have noticed that the Solver Options dialog box provides an option called Use Automatic Scaling (see Figure 3.14). If you select this option, Solver attempts to rescale the data automatically before solving the problem. Although this option is effective, you should not rely solely on it to solve all scaling problems that occur in your models.

Scaling and Linear Models

When the Standard LP Simplex solving option is selected, Solver conducts several internal tests to verify that the model is truly linear in the objective and constraints. If Solver's tests indicate that the model is not linear, a dialog box appears indicating that the conditions for linearity are not satisfied. The internal tests Solver applies are nearly 100% accurate but sometimes indicate that the model is not linear when, in fact, it is. This often occurs when a model is poorly scaled. If you encounter this message and you are certain that your model is linear, re-solving the model might result in Solver identifying the optimal solution. If this does not work, try reformulating your model so that it is more evenly scaled.

3.11.6 IMPLEMENTING THE MODEL

One way to implement this model in a spreadsheet is shown in Figure 3.28 (and in the file Fig3-28.xls on your data disk). In this spreadsheet, cells B5 through E5 contain the costs of the different types of feeds. The percentage of the different nutrients found in each type of feed is listed in cells B10 through E12.

FIGURE 3.28

Spreadsheet model for Agri-Pro's blending problem

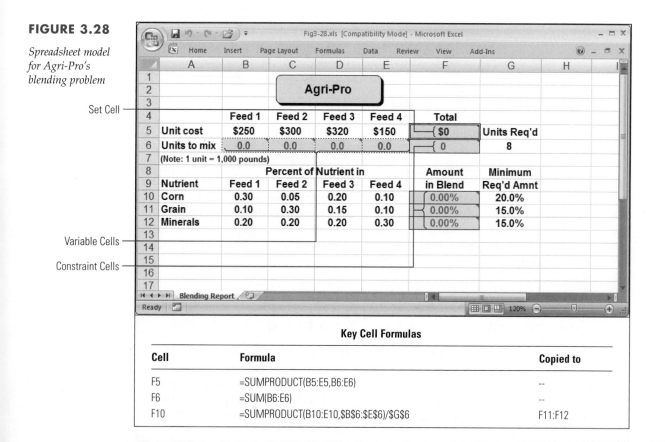

Cell	Formula	Copied to
F5	=SUMPRODUCT(B5:E5,B6:E6)	--
F6	=SUM(B6:E6)	--
F10	=SUMPRODUCT(B10:E10,$B$6:$E$6)/$G$6	F11:F12

Cell G6 contains the total amount of feed (in 1,000s of pounds) required for the order, and the minimum percentage of the three types of nutrients required by the customer order are entered in cells G10 through G12. Notice that the values in column G correspond to the RHS values for the various constraints in the model.

In this spreadsheet, cells B6, C6, D6, and E6 are reserved to represent the decision variables X_1, X_2, X_3, and X_4. These cells ultimately will indicate how much of each type of feed should be mixed together to fill the order. The objective function for the problem is implemented in cell F5 using the formula:

Formula for cell F5:   =SUMPRODUCT(B5:E5,B6:E6)

The LHS formula for the first constraint involves calculating the sum of the decision variables. This relationship is implemented in cell F6 as:

Formula for cell F6:   =SUM(B6:E6)

The RHS for this constraint is in cell G6. The LHS formulas for the other three constraints are implemented in cells F10, F11, and F12. Specifically, the LHS formula for the second constraint (representing the proportion of corn in the mix) is implemented in cell F10 as:

Formula for cell F10:   =SUMPRODUCT(B10:E10,$B$6:$E$6)/$G$6
(Copy to F11 through F12.)

This formula is then copied to cells F11 and F12 to implement the LHS formulas for the remaining two constraints. Again, cells G10 through G12 contain the RHS values for these constraints.

Notice that this model is implemented in a user-friendly way. Each constraint cell has a logical interpretation that communicates important information. For any given values for the variable cells (B6 through E6) totaling 8,000, the constraint cells (F10 through F12) indicate the *actual* percentage of corn, grain, and minerals in the mix.

3.11.7 SOLVING THE MODEL

Figure 3.29 shows the Solver parameters required to solve this problem. The optimal solution is shown in Figure 3.30.

FIGURE 3.29

Solver parameters for the blending problem

FIGURE 3.30

Optimal solution to Agri-Pro's blending problem

3.11.8 ANALYZING THE SOLUTION

The optimal solution shown in Figure 3.30 indicates that the 8,000 pound feed order is produced at the lowest possible cost by mixing 4,500 pounds of feed 1 ($X_1 = 4.5$) with 2,000 pounds of feed 2 ($X_2 = 2$) and 1,500 pounds of feed 4 ($X_4 = 1.5$). Cell F6 indicates this produces exactly 8,000 pounds of feed. Furthermore, cells F10 through F12 indicate this mix contains 20% corn, 15% grain, and 21.88% minerals. The total cost of producing this mix is $1,950, as indicated by cell F5.

Have You Seen LP at Your Grocery Store?

The next time you are at your local grocery store, make a special trip down the aisle where the pet food is located. On the back of just about any bag of dog or cat food, you should see the following sort of label (taken directly from the author's dog's favorite brand of food):

This product contains:

- At least 21% crude protein
- At least 8% crude fat
- At most 4.5% crude fiber
- At most 12% moisture

In making such statements, the manufacturer guarantees that these nutritional requirements are met by the product. Various ingredients (such as corn, soybeans, meat and bone meal, animal fat, wheat, and rice) are blended to make the product. Most companies are interested in determining the blend of ingredients that satisfies these requirements in the least costly way. Not surprisingly, almost all of the major pet food manufacturing companies use LP extensively in their production process to solve this type of blending problem.

3.12 A Production and Inventory Planning Problem

One of the most fundamental problems facing manufacturing companies is that of planning their production and inventory levels. This process considers demand forecasts and resource constraints for the next several time periods and determines production and inventory levels for each of these time periods so as to meet the anticipated demand in the most economical way. As the following example illustrates, the multiperiod nature of these problems can be handled very conveniently in a spreadsheet to greatly simplify the production planning process.

> The Upton Corporation manufactures heavy-duty air compressors for the home and light industrial markets. Upton is presently trying to plan its production and inventory levels for the next six months. Because of seasonal fluctuations in utility and raw material costs, the per unit cost of producing air compressors varies from month to month—as does the demand for air compressors. Production capacity also varies from month to month due to differences in the number of working days, vacations, and scheduled maintenance and training. The following table summarizes the monthly production costs, demands, and production capacity Upton's management expects to face over the next six months.

	Month					
	1	**2**	**3**	**4**	**5**	**6**
Unit Production Cost	$ 240	$ 250	$ 265	$ 285	$ 280	$ 260
Units Demanded	1,000	4,500	6,000	5,500	3,500	4,000
Maximum Production	4,000	3,500	4,000	4,500	4,000	3,500

> Given the size of Upton's warehouse, a maximum of 6,000 units can be held in inventory at the end of any month. The owner of the company likes to keep at least 1,500 units in inventory as safety stock to meet unexpected demand contingencies. To maintain a stable workforce, the company wants to produce no less than one half of its maximum production capacity each month. Upton's controller estimates that the cost of carrying a unit in any given month is approximately equal to 1.5% of the unit production cost in the same month. Upton estimates the number of units carried in inventory each month by averaging the beginning and ending inventory for each month.
>
> There are 2,750 units currently in inventory. Upton wants to identify the production and inventory plan for the next six months that will meet the expected demand each month while minimizing production and inventory costs.

3.12.1 DEFINING THE DECISION VARIABLES

The basic decision Upton's management team faces is how many units to manufacture in each of the next six months. We will represent these decision variables as follows:

$$P_1 = \text{number of units to produce in month 1}$$
$$P_2 = \text{number of units to produce in month 2}$$
$$P_3 = \text{number of units to produce in month 3}$$
$$P_4 = \text{number of units to produce in month 4}$$
$$P_5 = \text{number of units to produce in month 5}$$
$$P_6 = \text{number of units to produce in month 6}$$

3.12.2 DEFINING THE OBJECTIVE FUNCTION

The objective in this problem is to minimize the total production and inventory costs. The total production cost is computed easily as:

$$\text{Production Cost} = 240P_1 + 250P_2 + 265P_3 + 285P_4 + 280P_5 + 260P_6$$

The inventory cost is a bit more tricky to compute. The cost of holding a unit in inventory each month is 1.5% of the production cost in the same month. So, the unit inventory cost is \$3.60 in month 1 (i.e., 1.5% × \$240 = \$3.60), \$3.75 in month 2 (i.e., 1.5% × \$250 = \$3.75), and so on. The number of units held each month is to be computed as the average of the beginning and ending inventory for the month. Of course, the beginning inventory in any given month is equal to the ending inventory from the previous month. So if we let B_i represent the beginning inventory for month i, the total inventory cost is given by:

$$\text{Inventory Cost} = 3.6(B_1 + B_2)/2 + 3.75(B_2 + B_3)/2 + 3.98(B_3 + B_4)/2$$
$$+ 4.28(B_4 + B_5)/2 + 4.20(B_5 + B_6)/2 + 3.9(B_6 + B_7)/2$$

Note that the first term in the previous formula computes the inventory cost for month 1 using B_1 as the beginning inventory for month 1 and B_2 as the ending inventory for month 1. Thus, the objective function for this problem is given as:

$$\text{MIN:} \quad \left. \begin{array}{l} 240P_1 + 250P_2 + 265P_3 + 285P_4 + 280P_5 + 260P_6 \\ + 3.6(B_1 + B_2)/2 + 3.75(B_2 + B_3)/2 + 3.98(B_3 + B_4)/2 \\ + 4.28(B_4 + B_5)/2 + 4.20(B_5 + B_6)/2 + 3.9(B_6 + B_7)/2 \end{array} \right\} \quad \text{total cost}$$

3.12.3 DEFINING THE CONSTRAINTS

There are two sets of constraints that apply to this problem. First, the number of units produced each month cannot exceed the maximum production levels stated in the problem. However, we also must make sure that the number of units produced each month is no less than one half of the maximum production capacity for the month. These conditions can be expressed concisely as follows:

$$2{,}000 \le P_1 \le 4{,}000 \qquad \} \text{ production level for month 1}$$
$$1{,}750 \le P_2 \le 3{,}500 \qquad \} \text{ production level for month 2}$$
$$2{,}000 \le P_3 \le 4{,}000 \qquad \} \text{ production level for month 3}$$
$$2{,}250 \le P_4 \le 4{,}500 \qquad \} \text{ production level for month 4}$$
$$2{,}000 \le P_5 \le 4{,}000 \qquad \} \text{ production level for month 5}$$
$$1{,}750 \le P_6 \le 3{,}500 \qquad \} \text{ production level for month 6}$$

These restrictions simply place the appropriate lower and upper limits on the values that each of the decision variables may assume. Similarly, we must ensure that the ending inventory each month falls between the minimum and maximum allowable inventory levels of 1,500 and 6,000, respectively. In general, the ending inventory for any month is computed as:

$$\text{Ending Inventory} = \text{Beginning Inventory} + \text{Units Produced} - \text{Units Sold}$$

Thus, the following restrictions indicate that the ending inventory in each of the next six months (after meeting the demand for the month) must fall between 1,500 and 6,000.

$$1,500 \leq B_1 + P_1 - 1,000 \leq 6,000 \qquad \} \text{ ending inventory for month 1}$$
$$1,500 \leq B_2 + P_2 - 4,500 \leq 6,000 \qquad \} \text{ ending inventory for month 2}$$
$$1,500 \leq B_3 + P_3 - 6,000 \leq 6,000 \qquad \} \text{ ending inventory for month 3}$$
$$1,500 \leq B_4 + P_4 - 5,500 \leq 6,000 \qquad \} \text{ ending inventory for month 4}$$
$$1,500 \leq B_5 + P_5 - 3,500 \leq 6,000 \qquad \} \text{ ending inventory for month 5}$$
$$1,500 \leq B_6 + P_6 - 4,000 \leq 6,000 \qquad \} \text{ ending inventory for month 6}$$

Finally, to ensure that the beginning balance in one month equals the ending balance from the previous month, we have the following additional restrictions:

$$B_2 = B_1 + P_1 - 1,000$$
$$B_3 = B_2 + P_2 - 4,500$$
$$B_4 = B_3 + P_3 - 6,000$$
$$B_5 = B_4 + P_4 - 5,500$$
$$B_6 = B_5 + P_5 - 3,500$$
$$B_7 = B_6 + P_6 - 4,000$$

3.12.4 IMPLEMENTING THE MODEL

The LP problem for Upton's production and inventory planning problem may be summarized as:

MIN:

$$\left. \begin{array}{l} 240P_1 + 250P_2 + 265P_3 + 285P_4 + 280P_5 + 260P_6 \\ + 3.6(B_1 + B_2)/2 + 3.75(B_2 + B_3)/2 + 3.98(B_3 + B_4)/2 \\ + 4.28(B_4 + B_5)/2 + 4.20(B_5 + B_6)/2 + 3.9(B_6 + B_7)/2 \end{array} \right\} \text{ total cost}$$

Subject to:

$$2,000 \leq P_1 \leq 4,000 \qquad \} \text{ production level for month 1}$$
$$1,750 \leq P_2 \leq 3,500 \qquad \} \text{ production level for month 2}$$
$$2,000 \leq P_3 \leq 4,000 \qquad \} \text{ production level for month 3}$$
$$2,250 \leq P_4 \leq 4,500 \qquad \} \text{ production level for month 4}$$
$$2,000 \leq P_5 \leq 4,000 \qquad \} \text{ production level for month 5}$$
$$1,750 \leq P_6 \leq 3,500 \qquad \} \text{ production level for month 6}$$
$$1,500 \leq B_1 + P_1 - 1,000 \leq 6,000 \qquad \} \text{ ending inventory for month 1}$$
$$1,500 \leq B_2 + P_2 - 4,500 \leq 6,000 \qquad \} \text{ ending inventory for month 2}$$
$$1,500 \leq B_3 + P_3 - 6,000 \leq 6,000 \qquad \} \text{ ending inventory for month 3}$$
$$1,500 \leq B_4 + P_4 - 5,500 \leq 6,000 \qquad \} \text{ ending inventory for month 4}$$
$$1,500 \leq B_5 + P_5 - 3,500 \leq 6,000 \qquad \} \text{ ending inventory for month 5}$$
$$1,500 \leq B_6 + P_6 - 4,000 \leq 6,000 \qquad \} \text{ ending inventory for month 6}$$

where:

$$B_2 = B_1 + P_1 - 1,000$$
$$B_3 = B_2 + P_2 - 4,500$$
$$B_4 = B_3 + P_3 - 6,000$$
$$B_5 = B_4 + P_4 - 5,500$$
$$B_6 = B_5 + P_5 - 3,500$$
$$B_7 = B_6 + P_6 - 4,000$$

FIGURE 3.31

Spreadsheet model for Upton's production problem

Variable Cells

Constraint Cells

Set Cell

Key Cell Formulas

Cell	Formula	Copied to
C9	=C6+C7-C8	D9:H9
D6	=C9	E6:H6
C18	=$B$18*C17	D18:H18
C20	=C17*C7	D20:H20
C21	=C18*(C6+C9)/2	D21:H21
H23	=SUM(C20:H21)	--

A convenient way of implementing this model is shown in Figure 3.31 (and file Fig3-31.xls on your data disk). Cells C7 through H7 in this spreadsheet represent the number of air compressors to produce in each month and therefore correspond to the decision variables (P_1 through P_6) in our model. We will place appropriate upper and lower bounds on these cells to enforce the restrictions represented by the first six constraints in our model. The estimated demands for each time period are listed just below the decision variables in cells C8 through H8.

With the beginning inventory level of 2,750 entered in cell C6, the ending inventory for month 1 is computed in cell C9 as follows:

$$\text{Formula for cell C9:} \qquad =C6+C7-C8$$

(Copy to cells D9 through H9.)

This formula can be copied to cells D9 through H9 to compute the ending inventory levels for each of the remaining months. We will place appropriate lower and upper limits on these cells to enforce the restrictions indicated by the second set of six constraints in our model.

To ensure that the beginning inventory in month 2 equals the ending inventory from month 1, we place the following formula in cell D6:

Formula for cell D6:   =C9

(Copy to cells E6 through H6.)

This formula can be copied to cells E6 through H6 to ensure that the beginning inventory levels in each month equal the ending inventory levels from the previous month. It is important to note that because the beginning inventory levels can be calculated directly from the ending inventory levels, there is no need to specify these cells as constraint cells to Solver.

With the monthly unit production costs entered in cell C17 through H17, the monthly unit carrying costs are computed in cells C18 through H18 as follows:

Formula for cell C18:   =$B$18*C17

(Copy to cells D18 through H18.)

The total monthly production and inventory costs are then computed in rows 20 and 21 as follows:

Formula for cell C20:   =C17*C7

(Copy to cells D20 through H20.)

Formula for cell C21:   =C18*(C6 + C9)/2

(Copy to cells D21 through H21.)

Finally, the objective function representing the total production and inventory costs for the problem is implemented in cell H23 as follows:

Formula for cell H23:   =SUM(C20:H21)

3.12.5 SOLVING THE MODEL

Figure 3.32 shows the Solver parameters required to solve this problem. The optimal solution is shown in Figure 3.33.

FIGURE 3.32

Solver parameters for the production problem

FIGURE 3.33

*Optimal solution
to Upton's
production problem*

3.12.6 ANALYZING THE SOLUTION

The optimal solution shown in Figure 3.33 indicates that Upton should produce 4,000 units in period 1, 3,500 units in period 2, 4,000 units in period 3, 4,250 units in period 4, 4,000 units in period 5, and 3,500 units in period 6. Although the demand for air compressors in month 1 can be met by the beginning inventory, production in month 1 is required to build inventory for future months in which demand exceeds the available production capacity. Notice that this production schedule calls for the company to operate at full production capacity in all months except month 4. Month 4 is expected to have the highest per unit production cost. Therefore, it is more economical to produce extra units in prior months and hold them in inventory for sale in month 4.

It is important to note that although the solution to this problem provides a production plan for the next six months, it does not bind Upton's management team to implement this particular solution throughout the next six months. At an operational level, the management team is most concerned with the decision that must be made now—namely, the number of units to schedule for production in month 1. At the end of month 1, Upton's management should update the inventory, demand, and cost estimates, and re-solve the model to identify the production plan for the next six months (presently months 2 through 7). At the end of month 2, this process should be repeated. Thus, multiperiod planning models such as this should be used repeatedly on a periodic basis as part of a rolling planning process.

3.13 A Multi-Period Cash Flow Problem

Numerous business problems involve decisions that have a ripple effect on future decisions. In the previous example, we saw how the manufacturing plans for one time period can affect the amount of resources available and the inventory carried in subsequent time periods. Similarly, many financial decisions involve multiple time periods because the amount of money invested or spent at one point in time directly affects the amount of money available in subsequent time periods. In these types of multi-period problems, it can be difficult to account for the consequences of a current decision on future time periods without an LP model. The formulation of such a model is illustrated next in an example from the world of finance.

> Taco-Viva is a small but growing restaurant chain specializing in Mexican fast food. The management of the company has decided to build a new location in Wilmington, North Carolina, and wants to establish a construction fund (or sinking fund) to pay for the new facility. Construction of the restaurant is expected to take six months and cost $800,000. Taco-Viva's contract with the construction company requires it to make payments of $250,000 at the end of the second and fourth months, and a final payment of $300,000 at the end of the sixth month when the restaurant is completed. The company can use four investment opportunities to establish the construction fund; these investments are summarized in the following table:

Investment	Available in Month	Months to Maturity	Yield at Maturity
A	1, 2, 3, 4, 5, 6	1	1.8%
B	1, 3, 5	2	3.5%
C	1, 4	3	5.8%
D	1	6	11.0%

> The table indicates that investment A will be available at the beginning of each of the next six months, and funds invested in this manner mature in one month with a yield of 1.8%. Funds can be placed in investment C only at the beginning of months 1 and/or 4, and mature at the end of three months with a yield of 5.8%.
> The management of Taco-Viva needs to determine the investment plan that allows them to meet the required schedule of payments while placing the least amount of money in the construction fund.

This is a multi-period problem because a six-month planning horizon must be considered. That is, Taco-Viva must plan which investment alternatives to use at various times during the next six months.

3.13.1 DEFINING THE DECISION VARIABLES

The basic decision faced by the management of Taco-Viva is how much money to place in each investment vehicle during each time period when the investment opportunities are available. To model this problem, we need different variables to represent each investment/time period combination. This can be done as:

$A_1, A_2, A_3, A_4, A_5, A_6$ = the amount of money (in $1,000s) placed in investment A at the beginning of months 1, 2, 3, 4, 5, and 6, respectively

B_1, B_3, B_5 = the amount of money (in $1,000s) placed in investment B at the beginning of months 1, 3, and 5, respectively

C_1, C_4 = the amount of money (in $1,000s) placed in investment C at the beginning of months 1 and 4, respectively

D_1 = the amount of money (in $1,000s) placed in investment D at the beginning of month 1

Notice that all variables are expressed in units of thousands of dollars to maintain a reasonable scale for this problem. So, keep in mind that when referring to the amount of money represented by our variables, we mean the amount in thousands of dollars.

3.13.2 DEFINING THE OBJECTIVE FUNCTION

Taco-Viva's management wants to minimize the amount of money it must place in the construction fund initially to cover the payments that will be due under the contract. At the beginning of month 1, the company wants to invest some amount of money that, along with its investment earnings, will cover the required payments without an additional infusion of cash from the company. Because $A_1, B_1, C_1,$ and D_1 represent the initial amounts invested by the company in month 1, the objective function for the problem is:

MIN: $A_1 + B_1 + C_1 + D_1$ } total cash invested at the beginning of month 1

3.13.3 DEFINING THE CONSTRAINTS

To formulate the cash-flow constraints for this problem, it is important to clearly identify: (1) when the different investments can be made, (2) when the different investments will mature, and (3) how much money will be available when each investment matures. Figure 3.34 summarizes this information.

The negative values, represented by -1 in Figure 3.34, indicate when dollars can flow *into* each investment. The positive values indicate how much these same dollars will be worth when the investment matures, or when dollars flow *out* of each investment. The double-headed arrow symbols indicate time periods in which funds remain in a particular investment. For example, the third row of the table in Figure 3.34 indicates that every dollar placed in investment C at the beginning of month 1 will be worth $1.058 when this investment matures three months later—at the *beginning* of month 4. (Note that the beginning of month 4 occurs at virtually the same instant as the *end* of month 3. Thus, there is no practical difference between the beginning of one time period and the end of the previous time period.)

Assuming that the company invests the amounts represented by $A_1, B_1, C_1,$ and D_1 at the beginning of month 1, how much money would be available to reinvest or make the required payments at the beginning of months 2, 3, 4, 5, 6, and 7? The answer to this question allows us to generate the set of cash-flow constraints needed for this problem.

As indicated by the second column of Figure 3.34, the only funds maturing at the beginning of month 2 are those placed in investment A at the beginning of month 1 (A_1). The value of the funds maturing at the beginning of month 2 is $1.018A_1$. Because no payments are required at the beginning of month 2, all the maturing funds

	Cash Inflow/Outflow at the Beginning of Month						
Investment	1	2	3	4	5	6	7
A_1	−1	1.018					
B_1	−1	⟷	1.035				
C_1	−1	⟷	⟷	1.058			
D_1	−1	⟷	⟷	⟷	⟷	⟷	1.11
A_2		−1	1.018				
A_3			−1	1.018			
B_3			−1	⟷	1.035		
A_4				−1	1.018		
C_4				−1	⟷	⟷	1.058
A_5					−1	1.018	
B_5					−1	⟷	1.035
A_6						−1	1.018
Req'd Payments (in $1,000s)	$0	$0	$250	$0	$250	$0	$300

FIGURE 3.34

Cash-flow summary table for Taco-Viva's investment opportunities

must be reinvested. But the only new investment opportunity available at the beginning of month 2 is investment A (A_2). Thus, the amount of money placed in investment A at the beginning of month 2 must be $1.018A_1$. This is expressed by the constraint:

$$1.018A_1 = A_2 + 0 \qquad \} \text{ cash flow for month 2}$$

This constraint indicates that the total amount of money maturing at the beginning of month 2 ($1.018A_1$) must equal the amount of money reinvested at the beginning of month 2 (A_2) plus any payment due in month 2 ($0).

Now, consider the cash flows that will occur during month 3. At the beginning of month 3, any funds that were placed in investment B at the beginning of month 1 (B_1) will mature and be worth a total of $1.035B_1$. Similarly, any funds placed in investment A at the beginning of month 2 (A_2) will mature and be worth a total of $1.018A_2$. Because a payment of $250,000 is due at the beginning of month 3, we must ensure that the funds maturing at the beginning of month 3 are sufficient to cover this payment, and that any remaining funds are placed in the investment opportunities available at the beginning of month 3 (A_3 and B_3). This requirement can be stated algebraically as:

$$1.035B_1 + 1.018A_2 = A_3 + B_3 + 250 \qquad \} \text{ cash flow for month 3}$$

This constraint indicates that the total amount of money maturing at the beginning of month 3 ($1.035B_1 + 1.018A_2$) must equal the amount of money reinvested at the beginning of month 3 ($A_3 + B_3$) plus the payment due at the beginning of month 3 ($250,000).

The same logic we applied to generate the cash-flow constraints for months 2 and 3 also can be used to generate cash-flow constraints for the remaining months. Doing so produces a cash-flow constraint for each month that takes on the general form:

$$\begin{pmatrix} \text{Total \$ amount} \\ \text{maturing at the} \\ \text{beginning} \\ \text{of the month} \end{pmatrix} = \begin{pmatrix} \text{Total \$ amount} \\ \text{reinvested at the} \\ \text{beginning} \\ \text{of the month} \end{pmatrix} + \begin{pmatrix} \text{Payment} \\ \text{due at the} \\ \text{beginning} \\ \text{of the month} \end{pmatrix}$$

Using this general definition of the cash flow relationships, the constraints for the remaining months are represented by:

$1.058C_1 + 1.018A_3 = A_4 + C_4$ } cash flow for month 4

$1.035B_3 + 1.018A_4 = A_5 + B_5 + 250$ } cash flow for month 5

$1.018A_5 = A_6$ } cash flow for month 6

$1.11D_1 + 1.058C_4 + 1.035B_5 + 1.018A_6 = 300$ } cash flow for month 7

To implement these constraints in the spreadsheet, we must express them in a slightly different (but algebraically equivalent) manner. Specifically, to conform to our general definition of an equality constraint ($f(X_1, X_2, \ldots, X_n) = b$) we need to rewrite the cash-flow constraints so that all the *variables* in each constraint appear on the LHS of the equal sign, and a numeric constant appears on the RHS of the equal sign. This can be done as:

$1.018A_1 - 1A_2 = 0$ } cash flow for month 2

$1.035B_1 + 1.018A_2 - 1A_3 - 1B_3 = 250$ } cash flow for month 3

$1.058C_1 + 1.018A_3 - 1A_4 - 1C_4 = 0$ } cash flow for month 4

$1.035B_3 + 1.018A_4 - 1A_5 - 1B_5 = 250$ } cash flow for month 5

$1.018A_5 - 1A_6 = 0$ } cash flow for month 6

$1.11D_1 + 1.058C_4 + 1.035B_5 + 1.018A_6 = 300$ } cash flow for month 7

There are two important points to note about this alternate expression of the constraints. First, each constraint takes on the following general form, which is algebraically equivalent to our previous general definition for the cash-flow constraints:

$$\begin{pmatrix} \text{Total \$ amount} \\ \text{maturing at the} \\ \text{beginning} \\ \text{of the month} \end{pmatrix} - \begin{pmatrix} \text{Total \$ amount} \\ \text{reinvested at the} \\ \text{beginning} \\ \text{of the month} \end{pmatrix} = \begin{pmatrix} \text{Payment} \\ \text{due at the} \\ \text{beginning} \\ \text{of the month} \end{pmatrix}$$

Although the constraints look slightly different in this form, they enforce the same relationships among the variables as expressed by the earlier constraints.

Second, the LHS coefficients in the alternate expression of the constraints correspond directly to the values listed in the cash-flow summary table in Figure 3.34. That is, the coefficients in the constraint for month 2 correspond to the values in the column for month 2 in Figure 3.34; the coefficients for month 3 correspond to the values in the column for month 3, and so on. This relationship is true for all the constraints and will be very helpful in implementing this model in the spreadsheet.

3.13.4 IMPLEMENTING THE MODEL

The LP model for Taco-Viva's construction fund problem is summarized as:

MIN: $A_1 + B_1 + C_1 + D_1$ } cash invested at beginning of month 1

Subject to:

$1.018A_1 - 1A_2$ = 0 } cash flow for month 2

$1.035B_1 + 1.018A_2 - 1A_3 - 1B_3$ = 250 } cash flow for month 3

$1.058C_1 + 1.018A_3 - 1A_4 - 1C_4$ = 0 } cash flow for month 4

$1.035B_3 + 1.018A_4 - 1A_5 - 1B_5$ = 250 } cash flow for month 5

$1.018A_5 - 1A_6$ = 0 } cash flow for month 6

$1.11D_1 + 1.058C_4 + 1.035B_5 + 1.018A_6 = 300$ } cash flow for month 7

$A_i, B_i, C_i, D_i, \geq 0$, for all i } nonnegativity conditions

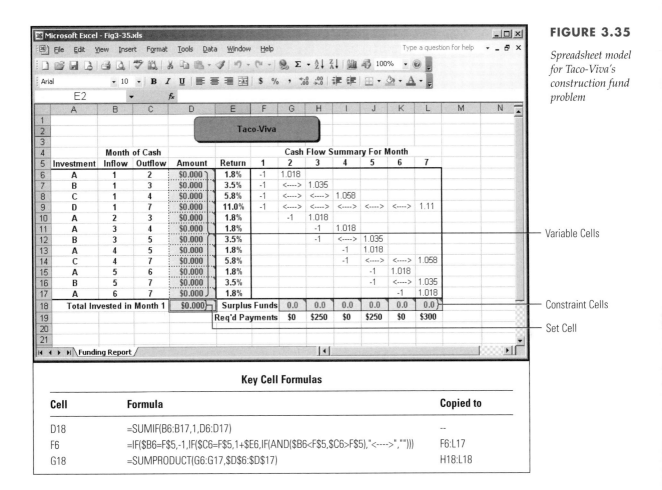

FIGURE 3.35

Spreadsheet model for Taco-Viva's construction fund problem

Key Cell Formulas

Cell	Formula	Copied to
D18	=SUMIF(B6:B17,1,D6:D17)	--
F6	=IF($B6=F$5,-1,IF($C6=F$5,1+$E6,IF(AND($B6<F$5,$C6>F$5),"<---->","")))	F6:L17
G18	=SUMPRODUCT(G6:G17,$D$6:$D$17)	H18:L18

One approach to implementing this model is shown in Figure 3.35 (and file Fig3-35.xls on your data disk). The first three columns of this spreadsheet summarize the different investment options that are available and the months in which money may flow into and out of these investments. Cells D6 through D17 represent the decision variables in our model and indicate the amount of money (in $1,000s) to be placed in each of the possible investments.

The objective function for this problem requires that we compute the total amount of money being invested in month 1. This was done in cell D18 as follows:

Formula for cell D18:   =SUMIF(B6:B17,1,D6:D17)

This SUMIF function compares the values in cells B6 through B17 to the value 1 (its second argument). If any of the values in B6 through B17 equal 1, it sums the corresponding values in cells D6 through D17. In this case, the values in cells B6 through B9 all equal 1; therefore, the function returns the sum of the values in cells D6 through D9. Note that although we could have implemented the objective using the formula SUM(D6:D9), the previous SUMIF formula makes for a more modifiable and reliable model. If any of the values in column B are changed to or from 1, the SUMIF function continues to represent the appropriate objective function, whereas the SUM function would not.

Our next job is to implement the cash inflow/outflow table described earlier in Figure 3.34. Recall that each row in Figure 3.34 corresponds to the cash flows associated with a particular investment alternative. This table can be implemented in our spreadsheet using the following formula:

Formula for cell F6: =IF($B6=F$5,-1,IF($C6=F$5,1+$E6,IF(AND($B6<F$5,$C6>F$5)," <--->","")))
(Copy to cells F6 through L17.)

This formula first checks to see if the "month of cash inflow" value in column B matches the month indicator value in row 5. If so, the formula returns the value -1. Otherwise, it goes on to check to see if the "month of cash outflow" value in column C matches the month indicator value in row 5. If so, the formula returns a value equal to 1 plus the return for the investment (from column E). If neither of the first two conditions are met, the formula next checks whether the current month indicator in row 5 is larger than the "month of cash inflow" value (column B) and smaller than the "month of cash outflow" value (column C). If so, the formula returns the characters "<--->" to indicate periods in which funds neither flow into or out of a particular investment. Finally, if none of the previous three conditions are met, the formula simply returns an empty (or null) string "". Although this formula looks a bit intimidating, it is simply a set of three nested IF functions. More important, it automatically updates the cash flow summary if any of the values in columns B, C, or E are changed, increasing the reliability and modifiability of the model.

Earlier, we noted that the values listed in columns 2 through 7 of the cash inflow/outflow table correspond directly to the coefficients appearing in the various cash-flow constraints. This property allows us to implement the cash-flow constraints in the spreadsheet conveniently. For example, the LHS formula for the cash-flow constraint for month 2 is implemented in cell G18 through the formula:

Formula in cell G18:   =SUMPRODUCT(G6:G17,$D$6:$D$17)
(Copy to H18 through L18.)

This formula multiplies each entry in the range G6 through G17 by the corresponding entry in the range D6 through D17 and then sums these individual products. This formula is copied to cells H18 through L18. (Notice that the SUMPRODUCT( ) formula treats cells containing labels and null strings as if they contained the value zero.) Take a moment now to verify that the formulas in cells G18 through L18 correspond to the LHS formulas of the cash-flow constraints in our model. Cells G19 through L19 list the RHS values for the cash-flow constraints.

3.13.5 SOLVING THE MODEL

To find the optimal solution to this model, we must indicate to Solver the set cell, variable cells, and constraint cells identified in Figure 3.35. Figure 3.36 shows the Solver parameters required to solve this model. The optimal solution is shown in Figure 3.37.

3.13.6 ANALYZING THE SOLUTION

The value of the set cell (D18) in Figure 3.37 indicates that a total of $741,363 must be invested to meet the payments on Taco-Viva's construction project. Cells D6 and D8 indicate that approximately $241,237 should be placed in investment A at the beginning of month 1 ($A_1 = 241.237$) and approximately $500,126 should be placed in investment C ($C_1 = 500.126$).

At the beginning of month 2, the funds placed in investment A at the beginning of month 1 will mature and will be worth $245,580 ($241,237 \times 1.018 = 245,580$). The value

FIGURE 3.36

Solver parameters for the construction fund problem

FIGURE 3.37

Optimal solution to Taco-Viva's construction fund problem

in cell D10 indicates that these funds should be placed back into investment A at the beginning of month 2 ($A_2 = 245.580$).

At the beginning of month 3, the first $250,000 payment is due. At that time, the funds placed in investment A at the beginning of month 2 will mature and will be worth $250,000 ($1.018 \times 245,580 = 250,000$) — allowing us to make this payment.

At the beginning of month 4, the funds placed in investment C at the beginning of month 1 will mature and will be worth $529,134. Our solution indicates that $245,580 of this amount should be placed in investment A ($A_4 = 245.580$) and that the rest should be reinvested in investment C ($C_4 = 283.554$).

If you trace through the cash flows for the remaining months, you will discover that our model is doing exactly what it was designed to do. The amount of money scheduled to mature at the beginning of each month is exactly equal to the amount of money scheduled to be reinvested after required payments are made. Thus, out of an infinite number of possible investment schedules, our LP model found the one schedule that requires the least amount of money up front.

3.13.7 MODIFYING THE TACO-VIVA PROBLEM TO ACCOUNT FOR RISK (OPTIONAL)

In investment problems like this, it is not uncommon for decision makers to place limits on the amount of risk they are willing to assume. For instance, suppose that the chief financial officer (CFO) for Taco-Viva assigned the following risk ratings to each of the possible investments on a scale from 1 to 10 (where 1 represents the least risk and 10 the greatest risk). We also will assume that the CFO wants to determine an investment plan where the weighted average risk level does not exceed 5.

Investment	Risk Rating
A	1
B	3
C	8
D	6

We will need to formulate an additional constraint for each time period to ensure that the weighted average risk level never exceeds 5. To see how this can be done, let's start with month 1.

In month 1, funds can be invested in A_1, B_1, C_1, and/or D_1, and each investment is associated with a different degree of risk. To calculate the weighted average risk during month 1, we must multiply the risk factors for each investment by the proportion of money in that investment. This is represented by:

$$\text{Weighted average risk in month 1} = \frac{1A_1 + 3B_1 + 8C_1 + 6D_1}{A_1 + B_1 + C_1 + D_1}$$

We can ensure that the weighted average risk in month 1 does not exceed the value 5 by including the following constraint in our LP model:

$$\frac{1A_1 + 3B_1 + 8C_1 + 6D_1}{A_1 + B_1 + C_1 + D_1} \leq 5 \quad \} \text{ risk constraint for month 1}$$

Now, consider month 2. According to the column for month 2 in our cash inflow/outflow table, the company can have funds invested in B_1, C_1, D_1, and/or A_2 during this month. Thus, the weighted average risk that occurs in month 2 is defined by:

$$\text{Weighted average risk in month 2} = \frac{3B_1 + 8C_1 + 6D_1 + 1A_2}{B_1 + C_1 + D_1 + A_2}$$

Again, the following constraint ensures that this quantity never exceeds 5:

$$\frac{3B_1 + 8C_1 + 6D_1 + 1A_2}{B_1 + C_1 + D_1 + A_2} \leq 5 \quad \} \text{ risk constraint for month 2}$$

The risk constraints for months 3 through 6 are generated in a similar manner, and appear as:

$$\frac{8C_1 + 6D_1 + 1A_3 + 3B_3}{C_1 + D_1 + A_3 + B_3} \leq 5 \quad \} \text{ risk constraint for month 3}$$

$$\frac{6D_1 + 3B_3 + 1A_4 + 8C_4}{D_1 + B_3 + A_4 + C_4} \leq 5 \quad \} \text{ risk constraint for month 4}$$

$$\frac{6D_1 + 8C_4 + 1A_5 + 3B_5}{D_1 + C_4 + A_5 + B_5} \leq 5 \quad \} \text{ risk constraint for month 5}$$

$$\frac{6D_1 + 8C_4 + 3B_5 + 1A_6}{D_1 + C_4 + B_5 + A_6} \leq 5 \quad \} \text{ risk constraint for month 6}$$

Although the risk constraints listed here have a very clear meaning, it is easier to implement these constraints in the spreadsheet if we state them in a different (but algebraically equivalent) manner. In particular, it is helpful to eliminate the fractions on the LHS of the inequalities by multiplying each constraint through by its denominator and re-collecting the variables on the LHS of the inequality. The following steps show how to rewrite the risk constraint for month 1:

1. Multiply both sides of the inequality by the denominator:

$$(A_1 + B_1 + C_1 + D_1) \frac{1A_1 + 3B_1 + 8C_1 + 6D_1}{A_1 + B_1 + C_1 + D_1} \leq (A_1 + B_1 + C_1 + D_1)5$$

to obtain:

$$1A_1 + 3B_1 + 8C_1 + 6D_1 \leq 5A_1 + 5B_1 + 5C_1 + 5D_1$$

2. Re-collect the variables on the LHS of the inequality sign:

$$(1 - 5)A_1 + (3 - 5)B_1 + (8 - 5)C_1 + (6 - 5)D_1 \leq 0$$

to obtain:

$$-4A_1 - 2B_1 + 3C_1 + 1D_1 \leq 0$$

Thus, the following two constraints are algebraically equivalent:

$$\frac{1A_1 + 3B_1 + 8C_1 + 6D_1}{A_1 + B_1 + C_1 + D_1} \leq 5 \quad \} \text{ risk constraint for month 1}$$

$$-4A_1 - 2B_1 + 3C_1 + 1D_1 \leq 0 \quad \} \text{ risk constraint for month 1}$$

The set of values for A_1, B_1, C_1, and D_1 that satisfies the first of these constraints also satisfies the second constraint (that is, these constraints have exactly the same set of feasible values). So, it does not matter which of these constraints we use to find the optimal solution to the problem.

The remaining risk constraints are simplified in the same way, producing the following constraints:

$-2B_1$	$+$	$3C_1$	$+$	$1D_1$	$-$	$4A_2$			$\leq$	0	} risk constraint for month 2
		$3C_1$	$+$	$1D_1$	$-$	$4A_3$	$-$	$2B_3$	$\leq$	0	} risk constraint for month 3
				$1D_1$	$-$	$2B_3$	$-$	$4A_4$	$+$	$3C_4$	$\leq$	0	} risk constraint for month 4
				$1D_1$	$+$	$3C_4$	$-$	$4A_5$	$-$	$2B_5$	$\leq$	0	} risk constraint for month 5
				$1D_1$	$+$	$3C_4$	$-$	$2B_5$	$-$	$4A_6$	$\leq$	0	} risk constraint for month 6

Notice that the coefficient for each variable in these constraints is simply the risk factor for the particular investment minus the maximum allowable weighted average risk value of 5. That is, all A_i variables have coefficients of $1 - 5 = -4$; all B_i variables have coefficients of $3 - 5 = -2$; all C_i variables have coefficients of $8 - 5 = 3$; and all D_i variables have coefficients of $6 - 5 = 1$. This observation will help us implement these constraints efficiently.

3.13.8 IMPLEMENTING THE RISK CONSTRAINTS

Figure 3.38 (and file Fig3-38.xls on your data disk) shows a split screen that illustrates an easy way to implement the risk constraints for this model. Earlier we noted that the coefficient for each variable in each risk constraint is simply the risk factor for the particular investment minus the maximum allowable weighted average risk value. Thus, the strategy in Figure 3.38 is to generate these values in the appropriate columns and rows of the spreadsheet so that the SUMPRODUCT( ) function can implement the LHS formulas for the risk constraints.

Recall that the risk constraint for each month involves only the variables representing investments that actually held funds during that month. For any given month, the investments that actually held funds during that month have the value −1 or contain a text entry starting with the "<" symbol (the first character of the "<---->" entries) in the

FIGURE 3.38

Spreadsheet model for Taco-Viva's revised construction fund problem

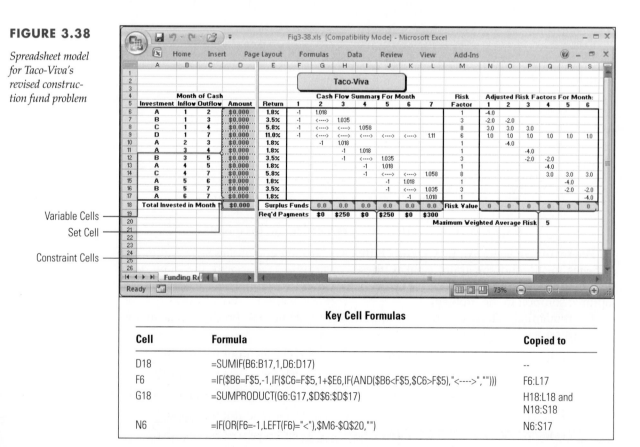

Cell	Formula	Copied to
D18	=SUMIF(B6:B17,1,D6:D17)	--
F6	=IF($B6=F$5,-1,IF($C6=F$5,1+$E6,IF(AND($B6<F$5,$C6>F$5),"<---->","")))	F6:L17
G18	=SUMPRODUCT(G6:G17,$D$6:$D$17)	H18:L18 and N18:S18
N6	=IF(OR(F6=-1,LEFT(F6)="<"),$M6-$Q$20,"")	N6:S17

corresponding column of the cash inflow/outflow summary table. For example, during month 2, funds can be invested in B_1, C_1, D_1, and/or A_2. The corresponding cells for month 2 in Figure 3.38 (cells G7, G8, G9, and G10, respectively) each contain either the value -1 or a text entry starting with the "<" symbol. Therefore, to generate the appropriate coefficients for the risk constraints, we can instruct the spreadsheet to scan the cash inflow/outflow summary for cells containing the value -1 or text entries starting with the "<" symbol, and return the correct risk constraint coefficients in the appropriate cells. To do this we enter the following formula in cell N6:

> Formula in cell N6:   =IF(OR(F6=-1,LEFT(F6)="<"),$M6-$Q$20,"")
> (Copy to N6 through S17.)

To generate the appropriate value in cell N6, the previous formula checks if cell F6 is equal to -1 or contains a text entry that starts with the "<" symbol. If either of these conditions is true, the function takes the risk factor for the investment from cell M6 and subtracts the maximum allowable risk factor found in cell Q20; otherwise, the function returns a null string (with a value of zero). This formula is copied to the remaining cells in the range N6 through S17, as shown in Figure 3.38.

The values in cells N6 through S17 in Figure 3.38 correspond to the coefficients in the LHS formulas for each of the risk constraints formulated earlier. Thus, the LHS formula for the risk constraint for month 1 is implemented in cell N18 as:

> Formula in cell N18:   =SUMPRODUCT(N6:N17,$D$6:$D$17)
> (Copy to O18 through S18.)

The LHS formulas for the remaining risk constraints are implemented by copying this formula to cells O18 through S18. We will tell Solver that these constraint cells must be less than or equal to zero.

3.13.9 SOLVING THE MODEL

To find the optimal solution to this model, we must communicate the appropriate information about the new risk constraints to Solver. Figure 3.39 shows the Solver parameters required to solve this model. The optimal solution is shown in Figure 3.40.

FIGURE 3.39

Solver parameters for the revised construction fund problem

FIGURE 3.40

Optimal solution to Taco-Viva's revised construction fund problem

Month of Cash					Cash Flow Summary For Month							Risk	Adjusted Risk Factors For Month:					
Investment	Inflow	Outflow	Amount	Return	1	2	3	4	5	6	7	Factor	1	2	3	4	5	6
A	1	2	$451.607	1.8%	-1	1.018						1	-4.0					
B	1	3	$0.000	3.5%	-1	<---->	1.035					3	-2.0	-2.0				
C	1	4	$290.682	5.8%	-1	<---->	<---->	1.058				8	3.0	3.0	3.0			
D	1	7	$0.000	11.0%	-1	<---->	<---->	<---->	<---->	<---->	1.11	6	1.0	1.0	1.0	1.0	1.0	1.0
A	2	3	$459.736	1.8%		-1	1.018					1		-4.0				
A	3	4	$218.012	1.8%			-1	1.018				1			-4.0			
B	3	5	$0.000	3.5%			-1	<---->	1.035			3			-2.0	-2.0		
A	4	5	$366.011	1.8%				-1	1.018			1				-4.0		
C	4	7	$163.466	5.8%				-1	<---->	<---->	1.058	8				3.0	3.0	3.0
A	5	6	$122.600	1.8%					-1	1.018		1					-4.0	
B	5	7	$0.000	3.5%					-1	<---->	1.035	3					-2.0	-2.0
A	6	7	$124.806	1.8%						-1	1.018	1						-4.0
Total Invested in Month 1			$742.289	Surplus Funds	0.0	250.0	0.0	250.0	0.0	300.0	Risk Value	-934	-967	0	-974	0	-9	
				Req'd Payments	$0	$250	$0	$250	$0	$300								
									Maximum Weighted Average Risk	5								

3.13.10 ANALYZING THE SOLUTION

The optimal solution to the revised Taco-Viva problem with risk constraints is quite different than the solution obtained earlier. In particular, the new solution requires that funds be placed in investment A in every time period. This is not too surprising given that investment A has the lowest risk rating. It may be somewhat surprising that of the remaining investments, B and D never are used. Although these investments have lower risk ratings than investment C, the combination of funds placed in investment A and C allows for the least amount of money to be invested in month 1 while meeting the scheduled payments and keeping the weighted average risk at or below the specified level.

3.14 Data Envelopment Analysis

Managers often are interested in determining how efficiently various units within a company operate. Similarly, investment analysts might be interested in comparing the efficiency of several competing companies within an industry. Data Envelopment Analysis (DEA) is an LP-based methodology for performing this type of analysis. DEA determines how efficiently an operating unit (or company) converts inputs to outputs when compared with other units. We will consider how DEA may be applied via the following example.

Mike Lister is a district manager for the Steak & Burger fast-food restaurant chain. The region Mike manages contains 12 company-owned units. Mike is in the process of evaluating the performance of these units during the past year to make recommendations on how much of an annual bonus to pay each unit's manager. He wants to base this decision, in part, on how efficiently each unit has been operated. Mike has collected the data shown in the following table on each of the 12 units. The outputs he has chosen include each unit's net profit (in $100,000s), average customer satisfaction rating, and average monthly cleanliness score. The inputs include total labor hours (in 100,000s) and total operating costs (in $1,000,000s). He wants to apply DEA to this data to determine an efficiency score of each unit.

	Outputs			Inputs	
Unit	Profit	Satisfaction	Cleanliness	Labor Hours	Operating Costs
1	5.98	7.7	92	4.74	6.75
2	7.18	9.7	99	6.38	7.42
3	4.97	9.3	98	5.04	6.35
4	5.32	7.7	87	3.61	6.34
5	3.39	7.8	94	3.45	4.43
6	4.95	7.9	88	5.25	6.31
7	2.89	8.6	90	2.36	3.23
8	6.40	9.1	100	7.09	8.69
9	6.01	7.3	89	6.49	7.28
10	6.94	8.8	89	7.36	9.07
11	5.86	8.2	93	5.46	6.69
12	8.35	9.6	97	6.58	8.75

3.14.1 DEFINING THE DECISION VARIABLES

Using DEA, the efficiency of an arbitrary unit i is defined as follows:

$$\text{Efficiency of unit } i = \frac{\text{Weighted sum of unit } i\text{'s outputs}}{\text{Weighted sum of unit } i\text{'s inputs}} = \frac{\sum_{j=1}^{n_O} O_{ij} w_j}{\sum_{j=1}^{n_I} I_{ij} v_j}$$

Here, O_{ij} represents the value of unit i on *output* j, I_{ij} represents the value of unit i on *input* j, w_j is a nonnegative weight assigned to output j, v_j is a nonnegative weight assigned to input j, n_O is the number of output variables, and n_I is the number of input variables. The problem in DEA is to determine values for the weights w_j and v_j. Thus, w_j and v_j represent the decision variables in a DEA problem.

3.14.2 DEFINING THE OBJECTIVE

A separate LP problem is solved for each unit in a DEA problem. However, for each unit the objective is the same: to maximize the weighted sum of that unit's outputs. For an arbitrary unit i, the objective is stated as:

$$\text{MAX: } \sum_{j=1}^{n_O} O_{ij} w_j$$

Thus, as each LP problem is solved, the unit under investigation is given the opportunity to select the best possible weights for itself (or the weights that maximize the weighted sum of its output), subject to the following constraints.

3.14.3 DEFINING THE CONSTRAINTS

It is impossible for any unit to be more than 100% efficient. So as each LP is solved, the unit under investigation cannot select weights for itself that would cause the efficiency for any unit (including itself) to be greater than 100%. Thus, for each individual unit, we require the weighted sum of the unit's outputs to be less than or equal to the weighted sum of its inputs (so the ratio of weighted outputs to weighted inputs does not exceed 100%).

$$\sum_{j=1}^{n_o} O_{kj}w_j \leq \sum_{j=1}^{n_I} I_{kj}v_j, \qquad \text{for } k = 1 \text{ to the number of units}$$

or equivalently,

$$\sum_{j=1}^{n_o} O_{kj}w_j - \sum_{j=1}^{n_I} I_{kj}v_j \leq 0, \quad \text{for } k = 1 \text{ to the number of units}$$

To prevent unbounded solutions, we also require the sum of the weighted inputs for the unit under investigation (unit i) to equal one.

$$\sum_{j=1}^{n_I} I_{ij}v_j = 1$$

Because the sum of weighted inputs for the unit under investigation must equal one and its sum of the weighted outputs (being maximized) cannot exceed this value, the maximum efficiency score for the unit under investigation is also one (or 100%). Thus, units that are efficient will have a DEA efficiency score of 100%.

Important Point

When applying DEA, it is assumed that for output variables "more is better" (e.g., profit) and for input variables "less is better" (e.g., costs). Any output or input variables that do not naturally conform to these rules should be transformed before applying DEA. For example, the percentage of defective products produced is not a good choice for an output because fewer defects is actually a good thing. However, the percentage of nondefective products produced would be an acceptable choice for an output because "more is better" in that case.

3.14.4 IMPLEMENTING THE MODEL

To evaluate the efficiency of unit 1 in our example problem, we would solve the following LP problem,

MAX:	$5.98w_1 + 7.7w_2 + 92w_3$	} weighted output for unit 1
Subject to:	$5.98w_1 + 7.7w_2 + 92w_3 - 4.74v_1 - 6.75v_2 \leq 0$	} efficiency constraint for unit 1
	$7.18w_1 + 9.7w_2 + 99w_3 - 6.38v_1 - 7.42v_2 \leq 0$	} efficiency constraint for unit 2
	and so on to . . .	
	$8.35w_1 + 9.6w_2 + 97w_3 - 6.58v_1 - 8.75v_2 \leq 0$	} efficiency constraint for unit 12
	$4.74v_1 + 6.75v_2 = 1$	} input constraint for unit 1
	$w_1, w_2, w_3, v_1, v_2 \geq 0$	} nonnegativity conditions

A convenient way to implement this model is shown in Figure 3.41 (and in the file Fig3-41.xls on your data disk).

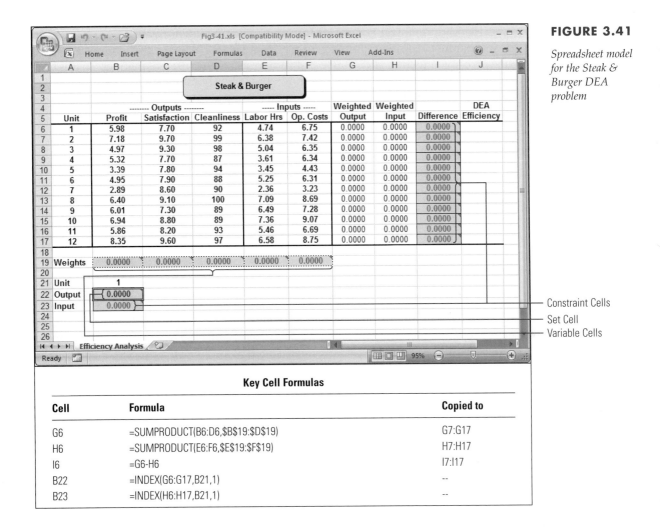

FIGURE 3.41

Spreadsheet model for the Steak & Burger DEA problem

Key Cell Formulas

Cell	Formula	Copied to
G6	=SUMPRODUCT(B6:D6,$B$19:$D$19)	G7:G17
H6	=SUMPRODUCT(E6:F6,$E$19:$F$19)	H7:H17
I6	=G6-H6	I7:I17
B22	=INDEX(G6:G17,B21,1)	--
B23	=INDEX(H6:H17,B21,1)	--

In Figure 3.41, cells B19 through F19 are reserved to represent the weights for each of the input and output variables. The weighted output for each unit is computed in column G as follows:

Formula for cell G6:   =SUMPRODUCT(B6:D6,$B$19:$D$19)
(Copy to G7 through G17.)

Similarly, the weighted input for each unit is computed in column H as:

Formula for cell H6:   =SUMPRODUCT(E6:F6,$E$19:$F$19)
(Copy to H7 through H17.)

The differences between the weighted outputs and weighted inputs are computed in column I. We will instruct Solver to constrain these values to be less than or equal to 0.

Formula for cell I6:   =G6-H6
(Copy to I7 through I17.)

The weighted output for unit 1 (computed in cell G6) implements the appropriate objective function and could be used as the set cell for Solver in this problem. Similarly, the weighted input for unit 1 is computed in cell H6 and could be constrained to equal 1 (as specified by the input constraint for unit 1 above). However, because we need to solve a separate LP problem for each of the 12 units, it will be more convenient to handle the objective function and input constraint in a slightly different manner. To this end, we reserve cell B21 to indicate the unit number currently under investigation. Cell B22 contains a formula that returns the weighted output for this unit from the list of weighted outputs in column G.

Formula for cell B22:   =INDEX(G6:G17,B21,1)

In general, the function INDEX(*range,row number,column number*) returns the value in the specified *row number* and *column number* of the given *range*. Because cell B21 contains the number 1, the previous formula returns the value in the first row and first column of the range G6:G17—or the value in cell G6. Thus, as long as the value of cell B21 represents a valid unit number from 1 to 12, the value in cell B22 will represent the appropriate objective function for the DEA model for that unit. Similarly, the input constraint requiring the weighted inputs for the unit in question to equal 1 can be implemented in cell B23 as follows:

Formula for cell B23:   =INDEX(H6:H17,B21,1)

So, for whatever unit number is listed in cell B21, cell B22 represents the appropriate objective function to be maximized and cell B23 represents the weighted input that must be constrained to equal 1. This arrangement greatly simplifies the process of solving the required series of DEA models.

3.14.5 SOLVING THE MODEL

To solve this model, we specify the set cells, variable cells, and constraints specified in Figure 3.42. Note that exactly the same Solver settings would be used to find the optimal DEA weights for any other unit. The optimal solution for unit 1 is shown in Figure 3.43. Notice that unit 1 achieves an efficiency score of 0.9667 and therefore is slightly inefficient.

FIGURE 3.42

Solver parameters for the DEA problem

FIGURE 3.43

Optimal DEA solution for unit 1

To complete the analysis for the remaining units, Mike could change the value in cell B21 manually to 2, 3, . . ., 12 and use Solver to reoptimize the worksheet for each unit and record their efficiency scores in column J. However, if there were 120 units rather than 12, this manual approach would become quite cumbersome. Fortunately, it is easy to write a simple macro in Excel to carry out this process for us automatically with the click of a button. To do this, turn on the Developer tab in the ribbon and place a command button on your worksheet (as shown in Figure 3.44) as follows:

1. Click Office button, Excel Options, Popular, Show Developer tab.
2. Click the Command Button icon on the Developer, Insert, Active X Controls menu.
3. Click and drag on your worksheet to draw a command button.

Next, we need to change a few properties of our newly created command button. To do this,

1. Click the Command Button to make sure it is selected.
2. Click the Properties icon in the Developer, Controls ribbon.

These actions cause the Properties window shown in Figure 3.45 to appear. This window lists several properties (or attributes) of the command button that you can change to customize its appearance and behavior. For present purposes, change the command button's property values as follows,

Property	New Value
(Name)	DEA
Caption	Run DEA
TakeFocusOnClick	False

FIGURE 3.44

*Using the Control
Toolbox to create a
command button*

FIGURE 3.45

*Adjusting the
properties of the
command button*

Design Mode

Properties

> ## Important Software Note
>
> When you place a command button on a worksheet, it is a good idea to set its "TakeFocusOnClick" property to False. This prevents the command button from receiving the focus when it is clicked. "Focus" refers to the object on the screen that is selected or has the computer's attention. An Excel macro cannot perform certain operations if a command button has the focus.

Next, double-click the command button. This should launch Excel's Visual Basic Editor and bring up the code window for the command button's click event. Initially, the click event will not have any commands in it. Insert the statements shown in Figure 3.46. These statements will be executed whenever the command button is clicked.

> ## Software Tip
>
> You can toggle back and forth easily between Excel and the Visual Basic Editor by pressing Alt+F11.

If you have any programming experience, you can probably follow the logic behind the programming code listed in Figure 3.46. In a nutshell, the For and Next statements define a loop of code that will be repeated 12 times. During the first execution of the loop, the variable "unit" will equal 1. During the second execution of the loop, the variable "unit" will equal 2, and so on. During each execution of the loop, the following operations take place:

Macro Statement	Purpose
RANGE("B21")=unit	Places the current value of "unit" (the number 1, 2, 3, . . ., or 12) into cell B21 on the worksheet.
SolverSolve UserFinish:=True	Tells Solver to solve the problem without displaying the usual Solver Results dialog box.
Range("J" & 5 + unit) = Range("B22")	Takes the optimal objective function value in cell B22 and places it in row "5 + unit" (that is, row 6, 7, . . ., or 17) in column J.

To call Solver from within a macro program, we must first set a reference to the Solver.xla file. You do this from within Excel's Visual Basic editor as follows,

1. Click Tools, References and check the box for Solver.
2. Click OK.

We can now test our command button to see if it works. To do this,

1. Close the Visual Basic editor window (or press Alt+F11).
2. Click the Design Mode icon on the Developer, Controls ribbon.
3. Click the Run DEA command button.

FIGURE 3.46

VBA code for the command button's click event

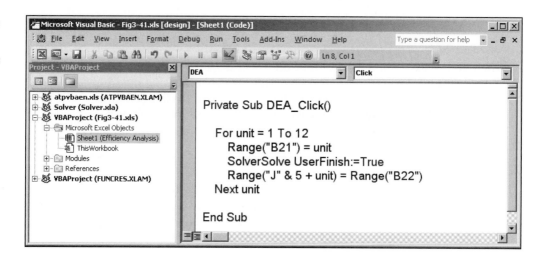

```
Private Sub DEA_Click()

    For unit = 1 To 12
        Range("B21") = unit
        SolverSolve UserFinish:=True
        Range("J" & 5 + unit) = Range("B22")
    Next unit

End Sub
```

If everything worked correctly, you should see the results shown in Figure 3.47 (or see the completed file Fig3-47.xls on your data disk).

Important Software Note

It is important to remember that command buttons and other controls become operational only after you exit design mode. If the Developer, Control ribbon before clicking the Design Mode icon, you might still be in design mode and your controls might not operate correctly.

FIGURE 3.47

DEA efficiency scores for all the units

Fig3-41.xls [Compatibility Mode] - Microsoft Excel

Steak & Burger

Unit	Profit	Outputs Satisfaction	Cleanliness	Inputs Labor Hrs	Op. Costs	Weighted Output	Weighted Input	Difference	DEA Efficiency
1	5.98	7.70	92	4.74	6.75	0.7248	0.7639	-0.0392	0.9667
2	7.18	9.70	99	6.38	7.42	0.8658	0.8658	0.0000	1.0000
3	4.97	9.30	98	5.04	6.35	0.6106	0.7316	-0.1211	0.8345
4	5.32	7.70	87	3.61	6.34	0.6467	0.6988	-0.0521	1.0000
5	3.39	7.80	94	3.45	4.43	0.4268	0.5089	-0.0821	0.8426
6	4.95	7.90	88	5.25	6.31	0.6044	0.7324	-0.1280	0.8259
7	2.89	8.60	90	2.36	3.23	0.3676	0.3676	0.0000	1.0000
8	6.40	9.10	100	7.09	8.69	0.7762	1.0055	-0.2293	0.7720
9	6.01	7.30	89	6.49	7.28	0.7271	0.8546	-0.1275	0.8572
10	6.94	8.80	89	7.36	9.07	0.8343	1.0486	-0.2143	0.7958
11	5.86	8.20	93	5.46	6.69	0.7113	0.7741	-0.0628	0.9188
12	8.35	9.60	97	6.58	8.75	1.0000	1.0000	0.0000	1.0000

| Weights | 0.1153 | 0.0000 | 0.0004 | 0.0223 | 0.0975 |

Unit	12
Output	1.0000
Input	1.0000

Run DEA

Efficiency Analysis

3.14.6 ANALYZING THE SOLUTION

The solution shown in Figure 3.47 indicates that units 2, 4, 7, and 12 are operating at 100% efficiency (in the DEA sense), while the remaining units are operating less efficiently. Note that an efficiency rating of 100% does not necessarily mean that a unit is operating in the best possible way. It simply means that no linear combination of the other units in the study results in a composite unit that produces at least as much output using the same or less input. On the other hand, for units that are DEA *inefficient*, there exists a linear combination of efficient units that results in a composite unit that produces at least as much output using the same or less input than the inefficient unit. The idea in DEA is that an inefficient unit should be able to operate as efficiently as this hypothetical composite unit formed from a linear combination of the efficient units.

For instance, unit 1 has an efficiency score of 96.67% and is, therefore, somewhat inefficient. Figure 3.48 (in file Fig3-48.xls on your data disk) shows that a weighted average of 26.38% of unit 4, plus 28.15% of unit 7, plus 45.07% of unit 12 produces a hypothetical composite unit with outputs greater than or equal to those of unit 1 and requiring less input than unit 1. The assumption in DEA is that unit 1 should have been able to achieve this same level of performance.

For any inefficient unit, you can determine the linear combination of efficient units that results in a more efficient composite unit as follows:

1. Solve the DEA problem for the unit in question.
2. In the Solver Results dialog box, select the Sensitivity report option.

FIGURE 3.48

Example of a composite unit that is more efficient than unit 1

FIGURE 3.49

Sensitivity report for unit 1

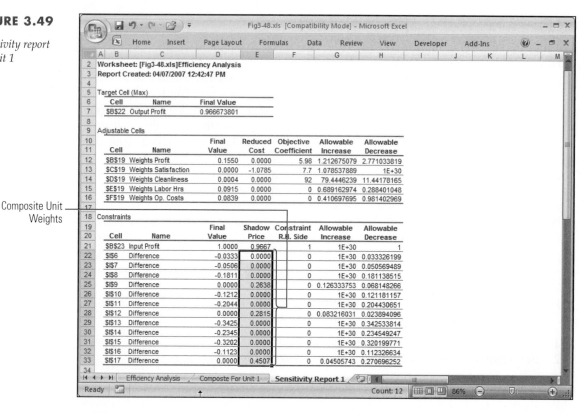

In the resulting sensitivity report, the absolute value of the Shadow Prices for the "Difference" constraints are the weights that should create a composite unit that is more efficient than the unit in question. The sensitivity report for unit 1 is shown in Figure 3.49.

Want To Know More?

To learn more about writing VBA macros in Excel, see *Excel 2007 Power Programming with VBA* by Wiley Publishing. To learn more about controlling Solver from within macros, click the Help button on the Solver Options dialog box (available in Premium Solver for Education).

3.15 Summary

This chapter described how to formulate an LP problem algebraically, implement it in a spreadsheet, and solve it using Solver. The decision variables in the algebraic formulation of a model correspond to the variable cells in the spreadsheet. The LHS formulas for each constraint in an LP model must be implemented in different cells in the spreadsheet. Also, a cell in the spreadsheet must represent the objective function in the LP model. Thus, there is a direct relationship between the various components of an algebraic formulation of an LP problem and its implementation in a spreadsheet.

There are many ways to implement a given LP problem in a spreadsheet. The process of building spreadsheet models is more an art than a science. A good spreadsheet implementation represents the problem in a way that clearly communicates its purpose, is reliable, auditable, and modifiable.

It is possible to use Excel's macro language (known as Visual Basic for Applications or VBA) to automate the process of solving LP models. This is particularly useful in problems in which an analyst might want to solve several related problems in succession.

3.16 References

Charnes, C., et al. *Data Envelopment Analysis: Theory, Methodology, and Application*, New York: Kluwer Academic Publishers, 1996.

Hilal, S., and W. Erickson. "Matching Supplies to Save Lives: Linear Programming the Production of Heart Valves." *Interfaces*, vol. 11, no. 6, 1981.

Lanzenauer, C., et al. "RRSP Flood: LP to the Rescue." *Interfaces*, vol. 17, no. 4, 1987.

McKay, A. "Linear Programming Applications on Microcomputers." *Journal of the Operational Research Society*, vol. 36, July 1985.

Roush, W., et al. "Using Chance-Constrained Programming for Animal Feed Formulation at Agway." *Interfaces*, vol. 24, no. 2, 1994.

Shogan, A. *Management Science*. Englewood Cliffs, NJ: Prentice Hall, 1988.

Subramanian, R., et al., "Coldstart: Fleet Assignment at Delta Airlines," *Interfaces*, vol. 24, no. 1, 1994.

Williams, H. *Model Building in Mathematical Programming*. New York: Wiley, 1990.

THE WORLD OF MANAGEMENT SCIENCE

Optimizing Production, Inventory, and Distribution at Kellogg

The Kellogg Company (http://www.kelloggs.com) is the largest cereal producer in the world and a leading producer of convenience foods. In 1999, Kellogg's worldwide sales totaled nearly $7 billion. Kellogg operates five plants in the United States and Canada and has seven core distribution centers and roughly fifteen co-packers that contract to produce or pack some of Kellogg's products. In the cereal business alone, Kellogg must coordinate the production of 80 products while inventorying and distributing over 600 stock keeping units with roughly 90 production lines and 180 packaging lines. Optimizing this many decision variables is obviously a daunting challenge.

Since 1990, Kellogg has been using a large-scale, multiperiod linear program, called the Kellogg Planning System (KPS), to guide production and distribution decisions. Most large companies like Kellogg employ some sort of enterprise resource planning (ERP). Kellogg's ERP systems is a largely custom, home-grown product, and KPS is a custom-developed tool to complement the ERP system.

An operational-level version of KPS is used at a weekly level of detail to help determine where products are produced and how finished products and in-process products are shipped between plants and distribution centers. A tactical-level version of KPS is used at a monthly level of detail to help establish plant budgets and make capacity and consolidation decisions. Kellogg attributes annual savings of $40–$45 million to the use of the KPS system.

Source: Brown, G., J. Keegan, B. Vigus, and K. Wood, "The Kellogg Company Optimizes Production, Inventory, and Distribution," *Interfaces*, Vol. 35, No. 6, 2001.

Questions and Problems

1. In creating the spreadsheet models for the problems in this chapter, cells in the spreadsheets had to be reserved to represent each of the decision variables in the algebraic models. We reserved these cells in the spreadsheets by entering values of zero in them. Why didn't we place some other value or formula in these cells? Would doing so have made any difference?

2. Four goals should be considered when trying to design an effective spreadsheet model: communication, reliability, auditability, and maintainability. We also noted that a spreadsheet design that results in formulas that can be copied is usually more effective than other designs. Briefly describe how using formulas that can be copied supports the four spreadsheet modeling goals.

3. Refer to question 13 at the end of Chapter 2. Implement a spreadsheet model for this problem and solve it using Solver.

4. Refer to question 14 at the end of Chapter 2. Implement a spreadsheet model for this problem and solve it using Solver.

5. Refer to question 17 at the end of Chapter 2. Implement a spreadsheet model for this problem and solve it using Solver.

6. Refer to question 18 at the end of Chapter 2. Implement a spreadsheet model for this problem and solve it using Solver.

7. Refer to question 19 at the end of Chapter 2. Implement a spreadsheet model for this problem and solve it using Solver.

8. Refer to question 20 at the end of Chapter 2. Implement a spreadsheet model for this problem and solve it using Solver.

9. Refer to question 21 at the end of Chapter 2. Implement a spreadsheet model for this problem and solve it using Solver.

10. Refer to question 22 at the end of Chapter 2. Implement a spreadsheet model for this problem and solve it using Solver.

11. Refer to question 23 at the end of Chapter 2. Implement a spreadsheet model for this problem and solve it using Solver.

12. A furniture manufacturer produces two types of tables (country and contemporary) using three types of machines. The time required to produce the tables on each machine is given in the following table.

Machine	Country	Contemporary	Total Machine Time Available per Week
Router	1.5	2.0	1,000
Sander	3.0	4.5	2,000
Polisher	2.5	1.5	1,500

Country tables sell for $350 and contemporary tables sell for $450. Management has determined that at least 20% of the tables made should be country and at least 30% should be contemporary. How many of each type of table should the company produce if it wants to maximize its revenue?

a. Formulate an LP model for this problem.
b. Create a spreadsheet model for this problem and solve it using Solver.
c. What is the optimal solution?
d. How will your spreadsheet model differ if there are 25 types of tables and 15 machine processes involved in manufacturing them?

13. Aire-Co produces home dehumidifiers at two different plants in Atlanta and Phoenix. The per unit cost of production in Atlanta and Phoenix is $400 and $360, respectively. Each plant can produce a maximum of 300 units per month. Inventory

holding costs are assessed at $30 per unit in beginning inventory each month. Aire-Co estimates the demand for its product to be 300, 400, and 500 units, respectively, over the next three months. Aire-Co wants to be able to meet this demand at minimum cost.

a. Formulate an LP model for this problem.
b. Implement your model in a spreadsheet and solve it.
c. What is the optimal solution?
d. How does the solution change if each plant is required to produce at least 50 units per month?
e. How does the solution change if each plant is required to produce at least 100 units per month?

14. The Molokai Nut Company (MNC) makes four different products from macadamia nuts grown in the Hawaiian Islands: chocolate-coated whole nuts (Whole), chocolate-coated nut clusters (Cluster), chocolate-coated nut crunch bars (Crunch), and plain roasted nuts (Roasted). The company is barely able to keep up with the increasing demand for these products. However, increasing raw material prices and foreign competition are forcing MNC to watch its margins to ensure that it is operating in the most efficient manner possible. To meet marketing demands for the coming week, MNC needs to produce at least 1,000 pounds of the Whole product, between 400 and 500 pounds of the Cluster product, no more than 150 pounds of the Crunch product, and no more than 200 pounds of Roasted product. Each pound of the Whole, Cluster, Crunch, and Roasted product contains, respectively, 60%, 40%, 20%, and 100% macadamia nuts, with the remaining weight made up of chocolate coating. The company has 1,100 pounds of nuts and 800 pounds of chocolate available for use in the next week. The various products are made using four different machines that hull the nuts, roast the nuts, coat the nuts in chocolate (if needed), and package the products. The following table summaries the time required by each product on each machine. Each machine has 60 hours of time available in the coming week.

Minutes Required per Pound

Machine	Whole	Cluster	Crunch	Roasted
Hulling	1.00	1.00	1.00	1.00
Roasting	2.00	1.50	1.00	1.75
Coating	1.00	0.70	0.20	0.00
Packaging	2.50	1.60	1.25	1.00

The selling price and variable cost associated with each pound of product is summarized below:

Per Pound Revenue and Costs

	Whole	Cluster	Crunch	Roasted
Selling Price	$5.00	$4.00	$3.20	$4.50
Variable Cost	$3.15	$2.60	$2.16	$3.10

a. Formulate an LP model for this problem.
b. Create a spreadsheet model for this problem and solve it using Solver.
c. What is the optimal solution?

15. A company is trying to determine how to allocate its $145,000 advertising budget for a new product. The company is considering newspaper ads and television commercials as its primary means for advertising. The following table summarizes the costs

of advertising in these different media and the number of new customers reached by increasing amounts of advertising.

Media & # of Ads	# of New Customers Reached	Cost per Ad
Newspaper: 1–10	900	$1,000
Newspaper: 11–20	700	$900
Newspaper: 21–30	400	$800
Television: 1–5	10,000	$12,000
Television: 6–10	7,500	$10,000
Television: 11–15	5,000	$8,000

For instance, each of the first ten ads the company places in newspapers will cost $1,000 and is expected to reach 900 new customers. Each of the next 10 newspaper ads will cost $900 and is expected to reach 700 new customers. Note that the number of new customers reached by increasing amounts of advertising decreases as the advertising saturates the market. Assume that the company will purchase no more than 30 newspaper ads and no more than 15 television ads.

a. Formulate an LP model for this problem to maximize the number of new customers reached by advertising.
b. Implement your model in a spreadsheet and solve it.
c. What is the optimal solution?
d. Suppose the number of new customers reached by 11–20 newspaper ads is 400 and the number of new customers reached by 21–30 newspaper ads is 700. Make these changes in your spreadsheet and reoptimize the problem. What is the new optimal solution? What (if anything) is wrong with this solution and why?

16. The Shop at Home Network sells various household goods during live television broadcasts. The company owns several warehouses to hold many of the goods it sells, but also leases extra warehouse space when needed. During the next five months the company expects that it will need to lease the following amounts of extra warehouse space:

Month	1	2	3	4	5
Square Feet Needed	20,000	30,000	40,000	35,000	50,000

At the beginning of any month the company can lease extra space for one or more months at the following costs:

Lease Term (months)	1	2	3	4	5
Cost per Sq. Ft. Leased	$55	$95	$130	$155	$185

So, for instance, at the start of month 1 the company can lease as much space as it wants for 4 months at a cost of $155 per square foot. Similarly, at the start of month 3 it can lease any amount of space for 2 months at a cost of $95 per square foot. The company wants to determine the least costly way of meeting its warehousing needs over the coming 5 months.

a. Formulate an LP model for this problem.
b. Create a spreadsheet model for this problem and solve it using Solver.
c. What is the optimal solution?
d. How much would it cost the company to meet its space needs if in each month it leases for one month exactly the amount of space required for the month?

17. A bank has $650,000 in assets to allocate among investments in bonds, home mortgages, car loans, and personal loans. Bonds are expected to produce a return of 10%, mortgages 8.5%, car loans 9.5%, and personal loans 12.5%. To make sure the portfolio is not too risky, the bank wants to restrict personal loans to no more than the 25% of the total portfolio. The bank also wants to ensure that more money is invested in mortgages than in personal loans. It also wants to invest more in bonds than personal loans.

   a. Formulate an LP model for this problem with the objective of maximizing the expected return on the portfolio.
   b. Implement your model in a spreadsheet and solve it.
   c. What it the optimal solution?

18. Valu-Com Electronics manufactures five different models of telecommunications interface cards for personal and laptop computers. As summarized in the following table, each of these devices requires differing amounts of printed circuit (PC) board, resistors, memory chips, and assembly.

Per Unit Requirements

	HyperLink	FastLink	SpeedLink	MicroLink	EtherLink
PC Board (square inches)	20	15	10	8	5
Resistors	28	24	18	12	16
Memory Chips	8	8	4	4	6
Assembly Labor (in hours)	0.75	0.6	0.5	0.65	1

The unit wholesale price and manufacturing cost for each model are as follows.

Per Unit Revenues and Costs

	HyperLink	FastLink	SpeedLink	MicroLink	EtherLink
Wholesale Price	$189	$149	$129	$169	$139
Manufacturing Cost	$136	$101	$ 96	$137	$101

   In their next production period, Valu-Com has 80,000 square inches of PC board, 100,000 resistors, 30,000 memory chips, and 5,000 hours of assembly time available. The company can sell all the product it can manufacture, but the marketing department wants to be sure that it produces at least 500 units of each product and at least twice as many FastLink cards as HyperLink cards while maximizing profit.

   a. Formulate an LP model for this problem.
   b. Create a spreadsheet model for this problem and solve it using Solver.
   c. What is the optimal solution?
   d. Could Valu-Com make more money if it schedules its assembly workers to work overtime?

19. A trust officer at the Blacksburg National Bank needs to determine how to invest $100,000 in the following collection of bonds to maximize the annual return.

Bond	Annual Return	Maturity	Risk	Tax-Free
A	9.5%	Long	High	Yes
B	8.0%	Short	Low	Yes
C	9.0%	Long	Low	No
D	9.0%	Long	High	Yes
E	9.0%	Short	High	No

The officer wants to invest at least 50% of the money in short-term issues and no more than 50% in high-risk issues. At least 30% of the funds should go into tax-free investments and at least 40% of the total annual return should be tax-free.

a. Formulate an LP model for this problem.

b. Create a spreadsheet model for this problem and solve it using Solver.

c. What is the optimal solution?

20. The Weedwacker Company manufactures two types of lawn trimmers: an electric model and a gas model. The company has contracted to supply a national discount retail chain with a total of 30,000 electric trimmers and 15,000 gas trimmers. However, Weedwacker's production capability is limited in three departments: production, assembly, and packaging. The following table summarizes the hours of processing time available and the processing time required by each department, for both types of trimmers:

| | Hours Required per Trimmer | | |
	Electric	Gas	Hours Available
Production	0.20	0.40	10,000
Assembly	0.30	0.50	15,000
Packaging	0.10	0.10	5,000

The company makes its electric trimmer in-house for $55 and its gas trimmer for $85. Alternatively, it can buy electric and gas trimmers from another source for $67 and $95, respectively. How many gas and electric trimmers should Weedwacker make and how many should it buy from its competitor to fulfill its contract in the least costly manner?

a. Formulate an LP model for this problem.

b. Create a spreadsheet model for this problem and solve it using Solver.

c. What is the optimal solution?

21. A manufacturer of prefabricated homes has decided to subcontract four components of the homes. Several companies are interested in receiving this business, but none can handle more than one subcontract. The bids made by the companies for the various subcontracts are summarized in the following table.

Bids by Companies
(in $1,000s) for Various Subcontracts

| | Company | | | |
Component	A	B	C	D
1	185	225	193	207
2	200	190	175	225
3	330	320	315	300
4	375	389	425	445

Assuming that all the companies can perform each subcontract equally well, to which company should each subcontract be assigned if the home manufacturer wants to minimize payments to the subcontractors?

a. Formulate an LP model for this problem.

b. Create a spreadsheet model for this problem and solve it using Solver.

c. What is the optimal solution?

22. Tarmac Chemical Corporation produces a special chemical compound—called CHEMIX—that is used extensively in high school chemistry classes. This compound must contain at least 20% sulfur, at least 30% iron oxide, and at least 30% but no

more than 45% potassium. Tarmac's marketing department has estimated that it will need at least 600 pounds of this compound to meet the expected demand during the coming school session. Tarmac can buy three compounds to mix together to produce CHEMIX. The makeup of these compounds is shown in the following table.

Compound	Sulfur	Iron Oxide	Potassium
1	20%	60%	20%
2	40%	30%	30%
3	10%	40%	50%

Compounds 1, 2, and 3 cost $5.00, $5.25, and $5.50 per pound, respectively. Tarmac wants to use an LP model to determine the least costly way of producing enough CHEMIX to meet the demand expected for the coming year.
a. Formulate an LP model for this problem.
b. Create a spreadsheet model for this problem and solve it using Solver.
c. What is the optimal solution?

23. Holiday Fruit Company buys oranges and processes them into gift fruit baskets and fresh juice. The company grades the fruit it buys on a scale from 1 (lowest quality) to 5 (highest quality). The following table summarizes Holiday's current inventory of fruit.

Grade	Supply (1000s of lbs)
1	90
2	225
3	300
4	100
5	75

Each pound of oranges devoted to fruit baskets results in a marginal profit of $2.50, whereas each pound devoted to fresh juice results in a marginal profit of $1.75. Holiday wants the fruit in its baskets to have an average quality grade of at least 3.75 and its fresh juice to have a average quality grade of at least 2.50.
a. Formulate an optimization model for this problem.
b. Implement your model in a spreadsheet and solve it.
c. What it the optimal solution?

24. Riverside Oil Company in eastern Kentucky produces regular and supreme gasoline. Each barrel of regular sells for $21 and must have an octane rating of at least 90. Each barrel of supreme sells for $25 and must have an octane rating of at least 97. Each of these types of gasoline are manufactured by mixing different quantities of the following three inputs:

Input	Cost per Barrel	Octane Rating	Barrels Available (in 1000s)
1	$17.25	100	150
2	$15.75	87	350
3	$17.75	110	300

Riverside has orders for 300,000 barrels of regular and 450,000 barrels of supreme. How should the company allocate the available inputs to the production of regular and supreme gasoline if it wants to maximize profits?
a. Formulate an LP model for this problem.
b. Create a spreadsheet model for this problem and solve it using Solver.
c. What is the optimal solution?

25. Maintenance at a major theme park in central Florida is an ongoing process that occurs 24 hours a day. Because it is a long drive from most residential areas to the park, employees do not like to work shifts of fewer than eight hours. These 8-hour shifts start every four hours throughout the day. The number of maintenance workers needed at different times throughout the day varies. The following table summarizes the minimum number of employees needed in each 4-hour time period.

Time Period	Minimum Employees Needed
12 a.m. to 4 a.m.	90
4 a.m. to 8 a.m.	215
8 a.m. to 12 p.m.	250
12 p.m. to 4 p.m.	165
4 p.m. to 8 p.m.	300
8 p.m. to 12 a.m.	125

The maintenance supervisor wants to determine the minimum number of employees to schedule that meets the minimum staffing requirements.
a. Formulate an LP model for this problem.
b. Create a spreadsheet model for this problem and solve it using Solver.
c. What is the optimal solution?

26. Radmore Memorial Hospital has a problem in its fluids analysis lab. The lab has available three machines that analyze various fluid samples. Recently, the demand for analyzing blood samples has increased so much that the lab director is having difficulty getting all the samples analyzed quickly enough and still completing the other fluid work that comes into the lab. The lab works with five types of blood specimens. Any machine can be used to process any of the specimens. However, the amount of time required by each machine varies depending on the type of specimen being analyzed. These times are summarized in the following table.

**Required Specimen
Processing Time in Minutes**

	Specimen Type				
Machine	1	2	3	4	5
A	3	4	4	5	3
B	5	3	5	4	5
C	2	5	3	3	4

Each machine can be used a total of 8 hours a day. Blood samples collected on a given day arrive at the lab and are stored overnight and processed the next day. So, at the beginning of each day, the lab director must determine how to allocate the various samples to the machines for analysis. This morning, the lab has 80 type-1 specimens, 75 type-2 specimens, 80 type-3 specimens, 120 type-4 specimens, and 60 type-5 specimens awaiting processing. The lab director wants to know how many of each type of specimen should be analyzed on each machine to minimize the total time that the machines are devoted to analyzing blood samples.
a. Formulate an LP model for this problem.
b. Create a spreadsheet model for this problem and solve it using Solver.
c. What is the optimal solution?
d. How much processing time will be available on each machine if this solution is implemented?
e. How would the model and solution change if the lab director wanted to balance the use of each machine so that each machine were used approximately the same amount of time?

27. Virginia Tech operates its own power generating plant. The electricity generated by this plant supplies power to the university and to local businesses and residences in the Blacksburg area. The plant burns three types of coal, which produce steam that drives the turbines that generate the electricity. The Environmental Protection Agency (EPA) requires that for each ton of coal burned, the emissions from the coal furnace smoke stacks contain no more than 2,500 parts per million (ppm) of sulfur and no more than 2.8 kilograms (kg) of coal dust. The following table summarizes the amounts of sulfur, coal dust, and steam that result from burning a ton of each type of coal.

Coal	Sulfur (in ppm)	Coal Dust (in kg)	Pounds of Steam Produced
1	1,100	1.7	24,000
2	3,500	3.2	36,000
3	1,300	2.4	28,000

The three types of coal can be mixed and burned in any combination. The resulting emission of sulfur or coal dust and the pounds of steam produced by any mixture are given as the weighted average of the values shown in the table for each type of coal. For example, if the coals are mixed to produce a blend that consists of 35% of coal 1, 40% of coal 2, and 25% of coal 3, the sulfur emission (in ppm) resulting from burning one ton of this blend is:

$$0.35 \times 1{,}100 + 0.40 \times 3{,}500 + 0.25 \times 1{,}300 = 2{,}110$$

The manager of this facility wants to determine the blend of coal that will produce the maximum pounds of steam per ton without violating the EPA requirements.
a. Formulate an LP model for this problem.
b. Create a spreadsheet model for this problem and solve it using Solver.
c. What is the optimal solution?
d. If the furnace can burn up to 30 tons of coal per hour, what is the maximum amount of steam that can be produced per hour?

28. Kentwood Electronics manufactures three components for stereo systems: CD players, tape decks, and stereo tuners. The wholesale price and manufacturing cost of each item are shown in the following table.

Component	Wholesale Price	Manufacturing Cost
CD Player	$150	$75
Tape Deck	$85	$35
Stereo Tuner	$70	$30

Each CD player produced requires 3 hours of assembly; each tape deck requires 2 hours of assembly; and each tuner requires 1 hour of assembly. The marketing department has indicated that it can sell no more than 150,000 CD players, 100,000 tape decks, and 90,000 stereo tuners. However, the demand is expected to be at least 50,000 units of each item, and Kentwood wants to meet this demand. If Kentwood has 400,000 hours of assembly time available, how many CD players, tape decks, and stereo tuners should it produce to maximize profits while meeting the minimum demand figures?
a. Formulate an LP model for this problem.
b. Create a spreadsheet model for this problem and solve it using Solver.
c. What is the optimal solution?

29. The Rent-A-Dent car rental company allows its customers to pick up a rental car at one location and return it to any of its locations. Currently, two locations (1 and 2) have 16 and 18 surplus cars, respectively, and four locations (3, 4, 5, and 6) each need 10 cars. The costs of getting the surplus cars from locations 1 and 2 to the other locations are summarized in the following table.

Costs of Transporting Cars Between Locations

	Location 3	Location 4	Location 5	Location 6
Location 1	$54	$17	$23	$30
Location 2	$24	$18	$19	$31

Because 34 surplus cars are available at locations 1 and 2, and 40 cars are needed at locations 3, 4, 5, and 6, some locations will not receive as many cars as they need. However, management wants to make sure that all the surplus cars are sent where they are needed, and that each location needing cars receives at least five.
a. Formulate an LP model for this problem.
b. Create a spreadsheet model for this problem and solve it using Solver.
c. What is the optimal solution?

30. The Sentry Lock Corporation manufactures a popular commercial security lock at plants in Macon, Louisville, Detroit, and Phoenix. The per unit cost of production at each plant is $35.50, $37.50, $39.00, and $36.25, respectively, and the annual production capacity at each plant is 18,000, 15,000, 25,000, and 20,000, respectively. Sentry's locks are sold to retailers through wholesale distributors in seven cities across the United States. The unit cost of shipping from each plant to each distributor is summarized in the following table along with the forecasted demand from each distributor for the coming year.

Unit Shipping Cost to Distributor in

Plants	Tacoma	San Diego	Dallas	Denver	St. Louis	Tampa	Baltimore
Macon	$2.50	$2.75	$1.75	$2.00	$2.10	$1.80	$1.65
Louisville	$1.85	$1.90	$1.50	$1.60	$1.00	$1.90	$1.85
Detroit	$2.30	$2.25	$1.85	$1.25	$1.50	$2.25	$2.00
Phoenix	$1.90	$0.90	$1.60	$1.75	$2.00	$2.50	$2.65
Demand	8,500	14,500	13,500	12,600	18,000	15,000	9,000

Sentry wants to determine the least expensive way of manufacturing and shipping locks from their plants to the distributors. Because the total demand from distributors exceeds the total production capacity for all the plants, Sentry realizes it will not be able to satisfy all the demand for its product, but wants to make sure each distributor will have the opportunity to fill at least 80% of the orders they receive.
a. Create a spreadsheet model for this problem and solve it.
b. What is the optimal solution?

31. A paper recycling company converts newspaper, mixed paper, white office paper, and cardboard into pulp for newsprint, packaging paper, and print stock quality paper. The following table summarizes the yield for each kind of pulp recovered from each ton of recycled material.

Recycling Yield

	Newsprint	Packaging	Print Stock
Newspaper	85%	80%	—
Mixed Paper	90%	80%	70%
White Office Paper	90%	85%	80%
Cardboard	80%	70%	—

For instance, a ton of newspaper can be recycled using a technique that yields 0.85 tons of newsprint pulp. Alternatively, a ton of newspaper can be recycled using a technique that yields 0.80 tons of packaging paper. Similarly, a ton of cardboard can be recycled to yield 0.80 tons of newsprint or 0.70 tons of packaging paper pulp. Note that newspaper and cardboard cannot be converted to print stock pulp using the techniques available to the recycler.

The cost of processing each ton of raw material into the various types of pulp is summarized in the following table, along with the amount of each of the four raw materials that can be purchased and their costs.

	Processing Costs per Ton			Purchase Cost Per Ton	Tons Available
	Newsprint	Packaging	Print Stock		
Newspaper	$6.50	$11.00	—	$15	600
Mixed Paper	$9.75	$12.25	$9.50	$16	500
White Office Paper	$4.75	$7.75	$8.50	$19	300
Cardboard	$7.50	$8.50	—	$17	400

The recycler wants to determine the least costly way of producing 500 tons of newsprint pulp, 600 tons of packaging paper pulp, and 300 tons of print stock quality pulp.
a. Create a spreadsheet model for this problem and solve it.
b. What is the optimal solution?

32. A winery has the following capacity to produce an exclusive dinner wine at either of its two vineyards at the indicated costs:

Vineyard	Capacity	Cost per Bottle
1	3,500 bottles	$23
2	3,100 bottles	$25

Four Italian restaurants around the country are interested in purchasing this wine. Because the wine is exclusive, they all want to buy as much as they need but will take whatever they can get. The maximum amounts required by the restaurants and the prices they are willing to pay are summarized in the following table.

Restaurant	Maximum Demand	Price
1	1,800 bottles	$69
2	2,300 bottles	$67
3	1,250 bottles	$70
4	1,750 bottles	$66

The costs of shipping a bottle from the vineyards to the restaurants are summarized in the following table.

	Restaurant			
Vineyard	1	2	3	4
1	$7	$8	$13	$9
2	$12	$6	$8	$7

The winery needs to determine the production and shipping plan that allows it to maximize its profits on this wine.
a. Formulate an LP model for this problem.
b. Create a spreadsheet model for this problem and solve it using Solver.
c. What is the optimal solution?

33. The Pitts Barbecue Company makes three kinds of barbecue sauce: Extra Hot, Hot, and Mild. Pitts' vice president of marketing estimates that the company can sell 8,000 cases of its Extra Hot sauce plus 10 extra cases for every dollar it spends promoting this sauce; 10,000 cases of Hot sauce plus 8 extra cases for every dollar spent promoting this sauce; and 12,000 cases of its Mild sauce plus 5 extra cases for every dollar spent promoting this sauce. Although each barbecue sauce sells for $10 per case, the cost of producing the different types of sauce varies. It costs the company $6 to produce a case of Extra Hot sauce, $5.50 to produce a case of Hot sauce, and $5.25 to produce a case of Mild sauce. The president of the company wants to make sure the company manufactures at least the minimum amounts of each sauce that the marketing vice president thinks the company can sell. A budget of $25,000 total has been approved for promoting these items, of which at least $5,000 must be spent advertising each item. How many cases of each type of sauce should be made and how do you suggest that the company allocate the promotional budget if it wants to maximize profits?
   a. Formulate an LP model for this problem.
   b. Create a spreadsheet model for this problem and solve it using Solver.
   c. What is the optimal solution?
34. Acme Manufacturing makes a variety of household appliances at a single manufacturing facility. The expected demand for one of these appliances during the next four months is shown in the following table along with the expected production costs and the expected capacity for producing these items.

		Month		
	1	2	3	4
Demand	420	580	310	540
Production Cost	$49.00	$45.00	$46.00	$47.00
Production Capacity	500	520	450	550

Acme estimates that it costs $1.50 per month for each unit of this appliance carried in inventory (estimated by averaging the beginning and ending inventory levels each month). Currently, Acme has 120 units in inventory on hand for this product. To maintain a level workforce, the company wants to produce at least 400 units per month. It also wants to maintain a safety stock of at least 50 units per month. Acme wants to determine how many of each appliance to manufacture during each of the next four months to meet the expected demand at the lowest possible total cost.
   a. Formulate an LP model for this problem.
   b. Create a spreadsheet model for this problem and solve it using Solver.
   c. What is the optimal solution?
   d. How much money could Acme save if it were willing to drop the restriction about producing at least 400 units per month?
35. Paul Bergey is in charge of loading cargo ships for International Cargo Company (ICC) at the port in Newport News, Virginia. Paul is preparing a loading plan for an ICC freighter destined for Ghana. An agricultural commodities dealer wants to transport the following products aboard this ship.

Commodity	Amount Available (tons)	Volume per Ton (cubic feet)	Profit per Ton ($)
1	4,800	40	70
2	2,500	25	50
3	1,200	60	60
4	1,700	55	80

Paul can elect to load any and/or all of the available commodities. However, the ship has three cargo holds with the following capacity restrictions:

Cargo Hold	Weight Capacity (tons)	Volume Capacity (cubic feet)
Forward	3,000	145,000
Center	6,000	180,000
Rear	4,000	155,000

More than one type of commodity can be placed in the same cargo hold. However, because of balance considerations, the weight in the forward cargo hold must be within 10% of the weight in the rear cargo hold and the center cargo hold must be between 40% to 60% of the total weight on board.

a. Formulate an LP model for this problem.
b. Create a spreadsheet model for this problem and solve it using Solver.
c. What is the optimal solution?

36. The Pelletier Corporation has just discovered that it will not have enough warehouse space for the next five months. The additional warehouse space requirements for this period are:

Month	1	2	3	4	5
Additional Space Needed (in 1000 sq ft)	25	10	20	10	5

To cover its space requirements, the firm plans to lease additional warehouse space on a short-term basis. Over the next five months, a local warehouse has agreed to lease Pelletier any amount of space for any number of months according to the following cost schedule.

Length of Lease (in months)	1	2	3	4	5
Cost per 1000 square feet	$300	$525	$775	$850	$975

This schedule of leasing options is available to Pelletier at the beginning of each of the next five months. For example, the company could elect to lease 5,000 square feet for 4 months beginning in month 1 (at a cost of $850 × 5) and lease 10,000 square feet for 2 months beginning in month 3 (at a cost of $525 × 10).

a. Formulate an LP model for this problem.
b. Create a spreadsheet model for this problem and solve it using Solver.
c. What is the optimal solution?

37. Carter Enterprises is involved in the soybean business in South Carolina, Alabama, and Georgia. The president of the company, Earl Carter, goes to a commodity sale once a month where he buys and sells soybeans in bulk. Carter uses a local warehouse for storing his soybean inventory. This warehouse charges $10 per average ton of soybeans stored per month (based on the average of the beginning and ending inventory each month). The warehouse guarantees Carter the capacity to store up to 400 tons of soybeans at the end of each month. Carter has estimated what he believes the price per ton of soybeans will be during each of the next six months. These prices are summarized in the following table.

Month	1	2	3	4	5	6
Price per Ton	$135	$110	$150	$175	$130	$145

Assume that Carter currently has 70 tons of soybeans stored in the warehouse. How many tons of soybeans should Carter buy and sell during each of the next six months to maximize his profit trading soybeans?

a. Formulate an LP model for this problem.
b. Create a spreadsheet model for this problem and solve it using Solver.
c. What is the optimal solution?

38. Jack Potts recently won $1,000,000 in Las Vegas and is trying to determine how to invest his winnings. He has narrowed his decision down to five investments, which are summarized in the following table.

Summary of Cash Inflows and Outflows
(at beginning of years)

	1	2	3	4
A	−1	0.50	0.80	
B		−1	⟷	1.25
C	−1	⟷	⟷	1.35
D			−1	1.13
E	−1	⟷	1.27	

If Jack invests $1 in investment A at the beginning of year 1, he will receive $0.50 at the beginning of year 2 and another $0.80 at the beginning of year 3. Alternatively, he can invest $1 in investment B at the beginning of year 2 and receive $1.25 at the beginning of year 4. Entries of "⟷" in the table indicate times when no cash inflows or outflows can occur. At the beginning of any year, Jack can place money in a money market account that is expected to yield 8% per year. He wants to keep at least $50,000 in the money market account at all times and doesn't want to place any more than $500,000 in any single investment. How would you advise Jack to invest his winnings if he wants to maximize the amount of money he'll have at the beginning of year 4?

a. Formulate an LP model for this problem.
b. Create a spreadsheet model for this problem and solve it using Solver.
c. What is the optimal solution?

39. Fred and Sally Merrit recently inherited a substantial amount of money from a deceased relative. They want to use part of this money to establish an account to pay for their daughter's college education. Their daughter, Lisa, will be starting college 5 years from now. The Merrits estimate that her first year college expenses will amount to $12,000 and increase $2,000 per year during each of the remaining three years of her education. The following investments are available to the Merrits:

Investment	Available	Matures	Return at Maturity
A	Every year	1 year	6%
B	1, 3, 5, 7	2 years	14%
C	1, 4	3 years	18%
D	1	7 years	65%

The Merrits want to determine an investment plan that will provide the necessary funds to cover Lisa's anticipated college expenses with the smallest initial investment.

a. Formulate an LP model for this problem.
b. Create a spreadsheet model for this problem and solve it using Solver.
c. What is the optimal solution?

40. Refer to the previous question. Suppose the investments available to the Merrits have the following levels of risk associated with them.

Investment	A	B	C	D
Risk Factor	1	3	6	8

If the Merrits want the weighted average risk level of their investments to not exceed 4, how much money will they need to set aside for Lisa's education and how should they invest it?

a. Formulate an LP model for this problem.
b. Create a spreadsheet model for this problem and solve it using Solver.
c. What is the optimal solution?

41. WinterWearhouse operates a clothing store specializing in ski apparel. Given the seasonal nature of its business, often there is somewhat of an imbalance between when bills must be paid for inventory purchased and when the goods actually are sold and cash is received. Over the next six months, the company expects cash receipts and requirements for bill paying as follows:

	Month					
	1	2	3	4	5	6
Cash Receipts	$100,000	$225,000	$275,000	$350,000	$475,000	$625,000
Bills Due	$400,000	$500,000	$600,000	$300,000	$200,000	$100,000

The company likes to maintain a cash balance of at least $20,000 and currently has $100,000 cash on hand. The company can borrow money from a local bank for the following term/rate structure: 1 month at 1%, 2 months at 1.75%, 3 months at 2.49%, 4 months at 3.22%, and 5 months at 3.94%. When needed, money is borrowed at the end of a month and repaid, with interest, at the end of the month in which the obligation is due. For instance, if the company borrows $10,000 for 2 months in month 3, it would have to pay back $10,175 at the end of month 5.

a. Create a spreadsheet model for this problem and solve it.
b. What is the optimal solution?
c. Suppose its bank limits WinterWearhouse to borrowing no more than $100,000 at each level in the term/rate structure. How would this restriction change the optimal solution?

42. The accounting firm of Coopers & Andersen is conducting a benchmarking survey to assess the satisfaction level of its clients versus clients served by competing accounting firms. The clients are divided into four groups:

Group 1: Large clients of Coopers & Andersen
Group 2: Small clients of Coopers & Andersen
Group 3: Large clients of other accounting firms
Group 4: Small clients of other accounting firms

A total of 4,000 companies are being surveyed either by telephone or via a two-way web-cam interview. The costs associated with surveying the different types of companies are summarized below:

	Survey Costs	
Group	Telephone	Webcam
1	$18	$40
2	$14	$35
3	$25	$60
4	$20	$45

Coopers & Andersen wants the survey to carry out the survey in the least costly way that meets the following conditions:

- At least 10% but not more than 50% of the total companies surveyed should come from each group.
- At least 50% of the companies surveyed should be clients of Coopers & Andersen.
- At least 25% of the surveys should be done via web cam.
- At least 50% of the large clients of Coopers & Anderson who are surveyed should be done via web cam.
- A maximum of 40% of those surveyed may be small companies.
- A maximum of 25% of the small companies surveyed should be done via web cam.

   a. Formulate an LP model for this problem.
   b. Create a spreadsheet model for this problem and solve it using Solver.
   c. What is the optimal solution?

43. The chief financial officer for Eagle's Beach Wear and Gift Shop is planning for the company's cash flows for the next six months. The following table summarizes the expected accounts receivables and planned payments for each of these months (in $100,000s).

	January	February	March	April	May	June
Accounts Receivable Balances Due	1.50	1.00	1.40	2.30	2.00	1.00
Planned Payments (net of discounts)	1.80	1.60	2.20	1.20	0.80	1.20

The company currently has a beginning cash balance of $400,000 and desires to maintain a balance of at least $25,000 in cash at the end of each month. To accomplish this, the company has several ways of obtaining short-term funds:

1. **Delay Payments.** In any month, the company's suppliers permit it to delay any or all payments for one month. However, for this consideration, the company forfeits a 2% discount that normally applies when payments are made on time. (Loss of this 2% discount is, in effect, a financing cost.)
2. **Borrow Against Accounts Receivables.** In any month, the company's bank will loan it up to 75% of the accounts receivable balances due that month. These loans must be repaid in the following month and incur an interest charge of 1.5%.
3. **Short-Term Loan.** At the beginning of January, the company's bank will also give it a 6-month loan to be repaid in a lump sum at the end of June. Interest on this loan is 1% per month and is payable at the end of each month.

Assume the company earns 0.5% interest each month on cash held at the beginning of the month. Create a spreadsheet model that the company can use to determine the least costly cash management plan (i.e., minimal net financing costs) for this 6-month period. What is the optimal solution?

44. The DotCom Corporation is implementing a pension plan for its employees. The company intends to start funding the plan with a deposit of $50,000 on January 1, 2008. It plans to invest an additional $12,000 one year later, and continue making additional investments (increasing by $2,000 per year) on January 1 of each year from 2010 through 2022. To fund these payments, the company plans to purchase a

number of bonds. Bond 1 costs $970 per unit and will pay a $65 coupon on January 1 of each year from 2009 through 2012 plus a final payment of $1065 on January 1, 2013. Bond 2 costs $980 and will pay a $73 coupon on January 1 of each year from 2009 through 2018 plus a final payment of $1073 on January 1, 2019. Bond 3 costs $1025 and will pay a $85 coupon on January 1 of each year from 2009 through 2021 plus a final payment of $1085 on January 1, 2022. The company's cash holdings earn an interest rate of 4.5%. Assume that the company wants to purchase bonds on January 1, 2008 and cannot buy them in fractional units. How much should the company invest in the various bonds and cash account to fund this plan through January 1, 2022 in the least costly way?

a. Create a spreadsheet model for this problem and solve it.
b. What is the optimal solution?

45. A natural gas trading company wants to develop an optimal trading plan for the next 10 days. The following table summarizes the estimated prices (per thousand cubic feet (cf)) at which the company can buy and sell natural gas during this time. The company may buy gas at the "Ask" price and sell gas at the "Bid" price.

Day	1	2	3	4	5	6	7	8	9	10
Bid	$3.06	$4.01	$6.03	$4.06	$4.01	$5.02	$5.10	$4.08	$3.01	$4.01
Ask	$3.22	$4.10	$6.13	$4.19	$4.05	$5.12	$5.28	$4.23	$3.15	$4.18

The company currently has 150,000 cf of gas in storage and has a maximum storage capacity of 500,000 cf. To maintain the required pressure in the gas transmission pipeline system, the company can inject no more than 200,000 cf into the storage facility each day and can extract no more than 180,000 cf per day. Assume that extractions occur in the morning and injections occur in the evening. The owner of the storage facility charges a storage fee of 5% of the market (bid) value of the average daily gas inventory. (The average daily inventory is computed as the average of each day's beginning and ending inventory.)

a. Create a spreadsheet model for this problem and solve it.
b. What is the optimal solution?
c. Assuming price forecasts for natural gas change on a daily basis, how would you suggest that the company in this problem actually use your model?

46. The Embassy Lodge hotel chain wants to compare its brand efficiency to that of its major competitors using DEA. Embassy collected the following data reported in industry trade publications. Embassy views customers' perceptions of satisfaction and value (scored from 0 to 100 where 100 is best) to be outputs produced as a function of the following inputs: price, convenience, room comfort, climate control, service, and food quality. (All inputs are expressed on scales where less is better.)

Brand	Satis-faction	Value	Price	Conven-ience	Room Comfort	Climate Control	Service	Food Quality
Embassy Lodge	85	82	70.00	2.3	1.8	2.7	1.5	3.3
Sheritown Inn	96	93	70.00	1.5	1.1	0.2	0.5	0.5
Hynton Hotel	78	87	75.00	2.2	2.4	2.6	2.5	3.2
Vacation Inn	87	88	75.00	1.8	1.6	1.5	1.8	2.3
Merrylot	89	94	80.00	0.5	1.4	0.4	0.9	2.6
FairPrice Inn	93	93	80.00	1.3	0.9	0.2	0.6	2.8
Nights Inn	92	91	85.00	1.4	1.3	0.6	1.4	2.1
Western Hotels	97	92	90.00	0.3	1.7	1.7	1.7	1.8

a. Compute the DEA efficiency for each brand.
b. Which brands are efficient?
c. Is Embassy Lodge efficient? If not, what input and output values should it aspire to, to become efficient?

47. Fidelity Savings & Loans (FS&L) operates several banking facilities throughout the Southeastern United States. The officers of FS&L want to analyze the efficiency of the various branch offices using DEA. The following data has been selected to represent appropriate input and output measures of each banking facility.

Branch	R.O.A.	New Loans	Satisfaction	Labor Hrs	Op. Costs
1	5.32	770	92	3.73	6.34
2	3.39	780	94	3.49	4.43
3	4.95	790	93	5.98	6.31
4	6.01	730	82	6.49	7.28
5	6.40	910	98	7.09	8.69
6	2.89	860	90	3.46	3.23
7	6.94	880	89	7.36	9.07
8	7.18	970	99	6.38	7.42
9	5.98	770	94	4.74	6.75
10	4.97	930	91	5.04	6.35

a. Identify the inputs and outputs for FS&L. Are they all measured on the appropriate scale for use with DEA?
b. Compute the DEA efficiency of each branch office.
c. Which offices are DEA efficient?
d. What input and output levels should branch 5 aspire to, to become efficient?

CASE 3.1   Putting the Link in the Supply Chain

Rick Eldridge is the new Vice President for operations at the The Golfer's Link (TGL), a company specializing in the production of quality, discount sets of golf clubs. Rick was hired primarily because of his expertise in supply chain management (SCM). SCM is the integrated planning and control of all resources in the logistics process from the acquisition of raw materials to the delivery of finished products to the end user. Because SCM seeks to optimize all activities in the supply chain including transactions between firms, Rick's first priority is ensuring that all aspects of production and distribution within TGF are operating optimally.

TGL produces three different lines of golf clubs for men, women, and junior golfers at manufacturing plants in Daytona Beach, FL, Memphis, TN, and Tempe, AZ. The plant in Tempe produces all three lines of clubs. The one in Daytona produces only the men's and women's lines, and the plant in Memphis produces only the women's and juniors' lines. Each line of clubs requires varying amounts of three raw materials that are sometimes in short supply: titanium, aluminum, and a distinctive rock maple wood that TGL uses in all of its drivers. The manufacturing process for each line of clubs at each plant is identical. Thus, the amount of each of these materials required in each set of the different lines of clubs is summarized below:

Resources Required per Club Set (in lbs)		
	Men's	Women's	Juniors'
Titanium	2.9	2.7	2.5
Aluminum	4.5	4	5
Rock Maple	5.4	5	4.8

The estimated amount of each of these key resources available at each plant during the coming month is given as:

| | **Estimated Resource Availability (in lbs)** | | |
	Daytona	**Memphis**	**Tempe**
Titanium	4500	8500	14500
Aluminum	6000	12000	19000
Rock Maple	9500	16000	18000

TGL's reputation for quality and affordability ensures that it can sell all the clubs it can make. The men's, women's, and juniors' lines generate wholesale revenues of $225, $195, and $165, respectively, regardless of where they are produced. Club sets are shipped from the production plants to distribution centers in Sacramento, CA, Denver, CO, and Pittsburgh, PA. Each month, the different distribution centers order the number of club sets in each of the three lines that they would like to receive. TGL's contract with this distributor requires filling at least 90% (but no more than 100%) of all distributor orders. Rick recently received the following distributor orders for the coming month:

| | **Number of Club Sets Ordered** | | |
	Men's	**Women's**	**Juniors'**
Sacramento	700	900	900
Denver	550	1000	1500
Pittsburgh	900	1200	1100

The cost of shipping a set of clubs to each distribution point from each production facility is summarized in the following table. Note again that Daytona does not produce juniors' club sets and Memphis does not produce men's club sets.

| | **Shipping Costs** | | | | | | | |
| | **Men's** | | **Women's** | | | **Juniors'** | | |
To/From	**Daytona**	**Tempe**	**Daytona**	**Memphis**	**Tempe**	**Memphis**	**Tempe**
Sacramento	$51	$10	$49	$33	$9	$31	$8
Denver	$28	$43	$27	$22	$42	$21	$40
Pittsburgh	$36	$56	$34	$13	$54	$12	$52

Rick has asked you to determine an optimal production and shipping plan for the coming month.

a. Create a spreadsheet model for this problem and solve it. What is the optimal solution?

b. If Rick wanted to improve this solution, what additional resources would be needed and where would they be needed? Explain.

c. What would TGL's optimal profit be if they were not required to supply at least 90% of each distributor's order?

d. Suppose TGL's agreement included the option of paying a $10,000 penalty if they cannot supply at least 90% of each the distributor's order but instead supply at least 80% of each distributor's order. Comment on the pros and cons of TGL exercising this option.

Foreign Exchange Trading at Baldwin Enterprises

CASE 3.2

Baldwin Enterprises is a large manufacturing company with operations and sales divisions located in the United States and several other countries. The CFO of the organization, Wes Hamrick, is concerned about the amount of money Baldwin has been paying in transaction costs in the foreign exchange markets and has asked you to help optimize Baldwin's foreign exchange treasury functions.

With operations in several countries, Baldwin maintains cash assets in several different currencies: U.S. dollars (USD), the European Union's euro (EUR), Great Britain's pound (GBP), Hong Kong dollars (HKD), and Japanese yen (JPY). To meet the different cash flow requirements associated with its operations around the world, Baldwin often must move funds from one location (and currency) to another. For instance, to pay an unexpected maintenance expense at its facility in Japan, Baldwin might need to convert some of its holdings in U.S. dollars to Japanese yen.

The foreign exchange (FX) market is a network of financial institutions and brokers in which individuals, businesses, banks, and governments buy and sell the currencies of different countries. They do so to finance international trade, invest or do business abroad, or speculate on currency price changes. The FX market operates 24 hours a day and represents the largest and most liquid marketplace in the global economy. On average, the equivalent of about $1.5 trillion in different currencies is traded daily in the FX market around the world. The liquidity of the market provides businesses with access to international markets for goods and services by providing foreign currency necessary for transactions worldwide (see:http://www.ny.frb.org/fxc).

The FX market operates in much the same way as a stock or commodity market; there is a bid price and ask price for each commodity (or, in this case, currency). A bid price is the price at which the market is willing to buy a particular currency and the ask price is the price at which the market is willing to sell a currency. The ask prices are typically slightly higher than the bid prices for the same currency—representing the transaction cost or the profit earned by the organizations that keep the market liquid.

The following table summarizes the current FX rates for the currencies Baldwin currently holds. The entries in this table represent the conversion rates from the row currencies to the column currencies.

Convert/To	USD	EUR	GBP	HKD	JPY
USD	1	1.01864	0.6409	7.7985	118.55
EUR	0.9724	1	0.6295	7.6552	116.41
GBP	1.5593	1.5881	1	12.154	184.97
HKD	0.12812	0.1304	0.0821	1	15.1005
JPY	0.00843	0.00856	0.0054	0.0658	1

For example, the table indicates that one British pound (GBP) can be exchanged (or sold) for 1.5593 U.S. dollars (USD). Thus, $1.5593 is the bid price, in U.S. dollars, for one British pound. Alternatively, the table indicates one U.S. dollar (USD) can be exchanged (sold) for 0.6409 British pounds (GBP). So, it takes about 1.5603 U.S. dollars (or 1/0.6409) to buy one British pound (or the ask price, in U.S. dollars, for one British pound is roughly $1.5603).

Notice that if you took one British pound, converted it to 1.5593 U.S. dollars, and then converted those 1.5593 dollars back to British pounds, you would end up with only

0.999355 British pounds (i.e., $1 \times 1.5593 \times 0.6409 = 0.999355$). The money that you lose in this exchange is the transaction cost.

Baldwin's current portfolio of cash holdings includes 2 million USD, 5 million EUR, 1 million GBP, 3 million HKD, and 30 million JPY. This portfolio is equivalent to $9,058,710 USD under the current exchange rates (given above). Wes has asked you to design a currency trading plan that would increase Baldwin's euro and yen holdings to 8 million EUR and 54 JPY, respectively, while maintaining the equivalent of at least $250,000 USD in each currency. Baldwin measures transaction costs as the change in the USD equivalent value of the portfolio.

a. Create a spreadsheet model for this problem and solve it.
b. What is the optimal trading plan?
c. What is the optimal transaction cost (in equivalent USD)?
d. Suppose that another executive thinks that holding $250,000 USD in each currency is excessive and wants to lower the amount to $50,000 USD in each currency. Does this help to lower the transaction cost? Why or why not?
e. Suppose the exchange rate for converting USD to GBP increased from 0.6409 to 0.6414. What would happen to the optimal solution in this case?

The Wolverine Retirement Fund
CASE 3.3

Kelly Jones is a financial analyst for Wolverine Manufacturing, a company that produces engine bearings for the automotive industry. Wolverine is hammering out a new labor agreement with its unionized workforce. One of the major concerns of the labor union is the funding of Wolverine's retirement plan for their hourly employees. The union believes that the company has not been contributing enough money to this fund to cover the benefits it will need to pay to retiring employees. Because of this, the union wants the company to contribute approximately $1.5 million dollars in additional money to this fund over the next 20 years. These extra contributions would begin with an extra payment of $20,000 at the end of one year with annual payments increasing by 12.35% per year for the next 19 years.

The union has asked the company to set up a sinking fund to cover the extra annual payments to the retirement fund. Wolverine's Chief Financial Officer and the union's chief negotiator have agreed that AAA-rated bonds recently issued by three different companies may be used to establish this fund. The following table summarizes the provisions of these bonds.

Company	Maturity	Coupon Payment	Price	Par Value
AC&C	15 years	$80	$847.88	$1,000
IBN	10 years	$90	$938.55	$1,000
MicroHard	20 years	$85	$872.30	$1,000

According to this table, Wolverine may buy bonds issued by AC&C for $847.88 per bond. Each AC&C bond will pay the bondholder $80 per year for the next 15 years, plus an extra payment of $1,000 (the par value) in the fifteenth year. Similar interpretations apply to the information for the IBN and MicroHard bonds. A money market fund yielding 5% may be used to hold any coupon payments that are not needed to meet the company's required retirement fund payment in any given year.

Wolverine's CFO has asked Kelly to determine how much money the company would have to invest and which bonds the company should buy to meet the labor union's demands.

a. If you were Kelly, what would you tell the CFO?
b. Suppose that the union insists on including one of the following stipulations into the agreement:
    1. No more than half of the total number of bonds purchased may be purchased from a single company.
    2. At least 10% of the total number of bonds must be purchased from each of the companies.
Which stipulation should Wolverine agree to?

CASE 3.4 Saving the Manatees

"So how am I going to spend this money," thought Tom Wieboldt as he sat staring at the pictures and posters of manatees around his office. An avid environmentalist, Tom is the president of "Friends of the Manatees"—a nonprofit organization trying to help pass legislation to protect manatees.

Manatees are large, gray-brown aquatic mammals with bodies that taper to a flat, paddle-shaped tail. These gentle and slow-moving creatures grow to an average adult length of 10 feet and weigh an average of 1,000 pounds. Manatees are found in shallow, slow-moving rivers, estuaries, saltwater bays, canals, and coastal areas. In the United States, manatees are concentrated in Florida in the winter, but can be found in summer months as far west as Alabama and as far north as Virginia and the Carolinas. They have no natural enemies, but loss of habitat is the most serious threat facing manatees today. Most human-related manatee deaths occur from collisions with motor boats.

Tom's organization has been supporting a bill before the Florida legislature to restrict the use of motor boats in areas known to be inhabited by manatees. This bill is scheduled to come up for a vote in the legislature. Tom recently received a phone call from a national environmental protection organization indicating that it will donate $300,000 to Friends of the Manatees to help increase public awareness about the plight of the manatees, and to encourage voters to urge their representatives in the state legislature to vote for this bill. Tom intends to use this money to purchase various types of advertising media to "get the message out" during the four weeks immediately preceding the vote.

Tom is considering several different advertising alternatives: newspapers, TV, radio, billboards, and magazines. A marketing consultant provided Tom with the following data on the costs and effectiveness of the various types of media being considered.

Advertising Medium	Unit Cost	Unit Impact Rating
Half-page, Daily paper	$800	55
Full-page, Daily paper	$1,400	75
Half-page, Sunday paper	$1,200	65
Full-page, Sunday paper	$1,800	80
Daytime TV spot	$2,500	85
Evening TV spot	$3,500	100
Highway Billboards	$750	35
15-second Radio spot	$150	45
30-second Radio spot	$300	55
Half-page, magazine	$500	50
Full-page, magazine	$900	60

According to the marketing consultant, the most effective type of advertising for this type of problem would be short TV ads during the evening prime-time hours.

Thus, this type of advertising was given a "unit impact rating" of 100. The other types of advertising were then given unit impact ratings that reflect their expected effectiveness relative to an evening TV ad. For instance, a half-page magazine ad is expected to provide half the effectiveness of an evening TV ad and is therefore given an impact rating of 50.

Tom wants to allocate the $300,000 to these different advertising alternatives in a way that will maximize the impact achieved. However, he realizes that it is important to spread his message via several different advertising channels, as not everyone listens to the radio and not everyone watches TV in the evenings.

The two most widely read newspapers in the state of Florida are the *Orlando Sentinel* and the *Miami Herald*. During the four weeks before the vote, Tom wants to have half-page ads in the daily (Monday-Saturday) versions of each of these papers at least three times per week. He also wants to have one full-page ad in the daily version of each paper the week before the vote, and he is willing to run more full-page ads if this would be helpful. He also wants to run full-page ads in the Sunday editions of each paper the Sunday before the vote. Tom never wants to run a full-page and half-page ad in a paper on the same day. So the maximum number of full and half-page ads that can be run in the daily papers should be 48 (i.e., 4 weeks × 6 days per week × 2 papers = 48). Similarly, the maximum number of full and half-page ads that can be run in the Sunday papers is eight.

Tom wants to have at least one and no more than three daytime TV ads every day during the four-week period. He also wants to have at least one ad on TV every night but no more than two per night.

There are 10 billboard locations throughout the state that are available for use during the four weeks before the vote. Tom definitely wants to have at least one billboard in each of the cities of Orlando, Tampa, and Miami.

Tom believes that the ability to show pictures of the cute, pudgy, lovable manatees in the print media offers a distinct advantage over radio ads. However, the radio ads are relatively inexpensive and might reach some people that the other ads will not reach. Thus, Tom wants to have at least two 15-second and at least two 30-second ads on the radio each day. However, he wants to limit the number of radio ads to five 15-second ads and five 30-second ads per day.

There are three different weekly magazines in which Tom can run ads. Tom wants to run full-page ads in each of the magazines at some point during the four-week period. However, he never wants to run full- and half-page ads in the same magazine in a given week. Thus, the total number of full- and half-page magazine ads selected should not exceed 12 (i.e., 4 weeks × 3 magazines × 1 ad per magazine per week = 12 ads).

Although Tom has some ideas about the minimum and maximum number of ads to run in the various types of media, he's not sure how much money this will take. And if he can afford to meet all the minimums, he's really confused about the best way to spend the remaining funds. So again Tom asks himself, "How am I going to spend this money?"

a. Create a spreadsheet model for this problem and solve it. What is the optimal solution?

b. Of the constraints Tom placed on this problem, which are "binding" or preventing the objective function from being improved further?

c. Suppose Tom was willing to increase the allowable number of evening TV ads. How much would this improve the solution?

d. Suppose Tom was willing to double the allowable number of radio ads aired each day. How much would this improve the solution?

Chapter 4

Sensitivity Analysis and the Simplex Method

4.0 Introduction

In Chapters 2 and 3, we studied how to formulate and solve LP models for a variety of decision problems. However, formulating and solving an LP model does not necessarily mean that the original decision problem has been solved. Several questions often arise about the optimal solution to an LP model. In particular, we might be interested in how sensitive the optimal solution is to changes in various coefficients of the LP model.

Businesses rarely know with certainty what costs will be incurred, or the exact amount of resources that will be consumed or available in a given situation or time period. Thus, management might be skeptical of optimal solutions obtained using models that assume that all relevant factors are known with certainty. Sensitivity analysis can help overcome this skepticism and provide a better picture of how the solution to a problem will change if different factors in the model change. Sensitivity analysis also can help answer several practical managerial questions that might arise about the solution to an LP problem.

4.1 The Purpose of Sensitivity Analysis

As noted in Chapter 2, any problem that can be stated in the following form is an LP problem:

$$\text{MAX (or MIN):} \quad c_1X_1 + c_2X_2 + \cdots + c_nX_n$$
$$\text{Subject to:} \quad a_{11}X_1 + a_{12}X_2 + \cdots + a_{1n}X_n \leq b_1$$
$$\vdots$$
$$a_{k1}X_1 + a_{k2}X_2 + \cdots + a_{kn}X_n \geq b_k$$
$$\vdots$$
$$a_{m1}X_1 + a_{m2}X_2 + \cdots + a_{mn}X_n = b_m$$

All the coefficients in this model (the c_j, a_{ij}, and b_i) represent numeric constants. So, when we formulate and solve an LP problem, we implicitly assume that we can specify the exact values for these coefficients. However, in the real world, these coefficients might change from day to day or minute to minute. For example, the price a company charges for its products can change on a daily, weekly, or monthly basis. Similarly, if a skilled machinist calls in sick, a manufacturer might have less capacity to produce items on a given machine than was originally planned.

Realizing that such uncertainties exist, a manager should consider how sensitive an LP model's solution is to changes or estimation errors that might occur in: (1) the objective function coefficients (the c_j), (2) the constraint coefficients (the a_{ij}), and (3) the RHS values for the constraints (the b_i). A manager also might ask a number of "What if?" questions about these values. For example, what if the cost of a product increases by 7%? What if a reduction in setup time allows for additional capacity on a given machine? What if a worker's suggestion results in a product requiring only two hours of labor rather than three? Sensitivity analysis addresses these issues by assessing the sensitivity of the solution to uncertainty or estimation errors in the model coefficients, and also the solution's sensitivity to changes in model coefficients that might occur because of human intervention.

4.2 Approaches to Sensitivity Analysis

You can perform sensitivity analysis on an LP model in several ways. If you want to determine the effect of some change in the model, the most direct approach is simply to change the model and re-solve it. This approach is suitable if the model does not take an excessive amount of time to change or solve. In addition, if you are interested in studying the consequences of *simultaneously* changing several coefficients in the model, this might be the only practical approach to sensitivity analysis.

Solver also provides some sensitivity information after solving an LP problem. As mentioned in Chapter 3, one of the benefits of using the simplex method to solve LP problems is its speed—it is considerably faster than the other optimization techniques offered by Solver. However, another advantage of using the simplex method is that it provides more sensitivity analysis information than the other techniques. In particular, the simplex method provides us with information about:

- The range of values the objective function coefficients can assume without changing the optimal solution
- The impact on the optimal objective function value of increases or decreases in the availability of various constrained resources
- The impact on the optimal objective function value of forcing changes in the values of certain decision variables away from their optimal values
- The impact that changes in constraint coefficients will have on the optimal solution to the problem

4.3 An Example Problem

We will again use the Blue Ridge Hot Tubs problem to illustrate the types of sensitivity analysis information available using Solver. The LP formulation of the problem is repeated here, where X_1 represents the number of Aqua-Spas and X_2 represents the number of Hydro-Luxes to be produced:

$$
\begin{array}{lll}
\text{MAX:} & 350X_1 + 300X_2 & \text{\} profit} \\
\text{Subject to:} & 1X_1 + 1X_2 \leq 200 & \text{\} pump constraint} \\
& 9X_1 + 6X_2 \leq 1{,}566 & \text{\} labor constraint} \\
& 12X_1 + 16X_2 \leq 2{,}880 & \text{\} tubing constraint} \\
& X_1, X_2 \geq 0 & \text{\} nonnegativity conditions}
\end{array}
$$

FIGURE 4.1

*Spreadsheet model
for the Blue Ridge
Hot Tubs product
mix problem*

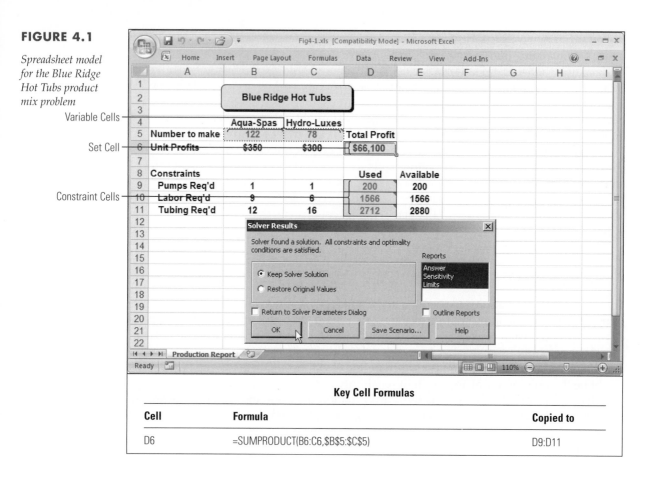

Key Cell Formulas

Cell	Formula	Copied to
D6	=SUMPRODUCT(B6:C6,$B$5:$C$5)	D9:D11

This model is implemented in the spreadsheet shown in Figure 4.1 (and file Fig4-1.xls on your data disk). (See Chapter 3 for details on the procedure used to create and solve this spreadsheet model.)

After solving the LP model, Solver displays the Solver Results dialog box, shown in Figure 4.1. This dialog box provides three report options: Answer, Sensitivity, and Limits. You can select any of these reports after a model has been solved. To select all three reports, highlight the reports, and then click OK. To access each report, click the appropriate tab at the bottom of the screen.

4.4 The Answer Report

Figure 4.2 shows the Answer Report for the Blue Ridge Hot Tubs problem. This report summarizes the solution to the problem, and is fairly self-explanatory. The first section of the report summarizes the original and final (optimal) value of the set cell. The next section summarizes the original and final (optimal) values of the adjustable (or changing) cells representing the decision variables.

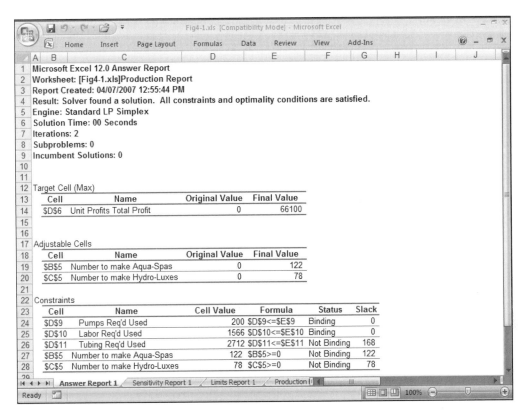

FIGURE 4.2

*Answer Report
for the hot tub
problem*

The final section of this report provides information about the constraints. In particular, the Cell Value column shows the final (optimal) value assumed by each constraint cell. Note that these values correspond to the final value assumed by the LHS formula of each constraint. The Formula column indicates the upper or lower bounds that apply to each constraint cell. The Status column indicates which constraints are binding and which are nonbinding. A constraint is **binding** if it is satisfied as a strict equality in the optimal solution; otherwise, it is **nonbinding**. Notice that the constraints for the number of pumps and amount of labor used are both binding, meaning that *all* the available pumps and labor hours will be used if this solution is implemented. Therefore, these constraints are preventing Blue Ridge Hot Tubs from achieving a higher level of profit.

Finally, the values in the Slack column indicate the difference between the LHS and RHS of each constraint. By definition, binding constraints have zero slack and nonbinding constraints have some positive level of slack. The values in the Slack column indicate that if this solution is implemented, all the available pumps and labor hours will be used, but 168 feet of tubing will be left over. The slack values for the nonnegativity conditions indicate the amounts by which the decision variables exceed their respective lower bounds of zero.

The Answer Report does not provide any information that could not be derived from the solution shown in the spreadsheet model. However, the format of this report gives a convenient summary of the solution that can be incorporated easily into a word-processing document as part of a written report to management.

> ## Report Headings
>
> When creating the reports described in this chapter, Solver will try to use various text entries from the original spreadsheet to generate meaningful headings and labels in the reports. Given the various ways in which a model can be implemented, Solver might not always produce meaningful headings. However, you can change any text entry to make the report more meaningful or descriptive.

4.5 The Sensitivity Report

Figure 4.3 shows the Sensitivity Report for the Blue Ridge Hot Tubs problem. This report summarizes information about the objective (or target cell), the variable (or adjustable) cells, and constraints for our model. This information is useful in evaluating how sensitive the optimal solution is to changes in various coefficients in the model.

FIGURE 4.3

Sensitivity Report for the hot tub problem

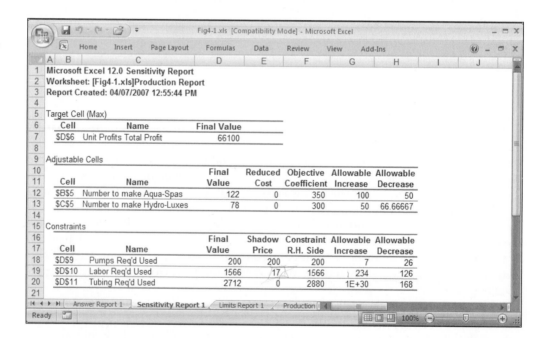

4.5.1 CHANGES IN THE OBJECTIVE FUNCTION COEFFICIENTS

Chapter 2 introduced the level-curve approach to solving a graphical LP problem and showed how to use this approach to solve the Blue Ridge Hot Tubs problem. This graphical solution is repeated in Figure 4.4 (and file Fig4-4.xls on your data disk).

FIGURE 4.4

Graph of original feasible region and optimal solution

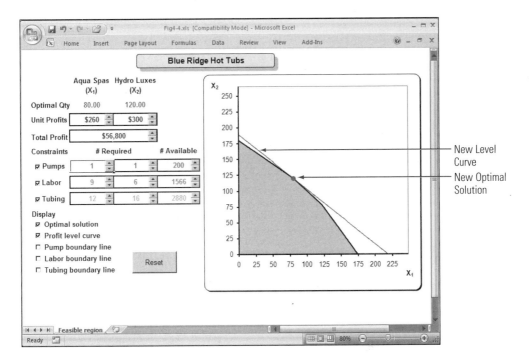

FIGURE 4.5

How a change in an objective function coefficient can change the slope of the level curve and the optimal solution

The slope of the original level curve in Figure 4.4 is determined by the coefficients in the objective function of the model (the values 350 and 300). In Figure 4.5, we can see that if the slope of the level curve were different, the extreme point represented by $X_1 = 80$, $X_2 = 120$ would be the optimal solution. Of course, the only way to change the level curve for the objective function is to change the coefficients in the objective function. So, if the objective function coefficients are at all uncertain, we might be interested in determining how much these values could change before the optimal solution would change.

For example, if the owner of Blue Ridge Hot Tubs does not have complete control over the costs of producing hot tubs (which is likely because he purchases the fiberglass hot tub shells from another company), the profit figures in the objective function of our LP model might not be the exact profits earned on hot tubs produced in the future. So before the manager decides to produce 122 Aqua-Spas and 78 Hydro-Luxes, he might want to determine how sensitive this solution is to the profit figures in the objective. That is, the manager might want to determine how much the profit figures could change before the optimal solution of $X_1 = 122$, $X_2 = 78$ would change. This information is provided in the Sensitivity Report shown in Figure 4.3.

The original objective function coefficients associated with the variable cells are listed in the Objective Coefficient column in Figure 4.3. The next two columns show the allowable increases and decreases in these values. For example, the objective function value associated with Aqua-Spas (or variable X_1) can increase by as much as $100 or decrease by as much as $50 without changing the optimal solution, assuming all other coefficients remain constant. (You can verify this by changing the profit coefficient for Aqua-Spas to any value in the range from $300 to $450 and re-solving the model.) Similarly, the objective function value associated with Hydro-Luxes (or variable X_2) can increase by $50 or decrease by approximately $66.67 without changing the optimal values of the decision variables, assuming all other coefficients remain constant. (Again, you can verify this by re-solving the model with different profit values for Hydro-Luxes.)

Software Note

When setting up a spreadsheet model for an LP problem for which you intend to generate a sensitivity report, it is a good idea to make sure that the cells corresponding to RHS values of constraints contain constants or formulas that do not involve the decision variables. Thus, any RHS formula related directly or indirectly to the decision variables should be moved algebraically to the left-hand side of the constraint before implementing your model. This will help to reduce problems in interpreting Solver's sensitivity report.

4.5.2 A NOTE ABOUT CONSTANCY

The phrase "assuming all other coefficients remain constant" in the previous paragraph reinforces that the allowable increases and decreases shown in the Sensitivity Report apply only if *all* the other coefficients in the LP model do not change. The objective coefficient for Aqua-Spas can assume any value from $300 to $450 without changing the optimal solution—*but this is guaranteed to be true only if all the other coefficients in the model remain constant (including the objective function coefficient for X_2).* Similarly, the objective function coefficient for X_2 can assume any value between $233.33 and $350 without changing the optimal solution—*but this is guaranteed to be true only if all the other coefficients in the model remain constant (including the objective function coefficient for X_1).* Later in this chapter, you will see how to determine whether the current solution remains optimal if changes are made in two or more objective coefficients at the same time.

4.5.3 ALTERNATE OPTIMAL SOLUTIONS

Sometimes, the allowable increase or allowable decrease for the objective function coefficient for one or more variables will equal zero. In the absence of degeneracy (to be described later), this indicates that alternate optimal solutions exist. Usually you can get Solver to produce an alternate optimal solution (when they exist) by: (1) adding a constraint to your model that holds the objective function at the current optimal value, and then (2) attempting to maximize or minimize the value of one of the decision variables that had an objective function coefficient with an allowable increase or decrease of zero. This approach sometimes involves some "trial and error" in step 2, but should cause Solver to produce an alternate optimal solution to your problem.

4.5.4 CHANGES IN THE RHS VALUES

As noted earlier, constraints that have zero slack in the optimal solution to an LP problem are called binding constraints. Binding constraints prevent us from further improving (that is, maximizing or minimizing) the objective function. For example, the Answer Report in Figure 4.2 indicates that the constraints for the number of pumps and hours of labor available are binding, whereas the constraint on the amount of tubing available is nonbinding. This is also evident in Figure 4.3 by comparing the Final Value column with the Constraint R.H. Side column. The values in the Final Value column represent the LHS values of each constraint at the optimal solution. A constraint is binding if its Final Value is equal to its Constraint R.H. Side value.

After solving an LP problem, you might want to determine how much better or worse the solution would be if we had more or less of a given resource. For example, Howie Jones might wonder how much more profit could be earned if additional pumps or labor hours were available. The Shadow Price column in Figure 4.3 provides the answers to such questions.

The **shadow price** for a constraint indicates the amount by which the objective function value changes given a unit *increase* in the RHS value of the constraint, assuming that all other coefficients remain constant. If a shadow price is positive, a unit increase in the RHS value of the associated constraint results in an increase in the optimal objective function value. If a shadow price is negative, a unit increase in the RHS value of the associated constraint results in a decrease in the optimal objective function value. To analyze the effects of decreases in the RHS values, you reverse the sign on the shadow price. That is, the negated shadow price for a constraint indicates the amount by which the optimal objective function value changes given a unit *decrease* in the RHS value of the constraint, assuming that all other coefficients remain constant. The shadow price values apply, provided that the increase or decrease in the RHS value falls within the allowable increase or allowable decrease limits in the Sensitivity Report for each constraint.

For example, Figure 4.3 indicates that the shadow price for the labor constraint is 16.67. Therefore, if the number of available labor hours increased by any amount in the range from 0 to 234 hours, the optimal objective function value changes (increases) by $16.67 for each additional labor hour. If the number of available labor hours decreased by any amount in the range from 0 to 126 hours, the optimal objective function value changes (decreases) by −$16.67 for each lost labor hour. A similar interpretation holds for the shadow price for the constraint on the number of pumps. (It is coincidental that the shadow price for the pump constraint (200) is the same as that constraint's RHS and Final Values.)

4.5.5 SHADOW PRICES FOR NONBINDING CONSTRAINTS

Now, let's consider the shadow price for the nonbinding tubing constraint. The tubing constraint has a shadow price of zero with an allowable increase of infinity and an allowable decrease of 168. Therefore, if the RHS value for the tubing constraint increases by *any* amount, the objective function value does not change (or changes by zero). This result is not surprising. Because the optimal solution to this problem leaves 168 feet of tubing unused, *additional* tubing will not produce a better solution. Furthermore, because the optimal solution includes 168 feet of unused tubing, we can reduce the RHS value of this constraint by 168 without affecting the optimal solution.

As this example illustrates, the shadow price of a nonbinding constraint is always zero. There is always some amount by which the RHS value of a nonbinding constraint can be changed without affecting the optimal solution.

4.5.6 A NOTE ABOUT SHADOW PRICES

One important point needs to be made concerning shadow prices. To illustrate this point, let's suppose that the RHS value of the labor constraint for our example problem increases by 162 hours (from 1,566 to 1,728) due to the addition of new workers. Because this increase is within the allowable increase listed for the labor constraint, you might expect that the optimal objective function value would increase by $16.67 \times 162 = $2,700$. That is, the new optimal objective function value would be approximately $68,800 ($66,100 + $16.67 \times 162 = $68,800). Figure 4.6 shows the re-solved model after increasing the RHS value for the labor constraint by 162 labor hours to 1,728.

FIGURE 4.6

Solution to the revised hot tub problem with 162 additional labor hours

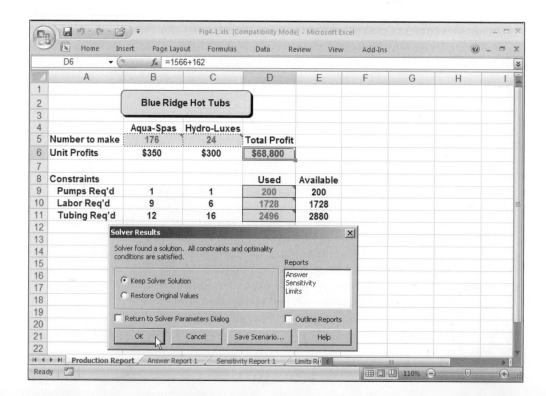

In Figure 4.6, the new optimal objective function value is $68,800, as expected. But this solution involves producing 176 Aqua-Spas and 24 Hydro-Luxes. That is, the optimal solution to the revised problem is *different* from the solution to the original problem shown in Figure 4.1. This is not surprising, because changing the RHS of a constraint also changes the feasible region for the problem. The effect of increasing the RHS of the labor constraint is shown graphically in Figure 4.7.

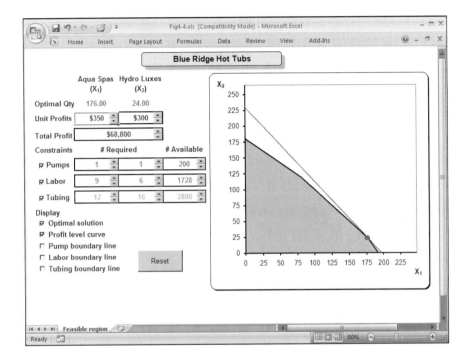

FIGURE 4.7

How a change in the RHS value of the labor constraint changes the feasible region and optimal solution

So, although shadow prices indicate how the objective function value changes if a given RHS value changes, they *do not* tell you which values the decision variables need to assume to achieve this new objective function value. Determining the new optimal values for the decision variables requires that you make the appropriate changes in the RHS value and re-solve the model.

Another Interpretation of Shadow Prices

Unfortunately, there is no one universally accepted way of reporting shadow prices for constraints. In some software packages, the signs of the shadow prices do not conform to the convention used by Solver. Regardless of which software package you use, there is another way to look at shadow prices that always should lead to a proper interpretation. The absolute value of the shadow price always indicates the amount by which the objective function will be *improved* if the corresponding constraint is *loosened*. A "less than or equal to" constraint is loosened by *increasing* its RHS value, whereas a "greater than or equal to" constraint is loosened by *decreasing* its RHS value. (The absolute value of the shadow price also can be interpreted as the amount by which the objective will be made *worse* if the corresponding constraint is *tightened*.)

4.5.7 SHADOW PRICES AND THE VALUE OF ADDITIONAL RESOURCES

In the previous example, an additional 162 hours of labor allowed us to increase profits by $2,700. A question then might arise as to how much we should be willing to pay to acquire these additional 162 hours of labor. The answer to this question is, "It depends. . . ."

If labor is a *variable* cost that was subtracted (along with other variable costs) from the selling price of the hot tubs to determine the marginal profits associated with each type of tub, we should be willing to pay up to $2,700 *above and beyond* what we ordinarily would pay to acquire 162 hours of labor. In this case, notice that both the original and revised profit figures of $66,100 and $68,800, respectively, represent the profit earned *after* the normal labor charge has been paid. Therefore, we could pay a premium of up to $2,700 to acquire the additional 162 hours of labor (or an extra $16.67 per additional labor hour) and still earn at least as much profit as we would have without the additional 162 hours of labor. Thus, if the normal labor rate is $12 per hour, we could pay up to $28.67 per hour to acquire each of the additional 162 hours of labor.

On the other hand, if labor is a sunk cost, which must be paid regardless of how many hot tubs are produced, it would not (or should not) have been subtracted from the selling price of the hot tubs in determining the marginal profit coefficients for each tub produced. In this case, we should be willing to pay a maximum of $16.67 per hour to acquire each of the additional 162 hours of labor.

4.5.8 OTHER USES OF SHADOW PRICES

Because shadow prices represent the marginal values of the resources in an LP problem, they can help us answer several other managerial questions that might arise. For example, suppose that Blue Ridge Hot Tubs is considering introducing a new model of hot tub called the Typhoon-Lagoon. Suppose that each unit of this new model requires 1 pump, 8 hours of labor, and 13 feet of tubing, and can be sold to generate a marginal profit of $320. Would production of this new model be profitable?

Because Blue Ridge Hot Tubs has limited resources, the production of any Typhoon-Lagoons would consume some of the resources currently devoted to the production of Aqua-Spas and Hydro-Luxes. So, producing Typhoon-Lagoons will reduce the number of pumps, labor hours, and tubing available for producing the other types of hot tubs. The shadow prices in Figure 4.3 indicate that each pump taken away from production of the current products will reduce profits by $200. Similarly, each labor hour taken away from the production of the current products will reduce profits by $16.67. The shadow price for the tubing constraint indicates that the supply of tubing can be reduced without adversely affecting profits.

Because each Typhoon-Lagoon requires 1 pump, 8 hours of labor, and 13 feet of tubing, the diversion of resources required to produce one unit of this new model would cause a reduction in profit of $200 × 1 + $16.67 × 8 + $0 × 13 = $333.33. This reduction would be partially offset by the $320 increase in profit generated by each Typhoon-Lagoon. The net effect of producing each Typhoon-Lagoon would be a $13.33 reduction in profit ($320 − $333.33 = −$13.33). Therefore, the production of Typhoon-Lagoons would not be profitable (although the company might choose to produce a small number of Typhoon-Lagoons to enhance its product line for marketing purposes).

Another way to determine whether or not Typhoon-Lagoons should be produced is to add this alternative to our model and solve the resulting LP problem. The LP model for this revised problem is represented as follows, where X_1, X_2, and X_3 represent the number of Aqua-Spas, Hydro-Luxes, and Typhoon-Lagoons to be produced, respectively:

MAX: $350X_1 + 300X_2 + 320X_3$ } profit
Subject to: $1X_1 + 1X_2 + 1X_3 \leq 200$ } pump constraint
              $9X_1 + 6X_2 + 8X_3 \leq 1{,}566$ } labor constraint
              $12X_1 + 16X_2 + 13X_3 \leq 2{,}880$ } tubing constraint
              $X_1, X_2, X_3 \geq 0$ } nonnegativity conditions

This model is implemented and solved in the spreadsheet, as shown in Figure 4.8. Notice that the optimal solution to this problem involves producing 122 Aqua-Spas ($X_1 = 122$), 78 Hydro-Luxes ($X_2 = 78$), and no Typhoon-Lagoons ($X_3 = 0$). So, as expected, the optimal solution does not involve producing Typhoon-Lagoons. Figure 4.9 shows the Sensitivity Report for our revised model.

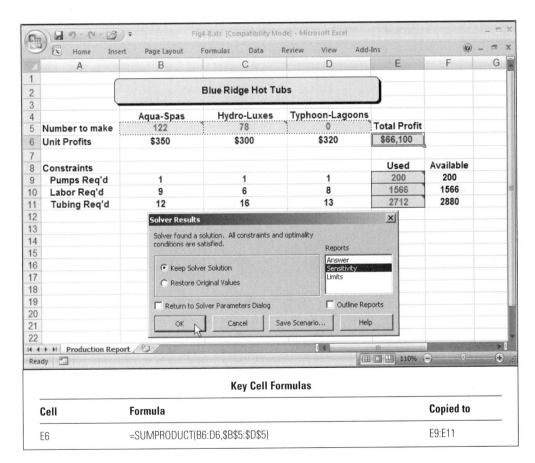

FIGURE 4.8

Spreadsheet model for the revised product mix problem with three hot tub models

4.5.9 THE MEANING OF THE REDUCED COSTS

The Sensitivity Report in Figure 4.9 for our revised model is identical to the sensitivity report for our original model *except* that it includes an additional row in the adjustable cells section. This row reports sensitivity information on the number of Typhoon-Lagoons

FIGURE 4.9

Sensitivity Report for the revised product mix problem with three hot tub models

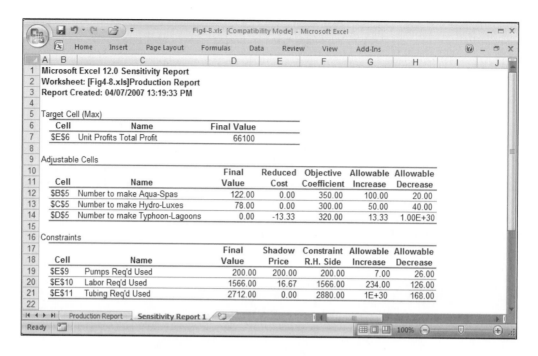

to produce. Notice that the Reduced Cost column indicates that the reduced cost value for Typhoon-Lagoons is −13.33. This is the same number that we calculated in the previous section when determining whether or not it would be profitable to produce Typhoon-Lagoons.

The reduced cost for each variable is equal to the per-unit amount that the product contributes to profits, minus the per-unit value of the resources it consumes (where the consumed resources are priced at their shadow prices). For example, the reduced cost of each variable in this problem is calculated as:

Reduced cost of Aqua-Spas $= 350 − 200 \times 1 − 16.67 \times 9 − 0 \times 12 = 0$

Reduced cost of Hydro-Luxes $= 300 − 200 \times 1 − 16.67 \times 6 − 0 \times 16 = 0$

Reduced cost of Typhoon-Lagoons $= 320 − 200 \times 1 − 16.67 \times 8 − 0 \times 13 = −13.33$

The allowable increase in the objective function coefficient for Typhoon-Lagoons equals 13.33. This means that the current solution will remain optimal provided that the marginal profit on Typhoon-Lagoons is less than or equal to $320 + $13.33 = $333.33 (because this would keep its reduced cost less than or equal to zero). However, if the marginal profit for Typhoon-Lagoons is more than $333.33, producing this product would be profitable and the optimal solution to the problem would change.

It is interesting to note that the shadow prices (marginal values) of the resources equate exactly with the marginal profits of the products that, at optimality, assume values between their simple lower and upper bounds. This will always be the case. In the optimal solution to an LP problem, the variables that assume values *between* their simple lower and upper bounds always have reduced cost values of zero. (In our example problem, all the variables have implicit simple upper bounds of positive infinity.) The variables with optimal values equal to their simple lower bounds have reduced cost values that are less than or equal to zero for maximization problems, or greater than or equal to zero for minimization problems. Variables with optimal values equal to their simple upper bounds have reduced cost values that are greater than or equal to zero for

FIGURE 4.10

*Summary of
optimal reduced
cost values*

Type of Problem	Optimal Value of Decision Variable	Optimal Value of Reduced Cost
Maximization	at simple lower bound	≤ 0
	between lower and upper bounds	$= 0$
	at simple upper bound	≥ 0
Minimization	at simple lower bound	≥ 0
	between lower and upper bounds	$= 0$
	at simple upper bound	≤ 0

maximization problems, or less than or equal to zero for minimization problems. Figure 4.10 summarizes these relationships.

Generally, at optimality, a variable assumes its largest possible value (or is set equal to its simple upper bound) if this variable helps improve the objective function value. In a maximization problem, the variable's reduced cost must be nonnegative to indicate that if the variable's value increased, the objective value would increase (improve). In a minimization problem, the variable's reduced cost must be nonpositive to indicate that if the variable's value increased, the objective value would decrease (improve).

Similar arguments can be made for the optimal reduced costs of variables at their lower bounds. At optimality, a variable assumes its smallest (lower bound) value if it cannot be used to improve the objective value. In a maximization problem, the variable's reduced cost must be nonpositive to indicate that if the variable's value increased, the objective value would decrease (worsen). In a minimization problem, the variable's reduced cost must be nonnegative to indicate that if the variable's value increased, the objective value would increase (worsen).

Key Points

Our discussion of Solver's sensitivity report highlights some key points concerning shadow prices and their relationship to reduced costs. These key points are summarized as:

- The shadow prices of resources equate the marginal value of the resources consumed with the marginal benefit of the goods being produced.
- Resources in excess supply have a shadow price (or marginal value) of zero.
- The reduced cost of a product is the difference between its marginal profit and the marginal value of the resources it consumes.
- Products whose marginal profits are less than the marginal value of the goods required for their production will not be produced in an optimal solution.

4.5.10 ANALYZING CHANGES IN CONSTRAINT COEFFICIENTS

Given what we know about reduced costs and shadow prices, we can now analyze how changes in some constraint coefficients affect the optimal solution to an LP problem. For example, it is unprofitable for Blue Ridge Hot Tubs to manufacture Typhoon-Lagoons assuming that each unit requires 8 hours of labor. However, what would happen if the product could be produced in only 7 hours? The reduced cost value for Typhoon-Lagoons is calculated as:

$$\$320 - \$200 \times 1 - \$16.67 \times 7 - \$0 \times 13 = \$3.31$$

Because this new reduced cost value is positive, producing Typhoon-Lagoons would be profitable in this scenario and the solution shown in Figure 4.8 no longer would be optimal. We could also reach this conclusion by changing the labor requirement for Typhoon-Lagoons in our spreadsheet model and re-solving the problem. In fact, we have to do this to determine the new optimal solution if each Typhoon-Lagoon requires only 7 hours of labor.

As another example, suppose that we wanted to know the maximum amount of labor that is required to assemble a Typhoon-Lagoon while keeping its production economically justifiable. The production of Typhoon-Lagoons would be profitable provided that the reduced cost for the product is greater than or equal to zero. If L_3 represents the amount of labor required to produce a Typhoon-Lagoon, we want to find the maximum value of L_3 that keeps the reduced cost for Typhoon-Lagoons greater than or equal to zero. That is, we want to find the maximum value of L_3 that satisfies the inequality:

$$\$320 - \$200 \times 1 - \$16.67 \times L_3 - \$0 \times 13 \geq 0$$

If we solve this inequality for L_3, we obtain:

$$L_3 \leq \frac{120}{16.67} = 7.20$$

Thus, the production of Typhoon-Lagoons would be economically justified provided that the labor required to produce them does not exceed 7.20 hours per unit. Similar types of questions can be answered using knowledge of the basic relationships between reduced costs, shadow prices, and optimality conditions.

4.5.11 SIMULTANEOUS CHANGES IN OBJECTIVE FUNCTION COEFFICIENTS

Earlier, we noted that the values in the Allowable Increase and Allowable Decrease columns in the Sensitivity Report for the objective function coefficients indicate the maximum amounts by which each objective coefficient can change without altering the optimal solution—*assuming that all other coefficients in the model remain constant*. A technique known as The 100% Rule determines whether the current solution remains optimal when more than one objective function coefficient changes. The following two situations could arise when applying this rule:

Case 1. All variables whose objective function coefficients change have non-zero reduced costs.

Case 2. At least one variable whose objective function coefficient changes has a reduced cost of zero.

In case 1, the current solution remains optimal provided that the objective function coefficient of each changed variable remains within the limits indicated in the Allowable Increase and Allowable Decrease columns of the Sensitivity Report.

Case 2 is a bit more tricky. In case 2, we must perform the following analysis where:

$\quad c_j \quad$ = the original objective function coefficient for variable X_j
$\quad \Delta c_j$ = the planned change in c_j
$\quad I_j \quad$ = the allowable increase in c_j given in the Sensitivity Report
$\quad D_j \quad$ = the allowable decrease in c_j given in the Sensitivity Report

$$r_j = \begin{cases} \dfrac{\Delta c_j}{I_j}, & \text{if } \Delta c_j \geq 0 \\[2ex] \dfrac{-\Delta c_j}{D_j}, & \text{if } \Delta c_j < 0 \end{cases}$$

Notice that r_j measures the ratio of the planned change in c_j to the maximum allowable change for which the current solution remains optimal. If only one objective function coefficient changed, the current solution remains optimal provided that $r_j \leq 1$ (or, if r_j is expressed as a percentage, it must be less than or equal to 100%). Similarly, if more than one objective function coefficient changes, the current solution will remain optimal provided that $\Sigma r_j \leq 1$. (Note that if $\Sigma r_j > 1$, the current solution might remain optimal, but this is not guaranteed.)

4.5.12 A WARNING ABOUT DEGENERACY

The solution to an LP problem sometimes exhibits a mathematical anomaly known as *degeneracy*. The solution to an LP problem is degenerate if the RHS values of any of the constraints have an allowable increase or allowable decrease of zero. The presence of degeneracy affects our interpretation of the values on the sensitivity report in a number of important ways:

1. When the solution is degenerate, the methods mentioned earlier for detecting alternate optimal solutions cannot be relied upon.
2. When a solution is degenerate, the reduced costs for the variable cells may not be unique. Additionally, in this case, the objective function coefficients for variable cells must change by at least as much as (and possibly more than) their respective reduced costs before the optimal solution would change.
3. When the solution is degenerate, the allowable increases and decreases for the objective function coefficients still hold and, in fact, the coefficients might have to be changed substantially beyond the allowable increase and decrease limits before the optimal solution changes.
4. When the solution is degenerate, the given shadow prices and their ranges still might be interpreted in the usual way but they might not be unique. That is, a different set of shadow prices and ranges also might apply to the problem (even if the optimal solution is unique).

So before interpreting the results on a sensitivity report, you always should check first to see if the solution is degenerate because this has important ramifications for how the numbers on the report should be interpreted. A complete description of the degeneracy anomaly goes beyond the intended scope of this book. However, degeneracy is sometimes caused by having redundant constraints in an LP model. *Extreme caution* (and perhaps consultation with an expert in mathematical programming) is in order if important business decisions are being made based on the sensitivity report for a degenerate LP problem.

4.6 The Limits Report

The Limits Report for the original Blue Ridge Hot Tubs problem is shown in Figure 4.11. This report lists the optimal value of the set cell. It then summarizes the optimal values for each variable cell and indicates what values the set cell assumes if each variable cell is set to its upper or lower limits. The values in the Lower Limits column indicate the smallest value that each variable cell can assume while the values of all other variable cells remain constant and all the constraints are satisfied. The values in the Upper Limits column indicate the largest value that each variable cell can assume while the values of all other variable cells remain constant and all the constraints are satisfied.

FIGURE 4.11

Limits Report for the original Blue Ridge Hot Tubs problem

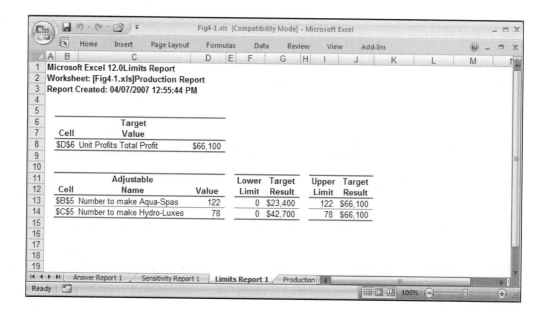

4.7 The Sensitivity Assistant Add-in (Optional)

This book comes with an Excel add-in called Sensitivity Assistant that provides two additional tools for performing sensitivity analysis on an *ad hoc* basis: Spider Tables and Solver Tables. A Spider Table summarizes the optimal value for one output cell as individual changes are made to various input cells. A Solver Table summarizes the optimal value of multiple output cells as changes are made to a single input cell. As illustrated in the following sections, these tools can be helpful in developing an understanding of how changes in various model parameters affect the optimal solution to a problem.

Installing the Sensitivity Assistant Add-In

To use the Sensitivity Assistant add-in, it must first be installed on your computer. To do this:

1. Copy the file Sensitivity.xla from the CD-ROM accompanying this book to the folder on your hard drive containing the file Solver.xla. (On most cases, this is the folder: *d*:\Program Files\Microsoft Office\Office12\Library\Solver.)

(Continued)

2. In Excel, click the Office button, Excel Options, Add-Ins, Go; browse to the Sensitivity.xla file and click OK.

This instructs your computer to open the Sensitivity Assistant add-in whenever you start Excel. It also causes the "Sensitivity Assistant . . ." option to be added to the Add-Ins ribbon in Excel. You can deactivate the Sensitivity Assistant add-in at any time by clicking the Office button, Excel Options, Add-Ins, Go command again.

4.7.1 CREATING SPIDER TABLES AND PLOTS

Recall that the optimal solution to the original Blue Ridge Hot Tubs problem involves producing 122 Aqua-Spas and 78 Hydro-Luxes for a total profit of $66,100. However, this solution assumes there will be exactly 200 pumps, 1,566 labor hours, and 2,880 feet of tubing available. In reality, pumps and tubing are sometimes defective, and workers sometimes call in sick. So, the owner of the company might wonder how sensitive the total profit is to changes in these resources. Although Solver's Sensitivity Report provides some information about this issue, a Spider Table and Plot is sometimes more helpful in communicating this information to management.

Again, a Spider Table summarizes the optimal value for one output cell as individual changes are made to various input cells. In this case, the output cell of interest is cell D6 representing total profit, and the input cells are E9, E10, and E11 representing the availability of pumps, labor, and tubing. Figure 4.12 (and file Fig4-12.xls on your data disk) shows how to set up a Spider Table for this problem.

The upper-left cell in a Spider Table should contain a formula referring to the output cell you want to track. Thus, in Figure 4.12, cell A14 contains a formula that returns the value of cell D6 representing total profit.

Formula for cell A14:   =D6

The remaining cells in the first row of a Spider Table should contain formulas referring to the input cells that you want to manipulate. Thus, cells B14, C14, and D14 contain formulas referring, respectively, to cells E9, E10, and E11, which represent the resource availability values that we want to manipulate.

Formula for cell B14:   =E9

Formula for cell C14:   =E10

Formula for cell D14:   =E11

The first cell in each remaining row of a Spider Table should contain a percentage value indicating an amount by which to adjust each of the input cells. Thus, in cells A15 through A25, we entered a series of percentages from 90% to 110%. The Spider Table tool will multiply the value of each of the input cells referenced in cells B14 through D14 by each of the percentages listed in cells A15 through A25, and will keep a record of the corresponding value of the output cell referenced in cell A14. Specifically, the Spider Table tool will first change the value in cell E9 (representing the number of pumps available) to 180 (or 90% of 200), re-solve the problem, and record the optimal profit in cell B15. It will then change the value in cell E9 to 184 (or 92% of 200), re-solve the problem, and record the optimal profit in cell B16. This process continues until all the input cells have been varied from 90% to 110% and the resulting optimal profit values recorded in the table.

FIGURE 4.12

Set up for creating a Spider Table and Plot

Key Cell Formulas		
Cell	Formula	Copied to
A14	=D6	--
B14	=E9	--
C14	=E10	--
D14	=E11	--

To complete the Spider Table, we would proceed through the following steps. The resulting table and plot is shown in Figure 4.13.

1. Select the range A14:D25
2. Click Add-Ins, Sensitivity Assistant
3. Select the Spider Table option
4. Click OK

The rationale for the name of this procedure should be readily apparent from the spider-like plot shown in Figure 4.13. The center point in the graph corresponds to the optimal solution to the original model with 100% of the pumps, labor, and tubing available. Each of the points in the graph show the effect on total profit of varying the original resource levels by the indicated percentage.

It is clear from Figure 4.13 that total profit is relatively insensitive to modest decreases or large increases in the availability of tubing. This is consistent with the sensitivity information regarding tubing shown earlier in Figure 4.9. The optimal solution to the original problem involved using all the pumps and all the labor hours, but only 2,712 feet of the 2,880 available feet of tubing. As a result, we could achieve the same level of profit even if the availability of tubing was reduced by 168 feet (or to about 94.2% of its original

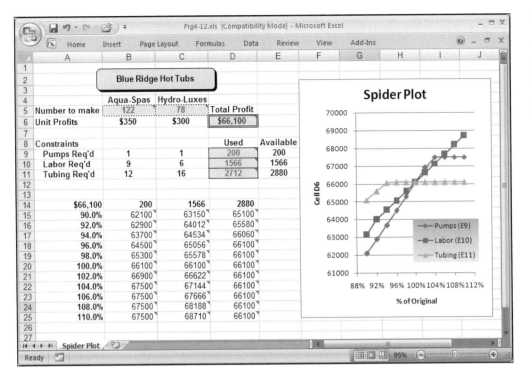

FIGURE 4.13

A Spider Table and Plot showing the relationship between profit and the availability of pumps, labor, and tubing

value). Similarly, because we are not using all of the available tubing, acquiring more tubing would only increase the surplus and not allow for any improvement in profit. Thus, our Spider Table and Plot suggest that the availability of tubing probably should not be a top concern in this problem. On the other hand, the Spider Plot suggests that changes in the availability of pumps and labor have a more pronounced effect on profit and the optimal solution to the problem.

Notes on Setting Up a Spider Table

1. The cell in the upper-left corner of the table range should contain a formula returning the value of the output cell you want to track.
2. The remaining cells in the first row of the table range should contain formulas referring to the input cells you want to manipulate.
3. The first cell in each remaining row of the table range should contain a percentage value indicating an amount by which to multiply each of the input cells.

4.7.2 CREATING A SOLVER TABLE

The Spider Plot in Figure 4.13 suggests that the total profit earned is most sensitive to changes in the available supply of pumps. We can create a Solver Table to study in greater detail the impact of changes in the available number of pumps. Recall that a Solver Table summarizes the optimal value of multiple output cells as changes are made

FIGURE 4.14

Set up for creating a Solver Table

Key Cell Formulas

Cell	Formula	Copied to
A14	=E9	--
B14	=B5	--
C14	=C5	--
D14	=D6	--
E14	=D9	--
F14	=D10	--
G14	=D11	--

to a single input cell. In this case, the single input we want to change is cell E9, which represents the number of pumps available. We might want to track what happens to several output cells, including the optimal number of Aqua-Spas and Hydro-Luxes (cells B5 and B6), the total profit (cell D6), and the total amount of pumps, labor, and tubing used (cells D9, D10, and D11). Figure 4.14 (and file Fig4-14.xls on your data disk) shows how to set up the Solver Table for this problem.

The upper-left cell in a Solver Table should contain a formula referring to the input cell you want to manipulate. Thus, cell A14 contains a formula referring to cell E9, which represents the available number of pumps.

Formula for cell A14:   =E9

The remaining cells in the first row of a Solver Table should contain formulas returning the values of the various output cells you want to track. Thus, cells B14 through G14 each contain a formula referring to one of our output cells.

Formula for cell B14:	=B5
Formula for cell C14:	=C5
Formula for cell D14:	=D6
Formula for cell E14:	=D9
Formula for cell F14:	=D10
Formula for cell G14	=D11

The first cell in each of the remaining rows of the Solver Table should contain a value to be assumed by the input cell. In this case, we entered values from 170 to 220 (in multiples of five) in cells A15 to A25 as representative values for the input cell (E9) representing the available number of pumps. The Solver Table tool will substitute each of the values in cells A15 through A25 into the input cell (E9), re-solve the problem, and then record the resulting values for the output cells referenced in the first row of the table range.

To complete the Solver Table, we would proceed through the following steps. The resulting table and plot is shown in Figure 4.15.

1. Select the range A14:G25.
2. Click Add-Ins, Sensitivity Assistant.
3. Select the Solver Table option.
4. Click OK.

Several interesting insights emerge from Figure 4.15. First, comparing columns A and E, as the number of available pumps increases from 170 up to 205, they are always all used. With about 175 pumps, we also begin to use all the available labor. However, when the number of available pumps increases to 210 or more, only 207 pumps can be used because we run out of both tubing and labor at that point. This suggests that the

FIGURE 4.15

Solver Table showing changes in the optimal solution, profit, and resource usage and the number of pumps changed

company should not be interested in getting more than 7 additional pumps unless it also can increase the amount of tubing and/or labor available.

Also note that the addition or subtraction of 5 pumps from the initial supply of 200 causes the optimal objective function value (column D) to change by $1,000. This suggests that if the company has 200 pumps, the marginal value of each pump is about $200 (i.e., $1000/5 = $200). Of course, this is equivalent to the *shadow price* of pumps shown earlier in Figure 4.9.

Finally, it is interesting to note that when the availability of pumps is between 175 and 205, each increase of 5 pumps causes the optimal number of Aqua-Spas to decrease by 10 and the optimal number of Hydro-Luxes to increase by 15. Thus, one advantage of the Solver Table over the Sensitivity Report is that it tells you not only how much the optimal value of the objective function changes as the number of pumps change, but it also can tell you how the optimal solution changes.

Notes on Setting Up a Solver Table

1. The cell in the upper-left corner of the table range should contain a formula referring to the input cell you want to manipulate.
2. The remaining cells in the first row of the table range should contain formulas returning the values of the output cells you want to track.
3. The first cell in each remaining row of the table range should contain a value to be assumed by the input cell.

4.7.3 COMMENTS

Additional Solver Tables and Spider Tables/Plots could be constructed to analyze every element of the model, including objective function and constraint coefficients. However, these techniques are considered 'computationally expensive' because they require the LP model to be solved repeatedly. For small problems such as Blue Ridge Hot Tubs, this is not really a problem. But as problem size and complexity increases, this approach to sensitivity analysis can become impractical.

4.8 The Simplex Method (Optional)

We have mentioned repeatedly that the simplex method is the preferred method for solving LP problems. This section provides an overview of the simplex method and shows how it relates to some of the items that appear on the Answer Report and the Sensitivity Report.

4.8.1 CREATING EQUALITY CONSTRAINTS USING SLACK VARIABLES

Because our original formulation of the LP model for the Blue Ridge Hot Tubs problem has only *two* decision variables (X_1 and X_2), you might be surprised to learn that Solver actually used *five* variables to solve this problem. As you saw in Chapter 2 when we plotted the boundary lines for the constraints in an LP problem, it is easier to work with "equal to" conditions rather than "less than or equal to," or "greater than or equal to" conditions. Similarly, the simplex method requires that *all* constraints in an LP model be expressed as equalities.

To solve an LP problem using the simplex method, Solver temporarily turns all inequality constraints into equality constraints by adding one new variable to each "less than or equal to" constraint and subtracting one new variable from each "greater than or equal to" constraint. The new variables used to create equality constraints are called **slack variables**.

For example, consider the less than or equal to constraint:

$$a_{k1}X_1 + a_{k2}X_2 + \cdots + a_{kn}X_n \leq b_k$$

Solver can turn this constraint into an equal to constraint by adding the nonnegative slack variable S_k to the LHS of the constraint:

$$a_{k1}X_1 + a_{k2}X_2 + \cdots + a_{kn}X_n + S_k = b_k$$

The variable S_k represents the amount by which $a_{k1}X_1 + a_{k2}X_2 + \cdots + a_{kn}X_n$ is less than b_k. Now consider the "greater than or equal to" constraint:

$$a_{k1}X_1 + a_{k2}X_2 + \cdots + a_{kn}X_n \geq b_k$$

Solver can turn this constraint into an "equal to" constraint by subtracting the nonnegative slack variable S_k from the LHS of the constraint:

$$a_{k1}X_1 + a_{k2}X_2 + \cdots + a_{kn}X_n - S_k = b_k$$

In this case, the variable S_k represents the amount by which $a_{k1}X_1 + a_{k2}X_2 + \cdots + a_{kn}X_n$ exceeds b_k.

To solve the original Blue Ridge Hot Tubs problem using the simplex method, Solver actually solved the following modified problem involving *five* variables:

MAX:	$350X_1 + 300X_2$	} profit
Subject to:	$1X_1 + 1X_2 + S_1 = 200$	} pump constraint
	$9X_1 + 6X_2 + S_2 = 1{,}566$	} labor constraint
	$12X_1 + 16X_2 + S_3 = 2{,}880$	} tubing constraint
	$X_1, X_2, S_1, S_2, S_3 \geq 0$	} nonnegativity conditions

We will refer to X_1 and X_2 as the **structural variables** in the model to distinguish them from the slack variables.

Recall that we did not set up slack variables in the spreadsheet or include them in the formulas in the constraint cells. Solver automatically sets up the slack variables it needs to solve a particular problem. The only time Solver even mentions these variables is when it creates an Answer Report like the one shown in Figure 4.2. The values in the Slack column in the Answer Report correspond to the optimal values of the slack variables.

4.8.2 BASIC FEASIBLE SOLUTIONS

After all the inequality constraints in an LP problem have been converted into equalities (by adding or subtracting appropriate slack variables), the constraints in the LP model represent a system (or collection) of linear equations. If there are a total of n variables in a system of m equations, one strategy for finding a solution to the system of equations is to select any m variables and try to find values for them that solve the system, assuming that all other variables are set equal to their lower bounds (which usually are zero). This strategy requires more variables than constraints in the system of equations—or that $n \geq m$.

The m variables selected to solve the system of equations in an LP model are sometimes called **basic variables**, whereas the remaining variables are called **nonbasic variables**. If a solution to the system of equations can be obtained using a given set of basic variables (while the nonbasic variables are all set equal to zero), that solution is called a **basic feasible solution**. Every basic feasible solution corresponds to one of the extreme points of the feasible region for the LP problem, and we know that the optimal solution to the LP problem also occurs at an extreme point. So, the challenge in LP is to find the set of basic variables (and their optimal values) that produce the basic feasible solution corresponding to the optimal extreme point of the feasible region.

Because our modified problem involves three constraints and five variables, we could select three basic variables in ten different ways to form possible basic feasible solutions for the problem. Figure 4.16 summarizes the results for these ten options.

The first five solutions in Figure 4.16 are feasible and, therefore, represent basic feasible solutions to this problem. The remaining solutions are infeasible because they violate the nonnegativity conditions. The best feasible alternative shown in Figure 4.16 corresponds to the optimal solution to the problem. In particular, if X_1, X_2, and S_3 are selected as basic variables and S_1 and S_2 are nonbasic and assigned their lower bound values

FIGURE 4.16

Possible basic feasible solutions for the original Blue Ridge Hot Tubs problem

	Basic Variables	Nonbasic Variables	Solution	Objective Value
1	S_1, S_2, S_3	X_1, X_2	$X_1=0, X_2=0,$ $S_1=200, S_2=1566, S_3=2880$	0
2	X_1, S_1, S_3	X_2, S_2	$X_1=174, X_2=0,$ $S_1=26, S_2=0, S_3=792$	60,900
3	X_1, X_2, S_3	S_1, S_2	$X_1=122, X_2=78,$ $S_1=0, S_2=0, S_3=168$	66,100
4	X_1, X_2, S_2	S_1, S_3	$X_1=80, X_2=120,$ $S_1=0, S_2=126, S_3=0$	64,000
5	X_2, S_1, S_2	X_1, S_3	$X_1=0, X_2=180,$ $S_1=20, S_2=486, S_3=0$	54,000
6*	X_1, X_2, S_1	S_2, S_3	$X_1=108, X_2=99,$ $S_1=-7, S_2=0, S_3=0$	67,500
7*	X_1, S_1, S_2	X_2, S_3	$X_1=240, X_2=0,$ $S_1=-40, S_2=-594, S_3=0$	84,000
8*	X_1, S_2, S_3	X_2, S_1	$X_1=200, X_2=0,$ $S_1=0, S_2=-234, S_3=480$	70,000
9*	X_2, S_2, S_3	X_1, S_1	$X_1=0, X_2=200,$ $S_1=0, S_2=366, S_3=-320$	60,000
10*	X_2, S_1, S_3	X_1, S_2	$X_1=0, X_2=261,$ $S_1=-61, S_2=0, S_3=-1296$	78,300

Note: * denotes infeasible solutions

(zero), we try to find values for X_1, X_2, and S_3 that satisfy the following constraints:

$$1X_1 + 1X_2 \qquad\quad = \quad 200 \qquad \} \text{ pump constraint}$$
$$9X_1 + 6X_2 \qquad\quad = 1{,}566 \qquad \} \text{ labor constraint}$$
$$12X_1 + 16X_2 + S_3 = 2{,}880 \qquad \} \text{ tubing constraint}$$

Notice that S_1 and S_2 in the modified "equal to" constraints are not included in the above constraint equations because we are assuming that the values of these nonbasic variables are equal to zero (their lower bounds). Using linear algebra, the simplex method determines that the values $X_1 = 122$, $X_2 = 78$, and $S_3 = 168$ satisfy the equations given above. So, a basic feasible solution to this problem is $X_1 = 122$, $X_2 = 78$, $S_1 = 0$, $S_2 = 0$, $S_3 = 168$. As indicated in Figure 4.16, this solution produces an objective function value of \$66,100. (Notice that the optimal values for the slack variables S_1, S_2, and S_3 also correspond to the values shown in the Answer Report in Figure 4.2 in the Slack column for constraint cells D9, D10, and D11.) Figure 4.17 shows the relationships between the basic feasible solutions listed in Figure 4.16 and the extreme points of the feasible region for this problem.

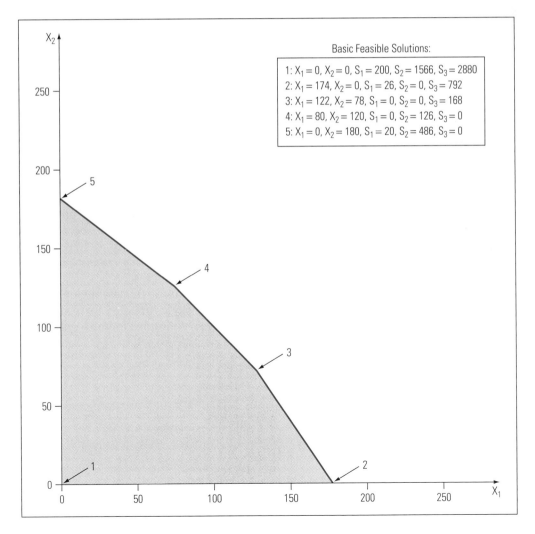

FIGURE 4.17

Illustration of the relationship between basic feasible solutions and extreme points

4.8.3 FINDING THE BEST SOLUTION

The simplex method operates by first identifying any basic feasible solution (or extreme point) for an LP problem, and then moving to an adjacent extreme point, if such a move improves the value of the objective function. When no adjacent extreme point has a better objective function value, the current extreme point is optimal and the simplex method terminates.

The process of moving from one extreme point to an adjacent one is accomplished by switching one of the basic variables with one of the nonbasic variables to create a new basic feasible solution that corresponds to the adjacent extreme point. For example, in Figure 4.17, moving from the first basic feasible solution (point 1) to the second basic feasible solution (point 2) involves making X_1 a basic variable and S_2 a nonbasic variable. Similarly, we can move from point 2 to point 3 by switching basic variables with nonbasic variables. So, starting at point 1 in Figure 4.17, the simplex method could move to point 2, then to the optimal solution at point 3. Alternatively, the simplex method could move from point 1 through points 5 and 4 to reach the optimal solution at point 3. Thus, although there is no guarantee that the simplex method will take the shortest route to the optimal solution of an LP problem, it will find the optimal solution eventually.

To determine whether switching a basic and nonbasic variable will result in a better solution, the simplex method calculates the reduced cost for each nonbasic variable to determine if the objective function could be improved if any of these variables are substituted for one of the basic variables. (Note that unbounded solutions are detected easily in the simplex method by the existence of a nonbasic variable that could improve the objective value by an infinite amount if it were made basic.) This process continues until no further improvement in the objective function value is possible.

4.9 Summary

This chapter described the methods for assessing how sensitive an LP model is to various changes that might occur in the model or its optimal solution. The impact of changes in an LP model can be analyzed easily by re-solving the model. Solver also provides a significant amount of sensitivity information automatically. For LP problems, the maximum amount of sensitivity information is obtained by solving the problem using the simplex method. Before using the information on the Sensitivity Report, you always should check first for the presence of degeneracy because this can have a significant effect on how one should interpret the numbers on this report.

The simplex method considers only the extreme points of the feasible region, and is an efficient way of solving LP problems. In this method, slack variables are introduced first to convert all constraints to "equal to" constraints. The simplex method systematically moves to better and better corner point solutions until no adjacent extreme point provides an improved objective function value.

4.10 References

Bazaraa, M. and J. Jarvis. *Linear Programming and Network Flows*. New York: Wiley, 1990.

Eppen, G., F. Gould and C. Schmidt. *Introductory Management Science*, 4th ed., Englewood Cliffs, NJ: Prentice-Hall, 1993.

Shogan, A. *Management Science*. Englewood Cliffs, NJ: Prentice Hall, 1988.

Wagner, H. and D. Rubin. "Shadow Prices: Tips and Traps for Managers and Instructors," *Interfaces*, vol. 20, no. 4, 1990.

Winston, W. *Operations Research: Applications and Algorithms*. Belmont, CA: Duxbury Press, 1994.

THE WORLD OF MANAGEMENT SCIENCE

Fuel Management and Allocation Model Helps National Airlines Adapt to Cost and Supply Changes

Fuel is a major component in the cost structure of an airline. Price and availability of fuel can vary from one air terminal to the next, and it is sometimes advantageous for an aircraft to carry more than the necessary minimum for the next leg of its route. Fuel loaded for the purpose of taking advantage of price or availability at a specific location is said to be tankered. A disadvantage of tankering is that fuel consumption increases when an aircraft is carrying more weight.

The use of LP to determine when and where to fuel aircraft saved National Airlines several million dollars during the first two years of implementation. In particular, National Airlines saw its average fuel costs drop 11.75% during a period when the average fuel cost for all domestic trunk airlines increased by 2.87%.

The objective function in the Fuel Management and Allocation Model consists of fuel costs and increases in operating costs from tankering. The constraints in the model address availability, minimum reserves, and aircraft capacities.

A particularly useful feature of the Fuel Management and Allocation Model is a series of reports that assist management in modifying the fuel-loading plan when sudden changes occur in availability or price. Shadow prices, along with the associated range of applicability, provide information about supply changes. Information about changes in price per gallon comes from the allowable increase and decrease for objective function coefficients.

For example, the availability report might indicate that the optimal quantity to purchase at Los Angeles from Shell West is 2,718,013 gallons; but if its supply decreases and fuel must be purchased from the next most attractive vendor, total cost would increase at the rate of $0.0478 per gallon (the shadow price). This fuel would be replaced by a prior purchase of up to 159,293 gallons from Shell East at New Orleans, tankered to Los Angeles.

The price report shows, for example, that vendor substitutions should be made if the current price of Shell West at Los Angeles, $0.3074, increases to $0.32583 or decreases to $0.27036. The report also indicates what that substitution should be.

Source: Darnell, D. Wayne and Carolyn Loflin, "National Airlines Fuel Management and Allocation Model," *Interfaces*, vol. 7, no. 2, February 1977, pp 1–16.

Questions and Problems

1. Howie Jones used the following information to calculate the profit coefficients for Aqua-Spas and Hydro-Luxes: pumps cost $225 each, labor costs $12 per hour, tubing costs $2 per foot. In addition to pumps, labor, and tubing, the production of Aqua-Spas and Hydro-Luxes consumes, respectively, $243 and $246 per unit in other resources that are not in short supply. Using this information, Howie calculated the marginal profits on Aqua-Spas and Hydro-Luxes as:

	Aqua-Spas	Hydro-Luxes
Selling Price	$950	$875
Pump Cost	−$225	−$225
Labor Cost	−$108	−$72
Tubing Cost	−$24	−$32
Other Variable Costs	−$243	−$246
Marginal Profit	$350	$300

Howie's accountant reviewed these calculations and thinks Howie made a mistake. For accounting purposes, factory overhead is assigned to products at a rate of $16 per labor hour. Howie's accountant argues that because Aqua-Spas require nine labor hours, the profit margin on this product should be $144 less. Similarly, because Hydro-Luxes require six labor hours, the profit margin on this product should be $96 less. Who is right and why?

2. A variable that assumes an optimal value between its lower and upper bounds has a reduced cost value of zero. Why must this be true? (*Hint:* What if such a variable's reduced cost value is not zero? What does this imply about the value of the objective function?)

3. Implement the following LP problem in a spreadsheet. Use Solver to solve the problem and create a Sensitivity Report. Use this information to answer the following questions:

$$\text{MAX:} \qquad 4X_1 + 2X_2$$
$$\text{Subject to:} \qquad 2X_1 + 4X_2 \le 20$$
$$3X_1 + 5X_2 \le 15$$
$$X_1, X_2 \ge 0$$

a. What range of values can the objective function coefficient for variable X_1 assume without changing the optimal solution?

b. Is the optimal solution to this problem unique, or are there alternate optimal solutions?

c. How much does the objective function coefficient for variable X_2 have to increase before it enters the optimal solution at a strictly positive level?

d. What is the optimal objective function value if X_2 equals 1?

e. What is the optimal objective function value if the RHS value for the second constraint changes from 15 to 25?

f. Is the current solution still optimal if the coefficient for X_2 in the second constraint changes from 5 to 1? Explain.

4. Implement the following LP model in a spreadsheet. Use Solver to solve the problem and create a Sensitivity Report. Use this information to answer the following questions:

$$\text{MAX:} \qquad 2X_1 + 4X_2$$
$$\text{Subject to:} \qquad -X_1 + 2X_2 \leq 8$$
$$X_1 + 2X_2 \leq 12$$
$$X_1 + X_2 \geq 2$$
$$X_1, X_2 \geq 0$$

a. Which of the constraints are binding at the optimal solution?
b. Is the optimal solution to this problem unique, or is there an alternate optimal solution?
c. What is the optimal solution to this problem if the value of the objective function coefficient for variable X_1 is zero?
d. How much can the objective function coefficient for variable X_2 decrease before changing the optimal solution?
e. Given the objective in this problem, if management could increase the RHS value for any of the constraints for identical costs, which would you choose to increase and why?

5. Implement the following LP model in a spreadsheet. Use Solver to solve the problem and create a Sensitivity Report. Use this information to answer the following questions:

$$\text{MIN:} \qquad 5X_1 + 3X_2 + 4X_3$$
$$\text{Subject to:} \qquad X_1 + X_2 + 2X_3 \geq 2$$
$$5X_1 + 3X_2 + 2X_3 \geq 1$$
$$X_1, X_2, X_3 \geq 0$$

a. What is the smallest value the objective function coefficient for X_3 can assume without changing the optimal solution?
b. What is the optimal objective function value if the objective function coefficient for X_3 changes to –1? (*Hint:* The answer to this question is not given in the Sensitivity Report. Consider what the new objective function is relative to the constraints.)
c. What is the optimal objective function value if the RHS value of the first constraint increases to 7?
d. What is the optimal objective function value if the RHS value of the first constraint decreases by 1?
e. Will the current solution remain optimal if the objective function coefficients for X_1 and X_3 both decrease by 1?

6. The CitruSun Corporation ships frozen orange juice concentrate from processing plants in Eustis and Clermont to distributors in Miami, Orlando, and Tallahassee. Each plant can produce 20 tons of concentrate each week. The company has just received orders of 10 tons from Miami for the coming week, 15 tons for Orlando, and 10 tons for Tallahassee. The cost per ton for supplying each of the distributors from each of the processing plants is shown in the following table.

	Miami	Orlando	Tallahassee
Eustis	$260	$220	$290
Clermont	$230	$240	$310

The company wants to determine the least costly plan for filling their orders for the coming week.
a. Formulate an LP model for this problem.
b. Implement the model in a spreadsheet and solve it.

   c. What is the optimal solution?

   d. Is the optimal solution degenerate?

   e. Is the optimal solution unique? If not, identify an alternate optimal solution for the problem.

   f. How would the solution change if the plant in Clermont is forced to shut for one day resulting in a loss of four tons of production capacity?

   g. What would the optimal objective function value be if the processing capacity in Eustis was reduced by five tons?

   h. Interpret the reduced cost for shipping from Eustis to Miami.

7. Use Solver to create Answer and Sensitivity Reports for question 15 at the end of Chapter 2 and answer the following questions:

   a. How much excess wiring and testing capacity exists in the optimal solution?

   b. What is the company's total profit if it has 10 additional hours of wiring capacity?

   c. By how much does the profit on alternators need to increase before their production is justified?

   d. Does the optimal solution change if the marginal profit on generators decreases by $50 and the marginal profit on alternators increases by $75?

   e. Suppose the marginal profit on generators decreases by $25. What is the maximum profit that can be earned on alternators without changing the optimal solution?

   f. Suppose the amount of wiring required on alternators is reduced to 1.5 hours. Does this change the optimal solution? Why or why not?

8. Use Solver to create Answer and Sensitivity Reports for question 18 at the end of Chapter 2 and answer the following questions:

   a. If the profit on Razors decreased to $35 would the optimal solution change?

   b. If the profit on Zoomers decreased to $35 would the optimal solution change?

   c. Interpret the shadow price for the supply of polymer.

   d. Why is the shadow price $0 for the constraint limiting the production of pocket bikes to no more than 700 units?

   e. Suppose the company could obtain 300 additional labor hours in production. What would the new optimal level of profit be?

9. Use Solver to create Answer and Sensitivity Reports for question 20 at the end of Chapter 2 and answer the following questions:

   a. How much can the price of watermelons drop before it is no longer optimal to plant any watermelons?

   b. How much does the price of cantaloupes have to increase before it is optimal to grow only cantaloupes?

   c. Suppose the price of watermelons drops by $60 per acre and the price of cantaloupes increases by $50 per acre. Is the current solution still optimal?

   d. Suppose the farmer can lease up to 20 acres of land from a neighboring farm to plant additional crops. How many acres should the farmer lease and what is the maximum amount he should pay to lease each acre?

10. Use Solver to create Answer and Sensitivity Reports for question 21 at the end of Chapter 2 and answer the following questions:

   a. If the profit on doors increased to $700 would the optimal solution change?

   b. If the profit on windows decreased to $200 would the optimal solution change?

   c. Explain the shadow price for the finishing process.

   d. If 20 additional hours of cutting capacity became available how much additional profit could the company earn?

e. Suppose another company wanted to use 15 hours of Sanderson's sanding capacity and was willing to pay $400 per hour to acquire it? Should Sanderson agree to this? How (if at all) would your answer change if the company instead wanted 25 hours of sanding capacity?

11. Create a Sensitivity Report for Electro-Poly's make vs. buy problem in section 3.8 of Chapter 3 and answer the following questions.
    a. Is the solution degenerate?
    b. How much can the cost of making model 1 slip rings increase before it becomes more economical to buy some of them?
    c. Suppose the cost of buying model 2 slip rings decreased by $9 per unit. Would the optimal solution change?
    d. Assume workers in the wiring area normally make $12 per hour and get 50% more when they work overtime. Should Electro-Poly schedule these employees to work overtime to complete this job? If so, how much money would this save?
    e. Assume workers in the harnessing area normally make $12 per hour and get 50% more when they work overtime. Should Electro-Poly schedule these employees to work overtime to complete this job? If so, how much money would this save?
    f. Create a Spider plot that shows the effect of varying each of the wiring and harnessing requirements (in cells B17 thru D18) to 90% of their current levels in 1% increments. If Electro-Poly wanted to invest in training or new technology to reduce one of these values, which one offers the greatest potential for cost savings?

12. Use Solver to create a Sensitivity Report for question 12 at the end of Chapter 3 and answer the following questions:
    a. If the company could get 50 more units of routing capacity, should they do it? If so, how much should they be willing to pay for it?
    b. If the company could get 50 more units of sanding capacity, should they do it? If so, how much should they be willing to pay for it?
    c. Suppose the polishing time on country tables could be reduced from 2.5 to 2 units per table. How much should the company be willing to pay to achieve this improvement in efficiency?
    d. Contemporary tables sell for $450. By how much would the selling price have to decrease before we would no longer be willing to produce contemporary tables? Does this make sense? Explain.

13. Use Solver to create a Sensitivity Report for question 18 at the end of Chapter 3 and answer the following questions:
    a. Which of the constraints in the problem are binding?
    b. If the company was going to eliminate one of its products, which should it be?
    c. If the company could buy 1,000 additional memory chips at the usual cost, should they do it? If so, how much would profits increase?
    d. Suppose the manufacturing costs used in this analysis were estimated hastily and are known to be somewhat imprecise. For which products would you want more precise cost estimates before implementing this solution?
    e. Create a Spider Plot showing the sensitivity of the total profit to the selling price of each product (adjusting the original values by 90%, 92%, . . ., 110%). According to this graph, total profit is most sensitive to which product?

14. Use Solver to create a Sensitivity Report for question 20 at the end of Chapter 3 and answer the following questions:
    a. How much would electric trimmers have to cost for the company to consider purchasing these items rather than making them?

b. If the cost to make gas trimmers increased to $90 per unit, how would the optimal solution change?

c. How much should the company be willing to pay to acquire additional capacity in the assembly area? Explain.

d. How much should the company be willing to pay to acquire additional capacity in the production area? Explain.

e. Prepare a Spider Plot showing the sensitivity of the total cost to changes in costs to make and the costs to buy (adjusting the original values by of 90%, 92%, . . ., 110%). Which of these costs is the total cost most sensitive to?

f. Suppose the hours of production capacity available is uncertain and could vary from 9,500 to 10,500. How does the optimal solution change for every 100-hour change in production capacity within this range?

15. Use Solver to create a Sensitivity Report for question 22 at the end of Chapter 3 and answer the following questions.

a. Suppose the cost of the first two compounds increases by $1.00 per pound and the cost of the third compound increases by $0.50 per pound. Does the optimal solution change?

b. How does the solution change if the maximum amount of potassium allowed decreases from 45% to 40%?

c. How much does the cost of the mix increase if the specifications for CHEMIX change to require at least 31% sulfur? (*Hint:* Remember that the shadow price indicates the impact on the objective function if the RHS value of the associated constraint increases by 1.)

16. Use Solver to create a Sensitivity Report for question 23 at the end of Chapter 3 and answer the following questions.

a. What is the maximum level profit that can be achieved for this problem?

b. Are there alternate optimal solutions to this problem? If so, identify the solution that allows the most grade 5 oranges to be used in fruit baskets while still achieving the maximum profit identified in part a.

c. If Holiday could acquire 1,000 more pounds of grade 4 oranges at a cost of $2.65 per 100 pounds, should they do it? Why?

d. Create a Spider Table and Plot showing the change in the total profit obtained by changing the required grade of fruit baskets and juice from 90% to 110% in 1% increments. If the department of agriculture wants to increase the required rating of one of these products, which product should the company lobby for?

17. Use Solver to create a Sensitivity Report for question 24 at the end of Chapter 3 and answer the following questions:

a. Are there alternate optimal solutions to this problem? Explain.

b. What is the highest possible octane rating for regular gasoline, assuming the company wants to maximize its profits? What is the octane rating for supreme gasoline at this solution?

c. What is the highest possible octane rating for supreme gasoline, assuming the company wants to maximize its profits? What is the octane rating for regular gasoline at this solution?

d. Which of the two profit-maximizing solutions identified in parts b and c would you recommend that the company implement? Why?

e. If the company could buy another 150 barrels of input 2 at a cost of $17 per barrel, should they do it? Why?

18. Use Solver to create a Sensitivity Report for question 28 at the end of Chapter 3 and answer the following questions:

a. What total profit level is realized if 100 extra hours of labor are available?

b. Assume a marginal labor cost of $11 per hour in determining the unit profits of each of the three products. How much should management pay to acquire 100 additional labor hours?

c. Interpret the reduced cost value for tuners. Why are more tuners not being produced?

19. Use Solver to create a Sensitivity Report for question 29 at the end of Chapter 3 and answer the following questions:

a. Is the optimal solution unique? How can you tell?

b. Which location is receiving the fewest cars?

c. Suppose a particular car at location 1 must be sent to location 3 to meet a customer's request. How much does this increase costs for the company?

d. Suppose location 6 must have at least eight cars shipped to it. What impact does this have on the optimal objective function value?

20. Refer to the previous question. Suppose location 1 has 15 cars available rather than 16. Create a Sensitivity Report for this problem and answer the following questions:

a. Is the optimal solution unique? How can you tell?

b. According to the Sensitivity Report, by how much should the total cost increase if we force a car to be shipped from location 1 to location 3?

c. Add a constraint to the model to force one car to be shipped from location 1 to location 3. By how much did the total cost increase?

21. Use Solver to create a Sensitivity Report for question 30 at the end of chapter 3 and answer the following questions:

a. Is the solution unique?

b. If Sentry wants to increase their production capacity to meet more of the demand for their product, which plant should they use? Explain.

c. If the cost of shipping from Phoenix to Tacoma increased to $1.98 per unit, would the solution change? Explain.

d. Could the company make more money if they relaxed the restriction that each distributor must receive at least 80% of the predicted demand? Explain.

e. How much extra should the company charge the distributor in Tacoma if this distributor insisted on receiving 8,500 units?

22. Use Solver to create a Sensitivity Report for question 31 at the end of Chapter 3 and answer the following questions.

a. Is the solution degenerate?

b. Is the solution unique?

c. How much should the recycler be willing to pay to acquire more cardboard?

d. If the recycler could buy 50 more tons of newspaper at a cost of $18 per ton, should they do it? Why or why not?

e. What is the recycler's marginal cost of producing each of the three different types of pulp?

f. By how much would the cost of converting white office paper into newsprint have to drop before it would become economical to use white office paper for this purpose?

g. By how much would the yield of newsprint pulp per ton of cardboard have to increase before it would become economical to use cardboard for this purpose?

23. Use Solver to create a Sensitivity Report for question 35 at the end of Chapter 3 and answer the following questions.

a. Is the solution degenerate?

b. Is the solution unique?

c. How much can the profit per ton on commodity 1 decrease before the optimal solution would change?

d. Create a Spider Table and Plot showing the change in the total profit obtained by changing the profit per ton on each commodity from 95% to 105% in 1% increments. If the shipping company wanted to increase the price of transporting one of the commodities, which one would have the greatest influence on total profits?

24. Use Solver to create a Sensitivity Report for question 36 at the end of Chapter 3 and answer the following questions.

   a. Is the solution degenerate?
   b. Is the solution unique?
   c. Use a Solver Table to determine the maximum price the Pelletier Corporation should be willing to pay for a two-month lease.
   d. Suppose the company is not certain that it will need exactly 20,000 sq.ft. in month 3 and believes that the actual amount needed may be as low as 15,000 sq.ft. or as high as 25,000 sq. ft. Use a Solver Table to determine if this would have any effect on the leasing arrangements the company selects in months 1 and 2.

25. Refer to question 45 in Chapter 3 and create a Solver table to answer the following questions.

   a. Suppose the gas producer needs an extra 50,000 cf of storage capacity for the next 10 days and wants to buy this capacity from the gas trading firm. What is the least amount of money the gas trading company should demand to provide this capacity?
   b. How much should the gas trading company be willing to pay to increase their available storage capacity by 500,000 cf?

26. Consider the following LP problem:

$$\text{MAX:} \qquad 4X_1 + 2X_2$$
$$\text{Subject to:} \qquad 2X_1 + 4X_2 \le 20$$
$$3X_1 + 5X_2 \le 15$$
$$X_1, X_2 \ge 0$$

   a. Use slack variables to rewrite this problem so that all its constraints are "equal to" constraints.
   b. Identify the different sets of basic variables that might be used to obtain a solution to the problem.
   c. Of the possible sets of basic variables, which lead to feasible solutions and what are the values for all the variables at each of these solutions?
   d. Graph the feasible region for this problem and indicate which basic feasible solution corresponds to each of the extreme points of the feasible region.
   e. What is the value of the objective function at each of the basic feasible solutions?
   f. What is the optimal solution to the problem?
   g. Which constraints are binding at the optimal solution?

27. Consider the following LP problem:

$$\text{MAX:} \qquad 2X_1 + 4X_2$$
$$\text{Subject to:} \qquad -X_1 + 2X_2 \le 8$$
$$X_1 + 2X_2 \le 12$$
$$X_1 + X_2 \ge 2$$
$$X_1, X_2 \ge 0$$

   a. Use slack variables to rewrite this problem so that all its constraints are "equal to" constraints.
   b. Identify the different sets of basic variables that might be used to obtain a solution to the problem.

c. Of the possible sets of basic variables, which lead to feasible solutions and what are the values for all the variables at each of these solutions?

d. Graph the feasible region for this problem and indicate which basic feasible solution corresponds to each of the extreme points of the feasible region.

e. What is the value of the objective function at each of the basic feasible solutions?

f. What is the optimal solution to the problem?

g. Which constraints are binding at the optimal solution?

28. Consider the following LP problem:

$$MIN: \quad 5X_1 + 3X_2 + 4X_3$$
$$Subject\ to: \quad X_1 + X_2 + 2X_3 \geq 2$$
$$5X_1 + 3X_2 + 2X_3 \geq 1$$
$$X_1, X_2, X_3 \geq 0$$

a. Use slack variables to rewrite this problem so that all its constraints are "equal to" constraints.

b. Identify the different sets of basic variables that might be used to obtain a solution to the problem.

c. Of the possible sets of basic variables, which lead to feasible solutions and what are the values for all the variables at each of these solutions?

d. What is the value of the objective function at each of the basic feasible solutions?

e. What is the optimal solution to the problem?

f. Which constraints are binding at the optimal solution?

29. Consider the following constraint, where S is a slack variable:

$$2X_1 + 4X_2 + S = 16$$

a. What was the original constraint before the slack variable was included?

b. What value of S is associated with each of the following points:

i) $X_1 = 2, X_2 = 2$

ii) $X_1 = 8, X_2 = 0$

iii) $X_1 = 1, X_2 = 3$

iv) $X_1 = 4, X_2 = 1$

30. Consider the following constraint, where S is a slack variable:

$$3X_1 + 4X_2 - S = 12$$

a. What was the original constraint before the slack variable was included?

b. What value of S is associated with each of the following points:

i) $X_1 = 5, X_2 = 0$

ii) $X_1 = 2, X_2 = 2$

iii) $X_1 = 7, X_2 = 1$

iv) $X_1 = 4, X_2 = 0$

A Nut Case

The Molokai Nut Company (MNC) makes four different products from macadamia nuts grown in the Hawaiian Islands: chocolate-coated whole nuts (Whole), chocolate-coated nut clusters (Cluster), chocolate-coated nut crunch bars (Crunch), and plain roasted nuts (Roasted). The company is barely able to keep up with the increasing demand for these products. However, increasing raw material prices and foreign competition are forcing MNC to watch its margins to ensure it is operating in the most efficient manner possible. To meet marketing demands for the coming week, MNC needs to produce at least 1,000 pounds of the Whole product, between 400 and 500 pounds of the Cluster product, no more than 150 pounds of the Crunch product, and no more than 200 pounds of Roasted product.

Each pound of the Whole, Cluster, Crunch, and Roasted product contains, respectively, 60%, 40%, 20%, and 100% macadamia nuts with the remaining weight made up of chocolate coating. The company has 1100 pounds of nuts and 800 pounds of chocolate available for use in the next week. The various products are made using four different machines that hull the nuts, roast the nuts, coat the nuts in chocolate (if needed), and package the products. The following table summarizes the time required by each product on each machine. Each machine has 60 hours of time available in the coming week.

Machine	Whole	Cluster	Crunch	Roasted
	Minutes Required per Pound			
Hulling	1.00	1.00	1.00	1.00
Roasting	2.00	1.50	1.00	1.75
Coating	1.00	0.70	0.20	0.00
Packaging	2.50	1.60	1.25	1.00

The controller recently presented management with the following financial summary of MNC's average weekly operations over the past quarter. From this report, the controller is arguing that the company should cease producing its Cluster and Crunch products.

	Whole	Cluster	Crunch	Roasted	Total
	Product				
Sales Revenue	$5,304	$1,800	$510	$925	$8,539
Variable Costs					
Direct materials	$1,331	$560	$144	$320	$2,355
Direct labor	$1,092	$400	$96	$130	$1,718
Manufacturing overhead	$333	$140	$36	$90	$599
Selling & Administrative	$540	$180	$62	$120	$902
Allocated Fixed Costs					
Manufacturing overhead	$688	$331	$99	$132	$1,250
Selling & Administrative	$578	$278	$83	$111	$1,050
Net Profit	$742	−$88	−$11	$22	$665
Units Sold	1040	500	150	200	1890
Net Profit Per Unit	$0.71	−$0.18	−$0.07	$0.11	$0.35

a. Do you agree with the controller's recommendation? Why or why not?
b. Formulate an LP model for this problem.
c. Create a spreadsheet model for this problem and solve it using Solver.
d. What is the optimal solution?
e. Create a sensitivity report for this solution and answer the following questions.
f. Is the solution degenerate?
g. Is the solution unique?

h. If MNC wanted to decrease the production on any product, which one would you recommend and why?
i. If MNC wanted to increase the production of any product, which one would you recommend and why?
j. Which resources are preventing MNS from making more money? If they could acquire more of this resource how much should they acquire & how much should they be willing to pay to acquire it?
k. How much should MNC be willing to pay to acquire more chocolate?
l. If the marketing department wanted to decrease the price of the Whole product by $0.25, would the optimal solution change?
m. Create a Spider plot showing the impact on net profit of changing each product's required time in the roasting process from between 70% to 130% of their original values in 5% increments. Interpret the information in the resulting chart.
n. Create a Spider plot showing the impact on net profit of changing the availability of nuts and chocolate from between 70% to 100% of their original values in 5% increments. Interpret the information in the resulting chart.

Parket Sisters

CASE 4.2

(Contributed by Jack Yurkiewicz, Lubin School of Business, Pace University, New York.)

Computers and word processors notwithstanding, the art of writing by hand recently entered a boom era. People are buying fountain pens again, and mechanical pencils are becoming more popular than ever. Joe Script, the president and CEO of Parket Sisters, a small but growing pen and pencil manufacturer, wants to establish a better foothold in the market. The writing market is divided into two main sectors. One, dominated by Mont Blanc, Cross, Parker Brothers, Waterman, Schaffer, and a few others, caters to people who want writing instruments. The product lines from these companies consist of pens and pencils of elaborate design, lifetime warranty, and high price. At the other end of the market are manufacturers like BIC, Pentel, and many companies from the far east, offering good quality items, low price, few trims, and limited diversity. These pens and pencils are meant to be used for a limited time and disposed of when the ink in a ballpoint pen runs out, or when the lead in a mechanical pencil won't retract or extend. In short, these items are not meant for repair.

Joe thinks that there must be a middle ground, and that is where he wants to position his company. Parket Sisters makes high-quality items, with limited trim and diversity, but also offers lifetime warranties. Furthermore, its pens and pencils are ergonomically efficient. Joe knows that some people want the status of the Mont Blanc Meisterstuck pen, for example, but he has never met a person who said that writing with such a pen is enjoyable. The pen is too large and clumsy for smooth writing. Parket Sisters' products, on the other hand, have a reputation for working well, are easy to hold and use, and cause limited "writer's fatigue."

Parket Sisters makes only three items—a ballpoint pen, a mechanical pencil, and a fountain pen. All are available in just one color, black, and are sold mostly in specialty stores and from better catalog companies. The per-unit profit of the items is $3.00 for the ballpoint pen, $3.00 for the mechanical pencil, and $5.00 for the fountain pen. These values take into account labor, the cost of materials, packing, quality control, and so on.

The company is trying to plan its production mix for each week. Joe believes that the company can sell any number of pens and pencils it produces, but production is currently limited by the available resources. Because of a recent strike and certain cash-flow problems, the suppliers of these resources are selling them to Parket Sisters in limited amounts. In particular, Joe can count on getting at most 1,000 ounces of plastic, 1,200 ounces of chrome, and 2,000 ounces of stainless steel each week from his suppliers, and these figures are not likely to change in the near future. Because of Joe's excellent reputation, the suppliers will sell Joe any amount (up to his limit) of the resources he needs when he requires them. That is, the suppliers do not require Joe to buy some fixed quantities of resources in advance of his production of pens and pencils; therefore, these resources can be considered variable costs rather than fixed costs for the pens and pencils.

Each ballpoint pen requires 1.2 ounces of plastic, 0.8 ounces of chrome, and 2 ounces of stainless steel. Each mechanical pencil requires 1.7 ounces of plastic, no chrome, and 3 ounces of stainless steel. Each fountain pen requires 1.2 ounces of plastic, 2.3 ounces of chrome, and 4.5 ounces of stainless steel. Joe believes LP could help him decide what his weekly product mix should consist of.

Getting his notes and notebooks, Joe grapples with the LP formulation. In addition to the constraints of the available resources, he recognizes that the model should include many other constraints (such as labor time availability and materials for packing). However, Joe wants to keep his model simple. He knows that eventually he'll have to take other constraints into account, but as a first-pass model, he'll restrict the constraints to just the three resources: plastic, chrome, and stainless steel.

With only these three constraints, Joe can formulate the problem easily as:

$$MAX: \quad 3.0X_1 + 3.0X_2 + 5.0X_3$$
$$\text{Subject to:} \quad 1.2X_1 + 1.7X_2 + 1.2X_3 \leq 1,000$$
$$0.8X_1 + 0X_2 + 2.3X_3 \leq 1,200$$
$$2.0X_1 + 3.0X_2 + 4.5X_3 \leq 2,000$$
$$X_1, X_2, X_3 \geq 0$$

where:

$$X_1 = \text{the number of ballpoint pens}$$
$$X_2 = \text{the number of mechanical pencils}$$
$$X_3 = \text{the number of fountain pens}$$

Joe's knowledge of Excel and the Solver feature is limited, so he asks you to enter and solve the problem for him, then answer the following questions. (Assume that each question is independent unless otherwise stated.)

a. What should the weekly product mix consist of, and what is the weekly net profit?
b. Is the optimal solution to question 1 degenerate? Explain your response.
c. Is the optimal solution from question 1 unique, or are there alternate answers to this question? Explain your response.
d. What is the marginal value of one more unit of chrome? Of plastic?
e. A local distributor has offered to sell Parket Sisters an additional 500 ounces of stainless steel for $0.60 per ounce more than it ordinarily pays. Should the company buy the steel at this price? Explain your response.
f. If Parket Sisters buys the additional 500 ounces of stainless steel noted in question 5, what is the new optimal product mix and what is the new optimal profit? Explain your response.
g. Suppose that the distributor offers to sell Parket Sisters some additional plastic at a price of only $1.00 over its usual cost of $5.00 per ounce. However, the distributor

will sell the plastic only in lot sizes of 500 ounces. Should Parket Sisters buy one such lot? Explain your response.

h. The distributor is willing to sell the plastic in lots of just 100 ounces instead of the usual 500-ounce lots, still at $1.00 over Parket Sisters' cost of $5.00 per ounce. How many lots (if any) should Parket Sisters buy? What is the optimal product mix if the company buys these lots, and what is the optimal profit?

i. Parket Sisters has an opportunity to sell some of its plastic for $6.50 per ounce to another company. The other company (which does not produce pens and pencils and, therefore, is not a competitor) wants to buy 300 ounces of plastic from Parket Sisters. Should Parket Sisters sell the plastic to the other company? What happens to Parket Sisters' product mix and overall profit if it does sell the plastic? Be as specific as possible.

j. The chrome supplier might have to fulfill an emergency order, and would be able to send only 1,000 ounces of chrome this week instead of the usual 1,200 ounces. If Parket Sisters receives only 1,000 ounces of chrome, what is the optimal product mix and optimal profit? Be as specific as possible.

k. The R&D department at Parket Sisters has been redesigning the mechanical pencil to make it more profitable. The new design requires 1.1 ounces of plastic, 2.0 ounces of chrome, and 2.0 ounces of stainless steel. If the company can sell one of these pencils at a net profit of $3.00, should it approve the new design? Explain your response.

l. If the per-unit profit on ballpoint pens decreases to $2.50, what is the optimal product mix and what is the company's total profit?

m. The marketing department suggested introducing a new felt tip pen that requires 1.8 ounces of plastic, 0.5 ounces of chrome, and 1.3 ounces of stainless steel. What profit must this product generate to make it worthwhile to produce?

n. What must the minimum per-unit profit of mechanical pencils be to make them worthwhile to produce?

o. Management believes that the company should produce at least 20 mechanical pencils per week to round out its product line. What effect would this have on overall profit? Give a numerical answer.

p. If the profit on a fountain pen is $6.75 instead of $5.00, what is the optimal product mix and optimal profit?

Kamm Industries

CASE 4.3

If your home or office is carpeted, there's a good chance that carpet came from Dalton, Georgia—also known as the "Carpet Capital of the World." Manufacturers in the Dalton area produce more than 70 percent of the total output of the $9 billion world-wide carpet industry. Competition in this industry is intense, which forces producers to strive for maximum efficiency and economies of scale. It also forces producers to continually evaluate investments in new technology.

Kamm Industries is one of the leading carpet producers in the Dalton area. Its owner, Geoff Kamm, has asked for your assistance in planning the production schedule for the next quarter (13 weeks). The company has orders for 15 different types of carpets that the company can produce on either of two types of looms: Dobbie looms and Pantera looms. Pantera looms produce standard tufted carpeting. Dobbie looms also can produce standard tufted carpeting, but they also allow the incorporation of designs (such as flowers or corporate logos) into the carpeting. The following table summarizes the orders for each type of carpet that must be produced in the coming quarter along with their production rates and costs on each type of loom, and the cost of subcontracting each order. Note that the first 4 orders involve special production requirements that can be achieved only on a Dobbie loom or via subcontracting. Assume that any portion of an order may be subcontracted.

Carpet	Demand Yds	Dobbie Yd/Hr	Dobbie Cost/Yd	Pantera Yd/Hr	Pantera Cost/Yd	Subcontract Cost/Yd
1	14,000	4.510	$2.66	na	na	$2.77
2	52,000	4.796	2.55	na	na	2.73
3	44,000	4.629	2.64	na	na	2.85
4	20,000	4.256	2.56	na	na	2.73
5	77,500	5.145	1.61	5.428	$1.60	1.76
6	109,500	3.806	1.62	3.935	1.61	1.76
7	120,000	4.168	1.64	4.316	1.61	1.76
8	60,000	5.251	1.48	5.356	1.47	1.59
9	7,500	5.223	1.50	5.277	1.50	1.71
10	69,500	5.216	1.44	5.419	1.42	1.63
11	68,500	3.744	1.64	3.835	1.64	1.80
12	83,000	4.157	1.57	4.291	1.56	1.78
13	10,000	4.422	1.49	4.558	1.48	1.63
14	381,000	5.281	1.31	5.353	1.30	1.44
15	64,000	4.222	1.51	4.288	1.50	1.69

Kamm currently owns and operates 15 Dobbie looms and 80 Pantera looms. To maximize efficiency and keep pace with demand, the company operates 24 hours a day, 7 days a week. Each machine is down for routine maintenance for approximately 2 hours per week. Create a spreadsheet model for this problem that can be used to determine the optimal production plan and answer the following questions.

a. What is the optimal production plan and associated cost?
b. Is the solution degenerate?
c. Is the solution unique?
d. What would happen to the total cost if one of the Dobbie machines broke and could not be used at all during the quarter?
e. What would happen to the total cost if an additional Dobbie machine was purchased and available for the quarter?
f. What would happen to the total cost if one of the Pantera machines broke and could not be used at all during the quarter?
g. What would happen to the total cost if an additional Pantera machine was purchased and available for the quarter?
h. Explain the shadow prices and the values in the "Allowable Increase" column of the Sensitivity Report for the products that are being outsourced.
i. How much money does it cost to produce carpet order 2? How much would the total cost decrease if that order were eliminated? Explain.
j. If the carpets in orders 5 through 15 all sell for the same amount, which type of carpet should Kamm encourage its sales force to sell more of? Why?
k. If the cost of buying the carpet in order 1 increased to $2.80 per yard, would the optimal solution change? Why?
l. If the cost of buying the carpet in order 15 decreased to $1.65 per yard, would the optimal solution change? Why?

Chapter 5

Network Modeling

5.0 Introduction

A number of practical decision problems in business fall into a category known as **network flow problems**. These problems share a common characteristic—they can be described or displayed in a graphical form known as a **network**. This chapter focuses on several types of network flow problems: transshipment problems, shortest path problems, maximal flow problems, transportation/assignment problems, and generalized network flow problems. Although specialized solution procedures exist for solving network flow problems, we will consider how to formulate and solve these problems as LP problems. We will also consider a different type of network problem known as the **minimum spanning tree problem**.

5.1 The Transshipment Problem

Let's begin our study of network flow problems by considering the transshipment problem. As you will see, most of the other types of network flow problems all can be viewed as simple variations of the transshipment problem. So, once you understand how to formulate and solve transshipment problems, the other types of problems will be easy to solve. The following example illustrates the transshipment problem.

> The Bavarian Motor Company (BMC) manufactures expensive luxury cars in Hamburg, Germany, and exports cars to sell in the United States. The exported cars are shipped from Hamburg to ports in Newark, New Jersey, and Jacksonville, Florida. From these ports, the cars are transported by rail or truck to distributors located in Boston, Massachusetts; Columbus, Ohio; Atlanta, Georgia; Richmond, Virginia; and Mobile, Alabama. Figure 5.1 shows the possible shipping routes available to the company along with the transportation cost for shipping each car along the indicated path.
>
> Currently, 200 cars are available at the port in Newark and 300 are available in Jacksonville. The numbers of cars needed by the distributors in Boston, Columbus, Atlanta, Richmond, and Mobile are 100, 60, 170, 80, and 70, respectively. BMC wants to determine the least costly way of transporting cars from the ports in Newark and Jacksonville to the cities where they are needed.

5.1.1 CHARACTERISTICS OF NETWORK FLOW PROBLEMS

Figure 5.1 illustrates a number of characteristics common to all network flow problems. All network flow problems can be represented as a collection of nodes connected by

FIGURE 5.1

*Network
representation of
the BMC
transshipment
problem*

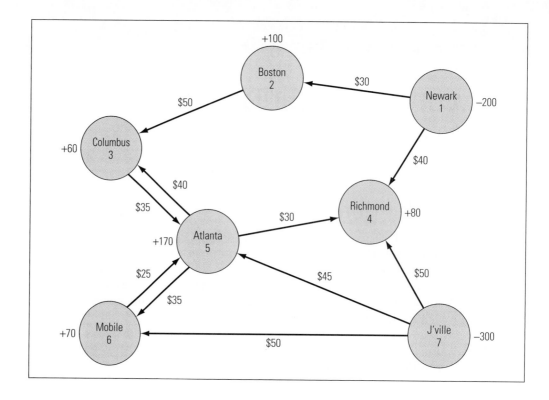

arcs. The circles in Figure 5.1 are called **nodes** in the terminology of network flow problems, and the lines connecting the nodes are called **arcs**. The arcs in a network indicate the valid paths, routes, or connections between the nodes in a network flow problem. When the lines connecting the nodes in a network are arrows that indicate a direction, the arcs in the network are called **directed arcs**. This chapter discusses directed arcs primarily but, for convenience, refers to them as arcs.

The notion of **supply nodes** (or sending nodes) and **demand nodes** (or receiving nodes) is another common element of network flow problems illustrated in Figure 5.1. The nodes representing the port cities of Newark and Jacksonville are both supply nodes because each has a supply of cars to send to other nodes in the network. Richmond represents a demand node because it demands to receive cars from the other nodes. All the other nodes in this network are transshipment nodes. **Transshipment nodes** can both send to and receive from other nodes in the network. For example, the node representing Atlanta in Figure 5.1 is a transshipment node because it can *receive* cars from Jacksonville, Mobile, and Columbus, and it also can send cars to Columbus, Mobile, and Richmond.

The net supply or demand for each node in the network is indicated by a positive or negative number next to each node. **Positive numbers** represent the *demand* at a given node, and **negative numbers** represent the *supply* available at a node. For example, the value +80 next to the node for Richmond indicates that the number of cars needs to increase by 80 — or that Richmond has a *demand* for 80 cars. The value −200 next to the node for Newark indicates that the number of cars can be reduced by 200 — or that Newark has a *supply* of 200 cars. A transshipment node can have either a net supply or demand, but not both. In this particular problem, all the transshipment nodes have demands. For example, the node representing Mobile in Figure 5.1 has a demand for 70 cars.

5.1.2 THE DECISION VARIABLES
FOR NETWORK FLOW PROBLEMS

The goal in a network flow model is to determine how many items should be moved (or flow) across each of the arcs. In our example, BMC needs to determine the least costly method of transporting cars along the various arcs shown in Figure 5.1 to distribute cars where they are needed. Thus, each of the arcs in a network flow model represents a decision variable. Determining the optimal flow for each arc is the equivalent of determining the optimal value for the corresponding decision variable.

It is customary to use numbers to identify each node in a network flow problem. In Figure 5.1, the number 1 identifies the node for Newark, 2 identifies the node for Boston, and so on. You can assign numbers to the nodes in any manner, but it is best to use a series of consecutive integers. The node numbers provide a convenient way to identify the decision variables needed to formulate the LP model for the problem. For each arc in a network flow model, you need to define one decision variable as:

X_{ij} = the number of items shipped (or flowing) *from* node *i to* node *j*

The network in Figure 5.1 for our example problem contains 11 arcs. Therefore, the LP formulation of this model requires the following 11 decision variables:

X_{12} = the number of cars shipped *from* node 1 (Newark) *to* node 2 (Boston)

X_{14} = the number of cars shipped *from* node 1 (Newark) *to* node 4 (Richmond)

X_{23} = the number of cars shipped *from* node 2 (Boston) *to* node 3 (Columbus)

X_{35} = the number of cars shipped *from* node 3 (Columbus) *to* node 5 (Atlanta)

X_{53} = the number of cars shipped *from* node 5 (Atlanta) *to* node 3 (Columbus)

X_{54} = the number of cars shipped *from* node 5 (Atlanta) *to* node 4 (Richmond)

X_{56} = the number of cars shipped *from* node 5 (Atlanta) *to* node 6 (Mobile)

X_{65} = the number of cars shipped *from* node 6 (Mobile) *to* node 5 (Atlanta)

X_{74} = the number of cars shipped *from* node 7 (Jacksonville) *to* node 4 (Richmond)

X_{75} = the number of cars shipped *from* node 7 (Jacksonville) *to* node 5 (Atlanta)

X_{76} = the number of cars shipped *from* node 7 (Jacksonville) *to* node 6 (Mobile)

5.1.3 THE OBJECTIVE FUNCTION
FOR NETWORK FLOW PROBLEMS

Each unit that flows from node *i* to node *j* in a network flow problem usually incurs some cost, c_{ij}. This cost might represent a monetary payment, a distance, or some other type of penalty. The objective in most network flow problems is to minimize the total cost, distance, or penalty that must be incurred to solve the problem. Such problems are known as *minimum cost network flow problems*.

In our example problem, different monetary costs must be paid for each car shipped across a given arc. For example, it costs $30 to ship each car from node 1 (Newark) to node 2 (Boston). Because X_{12} represents the number of cars shipped from Newark to Boston, the total cost incurred by cars shipped along this path is determined by $30X_{12}$. Similar calculations can be done for the other arcs in the network. Because BMC is interested in minimizing the total shipping costs, the objective function for this problem is expressed as:

$$\text{MIN:} \quad +30X_{12} + 40X_{14} + 50X_{23} + 35X_{35} + 40X_{53} + 30X_{54}$$
$$+ 35X_{56} + 25X_{65} + 50X_{74} + 45X_{75} + 50X_{76}$$

5.1.4 THE CONSTRAINTS FOR NETWORK FLOW PROBLEMS

Just as the number of arcs in the network determines the number of variables in the LP formulation of a network flow problem, the number of nodes determines the number of constraints. In particular, there must be one constraint for each node. A simple set of rules, known as the *Balance-of-Flow Rules*, applies to constructing the constraints for minimum cost network flow problems. These rules are summarized as follows:

For Minimum Cost Network Flow Problems Where:	Apply This Balance-of-Flow Rule at Each Node:
Total Supply > Total Demand	Inflow − Outflow ≥ Supply or Demand
Total Supply < Total Demand	Inflow − Outflow ≤ Supply or Demand
Total Supply = Total Demand	Inflow − Outflow = Supply or Demand

Note that if the total supply in a network flow problem is less than the total demand, then it will be impossible to satisfy all the demand. The balance-of-flow rule listed for this case assumes that you want to determine the least costly way of distributing the available supply—knowing that it is impossible to satisfy all the demand.

So to apply the correct balance-of-flow rule, we first must compare the total supply in the network to the total demand. In our example problem, there is a total supply of 500 cars and a total demand for 480 cars. Because the total supply exceeds the total demand, we will use the first balance-of-flow rule to formulate our example problem. That is, at each node, we will create a constraint of the form:

$$\text{Inflow} - \text{Outflow} \geq \text{Supply or Demand}$$

For example, consider node 1 (Newark) in Figure 5.1. No arcs flow into this node but two arcs (represented by X_{12} and X_{14}) flow out of the node. According to the balance-of-flow rule, the constraint for this node is:

Constraint for node 1: $-X_{12} - X_{14} \geq -200$

Notice that the supply at this node is represented by -200 following the convention we established earlier. If we multiply both sides of this equation by -1, we see that it is equivalent to $+X_{12} + X_{14} \leq +200$. (Note that multiplying an inequality by -1 reverses the direction of the inequality.) This constraint indicates that the total number of cars flowing out of Newark must not exceed 200. So, if we include either form of this constraint in the model, we can ensure that no more than 200 cars will be shipped from Newark.

Now consider the constraint for node 2 (Boston) in Figure 5.1. Because Boston has a demand for 100 cars, the balance-of-flow rule requires that the total number of cars coming into Boston from Newark (via X_{12}) minus the total number of cars being shipped out of Boston to Columbus (via X_{23}) must leave at least 100 cars in Boston. This condition is imposed by the constraint:

Constraint for node 2: $+X_{12} - X_{23} \geq +100$

Note that this constraint makes it possible to leave more than the required number of cars in Boston (e.g., 200 cars could be shipped into Boston and only 50 shipped out, leaving 150 cars in Boston). However, because our objective is to minimize costs, we can be sure that an excess number of cars will never be shipped to any city, because that would result in unnecessary costs being incurred.

Using the balance-of-flow rule, the constraints for each of the remaining nodes in our example problem are represented as:

Constraint for node 3: $+X_{23} + X_{53} - X_{35} \geq +60$

Constraint for node 4: $+X_{14} + X_{54} + X_{74} \geq +80$

Constraint for node 5: $+X_{35} + X_{65} + X_{75} - X_{53} - X_{54} - X_{56} \geq +170$

Constraint for node 6: $+X_{56} + X_{76} - X_{65} \geq +70$

Constraint for node 7: $-X_{74} - X_{75} - X_{76} \geq -300$

Again, each constraint indicates that the flow into a given node minus the flow out of that same node must be greater than or equal to the supply or demand at the node. So, if you draw a graph of a network flow problem like the one in Figure 5.1, it is easy to write out the constraints for the problem by following the balance-of-flow rule. Of course, we also need to specify the following nonnegativity condition for all the decision variables because negative flows should not occur on arcs:

$$X_{ij} \geq 0 \text{ for all } i \text{ and } j$$

5.1.5 IMPLEMENTING THE MODEL IN A SPREADSHEET

The formulation for the BMC transshipment problem is summarized as:

$$\text{MIN:} \quad \left. \begin{array}{l} +30X_{12} + 40X_{14} + 50X_{23} + 35X_{35} + 40X_{53} \\ +30X_{54} + 35X_{56} + 25X_{65} + 50X_{74} + 45X_{75} \\ +50X_{76} \end{array} \right\} \text{ total shipping cost}$$

Subject to:

$-X_{12} - X_{14} \geq -200$ } flow constraint for node 1

$+X_{12} - X_{23} \geq +100$ } flow constraint for node 2

$+X_{23} + X_{53} - X_{35} \geq +60$ } flow constraint for node 3

$+X_{14} + X_{54} + X_{74} \geq +80$ } flow constraint for node 4

$+X_{35} + X_{65} + X_{75} - X_{53} - X_{54} - X_{56} \geq +170$ } flow constraint for node 5

$+X_{56} + X_{76} - X_{65} \geq +70$ } flow constraint for node 6

$-X_{74} - X_{75} - X_{76} \geq -300$ } flow constraint for node 7

$X_{ij} \geq 0 \text{ for all } i \text{ and } j$ } nonnegativity conditions

A convenient way to implement this type of problem is shown in Figure 5.2 (and in the file Fig5-2.xls on your data disk). In this spreadsheet, cells B6 through B16 are used to represent the decision variables for our model (or the number of cars that should flow between each of the cities listed). The unit cost of transporting cars between each city is listed in column G. The objective function for the model is then implemented in cell G18 as follows:

Formula for cell G18:   =SUMPRODUCT(B6:B16,G6:G16)

To implement the LHS formulas for the constraints in this model, we need to compute the total inflow minus the total outflow for each node. This is done in cells K6 through K12 as follows:

Formula for cell K6:   =SUMIF($E$6:$E$16,I6,$B$6:$B$16)−

(Copy to cells K7 through K12.)   SUMIF($C$6:$C$16,I6,$B$6:$B$16)

FIGURE 5.2

Spreadsheet implementation of the BMC transshipment problem

Constraint Cells

Variable Cells

Set Cell

Key Cell Formulas

Cell	Formula	Copied to
D6	=VLOOKUP(C6,$I$6:$J$12,2)	D7:D16 and F6:F16
G18	=SUMPRODUCT(B6:B16,G6:G16)	--
K6	=SUMIF($E$6:$E$16,I6,$B$6:$B$16)-SUMIF($C$6:$C$16,I6,$B$6:$B$16)	K7:K12

The first SUMIF function in this formula compares the values in the range E6 through E16 to the value in I6 and, if a match occurs, sums the corresponding value in the range B6 through B16. Of course, this gives us the total number of cars flowing *into* Newark (which in this case will always be zero because none of the values in E6 through E16 match the value in I6). The next SUMIF function compares the values in the range C6 through C16 to the value in I6 and, if a match occurs, sums the corresponding values in the range B6 through B16. This gives us the total number of cars flowing *out of* Newark (which in this case will always equal the values in cells B6 and B7 because these are the only arcs flowing out of Newark). Copying this formula to cells K7 though K12 allows us to easily calculate the total inflow minus the total outflow for each of the nodes in our problem. The RHS values for these constraint cells are shown in cells L6 though L12.

Figure 5.3 shows the Solver parameters and options required to solve this model. The optimal solution to the problem is shown in Figure 5.4.

5.1.6 ANALYZING THE SOLUTION

Figure 5.4 shows the optimal solution for BMC's transshipment problem. The solution indicates that 120 cars should be shipped from Newark to Boston ($X_{12} = 120$), 80 cars from Newark to Richmond ($X_{14} = 80$), 20 cars from Boston to Columbus ($X_{23} = 20$), 40 cars from Atlanta to Columbus ($X_{53} = 40$), 210 cars from Jacksonville to Atlanta ($X_{75} = 210$), and 70 cars from Jacksonville to Mobile ($X_{76} = 70$). Cell G18 indicates that

FIGURE 5.3

Solver parameters for the BMC transshipment problem

FIGURE 5.4

Optimal solution to the BMC transshipment problem

the total cost associated with this shipping plan is $22,350. The values of the constraint cells in K6 and K12 indicate, respectively, that all 200 cars available at Newark are being shipped and only 280 of the 300 cars available at Jacksonville are being shipped. A comparison of the remaining constraint cells in K7 through K11 with their RHS values in L7 through L11 reveals that the demand at each of these cities is being met by the net flow of cars through each city.

This solution is summarized graphically, as shown in Figure 5.5. The values in the boxes next to each arc indicate the optimal flows for the arcs. The optimal flow for all the other arcs in the problem, which are not shown in Figure 5.5, is 0. Notice that the amount flowing into each node minus the amount flowing out of each node is equal

FIGURE 5.5

Network representation of the optimal solution for the BMC transshipment problem

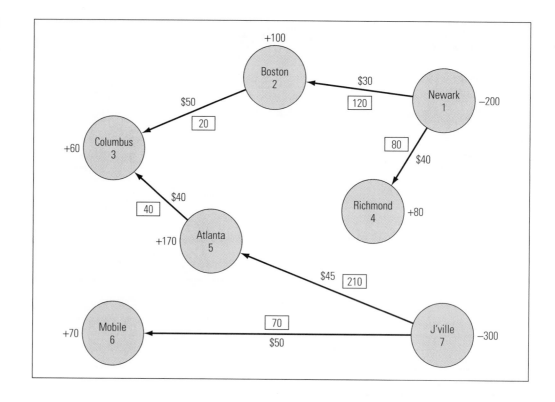

to the supply or demand at the node. For example, 210 cars are being shipped from Jacksonville to Atlanta. Atlanta will keep 170 of the cars (to satisfy the demand at this node) and send the extra 40 to Columbus.

5.2 The Shortest Path Problem

In many decision problems, we need to determine the shortest (or least costly) route or path through a network from a starting node to an ending node. For example, many cities are developing computerized models of their highways and streets to help emergency vehicles identify the quickest route to a given location. Each street intersection represents a potential node in a network, and the streets connecting the intersections represent arcs. Depending on the day of the week and the time of day, the time required to travel various streets can increase or decrease due to changes in traffic patterns. Road construction and maintenance also affect traffic flow patterns. So, the quickest route (or shortest path) for getting from one point in the city to another can change frequently. In emergency situations, lives or property can be lost or saved depending on how quickly emergency vehicles arrive where they are needed. The ability to quickly determine the shortest path to the location of an emergency situation is extremely useful in these situations. The following example illustrates another application of the shortest path problem.

The American Car Association (ACA) provides a variety of travel-related services to its members, including information on vacation destinations, discount hotel reservations, emergency road assistance, and travel route planning. This last service, travel route planning, is one of its most popular services. When members of the ACA are planning to take a driving trip, they call the organization's toll-free 800 number and indicate what cities they will be traveling from and to. The ACA then

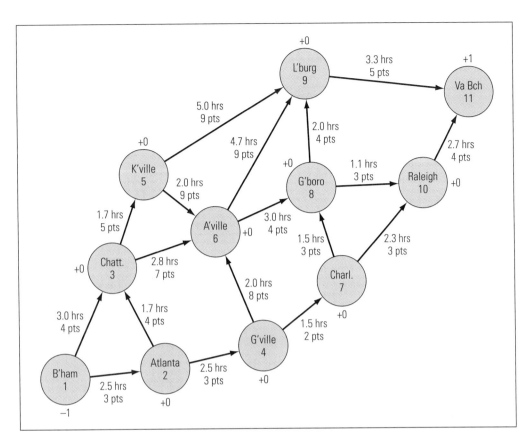

FIGURE 5.6

Network of possible routes for the ACA's shortest path problem

determines an optimal route for traveling between these cities. The ACA's computer databases of major highways and interstates are kept up-to-date with information on construction delays and detours and estimated travel times along various segments of roadways.

Members of the ACA often have different objectives in planning driving trips. Some are interested in identifying routes that minimize travel times. Others, with more leisure time on their hands, want to identify the most scenic route to their desired destination. The ACA wants to develop an automated system for identifying an optimal travel plan for its members.

To see how the ACA could benefit by solving shortest path problems, consider the simplified network shown in Figure 5.6 for a travel member who wants to drive from Birmingham, Alabama to Virginia Beach, Virginia. The nodes in this graph represent different cities and the arcs indicate the possible travel routes between the cities. For each arc, Figure 5.6 lists both the estimated driving time to travel the road represented by each arc and the number of points that route has received on the ACA's system for rating the scenic quality of the various routes.

Solving this problem as a network flow model requires the various nodes to have some supply or demand. In Figure 5.6, node 1 (Birmingham) has a supply of 1, node 11 (Virginia Beach) has a demand of 1, and all other nodes have a demand (or supply) of 0. If we view this model as a transshipment problem, we want to find either the quickest way or the most scenic way of shipping 1 unit of flow from node 1 to node 11. The route this unit of supply takes corresponds to either the shortest path or the most scenic path through the network, depending on which objective is being pursued.

5.2.1 AN LP MODEL FOR THE EXAMPLE PROBLEM

Using the balance-of-flow rule, the LP model to minimize the driving time in this problem is represented as:

$$\text{MIN:} \quad +2.5X_{12} + 3X_{13} + 1.7X_{23} + 2.5X_{24} + 1.7X_{35} + 2.8X_{36} + 2X_{46} + 1.5X_{47} + 2X_{56} + 5X_{59}$$
$$+ 3X_{68} + 4.7X_{69} + 1.5X_{78} + 2.3X_{7,10} + 2X_{89} + 1.1X_{8,10} + 3.3X_{9,11} + 2.7X_{10,11}$$

Subject to:

$$
\begin{array}{lrl}
-X_{12} - X_{13} & = -1 & \text{\} flow constraint for node 1} \\
+X_{12} - X_{23} - X_{24} & = 0 & \text{\} flow constraint for node 2} \\
+X_{13} + X_{23} - X_{35} - X_{36} & = 0 & \text{\} flow constraint for node 3} \\
+X_{24} - X_{46} - X_{47} & = 0 & \text{\} flow constraint for node 4} \\
+X_{35} - X_{56} - X_{59} & = 0 & \text{\} flow constraint for node 5} \\
+X_{36} + X_{46} + X_{56} - X_{68} - X_{69} & = 0 & \text{\} flow constraint for node 6} \\
+X_{47} - X_{78} - X_{7,10} & = 0 & \text{\} flow constraint for node 7} \\
+X_{68} + X_{78} - X_{89} - X_{8,10} & = 0 & \text{\} flow constraint for node 8} \\
+X_{59} + X_{69} + X_{89} - X_{9,11} & = 0 & \text{\} flow constraint for node 9} \\
+X_{7,10} + X_{8,10} - X_{10,11} & = 0 & \text{\} flow constraint for node 10} \\
+X_{9,11} + X_{10,11} & = +1 & \text{\} flow constraint for node 11} \\
X_{ij} \geq 0 \text{ for all } i \text{ and } j & & \text{\} nonnegativity conditions}
\end{array}
$$

Because the total supply equals the total demand in this problem, the constraints should be stated as equalities. The first constraint in this model ensures that the 1 unit of supply available at node 1 is shipped to node 2 or node 3. The next nine constraints indicate that anything flowing to nodes 2 though node 10 must also flow out of these nodes because each has a demand of 0. For example, if the unit of supply leaves node 1 for node 2 (via X_{12}), the second constraint ensures that it will leave node 2 for node 3 or node 4 (via X_{23} or X_{24}). The last constraint indicates that the unit ultimately must flow to node 11. Thus, the solution to this problem indicates the quickest route for getting from node 1 (Birmingham) to node 11 (Virginia Beach).

5.2.2 THE SPREADSHEET MODEL AND SOLUTION

The optimal solution to this problem shown in Figure 5.7 (and in the file Fig5-7.xls on your data disk) was obtained using the Solver parameters and options shown in Figure 5.8. Notice that this model includes calculations of both the total expected driving time (cell G26) and total scenic rating points (cell H26) associated with any solution. Either of these cells can be chosen as the objective function according to the client's desires. However, the solution shown in Figure 5.7 minimizes the expected driving time.

The optimal solution shown in Figure 5.7 indicates that the quickest travel plan involves driving from node 1 (Birmingham) to node 2 (Atlanta), then to node 4 (Greenville), then to node 7 (Charlotte), then to node 10 (Raleigh), and finally to node 11 (Virginia Beach). The total expected driving time along this route is 11.5 hours. Also note that this route receives a rating of 15 points on the ACA's scenic rating scale.

FIGURE 5.7

Spreadsheet model and solution showing the route that minimizes estimated driving time for the ACA's shortest path problem

Constraint Cells

Variable Cells

Set Cell

Key Cell Formulas

Cell	Formula	Copied to
D7	=VLOOKUP(C7,$J$7:$K$17,2)	D8:D24 and F7:F24
G26	=SUMPRODUCT(G7:G24,$B$7:$B$24)	H26
L7	=SUMIF($E$7:$E$24,J7,$B$7:$B$24)-SUMIF($C$7:$C$24,J7,$B$7:$B$24)	L8:L17

FIGURE 5.8

Solver parameters for the ACA's shortest path problem

FIGURE 5.9

Solution showing the most scenic route

Select Route?	From		To		Driving Time	Scenic Rating		Nodes		Net Flow	Supply/Demand
1.0	1	Birmingham	2	Atlanta	2.5	3		1	Birmingham	-1	-1
0.0	1	Birmingham	3	Chattanooga	3.0	4		2	Atlanta	0	0
1.0	2	Atlanta	3	Chattanooga	1.7	4		3	Chattanooga	0	0
0.0	2	Atlanta	4	Greenville	2.5	3		4	Greenville	0	0
1.0	3	Chattanooga	5	Knoxville	1.7	5		5	Knoxville	0	0
0.0	3	Chattanooga	6	Asheville	2.8	7		6	Asheville	0	0
0.0	4	Greenville	6	Asheville	2.0	8		7	Charlotte	0	0
0.0	4	Greenville	7	Charlotte	1.5	2		8	Greensboro	0	0
1.0	5	Knoxville	6	Asheville	2.0	9		9	Lynchburg	0	0
0.0	5	Knoxville	9	Lynchburg	5.0	9		10	Raleigh	0	0
0.0	6	Asheville	8	Greensboro	3.0	4		11	Virginia Beach	1	1
1.0	6	Asheville	9	Lynchburg	4.7	9					
0.0	7	Charlotte	8	Greensboro	1.5	3					
0.0	7	Charlotte	10	Raleigh	2.3	3					
0.0	8	Greensboro	9	Lynchburg	2.0	4					
0.0	8	Greensboro	10	Raleigh	1.1	3					
1.0	9	Lynchburg	11	Virginia Beach	3.3	5					
0.0	10	Raleigh	11	Virginia Beach	2.7	4					
				Total	15.9	35					

American Car Association

Using this spreadsheet, we also can determine the most scenic route by instructing Solver to maximize the value in cell H26. Figure 5.9 shows the optimal solution obtained in this case. This travel plan involves driving from Birmingham to Atlanta, to Chattanooga, to Knoxville, to Asheville, to Lynchburg, and finally, to Virginia Beach. This itinerary receives a rating of 35 points on the ACA's scenic rating scale but takes almost 16 hours of driving time.

5.2.3 NETWORK FLOW MODELS AND INTEGER SOLUTIONS

Up to this point, each of the network flow models that we have solved generated integer solutions. If you use the simplex method to solve any minimum cost network flow model having integer constraint RHS values, then the optimal solution automatically assumes integer values. This property is helpful because the items flowing through most network flow models represent discrete units (such as cars or people).

Sometimes, it is tempting to place additional constraints (or side constraints) on a network model. For example, in the ACA problem, suppose that the customer wants to get to Virginia Beach in the most scenic way possible within 14 hours of driving time. We can easily add a constraint to the model to keep the total driving time G26 less than or equal to 14 hours. If we then re-solve the model to maximize the scenic rating in cell H26, we obtain the solution shown in Figure 5.10.

Unfortunately, this solution is useless because it produces fractional results. Thus, if we add *side constraints* to network flow problems that do not obey the balance-of-flow rule, we can no longer ensure that the solution to the LP formulation of the problems

FIGURE 5.10

Example of a non-integer solution to a network problem with side constraints

will be integral. If integer solutions are needed for such problems, the integer programming techniques discussed in Chapter 6 must be applied.

5.3 The Equipment Replacement Problem

The equipment replacement problem is a common type of business problem that can be modeled as a shortest path problem. This type of problem involves determining the least costly schedule for replacing equipment over a specified length of time. Consider the following example.

> Jose Maderos is the owner of Compu-Train, a small company that provides hands-on software education and training for businesses in and around Boulder, Colorado. Jose leases the computer equipment used in his business and he likes to keep the equipment up-to-date so that it will run the latest, state-of-the-art software in an efficient manner. Because of this, Jose wants to replace his equipment at least every two years.
>
> Jose is currently trying to decide between two different lease contracts his equipment supplier has proposed. Under both contracts Jose would be required to pay $62,000 initially to obtain the equipment he needs. However, the two contracts differ in terms of the amount Jose would have to pay in subsequent years to replace his equipment. Under the first contract, the price to acquire new equipment would increase by 6% per year, but he would be given a trade-in credit of 60% for any equipment that is one year old and 15% for any equipment that is two years old. Under the second contract, the price to acquire new equipment would increase by just 2% per year, but he would only be given a trade-in credit of 30% for any equipment that is one year old and 10% for any equipment that is two years old.

FIGURE 5.11

Network representation of Compu-Train's first contract alternative for their equipment replacement problem

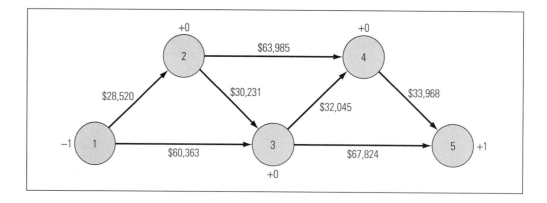

Jose realizes that no matter what he does, he will have to pay $62,000 to obtain the equipment initially. However, he wants to determine which contract would allow him to minimize the remaining leasing costs over the next five years and when he should replace his equipment under the selected contract.

Each of the two contracts Jose is considering can be modeled as a shortest path problem. Figure 5.11 shows how this would be accomplished for the first contract under consideration. Each node corresponds to a point in time during the next five years when Jose can replace his equipment. Each arc in this network represents a choice available to Jose. For example, the arc from node 1 to node 2 indicates that Jose can keep the equipment he initially acquires for one year and then replace it (at the beginning of year 2) for a net cost of $28,520 ($62,000 × 1.06 − 0.6 × $62,000 = $28,520). Alternatively, the arc from node 1 to node 3 indicates that Jose can keep his initial equipment for two years and replace it at the beginning of year 3 for a net cost of $60,363 ($62,000 × 1.06² − 0.15 × $62,000 = $60,363).

The arc from node 2 to node 3 indicates that if Jose replaces his initial equipment at the beginning of year 2, he can keep the new equipment for one year and replace it at the beginning of year 3 at a net cost of $30,231 ($62,000 × 1.06² − 0.60 × ($62,000 × 1.06) = $30,231). The remaining arcs and costs in the network can be interpreted in the same way. Jose's decision problem is to determine the least costly (or shortest) way of getting from node 1 to node 5 in this network.

5.3.1 THE SPREADSHEET MODEL AND SOLUTION

The LP formulation of Jose's decision problem can be generated from the graph in Figure 5.11 using the balance-of-flow rule in the same manner as the previous network flow problems. The spreadsheet model for this problem was implemented as shown in Figure 5.12 (and in the file Fig5-12.xls on your data disk) and solved using the settings shown in Figure 5.13. To assist Jose in comparing the two different alternatives he faces, notice that an area of the spreadsheet in Figure 5.12 has been reserved to represent assumptions about the annual increase in leasing costs (cell G5), and the trade-in values for one- and two-year old equipment (cells G6 and G7). The rest of the spreadsheet model uses these assumed values to compute the various costs. This enables us to change any of the assumptions and re-solve the model very easily.

The optimal solution to this problem shows that under the provisions of the first contract, Jose should replace his equipment at the beginning of each year at a total cost of $124,764. This amount is in addition to the $62,000 he has to pay up front at the beginning of year 1.

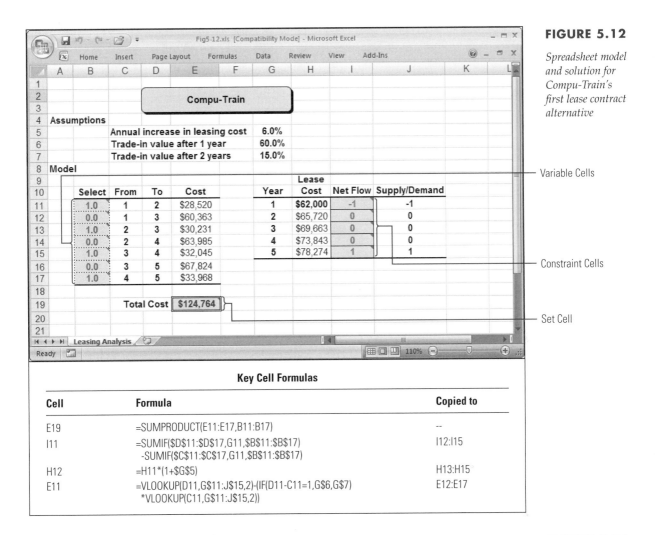

FIGURE 5.12

Spreadsheet model and solution for Compu-Train's first lease contract alternative

— Variable Cells

— Constraint Cells

— Set Cell

Key Cell Formulas

Cell	Formula	Copied to
E19	=SUMPRODUCT(E11:E17,B11:B17)	--
I11	=SUMIF($D$11:$D$17,G11,$B$11:$B$17) -SUMIF($C$11:$C$17,G11,$B$11:$B$17)	I12:I15
H12	=H11*(1+$G$5)	H13:H15
E11	=VLOOKUP(D11,G$11:J$15,2)-(IF(D11-C11=1,G$6,G$7) *VLOOKUP(C11,G$11:J$15,2))	E12:E17

FIGURE 5.13

Solver parameters for Compu-Train's equipment replacement problem

FIGURE 5.14

Solution for Compu-Train's second lease contract alternative

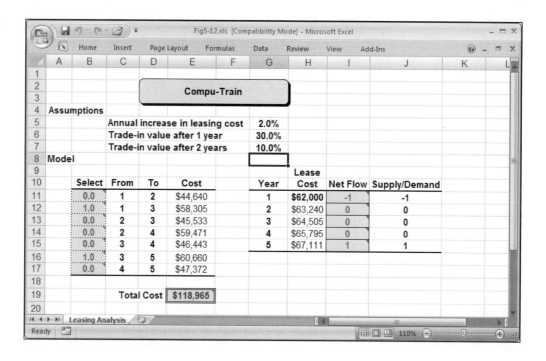

To determine the optimal replacement strategy and costs associated with the second contract, Jose could simply change the assumptions at the top of the spreadsheet and re-solve the model. The results of this are shown in Figure 5.14.

The optimal solution to this problem shows that under the provisions of the second contract, Jose should replace his equipment at the beginning of years 3 and 5 at a total cost of $118,965. Again, this amount is in addition to the $62,000 he has to pay up front at the beginning of year 1. Although the total costs under the second contract are lower than under the first, under the second contract Jose would be working with older equipment during years 2 and 4. Thus, although the solution to these two models makes the financial consequences of the two different alternatives clear, Jose still must decide for himself whether the benefits of the financial cost savings under the second contract outweigh the non-financial costs associated with using slightly out-of-date equipment during years 2 and 4. Of course, regardless of which contract Jose decides to go with, he will get to reconsider whether or not to upgrade his equipment at the beginning of each of the next 4 years.

Summary of Shortest Path Problems

You can model any shortest path problem as a transshipment problem by assigning a supply of 1 to the starting node, a demand of 1 to the ending node, and a demand of 0 to all other nodes in the network. Because the examples presented here involved only a small number of paths through each of the networks, it might have been easier to solve these problems simply by enumerating the paths and calculating the total distance of each one. However, in a problem with many nodes and arcs, an automated LP model is preferable to a manual solution approach.

5.4 Transportation/Assignment Problems

Chapter 3 presented an example of another type of network flow problem known as the transportation/assignment problem. The example involved the Tropicsun Company—a grower and distributor of fresh citrus products. The company wanted to determine the least expensive way to transport freshly picked fruit from three citrus groves to three processing plants. The network representation of the problem is repeated in Figure 5.15.

The network shown in Figure 5.15 differs from the earlier network flow problems in this chapter because it contains no transshipment nodes. Each node in Figure 5.15 is either a sending node or a receiving node. The lack of transshipment nodes is the key feature that distinguishes transportation/assignment problems from other types of network flow problems. As you saw in Chapter 3, this property allows you to set up and solve transportation/assignment problems conveniently in a matrix format in the spreadsheet. Although it is possible to solve transportation/assignment problems in the same way in which we solved transshipment problems, it is much easier to implement and solve these problems using the matrix approach described in Chapter 3.

Sometimes, transportation/assignment problems are *sparse* or not fully interconnected (meaning that not all the supply nodes have arcs connecting them to all the demand nodes). These "missing" arcs can be handled conveniently in the matrix approach to implementation by assigning arbitrarily large costs to the variable cells representing these arcs so that flow on these arcs becomes prohibitively expensive. However, as the number of missing arcs increases, the matrix approach to implementation becomes less and less computationally efficient compared to the procedure described in this chapter.

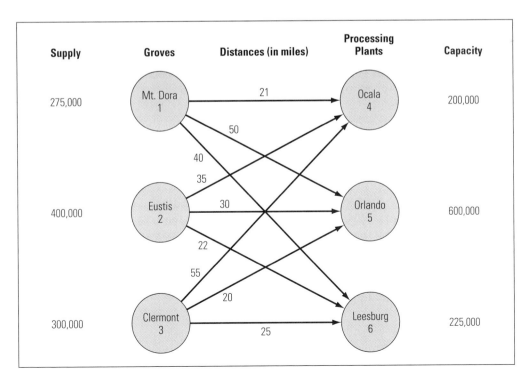

FIGURE 5.15

Network representation of Tropicsun's transportation/ assignment problem

5.5 Generalized Network Flow Problems

In all of the network problems we have considered so far, the amount of flow that exited an arc was always the same as the amount that entered the arc. For example, if we put 40 cars on a train in Jacksonville and sent them to Atlanta, the same 40 cars came off the train in Atlanta. However, there are numerous examples of network flow problems in which a gain or loss occurs on flows across arcs. For instance, if oil or gas is shipped through a leaky pipeline, the amount of oil or gas arriving at the intended destination will be less than the amount originally placed in the pipeline. Similar loss-of-flow examples occur as a result of evaporation of liquids, spoilage of foods and other perishable items, or imperfections in raw materials entering production processes that result in a certain amount of scrap. Many financial cash flow problems can be modeled as network flow problems in which flow gains (or increases) occur in the form of interest or dividends as money flows through various investments. The following example illustrates the modeling changes required to accommodate these types of problems.

Nancy Grant is the owner of Coal Bank Hollow Recycling, a company that specializes in collecting and recycling paper products. Nancy's company uses two different recycling processes to convert newspaper, mixed paper, white office paper, and cardboard into paper pulp. The amount of paper pulp extracted from the recyclable materials and the cost of extracting the pulp differs depending on which recycling process is used. The following table summarizes the recycling processes:

Material	Recycling Process 1		Recycling Process 2	
	Cost per ton	Yield	Cost per Ton	Yield
Newspaper	$13	90%	$12	85%
Mixed Paper	$11	80%	$13	85%
White Office Paper	$9	95%	$10	90%
Cardboard	$13	75%	$14	85%

For instance, every ton of newspaper subjected to recycling process 1 costs $13 and yields 0.9 tons of paper pulp. The paper pulp produced by the two different recycling processes goes through other operations to be transformed into pulp for newsprint, packaging paper, or print stock quality paper. The yields associated with transforming the recycled pulp into pulp for the final products are summarized in the following table:

Pulp Source	Newsprint Pulp		Packaging Paper Pulp		Print Stock Pulp	
	Cost per Ton	Yield	Cost per Ton	Yield	Cost per Ton	Yield
Recycling Process 1	$5	95%	$6	90%	$8	90%
Recycling Process 2	$6	90%	$8	95%	$7	95%

For instance, a ton of pulp exiting recycling process 2 can be transformed into 0.95 tons of packaging paper at a cost of $8.

Nancy currently has 70 tons of newspaper, 50 tons of mixed paper, 30 tons of white office paper, and 40 tons of cardboard. She wants to determine the most efficient way of converting these materials into 60 tons of newsprint pulp, 40 tons of packaging paper pulp, and 50 tons of print stock pulp.

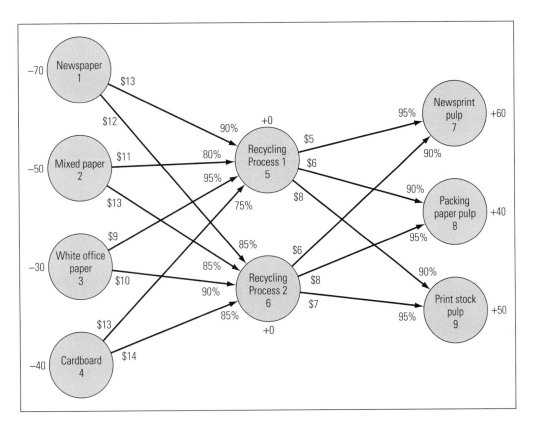

FIGURE 5.16

Graphical representation of Coal Bank Hollow Recycling's generalized network flow problem

Figure 5.16 shows how Nancy's recycling problem can be viewed as a generalized network flow problem. The arcs in this graph indicate the possible flow of recycling material through the production process. On each arc, we have listed both the cost of flow along the arc and the reduction factor that applies to flow along the arc. For instance, the arc from node 1 to node 5 indicates that each ton of newspaper going to recycling process 1 costs \$13 and yields 0.90 tons of paper pulp.

5.5.1 FORMULATING AN LP MODEL FOR THE RECYCLING PROBLEM

To formulate the LP model for this problem algebraically, we defined the decision variable X_{ij} to represent the tons of product flowing from node i to node j. The objective is then stated in the usual way as follows:

MIN: $13X_{15} + 12X_{16} + 11X_{25} + 13X_{26} + 9X_{35} + 10X_{36} + 13X_{45} + 14X_{46} + 5X_{57}$
$+ 6X_{58} + 8X_{59} + 6X_{67} + 8X_{68} + 7X_{69}$

The constraints for this problem may be generated using the balance-of-flow rule for each node. The constraints for the first four nodes (representing the supply of newspaper, mixed paper, white office paper, and cardboard, respectively) are given by:

$$-X_{15} - X_{16} \geq -70 \qquad \} \text{ flow constraint for node 1}$$
$$-X_{25} - X_{26} \geq -50 \qquad \} \text{ flow constraint for node 2}$$
$$-X_{35} - X_{36} \geq -30 \qquad \} \text{ flow constraint for node 3}$$
$$-X_{45} - X_{46} \geq -40 \qquad \} \text{ flow constraint for node 4}$$

These constraints simply indicate that the amount of product flowing out of each of these nodes may not exceed the supply available at each node. (Recall that the constraint given for node 1 is equivalent to $+X_{15} + X_{16} \leq +70$.)

Applying the balance-of-flow rule at nodes 5 and 6 (representing the two recycling processes) we obtain:

$+0.9X_{15} + 0.8X_{25} + 0.95X_{35} + 0.75X_{45} - X_{57} - X_{58} - X_{59} \geq 0$ } flow constraint for node 5

$+0.85X_{16} + 0.85X_{26} + 0.9X_{36} + 0.85X_{46} - X_{67} - X_{68} - X_{69} \geq 0$ } flow constraint for node 6

To better understand the logic of these constraints, we will rewrite them in the following algebraically equivalent manner:

$+0.9X_{15} + 0.8X_{25} + 0.95X_{35} + 0.75X_{45} \geq +X_{57} + X_{58} + X_{59}$ } equivalent flow constraint for node 5

$+0.85X_{16} + 0.85X_{26} + 0.9X_{36} + 0.85X_{46} \geq +X_{67} + X_{68} + X_{69}$ } equivalent flow constraint for node 6

Notice that the constraint for node 5 requires that the amount being shipped from node 5 (given by $X_{57} + X_{58} + X_{59}$) cannot exceed the net amount that would be available at node 5 (given by $0.9X_{15} + 0.8X_{25} + 0.95X_{35} + 0.75X_{45}$). Thus, here the yield factors come into play in determining the amount of product that would be available from the recycling processes. A similar interpretation applies to the constraint for node 6.

Finally, applying the balance-of-flow rule to nodes 7, 8, and 9 we obtain the constraints:

$+0.95X_{57} + 0.90X_{67} \geq 60$ } flow constraint for node 7

$+0.9X_{58} + 0.95X_{68} \geq 40$ } flow constraint for node 8

$+0.9X_{59} + 0.95X_{69} \geq 50$ } flow constraint for node 9

The constraint for node 7 ensures that the final amount of product flowing to node 7 ($0.95X_{57} + 0.90X_{67}$) is sufficient to meet the demand for pulp at this node. Again, similar interpretations apply to the constraints for nodes 8 and 9.

5.5.2 IMPLEMENTING THE MODEL

The model for Coal Bank Hollow Recycling's generalized network flow problem is summarized as:

MIN: $13X_{15} + 12X_{16} + 11X_{25} + 13X_{26} + 9X_{35} + 10X_{36} + 13X_{45} + 14X_{46} + 5X_{57}$
$+ 6X_{58} + 8X_{59} + 6X_{67} + 8X_{68} + 7X_{69}$

Subject to:

$-X_{15} - X_{16} \geq -70$ } flow constraint for node 1

$-X_{25} - X_{26} \geq -50$ } flow constraint for node 2

$-X_{35} - X_{36} \geq -30$ } flow constraint for node 3

$-X_{45} - X_{46} \geq -40$ } flow constraint for node 4

$+0.9X_{15} + 0.8X_{25} + 0.95X_{35} + 0.75X_{45} - X_{57} - X_{58} - X_{59} \geq 0$ } flow constraint for node 5

$+0.85X_{16} + 0.85X_{26} + 0.9X_{36} + 0.85X_{46} - X_{67} - X_{68} - X_{69} \geq 0$} flow constraint for node 6

$+0.95X_{57} + 0.90X_{67} \geq 60$ } flow constraint for node 7

$+0.9X_{58} + 0.95X_{68} \geq 40$ } flow constraint for node 8

$+0.9X_{59} + 0.95X_{69} \geq 50$ } flow constraint for node 9

$X_{ij} \geq 0$ for all i and j } nonnegativity conditions

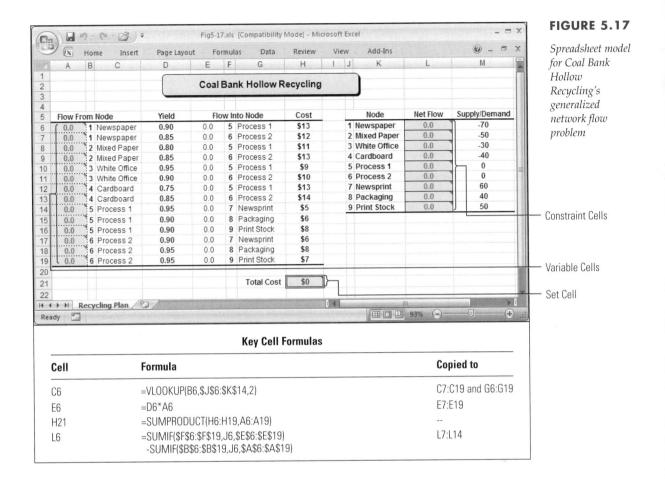

FIGURE 5.17

Spreadsheet model for Coal Bank Hollow Recycling's generalized network flow problem

Key Cell Formulas

Cell	Formula	Copied to
C6	=VLOOKUP(B6,$J$6:$K$14,2)	C7:C19 and G6:G19
E6	=D6*A6	E7:E19
H21	=SUMPRODUCT(H6:H19,A6:A19)	--
L6	=SUMIF($F$6:$F$19,J6,$E$6:$E$19) -SUMIF($B$6:$B$19,J6,$A$6:$A$19)	L7:L14

In all the other network flow models we have seen up to this point, all the coefficients in all the constraints were implicitly always +1 or −1. This is not true in the above model. Thus, we must give special attention to the coefficients in the constraints as we implement this model in the spreadsheet. One approach to implementing this problem is shown in Figure 5.17 (and the file Fig5-17.xls on your data disk).

The spreadsheet in Figure 5.17 is very similar to those of the other network flow problems we have solved. Cells A6 through A19 represent the decision variables (arcs) for our model, and the corresponding unit cost associated with each variable is listed in the range from H6 through H19. The objective function is implemented in cell H21 as:

Formula for cell H21:   =SUMPRODUCT(H6:H19,A6:A19)

To implement the LHS formulas for our constraints, we no longer can simply sum the variables flowing into each node and subtract the variables flowing out of the nodes. Instead, we first need to multiply the variables flowing into a node by the appropriate yield factor. With the yield factors entered in column D, the yield-adjusted flow for each arc is computed in column E as follows:

Formula for cell E6:   =A6*D6

(Copy to cells E7 through E19.)

FIGURE 5.18

Solver parameters for the recycling problem

Now, to implement the LHS formulas for each node in cells L6 through L14, we will sum the yield-adjusted flows into each node and subtract the raw flow out of each node. This may be done as follows:

Formula for cell L6:   = SUMIF($F$6:$F$19,J6,$E$6:$E$19)–
(Copy to cells L7 through L14.)   SUMIF($B$6:$B$19,J6,$A$6:$A$19)

Notice that the first SUMIF function in this formula sums the appropriate yield-adjusted flows in column E while the second SUMIF sums the appropriate raw flow values from column A. Thus, although this formula is very similar to the ones used in earlier models, there is a critical difference here that must be carefully noted and understood. The RHS values for these constraint cells are listed in cells M6 through M14.

5.5.3 ANALYZING THE SOLUTION

The Solver parameters used to solve this problem are shown in Figure 5.18 and the optimal solution is shown in Figure 5.19.

In this solution, 43.4 tons of newspaper, 50 tons of mixed paper, and 30 tons of white office paper are assigned to recycling process 1 (i.e., $X_{15} = 43.4$, $X_{25} = 50$, $X_{35} = 30$). This recycling process then yields a total of 107.6 tons of pulp (i.e., $0.9 \times 43.3 + 0.8 \times 50 + 0.95 \times 30 = 107.6$) of which 63.2 tons are allocated to the production of newsprint pulp ($X_{57} = 63.2$) and 44.4 tons are allocated to the production of pulp for packaging paper ($X_{58} = 44.4$). This allows us to meet the demand for 60 tons of newsprint pulp ($0.95 \times 63.2 = 60$) and 40 tons of packaging paper ($0.90 \times 44.4 = 40$).

The remaining 26.6 tons of newspaper are combined with 35.4 tons of cardboard in recycling process 2 (i.e., $X_{16} = 26.6$, $X_{46} = 35.4$). This results in a yield of 52.6 tons of pulp (i.e., $0.85 \times 26.6 + 0.85 \times 35.4 = 52.6$), which is all devoted to the production of 50 tons of print stock quality pulp ($0.95 \times 52.6 = 50$).

It is important for Nancy to note that this production plan calls for the use of all her supply of newspaper, mixed paper, and white office paper, but leaves about 4.6 tons of cardboard left over. Thus, she should be able to lower her total costs further by acquiring more newspaper, mixed paper, or white office paper. It would be wise for her to see if she could trade her surplus cardboard to another recycler for the material that she lacks.

FIGURE 5.19

*Optimal solution
to Coal Bank
Hollow
Recycling's
generalized
network flow
problem*

Flow From Node			Yield	Flow Into Node			Cost		Node	Net Flow	Supply/Demand
43.4	1	Newspaper	0.90	39.1	5	Process 1	$13	1	Newspaper	-70.0	-70
26.6	1	Newspaper	0.85	22.6	6	Process 2	$12	2	Mixed Paper	-50.0	-50
50.0	2	Mixed Paper	0.80	40.0	5	Process 1	$11	3	White Office	-30.0	-30
0.0	2	Mixed Paper	0.85	0.0	6	Process 2	$13	4	Cardboard	-35.4	-40
30.0	3	White Office	0.95	28.5	5	Process 1	$9	5	Process 1	0.0	0
0.0	3	White Office	0.90	0.0	6	Process 2	$10	6	Process 2	0.0	0
0.0	4	Cardboard	0.75	0.0	5	Process 1	$13	7	Newsprint	60.0	60
35.4	4	Cardboard	0.85	30.1	6	Process 2	$14	8	Packaging	40.0	40
63.2	5	Process 1	0.95	60.0	7	Newsprint	$5	9	Print Stock	50.0	50
44.4	5	Process 1	0.90	40.0	8	Packaging	$6				
0.0	5	Process 1	0.90	0.0	9	Print Stock	$8				
0.0	6	Process 2	0.90	0.0	7	Newsprint	$6				
0.0	6	Process 2	0.95	0.0	8	Packaging	$8				
52.6	6	Process 2	0.95	50.0	9	Print Stock	$7				

Total Cost $3,149

5.5.4 GENERALIZED NETWORK FLOW PROBLEMS AND FEASIBILITY

In generalized network flow problems, the gains and/or losses associated with flows across each arc *effectively* increase and/or decrease the supply available in the network. For example, consider what happens in Figure 5.16 if the supply of newspaper is reduced to 55 tons. Although it *appears* that the total supply in the network (175 tons) still exceeds the total demand (150 tons), if we try to solve the modified problem, Solver will tell us that the problem has no feasible solution. (You may verify this on your own.) So we are not able to satisfy all of the demand due to the loss of material that occurs in the production process.

The point being made here is that with generalized network flow problems, you cannot always tell before solving the problem if the total supply is adequate to meet the total demand. As a result, you cannot always know which balance-of-flow rule to apply. When the issue is unclear, it is safest[1] to first assume that all the demand can be met and (according to the balance-of-flow rule) use constraints of the form: Inflow − Outflow ≥ Supply or Demand. If the resulting problem is infeasible (and there are no errors in the model!), then we know all the demand cannot be satisfied and (according to the balance-of-flow rule) use constraints of the form: Inflow − Outflow ≤ Supply or Demand. In this later case, the solution will identify the least costly way of using the available supply to meet as much of the demand as possible.

Figures 5.20 and 5.21 show, respectively, the Solver parameters and optimal solution for this revised recycling problem with 55 tons of newspaper. Note that this solution uses all of the available supply of each of the recycling materials. Although the solution satisfies all the demand for newsprint pulp and packaging paper pulp, it falls almost 15 tons short of the total demand for print stock pulp.

[1] See question 3 at the end of this chapter for more on this issue.

FIGURE 5.20

Solver parameters for modified recycling problem

FIGURE 5.21

Optimal solution to modified recycling problem

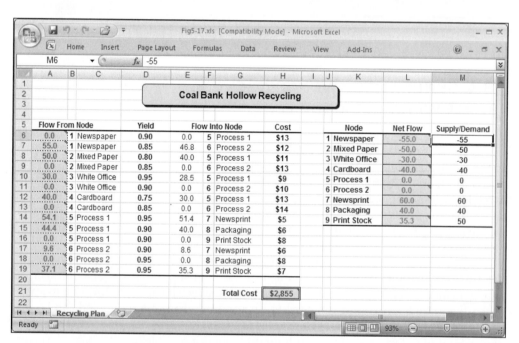

Important Modeling Point

For generalized network flow problems, the gains and/or losses associated with flows across each arc *effectively* increase and/or decrease the supply available in the network. As a result, it is sometimes difficult to tell in advance whether the total supply is adequate to meet the total demand in a generalized network flow problem. When in doubt, it is best to assume that the total supply is capable of satisfying the total demand and use Solver to prove (or refute) this assumption.

5.6 Maximal Flow Problems

The maximal flow problem (or max flow problem) is a type of network flow problem in which the goal is to determine the maximum amount of flow that can occur in the network. In a maximal flow problem, the amount of flow that can occur over each arc is limited by some capacity restriction. This type of network might be used to model the flow of oil in a pipeline (in which the amount of oil that can flow through a pipe in a unit of time is limited by the diameter of the pipe). Traffic engineers also use this type of network to determine the maximum number of cars that can travel through a collection of streets with different capacities imposed by the number of lanes in the streets and speed limits. The following example illustrates a max flow problem.

5.6.1 AN EXAMPLE OF A MAXIMAL FLOW PROBLEM

The Northwest Petroleum Company operates an oil field and refinery in Alaska. The crude obtained from the oil field is pumped through the network of pumping substations shown in Figure 5.22 to the company's refinery located 500 miles from the oil field. The amount of oil that can flow through each of the pipelines, represented by the arcs in the network, varies due to differing pipe diameters. The numbers next to the arcs in the network indicate the maximum amount of oil that can flow through the various pipelines (measured in thousands of barrels per hour). The company wants to determine the maximum number of barrels per hour that can flow from the oil field to the refinery.

The max flow problem appears to be very different from the network flow models described earlier because it does not include specific supplies or demands for the nodes. However, you can solve the max flow problem in the same way as a transshipment

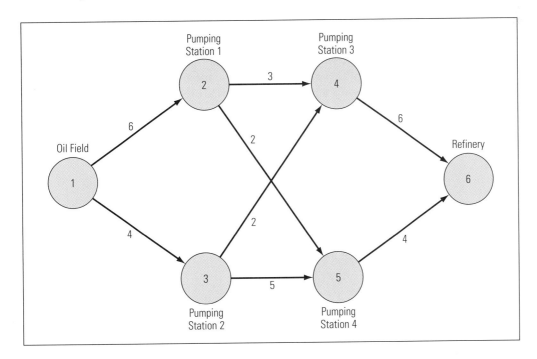

FIGURE 5.22

Network representation of Northwest Petroleum's oil refinery operation

FIGURE 5.23

Network structure of Northwest Petroleum's max flow problem

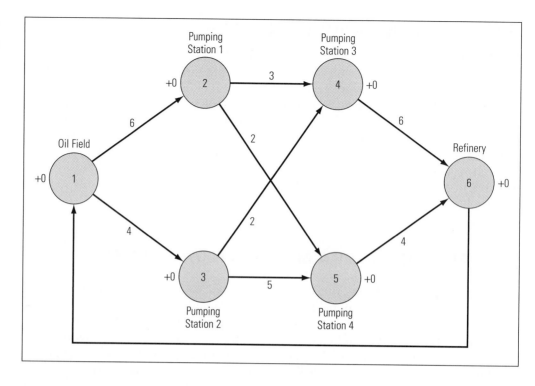

problem if you add a return arc from the ending node to the starting node, assign a demand of 0 to all the nodes in the network, and attempt to maximize the flow over the return arc. Figure 5.23 shows these modifications to the problem.

To understand the network in Figure 5.23, suppose that k units are shipped from node 6 to node 1 (where k represents some integer). Because node 6 has a supply of 0, it can send k units to node 1 only if these units can be returned through the network to node 6 (to balance the flow at node 6). The capacities on the arcs limit how many units can be returned to node 6. Therefore, the maximum flow through the network corresponds to the largest number of units that can be shipped from node 6 to node 1 and then returned through the network to node 6 (to balance the flow at this node). We can solve an LP model to determine the maximal flow by maximizing the flow from node 6 to node 1, given appropriate upper bounds on each arc and the usual balance-of-flow constraints. This model is represented as:

$$\text{MAX:} \qquad X_{61}$$

$$\text{Subject to:} \qquad +X_{61} - X_{12} - X_{13} = 0$$
$$+X_{12} - X_{24} - X_{25} = 0$$
$$+X_{13} - X_{34} - X_{35} = 0$$
$$+X_{24} + X_{34} - X_{46} = 0$$
$$+X_{25} + X_{35} - X_{56} = 0$$
$$+X_{46} + X_{56} - X_{61} = 0$$

with the following bounds on the decision variables:

$$0 \le X_{12} \le 6 \qquad 0 \le X_{25} \le 2 \qquad 0 \le X_{46} \le 6$$
$$0 \le X_{13} \le 4 \qquad 0 \le X_{34} \le 2 \qquad 0 \le X_{56} \le 4$$
$$0 \le X_{24} \le 3 \qquad 0 \le X_{35} \le 5 \qquad 0 \le X_{61} \le \infty$$

5.6.2 THE SPREADSHEET MODEL AND SOLUTION

This model is implemented in the spreadsheet shown in Figure 5.24 (and in the file Fig5-24.xls on your data disk). This spreadsheet model differs from the earlier network models in a few minor, but important, ways. First, column G in Figure 5.24 represents the upper bounds for each arc. Second, the objective function (or set cell) is represented by cell B16, which contains the formula:

$$\text{Formula in cell B16:} \qquad =\text{B14}$$

Cell B14 represents the flow from node 6 to node 1 (or X_{61}). This cell corresponds to the variable that we want to maximize in the objective function of the LP model. The Solver parameters and options shown in Figure 5.25 are used to obtain the optimal solution shown in Figure 5.24.

Because the arcs leading to node 6 (X_{46} and X_{56}) have a total capacity for 10 units of flow, it might be surprising to learn that only 9 units can flow through the network. However, the optimal solution shown in Figure 5.24 indicates that the maximal flow through the network is just 9 units.

The optimal flows identified in Figure 5.24 for each arc are shown in the boxes next to the capacities for each arc in Figure 5.26. In Figure 5.26, the arc from node 5 to node 6 is at its full capacity of 4 units, whereas the arc from node 4 to node 6 is 1 unit below its full capacity of 6 units. Although the arc from node 4 to node 6 can carry 1 additional unit of flow, it is prevented from doing so because all the arcs flowing to node 4 (X_{24} and X_{34}) are at full capacity.

FIGURE 5.24

Spreadsheet model and solution to Northwest Petroleum's max flow problem

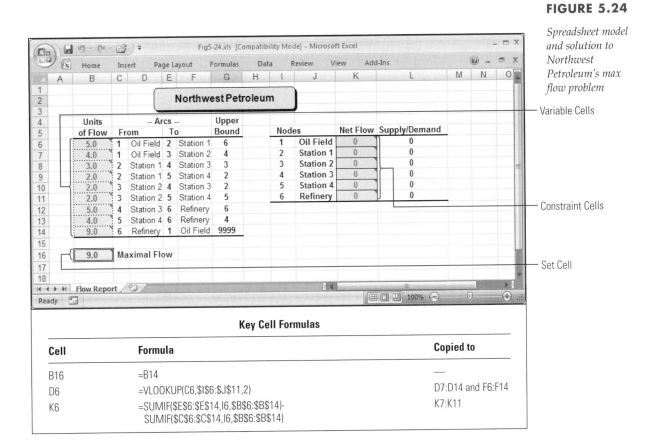

Key Cell Formulas

Cell	Formula	Copied to
B16	=B14	—
D6	=VLOOKUP(C6,$I$6:$J$11,2)	D7:D14 and F6:F14
K6	=SUMIF($E$6:$E$14,I6,$B$6:$B$14)- SUMIF($C$6:$C$14,I6,$B$6:$B$14)	K7:K11

FIGURE 5.25

Solver parameters for Northwest Petroleum's max flow problem

FIGURE 5.26

Network representation of the solution to Northwest Petroleum's max flow problem

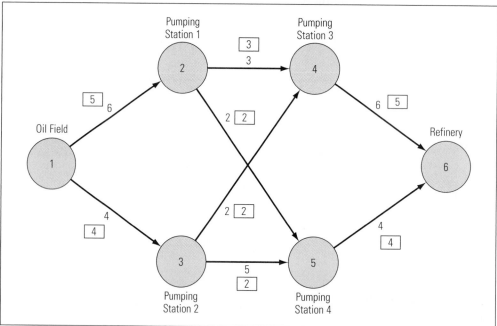

A graph like Figure 5.26, which summarizes the optimal flows in a max flow problem, is helpful in identifying where increases in flow capacity would be most effective. For example, from this graph, we can see that even though X_{24} and X_{34} are both at full capacity, increasing their capacity will not necessarily increase the flow through the network. Increasing the capacity of X_{24} would allow for an increased flow through the network because an additional unit could then flow from node 1 to node 2 to node 4 to node 6. However, increasing the capacity of X_{34} would not allow for an increase in the total flow because the arc from node 1 to node 3 is already at full capacity.

5.7 Special Modeling Considerations

A number of special conditions can arise in network flow problems that require a bit of creativity to model accurately. For example, it is easy to impose minimum or maximum flow restrictions on individual arcs in the networks by placing appropriate lower and upper bounds on the corresponding decision variables. However, in some network flow problems, minimum or maximum flow requirements may apply to the *total* flow emanating from a given node. For example, consider the network flow problem shown in Figure 5.27.

Now suppose that the total flow into node 3 must be at least 50 and the total flow into node 4 must be at least 60. We could enforce these conditions easily with the following constraints:

$$X_{13} + X_{23} \geq 50$$
$$X_{14} + X_{24} \geq 60$$

Unfortunately, these constraints do not conform to the balance-of-flow rule and would require us to impose *side constraints* on the model. An alternative approach to modeling this problem is shown in Figure 5.28.

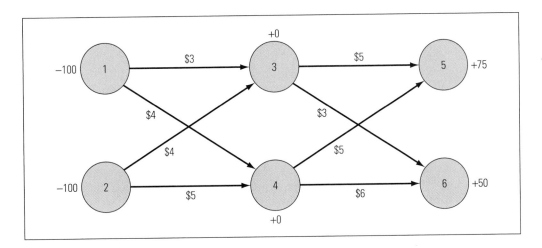

FIGURE 5.27

Example network flow problem

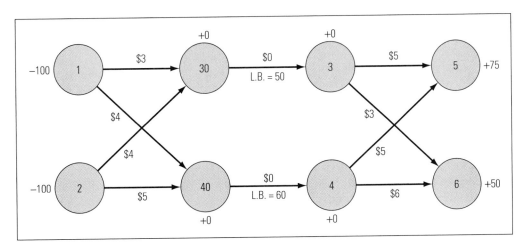

FIGURE 5.28

Revised network flow problem with lower bounds on the total flow into nodes 3 and 4

FIGURE 5.29

*Alternative
networks allowing
two different types
of flow between
two nodes*

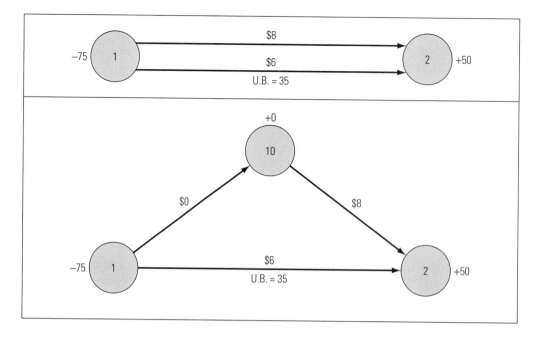

Two additional nodes and arcs were inserted in Figure 5.28. Note that the arc from node 30 to node 3 has a lower bound (L.B.) of 50. This will ensure that at least 50 units flow into node 3. Node 3 then must distribute this flow to nodes 5 and 6. Similarly, the arc connecting node 40 to node 4 ensures that at least 60 units will flow into node 4. The additional nodes and arcs added to Figure 5.28 are sometimes referred to as *dummy nodes* and *dummy arcs*.

As another example, consider the network in the upper portion of Figure 5.29 in which the flow between two nodes can occur at two different costs. One arc has a cost of $6 per unit of flow and an upper bound (U.B.) of 35. The other arc has a cost of $8 per unit of flow with no upper bound on the amount of flow allowed. Note that the minimum cost solution is to send 35 units of flow from node 1 to node 2 across the $6 arc and 15 units from node 1 to node 2 across the $8 arc.

To model this problem mathematically, we would like to have two arcs called X_{12} because both arcs go from node 1 to node 2. However, if both arcs are called X_{12}, there is no way to distinguish one from the other! A solution to this dilemma is shown in the lower portion of Figure 5.29 in which we inserted a dummy node and a dummy arc. Thus, there are now two distinct arcs flowing into node 2: X_{12} and $X_{10,2}$. Flow from node 1 to node 2 across the $8 arc now must first go through node 10.

As a final example, note that upper bounds (or capacity restrictions) on the arcs in a network flow might *effectively* limit the amount of supply that can be sent through the network to meet the demand. As a result, in a network flow problem with flow restrictions (upper bounds) on the arcs, it is sometimes difficult to tell in advance whether the total demand can be met—even if the total supply available exceeds the total demand. This again creates a potential problem in knowing which balance-of-flow rule to use. Consider the example in Figure 5.30.

The upper portion of Figure 5.30 shows a network with a total supply of 200 and total demand of 155. Because the total supply appears to exceed the total demand, we are inclined to apply the balance-of-flow rule that would generate constraints of the form: Inflow − Outflow ≥ Supply or Demand. This balance of flow rule requires the total

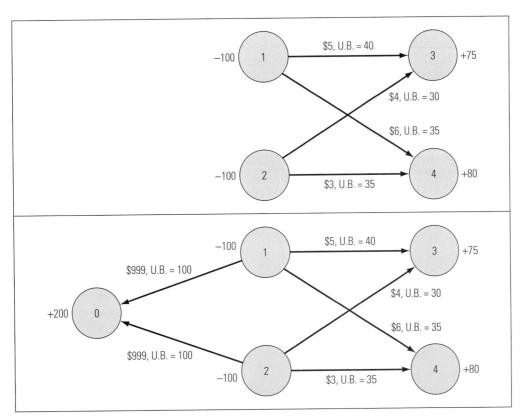

FIGURE 5.30

Example of using a dummy demand node

inflow to nodes 3 and 4 to be greater than or equal to their demands of 75 and 80, respectively. However, the upper bounds on the arcs leading into node 3 limit the total flow into this node to 70 units. Similarly, the total flow into node 4 is limited to 70. As a result, there is no feasible solution to the problem. In this case, we cannot resolve the infeasibility by reversing the constraints to be of the form: Inflow − Outflow ≤ Supply or Demand. Although this allows for less than the total amount demanded to be sent to nodes 3 and 4, it now *requires* all the supply to be sent out of nodes 1 and 2. Clearly, some of the 200 units of supply available from nodes 1 and 2 will have nowhere to go if the total flow into nodes 3 and 4 cannot exceed 140 units (as required by the upper bounds on the arcs).

A solution to this predicament is shown in the bottom half of Figure 5.30. Here, we added a dummy demand node (node 0) that is connected directly to nodes 1 and 2 with arcs that impose very large costs on flows to the dummy node. Note that the demand at this dummy node is equal to the total supply in the network. Now, the total demand exceeds the total supply so the balance-of-flow rule mandates we use constraints of the form: Inflow − Outflow ≤ Supply or Demand. Again, this allows for less than the total amount demanded to be sent to nodes 0, 3, and 4 but *requires* all the supply to be sent out of nodes 1 and 2. Due to the large costs associated with flows from nodes 1 and 2 to the dummy demand node, Solver will ensure that as much of the supply as possible is first sent to nodes 3 and 4. Any remaining supply at nodes 1 and 2 would then be sent to the dummy node. Of course, flows to the dummy node actually represent excess supply or inventory at nodes 1 and 2 that would not actually be shipped anywhere or incur any costs. But using a dummy node in this manner allows us to model and solve the problem accurately.

Dummy nodes and arcs can be helpful in modeling a variety of situations that occur naturally in network problems. The techniques illustrated here are three "tricks of the trade" in network modeling and might prove useful in some of the problems at the end of this chapter.

5.8 Minimal Spanning Tree Problems

Another type of network problem is known as the minimal spanning tree problem. This type of problem cannot be solved as an LP problem, but is solved easily using a simple manual algorithm.

For a network with n nodes, a **spanning tree** is a set of $n - 1$ arcs that connects all the nodes and contains no loops. A minimum spanning tree problem involves determining the set of arcs that connects all the nodes in a network while minimizing the total length (or cost) of the selected arcs. Consider the following example.

> Jon Fleming is responsible for setting up a local area network (LAN) in the design engineering department of Windstar Aerospace Company. A LAN consists of a number of individual computers connected to a centralized computer or file server. Each computer in the LAN can access information from the file server and communicate with the other computers in the LAN.
>
> Installing a LAN involves connecting all the computers together with communications cables. Not every computer has to be connected directly to the file server, but there must be some link between each computer in the network. Figure 5.31 summarizes all the possible connections that Jon could make. Each node in this figure represents one of the computers to be included in the LAN. Each line connecting the nodes represents a possible connection between pairs of computers. The dollar amount on each line represents the cost of making the connection.

The arcs in Figure 5.31 have no specific directional orientation, indicating that information can move in either direction across the arcs. Also note that the communication

FIGURE 5.31

Network representation of Windstar Aerospace's minimal spanning tree problem

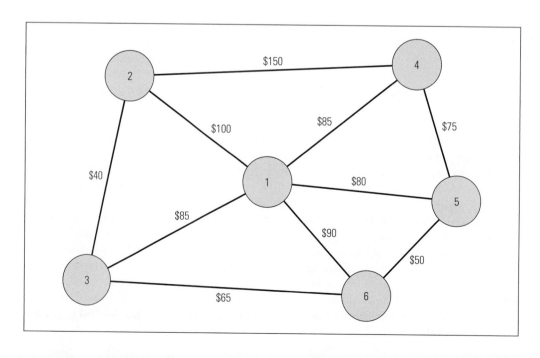

links represented by the arcs do not exist yet. Jon's challenge is to determine which links to establish. Because the network involves $n = 6$ nodes, a spanning tree for this problem consists of $n - 1 = 5$ arcs that results in a path existing between any pair of nodes. The objective is to find the minimal (least costly) spanning tree for this problem.

5.8.1 AN ALGORITHM FOR THE MINIMAL SPANNING TREE PROBLEM

You can apply a simple algorithm to solve minimal spanning tree problems. The steps to this algorithm are:

1. Select any node. Call this the current subnetwork.
2. Add to the current subnetwork the cheapest arc that connects any node within the current subnetwork to any node not in the current subnetwork. (Ties for the cheapest arc can be broken arbitrarily.) Call this the current subnetwork.
3. If all the nodes are in the subnetwork, stop; this is the optimal solution. Otherwise, return to step 2.

5.8.2 SOLVING THE EXAMPLE PROBLEM

You can program this algorithm easily or, for simple problems, execute it manually. The following steps illustrate how to execute the algorithm manually for the example problem shown in Figure 5.31.

Step 1. If we select node 1 in Figure 5.31, then node 1 is the current subnetwork.

Step 2. The cheapest arc connecting the current subnetwork to a node not in the current subnetwork is the $80 arc connecting nodes 1 and 5. This arc and node 5 are added to the current subnetwork.

Step 3. Four nodes (nodes 2, 3, 4, and 6) remain unconnected—therefore, return to step 2.

Step 2. The cheapest arc connecting the current subnetwork to a node not in the current subnetwork is the $50 arc connecting nodes 5 and 6. This arc and node 6 are added to the current subnetwork.

Step 3. Three nodes (nodes 2, 3, and 4) remain unconnected—therefore, return to step 2.

Step 2. The cheapest arc connecting the current subnetwork to a node not in the current subnetwork is the $65 arc connecting nodes 6 and 3. This arc and node 3 are added to the current subnetwork.

Step 3. Two nodes (nodes 2 and 4) remain unconnected—therefore, return to step 2.

Step 2. The cheapest arc connecting the current subnetwork to a node not in the current subnetwork is the $40 arc connecting nodes 3 and 2. This arc and node 2 are added to the current subnetwork.

Step 3. One node (node 4) remains unconnected—therefore, return to step 2.

Step 2. The cheapest arc connecting the current subnetwork to a node not in the current subnetwork is the $75 arc connecting nodes 5 and 4. This arc and node 4 are added to the current subnetwork.

Step 3. All the nodes are now connected. Stop; the current subnetwork is optimal.

Figure 5.32 shows the optimal (minimal) spanning tree generated by this algorithm. The algorithm described here produces the optimal (minimal) spanning tree regardless

FIGURE 5.32

Optimal solution to Windstar Aerospace's minimal spanning tree problem

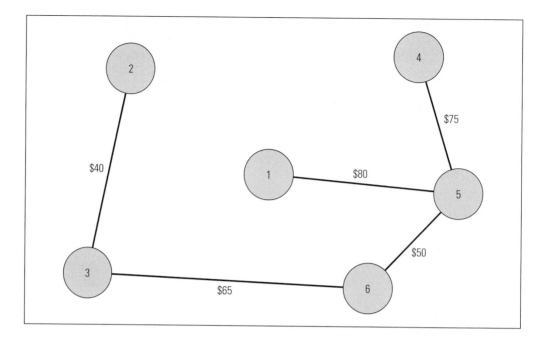

of which node is selected initially in step 1. You can verify this by solving the example problem again starting with a different node in step 1.

5.9 Summary

This chapter presented several business problems modeled as network flow problems, including transshipment problems, shortest path problems, maximal flow problems, transportation/assignment problems, and generalized network flow models. It also introduced the minimal spanning tree problem and presented a simple algorithm for solving this type of problem manually.

Although special algorithms exist for solving network flow problems, you can also formulate and solve them as LP problems. The constraints in an LP formulation of a network flow problem have a special structure that enables you to implement and solve these models easily in a spreadsheet. Although there might be more efficient ways of solving network flow problems, the methods discussed in this chapter are often the most practical. For extremely complex network flow problems, you might need to use a specialized algorithm. Unfortunately, you are unlikely to find this type of software at your local software store. However, various network optimization packages can be found in the technical/scientific directories on the Internet.

5.10 References

Glassey, R. and V. Gupta. "A Linear Programming Analysis of Paper Recycling," *Studies in Mathematical Programming*. New York: North–Holland, 1978.

Glover, F. and D. Klingman. "Network Applications in Industry and Government," *AIIE Transactions*, vol. 9, no. 4, 1977.

Glover, F., D. Klingman, and N. Phillips. *Network Models and Their Applications in Practice*. New York: Wiley, 1992.

Hansen, P. and R. Wendell. "A Note on Airline Commuting," *Interfaces*, vol. 11, no. 12, 1982.

Phillips, D. and A. Diaz. *Fundamentals of Network Analysis*. Englewood Cliffs, NJ: Prentice Hall, 1981.

Vemuganti, R., et al. "Network Models for Fleet Management," *Decision Sciences*, vol. 20, Winter 1989.

THE WORLD OF MANAGEMENT SCIENCE

Yellow Freight System Boosts Profits and Quality with Network Optimization

One of the largest motor carriers in the United States, Yellow Freight System, Inc. of Overland Park, Kansas, uses network modeling and optimization to assist management in load planning, routing empty trucks, routing trailers, dropping or adding direct service routes, and strategic planning of terminal size and location. The system, called SYSNET, operates on a network of Sun workstations optimizing over a million network flow variables. The company also uses a tactical planning room equipped with graphical display tools that allow planning meetings to be conducted interactively with the system.

The company competes in the less—than—truckload (LTL) segment of the trucking market. That is, they contract for shipments of any size, regardless of whether the shipment fills the trailer. To operate efficiently, Yellow Freight must consolidate and transfer shipments at 23 break—bulk terminals located throughout the United States. At these terminals, shipments might be reloaded into different trailers depending on the final destination. Each break—bulk terminal serves several end—of—line terminals, in a hub—and—spoke network. Normally, shipments are sent by truck to the break—bulk dedicated to the origination point. Local managers occasionally try to save costs by loading direct, which means bypassing a break—bulk and sending a truckload of consolidated shipments directly to the final destination. Before SYSNET, these decisions were made in the field without accurate information on how they would affect costs and reliability in the entire system.

Since its implementation in 1989, SYSNET has scored high with upper management. Often, the first response to a new proposal is, "Has it been run through SYSNET?" The benefits attributed to the new system include:

- an increase of 11.6% in freight loaded directly, saving $4.7 million annually
- better routing of trailers, saving $1 million annually
- savings of $1.42 million annually by increasing the average number of pounds loaded per trailer
- reduction in claims for damaged merchandise
- a 27% reduction in the number of late deliveries
- tactical planning projects with SYSNET in 1990 that identified $10 million in annual savings

Equally important has been the effect on the management philosophy and culture at Yellow Freight. Management now has greater control over network operations; tradition, intuition, and "gut feel" have been replaced with formal analytical tools; and Yellow Freight is better able to act as a partner with customers in total quality management and just—in—time inventory systems.

Source: Braklow, John W., William W. Graham, Stephen M. Hassler, Ken E. Peck and Warren B. Powell, "Interactive Optimization Improves Service and Performance for Yellow Freight System," *Interfaces*, 22:1, January—February 1992, pages 147—172.

Questions and Problems

1. This chapter followed the convention of using negative numbers to represent the supply at a node and positive numbers to represent the demand at a node. Another convention is just the opposite—using positive numbers to represent supply and negative numbers to represent demand. How would the balance-of-flow rule presented in this chapter need to be changed to accommodate this alternate convention?

2. To use the balance-of-flow rule presented in this chapter, constraints for supply nodes must have negative RHS values. Some LP software packages cannot solve problems in which the constraints have negative RHS values. How should the balance-of-flow rules be modified to produce LP models that can be solved with such software packages?

3. Consider the revised Coal Bank Hollow recycling problem discussed in section 5.5.4 of this chapter. We said that it is safest to assume the supply in a generalized network flow problem is capable of meeting the demand (until Solver proves otherwise).

   a. Solve the problem in Figure 5.17 (and file Fig5-17.xls on your data disk) assuming 80 tons of newspaper is available and that the supply is NOT adequate to meet the demand. How much of each of the raw recycling materials is used? How much demand for each product is met? What is the cost of this solution?

   b. Solve the problem again assuming that the supply is adequate to meet the demand. How much of each of the raw recycling materials is used? How much demand for each product is met? What is the cost of this solution?

   c. Which one is better? Why?

   d. Suppose there are 55 tons of newspaper available. Figure 5.21 shows the least cost solution for distributing the supply in this case. In that solution, the demand for newsprint pulp and packaging pulp is met but we are almost 15 tons short on print stock pulp. How much can this shortage be reduced (without creating shortages of the other products) and how much extra would it cost to do so?

4. Consider the generalized transportation problem shown in Figure 5.33. How can this problem be transformed into an equivalent transportation problem? Draw the network for the equivalent problem.

FIGURE 5.33

Graph of a generalized network flow problem

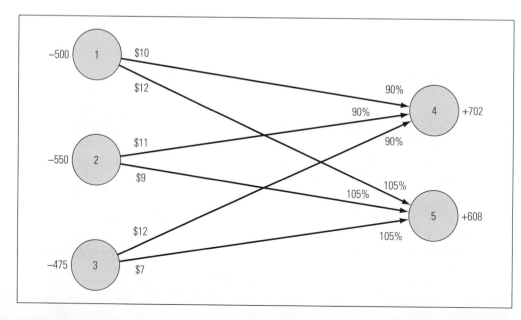

5. Draw the network representation of the following network flow problem.

MIN: $+7X_{12} + 6X_{14} + 3X_{23} + 4X_{24} + 5X_{32} + 9X_{43} + 8X_{52} + 5X_{54}$

Subject to: $-X_{12} - X_{14} = -5$

$+X_{12} + X_{52} + X_{32} - X_{23} - X_{24} = +4$

$-X_{32} + X_{23} + X_{43} = +8$

$+X_{14} + X_{24} + X_{54} - X_{43} = +0$

$-X_{52} - X_{54} = -7$

$X_{ij} \geq 0$ for all i and j

6. Draw the network representation of the following network flow problem. What kind of network flow problem is this?

MIN: $+2X_{13} + 6X_{14} + 5X_{15} + 4X_{23} + 3X_{24} + 7X_{25}$

Subject to: $-X_{13} - X_{14} - X_{15} = -8$

$-X_{23} - X_{24} - X_{25} = -7$

$+X_{13} + X_{23} \qquad\qquad = +5$

$+X_{14} + X_{24} \qquad\qquad = +5$

$+X_{15} + X_{25} \qquad\qquad = +5$

$X_{ij} \geq 0$ for all i and j

7. Refer to the equipment replacement problem discussed in section 5.3 of this chapter. In addition to the lease costs described for the problem, suppose that it costs Compu-Train $2,000 extra in labor costs whenever they replace their existing computers with new ones. What effect does this have on the formulation and solution of the problem? Which of the two leasing contracts is optimal in this case?

8. Suppose the X's in the following table indicate locations where fire sprinkler heads need to be installed in an existing building. The S indicates the location of the water source to supply these sprinklers. Assume that pipe can be run only vertically or horizontally (not diagonally) between the water source and the sprinkler heads.

	1	2	3	4	5	6	7
1		X					
2	X	X	X		X	X	X
3	X		X		X	X	X
4	X	X	X			X	X
5	X	X	X		X		X
6							
7	X						
8				S			X

a. Create a spanning tree showing how water can be brought to all the sprinkler heads using a minimal amount of pipe.

b. Suppose that it takes 10 feet of pipe to connect each cell in the table to each adjacent cell. How much pipe does your solution require?

9. SunNet is a residential Internet Service Provider (ISP) in the central Florida area. Presently, the company operates one centralized facility that all of its clients call into for Internet access. To improve service, the company is planning to open three satellite offices in the cities of Pine Hills, Eustis, and Sanford. The company has identified five different regions to be serviced by these three offices. The following table summarizes the number of customers in each region, the service capacity at each

office, and the average monthly per customer cost of providing service to each region from each office. Table entries of "n.a." indicate infeasible region-to-service-center combinations. SunNet would like to determine how many customers from each region to assign to each service center to minimize cost.

Region	Pine Hills	Eustis	Sanford	Customers
1	$6.50	$7.50	n.a.	30,000
2	$7.00	$8.00	n.a.	40,000
3	$8.25	$7.25	$6.75	25,000
4	n.a.	$7.75	$7.00	35,000
5	n.a.	$7.50	$6.75	33,000
Capacity	60,000	70,000	40,000	

a. Draw a network flow model to represent this problem.
b. Implement your model in Excel and solve it.
c. What is the optimal solution?

10. Acme Manufacturing makes a variety of household appliances at a single manufacturing facility. The expected demand for one of these appliances during the next four months is shown in the following table along with the expected production costs and the expected capacity for producing these items.

	Month			
	1	2	3	4
Demand	420	580	310	540
Production Cost	$49.00	$45.00	$46.00	$47.00
Production Capacity	500	520	450	550

Acme estimates that it costs $1.50 per month for each unit of this appliance carried in inventory at the end of each month. Currently, Acme has 120 units in inventory on hand for this product. To maintain a level workforce, the company wants to produce at least 400 units per month. They also want to maintain a safety stock of at least 50 units per month. Acme wants to determine how many of each appliance to manufacture during each of the next four months to meet the expected demand at the lowest possible total cost.

a. Draw a network flow model for this problem.
b. Create a spreadsheet model for this problem and solve it using Solver.
c. What is the optimal solution?
d. How much money could Acme save if they were willing to drop the restriction about producing at least 400 units per month?

11. Sunrise Swimwear manufactures ladies' swimwear in January through June of each year that is sold through retail outlets in March through August. The following table summarizes the monthly production capacity and retail demand (in 1000s), and inventory carrying costs (per 1000).

Month	Capacity	Demand	Carrying Cost	
			First Month	Other Months
January	16	—	$110	$55
February	18	—	$110	$55
March	20	14	$120	$55
April	28	20	$135	$55
May	29	26	$150	$55
June	36	33	$155	$55
July	—	28	—	—
August	—	10	—	—

a. Draw a network flow representation of this problem.
b. Implement a spreadsheet model for this problem.
c. What is the optimal solution?

12. Jacobs Manufacturing produces a popular custom accessory for pickup trucks at plants in Huntington, West Virginia and Bakersfield, California, and ships them to distributors in Dallas, Texas; Chicago, Illinois; Denver, Colorado; and Atlanta, Georgia. The plants in Huntington and Bakersfield have, respectively, the capacity to produce 3,000 and 4,000 units per month. For the month of October, costs of shipping a carton of 10 units from each plant to each distributor are summarized in the following table:

| | Shipping Cost per Container | | | |
	Dallas	Chicago	Denver	Atlanta
Huntington	$19	$15	$14	$12
Bakersfield	$16	$18	$11	$13

Jacobs has been notified that these shipping rates will each increase by $1.50 on November 1. Each distributor has ordered 1,500 units of Jacobs' product for October and 2,000 units for November. In any month, Jacobs can send each distributor up to 500 units more than they have ordered if Jacobs provides a $2 per unit discount on the excess (which the distributor must hold in inventory from one month to the next). In October, the per unit cost of production in Huntington and Bakersfield are $12 and $16, respectively. In November, Jacobs expects the cost of production at both plants to be $14 per unit. The company wants to develop production and distribution plan for the months of October and November that would allow them to meet the expected demand from each distributor at the minimum cost.

a. Draw a network flow model for this problem.
b. Implement your model in a spreadsheet and solve it.
c. What is the optimal solution?

13. A construction company wants to determine the optimal replacement policy for the earth mover it owns. The company has a policy of not keeping an earth mover for more than five years, and has estimated the annual operating costs and trade-in values for earth movers during each of the five years they might be kept as:

| | Age in Years | | | | |
	0-1	1-2	2-3	3-4	4-5
Operating Cost	$8,000	$9,100	$10,700	$9,200	$11,000
Trade-in Value	$14,000	$9,000	$6,000	$3,500	$2,000

Assume that new earth movers currently cost $25,000 and are increasing in cost by 4.5% per year. The company wants to determine when it should plan on replacing its current, 2-year-old earth mover. Use a 5-year planning horizon.

a. Draw the network representation of this problem.
b. Write out the LP formulation of this problem.
c. Solve the problem using Solver. Interpret your solution.

14. The Ortega Food Company needs to ship 100 cases of hot tamales from its warehouse in San Diego to a distributor in New York City at minimum cost. The costs associated with shipping 100 cases between various cities are:

From	Los Angeles	Denver	St. Louis	To Memphis	Chicago	New York
San Diego	5	13	—	45	—	105
Los Angeles	—	27	19	50	—	95
Denver	—	—	14	30	32	—
St. Louis	—	14	—	35	24	—
Memphis	—	—	35	—	18	25
Chicago	—	—	24	18	—	17

a. Draw the network representation of this problem.
b. Write out the LP formulation of this problem.
c. Solve the problem using Solver. Interpret your solution.

15. A cotton grower in south Georgia produces cotton on farms in Statesboro and Brooklet, ships it to cotton gins in Claxton and Millen, where it is processed, and then sends it to distribution centers in Savannah, Perry, and Valdosta, where it is sold to customers for $60 per ton. Any surplus cotton is sold to a government warehouse in Hinesville for $25 per ton. The cost of growing and harvesting a ton of cotton at the farms in Statesboro and Brooklet is $20 and $22, respectively. There are presently 700 and 500 tons of cotton available in Statesboro and Brooklet, respectively. The cost of transporting the cotton from the farms to the gins and the government warehouse is shown in the following table:

	Claxton	Millen	Hinesville
Statesboro	$4.00	$3.00	$4.50
Brooklet	$3.5	$3.00	$3.50

The gin in Claxton has the capacity to process 700 tons of cotton at a cost of $10 per ton. The gin in Millen can process 600 tons at a cost of $11 per ton. Each gin must use at least one half of its available capacity. The cost of shipping a ton of cotton from each gin to each distribution center is summarized in the following table:

	Savannah	Perry	Valdosta
Claxton	$10	$16	$15
Millen	$12	$18	$17

Assume that the demand for cotton in Savannah, Perry, and Valdosta is 400, 300, and 450 tons, respectively.
a. Draw a network flow model to represent this problem.
b. Implement your model in Excel and solve it.
c. What is the optimal solution?

16. The blood bank wants to determine the least expensive way to transport available blood donations from Pittsburg and Staunton to hospitals in Charleston, Roanoke, Richmond, Norfolk, and Suffolk. The supply and demand for donated blood is shown in Figure 5.34 along with the unit cost of shipping along each possible arc.
a. Create a spreadsheet model for this problem.
b. What is the optimal solution?
c. Suppose that no more than 1000 units of blood can be transported over any one arc. What is the optimal solution to this revised problem?

17. A furniture manufacturer has warehouses in cities represented by nodes 1, 2, and 3 in Figure 5.35. The values on the arcs indicate the per unit shipping costs required to transport living room suites between the various cities. The supply of living room

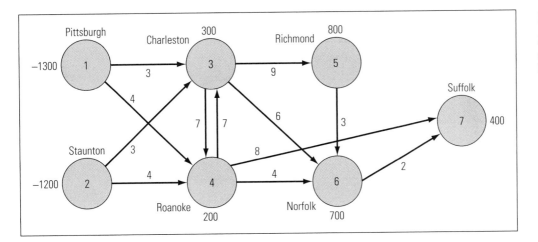

FIGURE 5.34

Network flow model for the blood bank problem

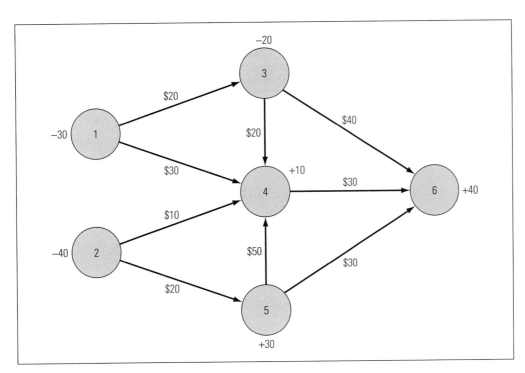

FIGURE 5.35

Network flow model for the furniture manufacturing problem

suites at each warehouse is indicated by the negative number next to nodes 1, 2, and 3. The demand for living room suites is indicated by the positive number next to the remaining nodes.

a. Identify the supply, demand, and transshipment nodes in this problem.

b. Use Solver to determine the least costly shipping plan for this problem.

18. The graph in Figure 5.36 represents various flows that can occur through a sewage treatment plant with the numbers on the arcs representing the maximum flow (in tons of sewage per hour) that can be accommodated. Formulate an LP model to determine the maximum tons of sewage per hour that can be processed by this plant.

19. A company has three warehouses that supply four stores with a given product. Each warehouse has 30 units of the product. Stores 1, 2, 3, and 4 require 20, 25, 30,

FIGURE 5.36

Network flow model for the sewage treatment plant

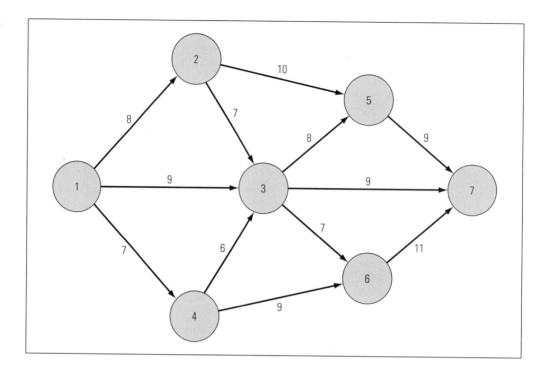

and 35 units of the product, respectively. The per unit shipping costs from each warehouse to each store are:

	Store			
Warehouse	1	2	3	4
1	5	4	6	5
2	3	6	4	4
3	4	3	3	2

a. Draw the network representation of this problem. What kind of problem is this?
b. Formulate an LP model to determine the least expensive shipping plan to fill the demands at the stores.
c. Solve the problem using Solver.
d. Suppose that shipments are not allowed between warehouse 1 and store 2 or between warehouse 2 and store 3. What is the easiest way to modify the spreadsheet so that you can solve this modified problem? What is the optimal solution to the modified problem?

20. A used-car broker needs to transport his inventory of cars from locations 1 and 2 in Figure 5.37 to used-car auctions being held at locations 4 and 5. The costs of transporting cars along each of the routes are indicated on the arcs. The trucks used to carry the cars can hold a maximum of 10 cars. Therefore, the maximum number of cars that can flow over any arc is 10.

a. Formulate an LP model to determine the least costly method of distributing the cars from locations 1 and 2 so that 20 cars will be available for sale at location 4, and 10 cars will be available for sale at location 5.
b. Use Solver to find the optimal solution to this problem.

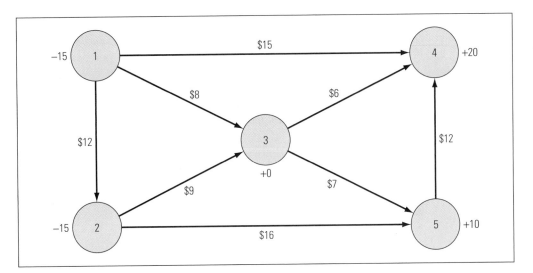

FIGURE 5.37

Network flow model for the used car problem

21. An information systems consultant who lives in Dallas must spend the majority of the month of March onsite with a client in San Diego. Her travel schedule for the month is as follows:

Leave Dallas	Leave San Diego
Monday, March 2	Friday, March 6
Monday, March 9	Thursday, March 12
Tuesday, March 17	Friday, March 20
Monday, March 23	Wednesday, March 25

The usual round-trip ticket price between Dallas and San Diego is $750. However, the airline offers a 25% discount if the dates on a round-trip ticket cover less than 7 nights and include a weekend. A 35% discount is offered for round-trip tickets covering 10 or more nights, and a 45% discount is available for round-trip tickets covering 20 or more nights. The consultant can purchase four round-trip tickets in any manner that allows her to leave Dallas and San Diego on the days indicated.
   a. Draw a network flow model for this problem.
   b. Implement the problem in a spreadsheet and solve it.
   c. What is the optimal solution? How much does this save for four full-cost round-trip tickets?
22. The Conch Oil Company needs to transport 30 million barrels of crude oil from a port in Doha, Qatar in the Persian Gulf to three refineries throughout Europe. The refineries are in Rotterdam, Netherlands; Toulon, France; and Palermo, Italy, and require 6 million, 15 million, and 9 million barrels, respectively. The oil can be transported to the refineries in three different ways. First, oil may be shipped from Qatar to Rotterdam, Toulon, and Palermo on supertankers traveling around Africa at costs of $1.20, $1.40, and $1.35 per barrel, respectively. Conch is contractually obligated to send at least 25% of its oil via these supertankers. Alternatively, oil can be shipped from Doha to Suez, Egypt, at a cost of $0.35 per barrel, then through the Suez Canal to Port Said at a cost of $0.20 per barrel, then from Port

Said to Rotterdam, Toulon, and Palermo at per barrel costs of $0.27, $0.23, and $0.19, respectively. Finally, up to 15 million barrels of the oil shipped from Doha to Suez can then be sent via pipeline Damietta, Egypt, at $0.16 per barrel. From Damietta, it can shipped to Rotterdam, Toulon, and Palermo at costs of $0.25, $0.20, and $0.15, respectively.

a. Draw a network flow model for this problem.
b. Implement your model in a spreadsheet and solve it.
c. What is the optimal solution?

23. Omega Airlines has several nonstop flights between Atlanta and Los Angeles every day. The schedules of these flights are shown in the following table.

Flight	Departs Atlanta	Arrives in L.A.	Flight	Departs L.A.	Arrive in Atlanta
1	6 am	8 am	1	5 am	9 am
2	8 am	10 am	2	6 am	10 am
3	10 am	Noon	3	9 am	1 pm
4	Noon	2 pm	4	Noon	4 pm
5	4 pm	6 pm	5	2 pm	6 pm
6	6 pm	8 pm	6	5 pm	9 pm
7	7 pm	9 pm	7	7 pm	11 pm

Omega wants to determine the optimal way of assigning flight crews to these different flights. The company wants to ensure that the crews always return to the city from which they left each day. FAA regulations require at least one hour of rest for flight crews between flights. However, flight crews become irritated if they are forced to wait for extremely long periods of time between flights, so Omega wants to find an assignment of flight schedules that minimizes these waiting periods.

a. Draw a network flow model for this problem.
b. Implement the problem in a spreadsheet and solve it.
c. What is the optimal solution? What is the longest period of time that a flight crew has to wait between flights, according to your solution?
d. Are there alternate optimal solutions to this problem? If so, do any alternate optimal solutions result in a smaller maximum waiting period between flights?

24. A residential moving company needs to move a family from city 1 to city 12 in Figure 5.38 where the numbers on the arcs represents the driving distance in miles between cities.

a. Create a spreadsheet model for this problem.
b. What is the optimal solution?
c. Suppose that the moving company gets paid by the mile and, as a result, wants to determine the longest path from city 1 to city 12. What is the optimal solution?
d. Now suppose that travel is permissible in either direction between cities 6 and 9. Describe the optimal solution to this problem.

25. Joe Jones wants to establish a construction fund (or sinking fund) to pay for a new bowling alley he is having built. Construction of the bowling alley is expected to take six months and cost $300,000. Joe's contract with the construction company requires him to make payments of $50,000 at the end of the second and fourth months, and a final payment of $200,000 at the end of the sixth month when the

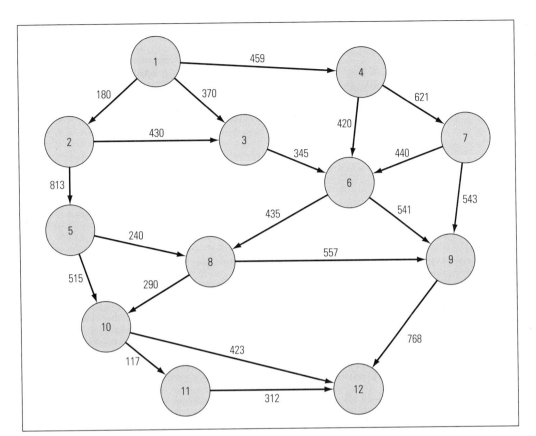

FIGURE 5.38

Network flow model for the moving company problem

bowling alley is completed. Joe has identified four investments that he can use to establish the construction fund; these investments are summarized in the following table:

Investment	Available in Month	Months to Maturity	Yield at Maturity
A	1, 2, 3, 4, 5, 6	1	1.2%
B	1, 3, 5	2	3.5%
C	1, 4	3	5.8%
D	1	6	11.0%

The table indicates that investment A will be available at the beginning of each of the next six months, and funds invested in this manner mature in one month with a yield of 1.2%. Similarly, funds can be placed in investment C only at the beginning of months 1 and/or 4, and mature at the end of three months with a yield of 5.8%. Joe wants to minimize the amount of money he must invest in month 1 to meet the required payments for this project.
a. Draw a network flow model for this problem.
b. Create a spreadsheet model for this problem and solve it.
c. What is the optimal solution?
26. Telephone calls for the YakLine, a discount long distance carrier, are routed through a variety of switching devices that interconnect various network hubs in different

cities. The maximum number of calls that can be handled by each segment of their network is shown in the following table:

Network Segments	Calls (in 1,000s)
Washington, DC to Chicago	800
Washington, DC to Kansas City	650
Washington, DC to Dallas	700
Chicago to Dallas	725
Chicago to Denver	700
Kansas City to Denver	750
Kansas City to Dallas	625
Denver to San Francisco	900
Dallas to San Francisco	725

YakLine wants to determine the maximum number of calls that can go from their east coast operations hub in Washington, DC to their west coast operations hub in San Francisco.

a. Draw a network flow model for this problem.
b. Create a spreadsheet model for this problem and solve it.
c. What is the optimal solution?

27. Union Express has 60 tons of cargo that needs to be shipped from Boston to Dallas. The shipping capacity on each of the routes Union Express planes fly each night is shown in the following table:

Nightly Flight Segments	Capacity (in tons)
Boston to Baltimore	30
Boston to Pittsburgh	25
Boston to Cincinnati	35
Baltimore to Atlanta	10
Baltimore to Cincinnati	5
Pittsburgh to Atlanta	15
Pittsburgh to Chicago	20
Cincinnati to Chicago	15
Cincinnati to Memphis	5
Atlanta to Memphis	25
Atlanta to Dallas	10
Chicago to Memphis	20
Chicago to Dallas	15
Memphis to Dallas	30
Memphis to Chicago	15

Will Union Express be able to move all 60 tons from Boston to Dallas in one night?

a. Draw a network flow model for this problem.
b. Create a spreadsheet model for the problem and solve it.
c. What is the maximum flow for this network?

28. E-mail messages sent over the Internet are broken up into electronic packets that may take a variety of different paths to reach their destination where the original message is reassembled. Suppose that the nodes in the graph shown in Figure 5.39 represent a series of computer hubs on the Internet and the arcs represent connections between them. Suppose that the values on the arcs represent the number of packets per minute (in 1,000,000s) that can be transmitted over each arc.

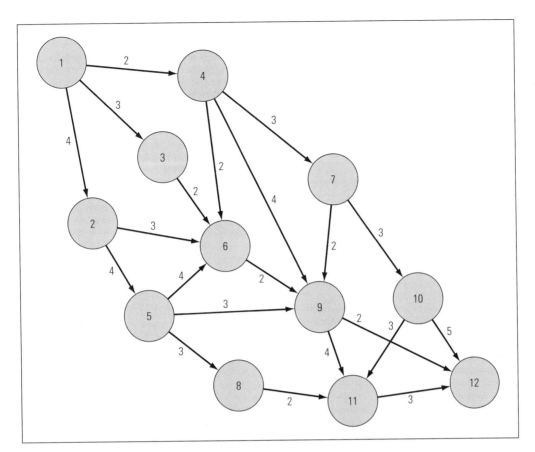

FIGURE 5.39

Network hubs and interconnections for the e-mail problem

a. Implement a network flow model to determine the maximum number of packets that can flow from node 1 to node 12 in one minute.
b. What is the maximum flow?
29. The Britts & Straggon company manufactures small engines at three different plants. From the plants, the engines are transported to two different warehouse facilities before being distributed to three wholesale distributors. The per unit manufacturing cost at each plant is shown in the following table in addition to the minimum required and maximum available daily production capacities.

Plant	Manufacturing Cost	Minimum Required Production	Maximum Production Capacity
1	$13	150	400
2	$15	150	300
3	$12	150	600

The unit cost of transporting engines from each plant to each warehouse is shown below.

Plant	Warehouse 1	Warehouse 2
1	$4	$5
2	$6	$4
3	$3	$5

FIGURE 5.40

Network flow model for the airport terminal problem

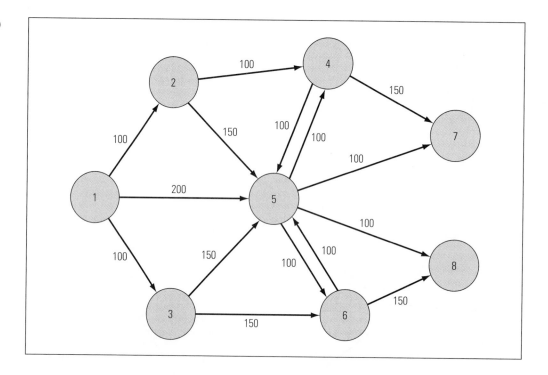

The unit cost of shipping engines from each warehouse to each distributor is shown in the following table along with the daily demand for each distributor.

Warehouse	Distributor 1	Distributor 2	Distributor 3
1	$6	$4	$3
2	$3	$5	$2
Demand	300	600	100

Each warehouse can process up to 500 engines per day.

a. Draw a network flow model to represent this problem.

b. Implement your model in Excel and solve it.

c. What is the optimal solution?

30. A new airport being built will have three terminals and two baggage pickup areas. An automated baggage delivery system has been designed to transport the baggage from each terminal to the two baggage pickup areas. This system is depicted graphically in Figure 5.40, where nodes 1, 2, and 3 represent the terminals, and nodes 7 and 8 represent the baggage pickup areas. The maximum number of bags per minute that can be handled by each part of the system is indicated by the value on each arc in the network.

a. Formulate an LP model to determine the maximum number of bags per minute that can be delivered by this system.

b. Use Solver to find the optimal solution to this problem.

31. Bull Dog Express runs a small airline that offers commuter flights between several cities in Georgia. The airline flies into and out of small airports only. These airports have limits on the number of flights Bull Dog Express can make each day. The airline can make five round-trip flights daily between Savannah and Macon, four round-trip flights daily between Macon and Albany, two round-trip flights daily between

Macon and Atlanta, two round-trip flights daily between Macon and Athens, two round-trip flights daily between Athens and Atlanta, and two round-trip flights daily from Albany to Atlanta. The airline wants to determine the maximum number of times connecting flights from Savannah to Atlanta can be offered in a single day.

a. Draw the network representation of this problem.

b. Formulate an LP model for this problem. What kind of problem is this?

c. Use Solver to determine the optimal solution to this problem.

32. The U.S. Department of Transportation (DOT) is planning to build a new interstate to run from Detroit, Michigan, to Charleston, South Carolina. Several different routes have been proposed. They are summarized in Figure 5.41, where node 1 represents Detroit and node 12 represents Charleston. The numbers on the arcs indicate the estimated construction costs of the various links (in millions of dollars). It is estimated that all of the routes will require approximately the same total driving time to make the trip from Detroit to Charleston. Thus, the DOT is interested in identifying the least costly alternative.

a. Formulate an LP model to determine the least costly construction plan.

b. Use Solver to determine the optimal solution to this problem.

33. A building contractor is designing the ductwork for the heating and air conditioning system in a new, single-story medical building. Figure 5.42 summarizes the possible connections between the primary air handling unit (node 1) and the various air outlets to be placed in the building (nodes 2 through 9). The arcs in the network represent possible ductwork connections, and the values on the arcs represent the feet of ductwork required.

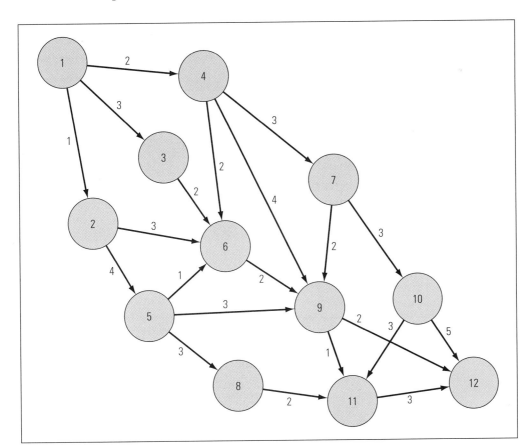

FIGURE 5.41

Possible routes for the interstate construction problem

FIGURE 5.42

Network representation of the ductwork problem

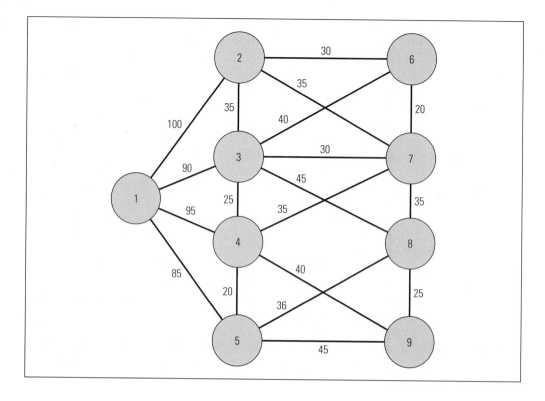

Starting at node 1, use the minimal spanning tree algorithm to determine how much ductwork should be installed to provide air access to each vent while requiring the least amount of ductwork.

34. The manager of catering services for the Roanoker Hotel has a problem. The banquet hall at the hotel is booked each evening during the coming week for groups who have reserved the following numbers of tables:

Day	Monday	Tuesday	Wednesday	Thursday	Friday
Tables Reserved	400	300	250	400	350

The hotel has 500 tablecloths that can be used for these banquets. However, the tablecloths used at each banquet will have to be cleaned before they can be used again. A local cleaning service will pick up the soiled tablecloths each evening after the banquet. It offers overnight cleaning for $2 per tablecloth, or 2-day service for $1 per tablecloth (*i.e.*, a tablecloth picked up Monday night can be ready Tuesday for $2 or ready for use Wednesday for $1). There are no tablecloth losses and all table-cloths must be cleaned. Due to the cleaner's capacity restrictions, the overnight service can be performed on up to only 250 tablecloths, and overnight service is not available on tablecloths picked up Friday night. All cloths used on Friday must be ready for use again by Monday. The hotel wants to determine the least costly plan for having its tablecloths cleaned.

a. Draw a network flow model for this problem. (*Hint:* Express the supplies and de-mands as minimum required and maximum allowable flows over selected arcs.)

b. Create a spreadsheet model for this problem and solve it. What is the optimal solution?

Hamilton & Jacobs

Hamilton & Jacobs (H&J) is a global investment company, providing start-up capital to promising new ventures around the world. Due to the nature of its business, H&J holds funds in a variety of countries and converts between currencies as needs arise in different parts of the world. Several months ago, the company moved $16 million into Japanese yen (JPY) when one U.S. dollar (USD) was worth 75 yen. Since that time, the value of the dollar has fallen sharply, where it now requires almost 110 yen to purchase one dollar.

Besides its holdings of yen, H&J also currently owns 6 million European EUROs and 30 million Swiss Francs (CHF). H&J's chief economic forecaster is predicting that all of the currencies it is presently holding will continue to gain strength against the dollar for the rest of the year. As a result, the company would like to convert all its surplus currency holdings back to U.S. dollars until the economic picture improves.

The bank H&J uses for currency conversions charges different transaction fees for converting between various currencies. The following table summarizes the transaction fees (expressed as a percentage of the amount converted) for US dollars (USD), Australian dollars (AUD), British pounds (GBP), European Euros (EURO), Indian Rupees (INR), Japanese yen (JPY), Singapore dollars (SGD), and Swiss Francs (CHF).

Transaction Fee Table

FROM/TO	USD	AUD	GBP	EUR	INR	JPY	SGD	CHF
USD	—	0.10%	0.50%	0.40%	0.40%	0.40%	0.25%	0.50%
AUD	0.10%	—	0.70%	0.50%	0.30%	0.30%	0.75%	0.75%
GBP	0.50%	0.70%	—	0.70%	0.70%	0.40%	0.45%	0.50%
EUR	0.40%	0.50%	0.70%	—	0.05%	0.10%	0.10%	0.10%
INR	0.40%	0.30%	0.70%	0.05%	—	0.20%	0.10%	0.10%
JPY	0.40%	0.30%	0.40%	0.10%	0.20%	—	0.05%	0.50%
SGD	0.25%	0.75%	0.45%	0.10%	0.10%	0.05%	—	0.50%
CHF	0.50%	0.75%	0.50%	0.10%	0.10%	0.50%	0.50%	—

Because it costs differing amounts to convert between various currencies, H&J determined that converting existing holdings directly into US dollars might not be the best strategy. Instead, it might be less expensive to convert existing holdings to an intermediate currency before converting the result back to US dollars. The following table summarizes the current exchange rates for converting from one currency to another.

Exchange Rate Table

From/To	USD	AUD	GBP	EUR	INR	JPY	SGD	CHF
USD	1	1.29249	0.55337	0.80425	43.5000	109.920	1.64790	1.24870
AUD	0.77370	1	0.42815	0.62225	33.6560	85.0451	1.27498	0.96612
GBP	1.80710	2.33566	1	1.45335	78.6088	198.636	2.97792	2.25652
EUR	1.24340	1.60708	0.68806	1	54.0879	136.675	2.04900	1.55263
INR	0.02299	0.02971	0.01272	0.01849	1	2.5269	0.03788	0.02871
JPY	0.00910	0.01176	0.00503	0.00732	0.39574	1	0.01499	0.01136
SGD	0.60683	0.78433	0.33581	0.48804	26.3972	66.7031	1	0.75775
CHF	0.80083	1.03507	0.44316	0.64407	34.8362	88.0275	1.31969	1

The exchange rate table indicates, for instance, that one Japanese yen can be converted into 0.00910 US dollars. So 100,000 yen would produce $910 US. However, the bank's 0.40% fee for this transaction would reduce the net amount received to

$910 \times (1 - 0.004) = \$906.36$. So H&J wants your assistance in determining the best way to convert all its non-US currency holdings back into US dollars.

a. Draw a network flow diagram for this problem.
b. Create a spreadsheet model for this problem and solve it.
c. What is the optimal solution?
d. If H&J converted each non-US currency it owns directly into US dollars, how many US dollars would it have?
e. Suppose that H&J wants to perform the same conversion but also leave $5 million in Australian dollars. What is the optimal solution in this case?

CASE 5.2   Old Dominion Energy

The United States is the biggest consumer of natural gas, and the second largest natural gas producer in the world. According to the U.S. Energy Information Administration (EIA), in 2001 the U.S. consumed 22.7 trillion cubic feet of natural gas. Stemming from phased deregulation, the transportation and delivery of natural gas from wellheads has grown since the '80s and there are now more than 278,000 miles of gas pipeline nationwide (see: http://www.platts.com/features/usgasguide/pipelines.shtml). With more electric power companies turning to natural gas as a cleaner-burning fuel, natural gas is expected to grow even more quickly over the next 20 years.

To ensure an adequate supply of natural gas, gas storage facilities have been built in numerous places along the pipeline. Energy companies can buy gas when prices are low and store it in these facilities for use or sale at a later date. Because energy consumption is influenced greatly by the weather (which is not entirely predictable), imbalances often arise in the supply and demand for gas in different parts of the country. Gas traders constantly monitor these market conditions and look for opportunities to sell gas from storage facilities when the price offered at a certain location is high enough. This decision is complicated because it costs different amounts of money to transport gas through different segments of the nationwide pipeline, and the capacity available in different parts of the pipeline is changing constantly. Thus, when traders see an opportunity to sell at a favorable price, they must quickly see how much capacity is available in the network and create deals with individual pipeline operators for the necessary capacity to move gas from storage to the buyer.

Bruce McDaniel is a gas trader for Old Dominion Energy (ODE), Inc. The network in Figure 5.43 represents a portion of the gas pipeline where ODE does business. The values next to each arc in this network are of the form (x,y) where x is the cost per thousand cubic feet (cf) of transporting gas along the arc, and y is the available transmission capacity of the arc in thousands of cubic feet. Note that the arcs in this network are bidirectional (i.e., gas can flow in either direction at the prices and capacities listed).

Bruce currently has 100,000 cf of gas in storage at Katy. Industrial customers in Joliet are offering $4.35 per thousand cf for up to 35,000 cf of gas. Buyers in Leidy are offering $4.63 per thousand cf for up to 60,000 cf of gas. Create a spreadsheet model to help Bruce answer the following questions.

a. Given the available capacity in the network, how much gas can be shipped from Katy to Leidy? From Katy to Joliet?
b. How much gas should Bruce offer to sell to Joliet and Leidy if he wants to maximize profits?
c. Is Bruce able to meet all the demand from both customers? If not, why not?
d. If Bruce wanted to try to pay more to obtain additional capacity on some of the pipelines, which ones should he investigate and why?

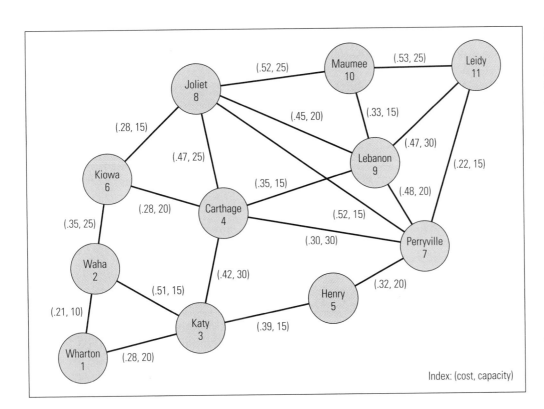

FIGURE 5.43

Gas pipeline network for Old Dominion Energy

Index: (cost, capacity)

US Express

US Express is an overnight package delivery company based in Atlanta, Georgia. Jet fuel is one of the largest operating costs incurred by the company and they want your assistance in managing this cost. The price of jet fuel varies considerably at different airports around the country. As a result, it seems that it might be wise to "fill up" on jet fuel at airports where it is least expensive. However, the amount of fuel an airliner burns depends, in part, on the weight of the plane—and excess fuel makes an airplane heavier and, therefore, less fuel-efficient. Similarly, more fuel is burned on flights from the east coast to the west coast (going against the jet stream) than from the west coast to the east coast (going with the jet stream).

The following table summarizes the flight schedule (or rotation) flown nightly by one of the company's planes. For each flight segment, the table summarizes the minimum required and maximum allowable amount of fuel on board at takeoff and the cost of fuel at each point of departure. The final column provides a linear function relating fuel consumption to the amount of fuel on board at takeoff.

Segment	Depart	Arrive	Minimum Fuel Level at Takeoff (in 1000s)	Maximum Fuel Level at Takeoff (in 1000s)	Cost per Gallon	Fuel used in Flight with G Gallons (in 1000s) on Board at Takeoff
1	Atlanta	San Francisco	21	31	$0.92	$3.20 + 0.45 \times G$
2	San Francisco	Los Angeles	7	20	$0.85	$2.25 + 0.65 \times G$
3	Los Angeles	Chicago	18	31	$0.87	$1.80 + 0.35 \times G$
4	Chicago	Atlanta	16	31	$1.02	$2.20 + 0.60 \times G$

For instance, if the plane leaves Atlanta for San Francisco with 25,000 gallons on board, it should arrive in San Francisco with approximately $25 - (3.2 + 0.45 \times 25) = 10.55$ thousand gallons of fuel.

The company has many other planes that fly different schedules each night, so the potential cost savings from efficient fuel purchasing is quite significant. But before turning you loose on all of their flight schedules, the company wants you to create a spreadsheet model to determine the most economical fuel purchasing plan for the previous schedule. (*Hint:* Keep in mind that the most fuel you would purchase at any departure point is the maximum allowable fuel level for takeoff at that point. Also, assume that whatever fuel is on board when the plane returns to Atlanta at the end of the rotation will still be on board when the plane leaves Atlanta the next evening.)

a. Draw the network diagram for this problem.
b. Implement the model for this problem in your spreadsheet and solve it.
c. How much fuel should US Express purchase at each departure point and what is the cost of this purchasing plan?

CASE 5.4   The Major Electric Corporation

Henry Lee is the Vice President of Purchasing for the consumer electronics division of the Major Electric Corporation (MEC). The company recently introduced a new type of video camcorder that has taken the market by storm. Although Henry is pleased with the strong demand for this product in the marketplace, it has been a challenge to keep up with MEC's distributors' orders of this camcorder. His current challenge is how to meet requests from MEC's major distributors in Pittsburgh, Denver, Baltimore, and Houston who have placed orders of 10,000, 20,000, 30,000, and 25,000 units, respectively, for delivery in two months (there is a one-month manufacturing and one-month shipping lead time for this product).

MEC has contracts with companies in Hong Kong, Korea, and Singapore who manufacture camcorders for the company under the MEC label. These contracts require MEC to order a specified minimum number of units each month at a guaranteed per unit cost. The contracts also specify the maximum number of units that may be ordered at this price. The following table summarizes these contracts:

	Monthly Purchasing Contract Provisions		
Supplier	**Unit Cost**	**Minimum Required**	**Maximum Allowed**
Hong Kong	$375	20,000	30,000
Korea	$390	25,000	40,000
Singapore	$365	15,000	30,000

MEC also has a standing contract with a shipping company to transport product from each of these suppliers to ports in San Francisco and San Diego. The cost of shipping from each supplier to each port is given in the following table along with the minimum required and maximum allowable number of shipping cartons each month:

	Monthly Shipping Contract Provisions					
	San Francisco Requirements			**San Diego Shipping Requirements**		
Supplier	**Cost per Container**	**Minimum Containers**	**Maximum Containers**	**Cost per Container**	**Minimum Containers**	**Maximum Containers**
Hong Kong	$2,000	5	20	$2,300	5	20
Korea	$1,800	10	30	$2,100	10	30
Singapore	$2,400	5	25	$2,200	5	15

Under the terms of this contract, MEC guarantees it will send at least 20 but no more than 65 shipping containers to San Francisco each month, and at least 30 but no more than 70 shipping containers to San Diego each month.

Each shipping container can hold 1,000 video cameras and ultimately will be trucked from the seaports on to the distributors. Again, MEC has a standing contract with a trucking company to provide trucking services each month. The cost of trucking a shipping container from each port to each distributor is summarized in the following table.

| | **Unit Shipping Cost per Container** | | | |
	Pittsburgh	**Denver**	**Baltimore**	**Houston**
San Francisco	$1,100	$850	$1,200	$1,000
San Diego	$1,200	$1,000	$1,100	$900

As with the other contracts, to obtain the prices given above, MEC is required to use a certain minimum amount of trucking capacity on each route each month and may not exceed certain maximum shipping amounts without incurring cost penalties. These minimum and maximum shipping restrictions are summarized in the following table.

| | **Minimum Required and Maximum Allowable Number of Shipping Containers per Month** | | | | | | | |
| | **Pittsburgh** | | **Denver** | | **Baltimore** | | **Houston** | |
	Min	**Max**	**Min**	**Max**	**Min**	**Max**	**Min**	**Max**
San Francisco	3	7	6	12	10	18	5	15
San Diego	4	6	5	14	5	20	10	20

Henry is left with the task of sorting through all this information to determine the least purchasing and distribution plan to fill the distributor's requests. But because he and his wife have tickets to the symphony for this evening, he has asked you to take a look at this problem and give him your recommendations at 9:00 tomorrow morning.
a. Create a network flow model for this problem. (*Hint:* Consider inserting intermediate nodes in your network to assist in meeting the minimum monthly purchase restrictions for each supplier and the minimum monthly shipping requirements for each port.)
b. Implement a spreadsheet model for this problem and solve it.
c. What is the optimal solution?

Chapter 6

Integer Linear Programming

6.0 Introduction

When some or all of the decision variables in an LP problem are restricted to assuming only integer values, the resulting problem is referred to as an **integer linear programming** (ILP) problem. Many practical business problems need integer solutions. For example, when scheduling workers, a company needs to determine the optimal number of employees to assign to each shift. If we formulate this problem as an LP problem, its optimal solution could involve allocating fractional numbers of workers (for example, 7.33 workers) to different shifts; but this is not an integer feasible solution. Similarly, if an airline is trying to decide how many 767s, 757s, and A-300s to purchase for its fleet, it must obtain an integer solution because the airline cannot buy fractions of planes.

This chapter discusses how to solve optimization problems in which certain decision variables must assume only integer values. This chapter also shows how the use of integer variables allows us to build more accurate models for a number of business problems.

6.1 Integrality Conditions

To illustrate some of the issues involved in an ILP problem, let's consider again the decision problem faced by Howie Jones, the owner of Blue Ridge Hot Tubs, described in Chapters 2, 3, and 4. This company sells two models of hot tubs, the Aqua-Spa and the Hydro-Lux, which it produces by purchasing prefabricated fiberglass hot tub shells and installing a common water pump and an appropriate amount of tubing. Each Aqua-Spa produced requires 1 pump, 9 hours of labor, and 12 feet of tubing, and contributes \$350 to profits. Each Hydro-Lux produced requires 1 pump, 6 hours of labor, and 16 feet of tubing, and contributes \$300 to profits. Assuming that the company has 200 pumps, 1,566 labor hours, and 2,880 feet of tubing available, we created the following LP formulation for this problem where X_1 and X_2 represent the number of Aqua-Spas and Hydro-Luxes to produce:

$$
\begin{array}{lll}
\text{MAX:} & 350X_1 + 300X_2 & \} \text{ profit} \\
\text{Subject to:} & 1X_1 + 1X_2 \leq 200 & \} \text{ pump constraint} \\
& 9X_1 + 6X_2 \leq 1{,}566 & \} \text{ labor constraint} \\
& 12X_1 + 16X_2 \leq 2{,}880 & \} \text{ tubing constraint} \\
& X_1, X_2 \geq 0 & \} \text{ nonnegativity conditions}
\end{array}
$$

Blue Ridge Hot Tubs is undoubtedly interested in obtaining the best possible *integer solution* to this problem because hot tubs can be sold only as discrete units. Thus, we can be sure that the company wants to find the *optimal integer solution* to this problem. So, in addition to the constraints stated previously, we add the following integrality condition to the formulation of the problem:

$$X_1 \text{ and } X_2 \text{ must be integers}$$

An **integrality condition** indicates that some (or all) of the variables in the formulation must assume only **integer values**. We refer to such variables as the integer variables in a problem. In contrast, variables that are not required to assume strictly integer values are referred to as **continuous variables**. Although it is easy to state integrality conditions for a problem, such conditions often make a problem more difficult (and sometimes impossible) to solve.

6.2 Relaxation

One approach to finding the optimal integer solution to a problem is to relax, or ignore, the integrality conditions and solve the problem as if it were a standard LP problem where all the variables are assumed to be continuous. This model is sometimes referred to as the **LP relaxation** of the original ILP problem. Consider the following ILP problem:

$$
\begin{aligned}
\text{MAX:} \quad & 2X_1 + 3X_2 \\
\text{Subject to:} \quad & X_1 + 3X_2 \leq 8.25 \\
& 2.5X_1 + X_2 \leq 8.75 \\
& X_1, X_2 \geq 0 \\
& X_1, X_2 \text{ must be integers}
\end{aligned}
$$

The LP relaxation for this problem is represented by:

$$
\begin{aligned}
\text{MAX:} \quad & 2X_1 + 3X_2 \\
\text{Subject to:} \quad & X_1 + 3X_2 \leq 8.25 \\
& 2.5X_1 + X_2 \leq 8.75 \\
& X_1, X_2 \geq 0
\end{aligned}
$$

The only difference between the ILP and its LP relaxation is that all integrality conditions imposed by the ILP are dropped in the relaxation. However, as illustrated in Figure 6.1, this change has a significant impact on the feasible regions for the two problems.

As shown in Figure 6.1, the feasible region for the ILP consists of only 11 discrete points. On the other hand, the feasible region for its LP relaxation consists of an infinite number of points represented by the shaded area. This figure illustrates an important point about the relationship between the feasible region of an ILP and its LP relaxation. The feasible region of the LP relaxation of an ILP problem *always* encompasses *all* the feasible integer solutions to the original ILP problem. Although the relaxed feasible region might include additional noninteger solutions, it will *not* include any integer solutions that are not feasible solutions to the original ILP.

6.3 Solving the Relaxed Problem

The LP relaxation of an ILP problem is often easy to solve using the simplex method. As explained in Chapter 2, an optimal solution to an LP problem occurs at one of the corner points of its feasible region (assuming that the problem has a bounded optimal solution). Thus, if we are extremely lucky, the optimal solution to the LP relaxation of an

FIGURE 6.1

Integer feasible region vs. LP feasible region

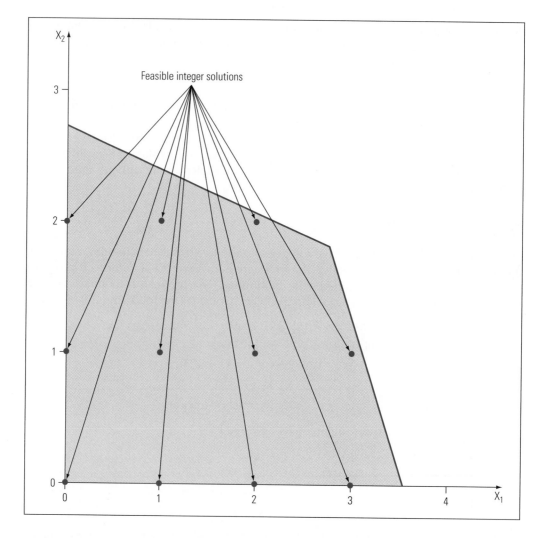

ILP problem might occur at an integer corner point of the relaxed feasible region. In this case, we find the optimal integer solution to the ILP problem simply by solving its LP relaxation. This is exactly what happened in Chapters 2 and 3 when we originally solved the relaxed LP model for the hot tub problem. Figure 6.2 (and the file Fig6-2.xls on your data disk) shows the solution to this problem.

The optimal solution to the relaxed LP formulation of the hot tub problem assigns integer values to the decision variables ($X_1 = 122$ and $X_2 = 78$). So in this case, the relaxed LP problem happens to have an integer-valued optimal solution. However, as you might expect, this will not always be the case.

Suppose, for example, that Blue Ridge Hot Tubs has only 1,520 hours of labor and 2,650 feet of tubing available during its next production cycle. The company might be interested in solving the following ILP problem:

MAX:	$350X_1 + 300X_2$	} profit
Subject to:	$1X_1 + 1X_2 \leq 200$	} pump constraint
	$9X_1 + 6X_2 \leq 1{,}520$	} labor constraint
	$12X_1 + 16X_2 \leq 2{,}650$	} tubing constraint
	$X_1, X_2 \geq 0$	} nonnegativity conditions
	X_1, X_2 must be integers	} integrality conditions

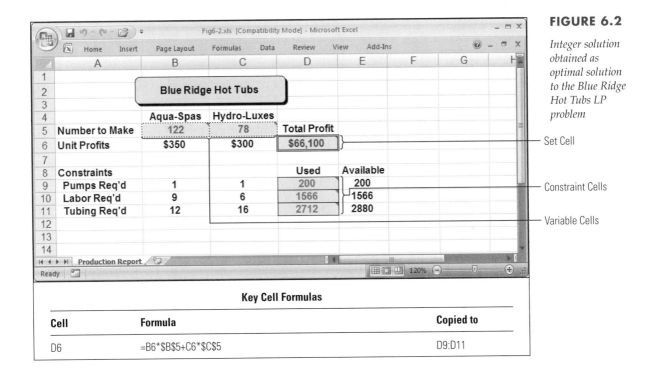

FIGURE 6.2

Integer solution obtained as optimal solution to the Blue Ridge Hot Tubs LP problem

— Set Cell

— Constraint Cells

— Variable Cells

Key Cell Formulas		
Cell	**Formula**	**Copied to**
D6	=B6*$B$5+C6*$C$5	D9:D11

If we relax the integrality conditions and solve the resulting LP problem, we obtain the solution shown in Figure 6.3. This solution indicates that producing 116.9444 Aqua-Spas and 77.9167 Hydro-Luxes will generate a maximum profit of $64,306. But this solution violates the integrality conditions stated in the original problem. As a general rule, the optimal solution to the LP relaxation of an ILP problem is not guaranteed to produce an integer solution. In such cases, other techniques must be applied to find the optimal integer solution for the problem being solved. (There are some exceptions to this rule. In particular, the network flow problems discussed in Chapter 5 often can be viewed as ILP problems. For reasons that go beyond the scope of this text, the LP relaxation of network flow problems always will have integer solutions if the supplies and/or demands at each node are integers and the problem is solved using the simplex method.)

6.4 Bounds

Before discussing how to solve ILP problems, an important point must be made about the relationship between the optimal solution to an ILP problem and the optimal solution to its LP relaxation: *The objective function value for the optimal solution to the ILP problem can never be better than the objective function value for the optimal solution to its LP relaxation.*

For example, the solution shown in Figure 6.3 indicates that if the company could produce (and sell) fractional numbers of hot tubs, it could make a maximum profit of $64,306 by producing 116.9444 Aqua-Spas and 77.9167 Hydro-Luxes. No other feasible solution (integer or otherwise) could result in a better value of the objective function. If a better feasible solution existed, the optimization procedure would have identified this better solution as optimal because our aim was to maximize the value of the objective function.

FIGURE 6.3

Noninteger solution obtained as optimal solution to the revised Blue Ridge Hot Tubs LP problem

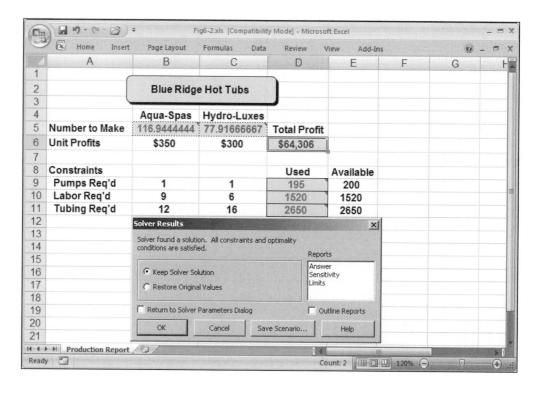

Although solving the LP relaxation of the revised hot tub problem might not provide the optimal integer solution to our original ILP problem, it does indicate that the objective function value of the optimal integer solution cannot possibly be greater than $64,306. This information can be important in helping us evaluate the quality of integer solutions we might discover during our search for the optimal solution.

Key Concept

For *maximization* problems, the objective function value at the optimal solution to the LP relaxation represents an *upper bound* on the optimal objective function value of the original ILP problem. For *minimization* problems, the objective function value at the optimal solution to the LP relaxation represents a *lower bound* on the optimal objective function value of the original ILP problem.

6.5 Rounding

As mentioned earlier, the solution to the LP relaxation of an ILP problem might satisfy the ILP problem's integrality conditions and, therefore, represent the optimal integer solution to the problem. But what should we do if this is not the case (as usually happens)? One technique that frequently is applied involves rounding the relaxed LP solution.

When the solution to the LP relaxation of an ILP problem does not result in an integer solution, it is tempting to think that simply rounding this solution will generate the optimal integer solution. Unfortunately, this is not the case. For example, if the values for the decision variables shown in Figure 6.3 are manually rounded up to their closest integer values, as shown in Figure 6.4, the resulting solution is infeasible. The company cannot manufacture 117 Aqua-Spas and 78 Hydro-Luxes because this would involve using more labor and tubing than are available.

Because rounding up does not always work, perhaps we should round down, or truncate, the values for the decision variables identified in the LP relaxation. As shown in Figure 6.5, this results in a feasible solution where 116 Aqua-Spas and 77 Hydro-Luxes are manufactured for a total profit of $63,700. However, this approach presents two possible problems. First, rounding down also could result in an infeasible solution, as shown in Figure 6.6.

FIGURE 6.4

Infeasible integer solution obtained by rounding up

FIGURE 6.5

Feasible integer solution obtained by rounding down

FIGURE 6.6

How rounding down can result in an infeasible integer solution

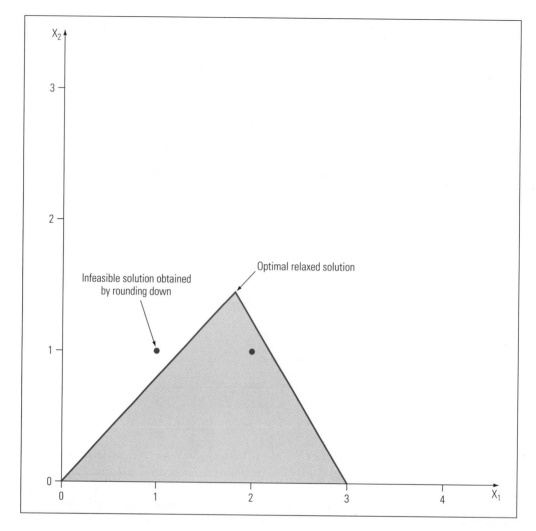

Another problem with rounding down is that even if it results in a feasible integer solution to the problem, there is no guarantee that it is the *optimal* integer solution. For example, the integer solution obtained by rounding down shown in Figure 6.5 produced a total profit of $63,700. However, as shown in Figure 6.7, a better integer solution exists for this problem. If the company produces 118 Aqua-Spas and 76 Hydro-Luxes, it can achieve a total profit of $64,100 (which is the optimal integer solution to this problem). Simply rounding the solution to the LP relaxation of an ILP problem is not guaranteed to provide the optimal integer solution. Although the integer solution obtained in this problem by rounding is very close to the optimal integer solution, rounding does not always work this well.

As we have seen, the solution to the LP relaxation of an ILP is not guaranteed to produce an integer solution, and rounding the solution to the LP relaxation is not guaranteed to produce the optimal integer solution. Therefore, we need another way to find the optimal integer solution to an ILP problem. Various procedures have been developed for this purpose. The most effective and widely used of these procedures is the branch-and-bound **(B&B) algorithm**. The B&B algorithm theoretically allows us to solve any ILP problem by solving a series of LP problems called candidate problems. For those who are interested, a discussion of how the B&B algorithm works is given at the end of this chapter.

FIGURE 6.7

Optimal integer solution to the revised Blue Ridge Hot Tubs problem

6.6 Stopping Rules

Finding the optimal solution for simple ILP problems sometimes can require the evaluation of hundreds of candidate problems. More complex problems can require the evaluation of thousands of candidate problems, which can be a very time-consuming task even for the fastest computers. For this reason, many ILP packages allow you to specify a suboptimality tolerance of X% (where X is some numeric value), which tells the B&B algorithm to stop when it finds an integer solution that is no more than X% worse than the optimal integer solution. This is another area where obtaining upper or lower bounds on the optimal integer solution can be helpful.

As noted earlier, if we relax all the integrality conditions in an ILP with a maximization objective and solve the resulting LP problem, the objective function value at the optimal solution to the relaxed problem provides an upper bound on the optimal integer solution. For example, when we relaxed the integrality conditions for the revised Blue Ridge Hot Tubs problem and solved it as an LP, we obtained the solution shown in Figure 6.3, which has an objective function value of $64,306. Thus, we know that the optimal integer solution to this problem cannot have an objective function value greater than $64,306. Now, suppose that the owner of Blue Ridge Hot Tubs is willing to settle for any integer solution to their problem that is no more than 5% below the optimal integer solution. It is easy to determine that 95% of $64,306 is $61,090 ($0.95 \times \$64,306 = \$61,090$). Therefore, any integer solution with an objective function value of at least $61,090 can be no worse than 5% below the optimal integer solution.

Specifying suboptimality tolerances can be helpful if you are willing to settle for a good but suboptimal solution to a difficult ILP problem. However, most B&B packages employ some sort of default suboptimality tolerance and, therefore, might produce a suboptimal solution to the ILP problem without indicating that a better solution might exist. (We will look at an example where this occurs shortly.) It is important to be aware of suboptimality tolerances because they can determine whether or not the true optimal solution to an ILP problem is found.

6.7 Solving ILP Problems Using Solver

Now that you have some understanding of the effort required to solve ILP problems, you can appreciate how using Solver simplifies this process. This section shows how to use Solver with the revised Blue Ridge Hot Tubs problem.

Figure 6.8 shows the Solver parameters required to solve the revised Blue Ridge Hot Tubs problem as a standard LP problem. However, none of these parameters indicate that the cells representing the decision variables (cells B5 and C5) must assume integer values. To communicate this to Solver, we need to add constraints to the problem by clicking the Add button.

Clicking this button displays the Add Constraint dialog box shown in Figure 6.9. In this dialog box, cells B5 through C5 are specified as the cell references for the additional constraints. Because we want these cells to assume only integer values, we need to select the **int** option from the drop-down menu, as shown in Figure 6.9.

After clicking the OK button, we return to the Solver Parameters dialog box shown in Figure 6.10. This dialog box now indicates that cells B5 and C5 are constrained to assume only integer values. We can now click the Solve button to determine the optimal solution to the problem, shown in Figure 6.11.

The Solver Results dialog box in Figure 6.11 indicates that Solver found a solution "within tolerance" that satisfies all constraints. Thus, we might suspect that the optimal integer solution to this problem involves producing 117 Aqua-Spas and 77 Hydro-Luxes for a total profit of $64,050. However, if you refer back to Figure 6.7, you will recall that

FIGURE 6.8

Solver parameters for the relaxed Blue Ridge Hot Tubs problem

FIGURE 6.9

Selecting integer constraints

FIGURE 6.10

Solver parameters for the revised Blue Ridge Hot Tubs problem with integer constraints

an even better integer solution to this problem can be obtained by producing 118 Aqua-Spas and 76 Hydro-Luxes for a total profit of $64,100. So why did Solver select an integer solution with a total profit of $64,050 when a better integer solution exists? The answer lies in Solver's suboptimality tolerance factor.

By default, Solver uses a suboptimality tolerance factor of 5%. So, when Solver found the integer solution with the objective function value of $64,050 shown in Figure 6.11, it determined that this solution was within 5% of the optimal integer solution and, therefore, it abandoned its search. (Note the message in Figure 6.11, "Solver found an integer solution within tolerance.") To ensure that Solver finds the best possible

FIGURE 6.11

Solution to the revised Blue Ridge Hot Tubs problem with integer constraints

solution to an ILP problem, we must change its suboptimality tolerance factor by clicking the Options button in the Solver Parameters dialog box and then click the Integer tab in the Solver Options dialog box. Figure 6.12 shows the resulting Integer Options dialog box.

As shown in Figure 6.12, you can set a number of options to control Solver's operations. The Tolerance option represents Solver's suboptimality tolerance value. To make sure that Solver finds the best possible solution to an ILP problem, we must change this setting from its default value of 0.05 to 0. If we do this and re-solve the current problem, we obtain the solution shown in Figure 6.13. This solution is the best possible integer solution to the problem.

FIGURE 6.12

Changing the suboptimality tolerance factor

FIGURE 6.13

Optimal integer solution to the revised Blue Ridge Hot Tubs problem

6.8 Other ILP Problems

Many decision problems encountered in business can be modeled as ILPs. As we have seen from the Blue Ridge Hot Tubs example, some problems that are initially formulated as LP problems might turn into ILP formulations if they require integer solutions. However, the importance of ILP extends beyond simply allowing us to obtain integer solutions to LP problems.

The ability to constrain certain variables to assume only integer values enables us to model a number of important conditions more accurately. For example, up to this point, we have not considered the impact of quantity discounts, setup or lump-sum costs, or batch size restrictions on a given decision problem. Without ILP techniques, we could not model these decision issues. We now consider several examples that illustrate the expanded modeling capabilities available through the use of integer variables.

6.9 An Employee Scheduling Problem

Anyone responsible for creating work schedules for several employees can appreciate the difficulties in this task. It can be very difficult to develop a feasible schedule, much less an optimal schedule. Trying to ensure that a sufficient number of workers is available when needed is a complicated task when you must consider multiple shifts, rest breaks, and lunch or dinner breaks. However, some sophisticated LP models have been devised to solve these problems. Although a discussion of these models is beyond the scope of this text, we will consider a simple example of an employee scheduling problem to give you an idea of how LP models are applied in this area.

Air-Express is an express shipping service that guarantees overnight delivery of packages anywhere in the continental United States. The company has various operations centers, called hubs, at airports in major cities across the country. Packages are received at hubs from other locations and then shipped to intermediate hubs or to their final destinations.

The manager of the Air-Express hub in Baltimore, Maryland, is concerned about labor costs at the hub and is interested in determining the most effective way to schedule workers. The hub operates seven days a week, and the number of packages it handles each day varies from one day to the next. Using historical data on the average number of packages received each day, the manager estimates the number of workers needed to handle the packages as:

Day of Week	Workers Required
Sunday	18
Monday	27
Tuesday	22
Wednesday	26
Thursday	25
Friday	21
Saturday	19

The package handlers working for Air-Express are unionized and are guaranteed a five-day work week with two consecutive days off. The base wage for the handlers is $655 per week. Because most workers prefer to have Saturday or Sunday off, the union has negotiated bonuses of $25 per day for its members who work on these days. The possible shifts and salaries for package handlers are:

Shift	Days Off	Wage
1	Sunday and Monday	$680
2	Monday and Tuesday	$705
3	Tuesday and Wednesday	$705
4	Wednesday and Thursday	$705
5	Thursday and Friday	$705
6	Friday and Saturday	$680
7	Saturday and Sunday	$655

The manager wants to keep the total wage expense for the hub as low as possible. With this in mind, how many package handlers should be assigned to each shift if the manager wants to have a sufficient number of workers available each day?

6.9.1 DEFINING THE DECISION VARIABLES

In this problem, the manager must decide how many workers to assign to each shift. Because there are seven possible shifts, we need the following seven decision variables:

$$X_1 = \text{the number of workers assigned to shift 1}$$
$$X_2 = \text{the number of workers assigned to shift 2}$$
$$X_3 = \text{the number of workers assigned to shift 3}$$
$$X_4 = \text{the number of workers assigned to shift 4}$$
$$X_5 = \text{the number of workers assigned to shift 5}$$
$$X_6 = \text{the number of workers assigned to shift 6}$$
$$X_7 = \text{the number of workers assigned to shift 7}$$

6.9.2 DEFINING THE OBJECTIVE FUNCTION

The objective in this problem is to minimize the total wages paid. Each worker on shift 1 and 6 is paid \$680 per week, and each worker on shift 7 is paid \$655. All other workers are paid \$705 per week. Thus, the objective of minimizing the total wage expense is expressed as:

$$\text{MIN:} \quad 680X_1 + 705X_2 + 705X_3 + 705X_4 + 705X_5 + 680X_6 + 655X_7 \} \text{ total wage expense}$$

6.9.3 DEFINING THE CONSTRAINTS

The constraints for this problem must ensure that at least 18 workers are scheduled for Sunday, at least 27 are scheduled for Monday, and so on. We need one constraint for each day of the week.

To make sure that at least 18 workers are available on Sunday, we must determine which decision variables represent shifts that are scheduled to work on Sunday. Because shifts 1 and 7 are the only shifts that have Sunday scheduled as a day off, the remaining shifts, 2 through 6, all are scheduled to work on Sunday. The following constraint ensures that at least 18 workers are available on Sunday:

$$0X_1 + 1X_2 + 1X_3 + 1X_4 + 1X_5 + 1X_6 + 0X_7 \geq 18 \qquad \} \text{ workers required on Sunday}$$

Because workers on shifts 1 and 2 have Monday off, the constraint for Monday should ensure that the sum of the variables representing the number of workers on the remaining shifts, 3 through 7, is at least 27. This constraint is expressed as:

$$0X_1 + 0X_2 + 1X_3 + 1X_4 + 1X_5 + 1X_6 + 1X_7 \geq 27 \qquad \} \text{ workers required on Monday}$$

Constraints for the remaining days of the week are generated easily by applying the same logic used in generating the previous two constraints. The resulting constraints are stated as:

$$1X_1 + 0X_2 + 0X_3 + 1X_4 + 1X_5 + 1X_6 + 1X_7 \geq 22 \qquad \} \text{ workers required on Tuesday}$$
$$1X_1 + 1X_2 + 0X_3 + 0X_4 + 1X_5 + 1X_6 + 1X_7 \geq 26 \qquad \} \text{ workers required on Wednesday}$$
$$1X_1 + 1X_2 + 1X_3 + 0X_4 + 0X_5 + 1X_6 + 1X_7 \geq 25 \qquad \} \text{ workers required on Thursday}$$
$$1X_1 + 1X_2 + 1X_3 + 1X_4 + 0X_5 + 0X_6 + 1X_7 \geq 21 \qquad \} \text{ workers required on Friday}$$
$$1X_1 + 1X_2 + 1X_3 + 1X_4 + 1X_5 + 0X_6 + 0X_7 \geq 19 \qquad \} \text{ workers required on Saturday}$$

Finally, all our decision variables must assume nonnegative integer values. These conditions are stated as:

$$X_1, X_2, X_3, X_4, X_5, X_6, X_7 \geq 0$$

All X_i must be integers

6.9.4 A NOTE ABOUT THE CONSTRAINTS

At this point, you might wonder why the constraints for each day are "greater than or equal to" rather than "equal to" constraints. For example, if Air-Express needs only 19 people on Saturday, why do we have a constraint that allows *more* than 19 people to be scheduled? The answer to this question relates to feasibility. Suppose we restate the problem so that all the constraints are "equal to" constraints. There are two possible outcomes for this problem: (1) it might have a feasible optimal solution, or (2) it might not have a feasible solution.

In the first case, if the formulation using "equal to" constraints has a feasible optimal solution, this same solution also must be a feasible solution to our formulation using "greater than or equal to" constraints. Because both formulations have the same objective function, the solution to our original formulation could not be worse (in terms of the optimal objective function value) than a formulation using "equal to" constraints.

In the second case, if the formulation using "equal to" constraints has no feasible solution, there is no schedule where the *exact* number of employees required can be scheduled each day. To find a feasible solution in this case, we would need to make the constraints less restrictive by allowing for more than the required number of employees to be scheduled (that is, using "greater than or equal to" constraints).

Therefore, using "greater than or equal to" constraints does not preclude a solution where the exact number of workers needed is scheduled for each shift, if such a schedule is feasible and optimal. If such a schedule is not feasible or not optimal, the formulation using "greater than or equal to constraints" also guarantees that a feasible optimal solution to the problem will be obtained.

6.9.5 IMPLEMENTING THE MODEL

The LP model for the Air-Express scheduling problem is summarized as:

MIN: $680X_1 + 705X_2 + 705X_3 + 705X_4 + 705X_5 + 680X_6 + 655X_7$ } total wage expense

Subject to:

$0X_1 + 1X_2 + 1X_3 + 1X_4 + 1X_5 + 1X_6 + 0X_7 \geq 18$ } workers required on Sunday
$0X_1 + 0X_2 + 1X_3 + 1X_4 + 1X_5 + 1X_6 + 1X_7 \geq 27$ } workers required on Monday
$1X_1 + 0X_2 + 0X_3 + 1X_4 + 1X_5 + 1X_6 + 1X_7 \geq 22$ } workers required on Tuesday
$1X_1 + 1X_2 + 0X_3 + 0X_4 + 1X_5 + 1X_6 + 1X_7 \geq 26$ } workers required on Wednesday
$1X_1 + 1X_2 + 1X_3 + 0X_4 + 0X_5 + 1X_6 + 1X_7 \geq 25$ } workers required on Thursday
$1X_1 + 1X_2 + 1X_3 + 1X_4 + 0X_5 + 0X_6 + 1X_7 \geq 21$ } workers required on Friday
$1X_1 + 1X_2 + 1X_3 + 1X_4 + 1X_5 + 0X_6 + 0X_7 \geq 19$ } workers required on Saturday
$X_1, X_2, X_3, X_4, X_5, X_6, X_7 \geq 0$

All X_i must be integers

A convenient way of implementing this model is shown in Figure 6.14 (and in the file Fig6-14.xls on your data disk). Each row in the table shown in this spreadsheet corresponds to one of the seven shifts in the problem. For each day of the week, entries have been made to indicate which shifts are scheduled to be on or off. For example, shift 1 is scheduled off Sunday and Monday, and works on the remaining days of the week. Notice that the values for each day of the week in Figure 6.14 correspond directly to the coefficients in the constraint in our LP model for the same day of the week. The required number of workers for each day is listed in cells B13 through H13 and corresponds to the RHS values of each constraint. The wages to be paid to each worker on the various shifts are listed in cells J5 through J11 and correspond to the objective function coefficients in our model.

Cells I5 through I11 indicate the number of workers assigned to each shift, and correspond to the decision variables X_1 through X_7 in our algebraic formulation of the LP model. The LHS formula for each constraint is implemented easily using the

FIGURE 6.14

Spreadsheet model for the Air-Express employee scheduling problem

SUMPRODUCT( ) function. For example, the formula in cell B12 implements the LHS of the constraint for the number of workers needed on Sunday as:

Formula for cell B12:   =SUMPRODUCT(B5:B11,$I$5:$I$11)

(Copy to C12 through H12 and J12.)

This formula is then copied to cells C12 through H12 to implement the LHS formulas of the remaining constraints. With the coefficients for the objective function entered in cells J5 through J11, the previous formula also is copied to cell J12 to implement the objective function for this model.

6.9.6 SOLVING THE MODEL

Figure 6.15 shows the Solver parameters required to solve this problem. The optimal solution is shown in Figure 6.16.

6.9.7 ANALYZING THE SOLUTION

The optimal solution to this problem is shown in Figure 6.16. This solution ensures that the available number of employees is at least as great as the required number of employees for each day. The minimum total wage expense associated with this solution is $22,540.

FIGURE 6.15

Solver parameters for the Air-Express scheduling problem

FIGURE 6.16

Optimal solution to the Air-Express employee scheduling problem

6.10 Binary Variables

As mentioned earlier, some LP problems naturally evolve into ILP problems when we realize that we need to obtain integer solutions. For example, in the Air-Express problem discussed in the previous section, we needed to determine the number of workers to assign to each of seven shifts. Because workers are discrete units, we needed to impose integrality conditions on the decision variables in this model representing the number of workers scheduled for each shift. To do so, we changed the continuous variables in the model into **general integer variables**, or variables that could assume any integer value (provided that the constraints of the problem are not violated). In many other situations, we might want to use **binary integer variables** (or binary variables), which can assume *only two* integer values: 0 and 1. Binary variables can be useful in several practical modeling situations, as illustrated in the following examples.

6.11 A Capital Budgeting Problem

In a capital budgeting problem, a decision maker is presented with several potential projects or investment alternatives and must determine which projects or investments to choose. The projects or investments typically require different amounts of various resources (for example, money, equipment, personnel) and generate different cash flows to the company. The cash flows for each project or investment are converted to a net present value (NPV). The problem is to determine which set of projects or investments to select to achieve the maximum possible NPV. Consider the following example:

> In his position as vice president of research and development (R&D) for CRT Technologies, Mark Schwartz is responsible for evaluating and choosing which R&D projects to support. The company received 18 R&D proposals from its scientists and engineers, and identified six projects as being consistent with the company's mission. However, the company does not have the funds available to undertake all six projects. Mark must determine which of the projects to select. The funding requirements for each project are summarized in the following table along with the NPV the company expects each project to generate.

Project	Expected NPV (in $1,000s)	Capital (in $1,000s) Required in				
		Year 1	Year 2	Year 3	Year 4	Year 5
1	$141	$ 75	$25	$20	$15	$10
2	$187	$ 90	$35	$ 0	$ 0	$30
3	$121	$ 60	$15	$15	$15	$15
4	$ 83	$ 30	$20	$10	$ 5	$ 5
5	$265	$100	$25	$20	$20	$20
6	$127	$ 50	$20	$10	$30	$40

> The company currently has $250,000 available to invest in new projects. It has budgeted $75,000 for continued support for these projects in year 2 and $50,000 per year for years 3, 4, and 5. Surplus funds in any year are reappropriated for other uses within the company and may not be carried over to future years.

6.11.1 DEFINING THE DECISION VARIABLES

Mark must decide which of the six projects to select. Thus, we need six variables to represent the alternatives under consideration. We will let $X_1, X_2, \ldots, X_6$ represent the six decision variables for this problem and assume they operate as:

$$X_i = \begin{cases} 1, \text{ if project } i \text{ is selected} \\ 0, \text{ otherwise} \end{cases} \quad i = 1, 2, \ldots, 6$$

Each decision variable in this problem is a binary variable that assumes the value 1 if the associated project is selected, or the value 0 if the associated project is not selected. In essence, each variable acts as an "on/off switch" to indicate whether or not a given project has been selected.

6.11.2 DEFINING THE OBJECTIVE FUNCTION

The objective in this problem is to maximize the total NPV of the selected projects. This is stated mathematically as:

$$\text{MAX:} \qquad 141X_1 + 187X_2 + 121X_3 + 83X_4 + 265X_5 + 127X_6$$

Notice that this objective function simply sums the NPV figures for the selected projects.

6.11.3 DEFINING THE CONSTRAINTS

We need one capital constraint for each year to ensure that the selected projects do not require more capital than is available. This set of constraints is represented by:

$$
\begin{aligned}
75X_1 + 90X_2 + 60X_3 + 30X_4 + 100X_5 + 50X_6 &\leq 250 \quad \}\text{ year 1 capital constraint} \\
25X_1 + 35X_2 + 15X_3 + 20X_4 + 25X_5 + 20X_6 &\leq 75 \quad \}\text{ year 2 capital constraint} \\
20X_1 + 0X_2 + 15X_3 + 10X_4 + 20X_5 + 10X_6 &\leq 50 \quad \}\text{ year 3 capital constraint} \\
15X_1 + 0X_2 + 15X_3 + 5X_4 + 20X_5 + 30X_6 &\leq 50 \quad \}\text{ year 4 capital constraint} \\
10X_1 + 30X_2 + 15X_3 + 5X_4 + 20X_5 + 40X_6 &\leq 50 \quad \}\text{ year 5 capital constraint}
\end{aligned}
$$

6.11.4 SETTING UP THE BINARY VARIABLES

In our formulation of this problem, we assume that each decision variable is a binary variable. We must include this assumption in the formal statement of our model by adding the constraints:

$$\text{All } X_i \text{ must be binary}$$

Important Software Note

Starting with Excel 8.0 in Office 97, Solver provides a feature that allows you to indicate that certain variable cells represent binary variables. When you are adding constraints, the drop-down list box (see Figure 6.9) used to indicate the type of constraint ("<=", ">=", "=", "int") includes another option labeled "bin" for binary. If you are using Excel 8.0 (or Premium Solver for Education), you can simply select the "bin" option for variable cells that represent binary variables. However, if you are using an older version of Excel, you might need to add three sets of constraints (">=0", "<=1", and integer) to any variable cells that you want Solver to treat as binary variables.

6.11.5 IMPLEMENTING THE MODEL

The ILP model for the CRT Technologies project selection problem is summarized as:

$$
\begin{aligned}
\text{MAX:} \qquad & 141X_1 + 187X_2 + 121X_3 + 83X_4 + 265X_5 + 127X_6 \\
\text{Subject to:} \qquad & 75X_1 + 90X_2 + 60X_3 + 30X_4 + 100X_5 + 50X_6 \leq 250 \\
& 25X_1 + 35X_2 + 15X_3 + 20X_4 + 25X_5 + 20X_6 \leq 75 \\
& 20X_1 + 0X_2 + 15X_3 + 10X_4 + 20X_5 + 10X_6 \leq 50 \\
& 15X_1 + 0X_2 + 15X_3 + 5X_4 + 20X_5 + 30X_6 \leq 50 \\
& 10X_1 + 30X_2 + 15X_3 + 5X_4 + 20X_5 + 40X_6 \leq 50 \\
& \text{All } X_i \text{ must be binary}
\end{aligned}
$$

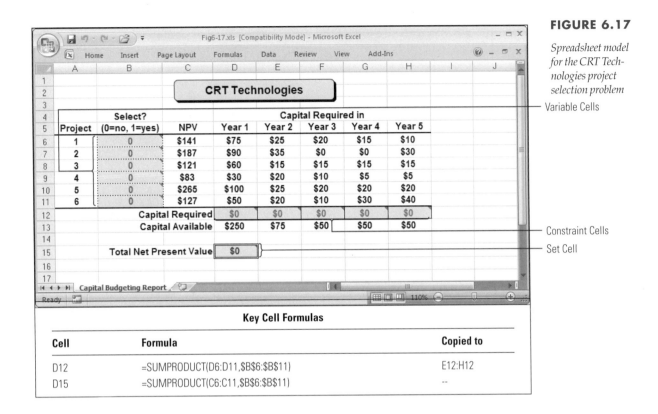

FIGURE 6.17

Spreadsheet model for the CRT Technologies project selection problem

— Variable Cells

— Constraint Cells

— Set Cell

This model is implemented in the spreadsheet shown in Figure 6.17 (and in the file Fig6-17.xls on your data disk). In this spreadsheet, the data for each project are listed in separate rows.

Cells B6 through B11 contain values of 0 to indicate that they are reserved for representing the six variables in our algebraic model. The LHS formula for the capital constraint is entered in cell D12, then copied to cells E12 through H12, as:

Formula for cell D12:   =SUMPRODUCT(D6:D11,$B$6:$B$11)
(Copy to E12 through H12.)

The RHS values for the constraints are listed in cells D13 through H13. Finally, the objective function of the model is implemented in cell D15 as:

Formula for cell D15:   =SUMPRODUCT(C6:C11,$B$6:$B$11)

6.11.6 SOLVING THE MODEL

To solve this model, we must tell Solver where we have implemented our objective function, decision variables, and constraints. The Solver Parameters dialog box shown in Figure 6.18 indicates that the objective function is implemented in cell D15 and that the decision variables are represented by cells B6 through B11. Also, notice that only two sets of constraints are specified for this problem.

The first set of constraints ensures that cells B6 through B11 will operate as binary variables. Notice that we implemented these constraints by referring to the cells in the spreadsheet that represent our decision variables—we do not have to set up separate

FIGURE 6.18

Solver parameters for the CRT Technologies project selection problem

cells in the spreadsheet to implement these constraints. The last set of constraints shown in the dialog box indicates that the values in cells D12 through H12 must be less than or equal to the values in cells D13 through H13 when the problem is solved. These conditions correspond to the capital constraints in the problem.

Because this model contains six decision variables and each variable can assume only one of two values, at most $2^6 = 64$ possible integer solutions exist for this problem. Some of these integer solutions will not fall in the feasible region, so we might suspect that this problem will not be too difficult to solve optimally. If we set the suboptimality tolerance factor to 0 (in the Integer Options dialog box) and solve the problem, we obtain the solution shown in Figure 6.19.

FIGURE 6.19

Optimal integer solution to the CRT Technologies project selection problem

FIGURE 6.20

A suboptimal heuristic solution to the CRT Technologies project selection problem

6.11.7 COMPARING THE OPTIMAL SOLUTION TO A HEURISTIC SOLUTION

The optimal solution shown in Figure 6.19 indicates that if CRT Technologies selects projects 1, 4, and 5, it can achieve a total NPV of $489,000. Although this solution does not use all of the capital available in each year, it is still the best possible integer solution to the problem.

Another approach to solving this problem is to create a ranked list of the projects in decreasing order by NPV and then select projects from this list, in order, until the capital is depleted. As shown in Figure 6.20, if we apply this heuristic to the current problem, we would select projects 5 and 2, but we could not select any more projects due to a lack of capital in year 5. This solution would generate a total NPV of $452,000. Again, we can see the potential benefit of optimization techniques over heuristic solution techniques.

6.12 Binary Variables and Logical Conditions

Binary variables can be used to model several logical conditions that might apply in a variety of problems. For example, in the CRT Technologies problem, several of the projects under consideration (for example, projects 1, 3, and 6) might represent alternative approaches for producing a certain part for a product. The company might want to limit the solution to include *no more than one* of these three alternatives. The following type of constraint accomplishes this restriction:

$$X_1 + X_3 + X_6 \le 1$$

Because X_1, X_3, and X_6 represent binary variables, no more than one of them can assume the value 1 and still satisfy the previous constraint. If we want to ensure that the solution includes *exactly one* of these alternatives, we could include the following constraint in our model:

$$X_1 + X_3 + X_6 = 1$$

As an example of another type of logical condition, suppose that project 4 involves a cellular communications technology that will not be available to the company unless it undertakes project 5. In other words, the company cannot select project 4 unless it also selects project 5. This type of relationship can be imposed on the solution with the constraint:

$$X_4 - X_5 \leq 0$$

The four possible combinations of values for X_4 and X_5 and their relationships to the previous constraint are summarized as:

Value of			
X_4	X_5	Meaning	Feasible?
0	0	Do not select either project	Yes
1	1	Select both projects	Yes
0	1	Select 5, but not 4	Yes
1	0	Select 4, but not 5	No

As indicated in this table, the previous constraint prohibits any solution in which project 4 is selected and project 5 is not selected.

As these examples illustrate, you can model certain logical conditions using binary variables. Several problems at the end of this chapter allow you to use binary variables (and your own creativity) to formulate models for decision problems that involve these types of logical conditions.

6.13 The Fixed-Charge Problem

In most of the LP problems discussed in earlier chapters, we formulated objective functions to maximize profits or minimize costs. In each of these cases, we associated a per-unit cost or per-unit profit with each decision variable to create the objective function. However, in some situations, the decision to produce a product results in a lump-sum cost, or fixed charge, in addition to a per-unit cost or profit. These types of problems are known as **fixed-charge** or fixed-cost problems. The following are some examples of fixed costs:

- the cost to lease, rent, or purchase a piece of equipment or a vehicle that will be required if a particular action is taken
- the setup cost required to prepare a machine or production line to produce a different type of product
- the cost to construct a new production line or facility that will be required if a particular decision is made
- the cost of hiring additional personnel that will be required if a particular decision is made

In each of these examples, the fixed costs are *new* costs that will be incurred if a particular action or decision is made. In this respect, fixed costs are different from **sunk costs**, which are costs that will be incurred regardless of what decision is made. Sunk costs are irrelevant for decision-making purposes because, by definition, decisions do not influence these costs. On the other hand, fixed costs are important factors in decision making because the decision determines whether or not these costs will be incurred. The following example illustrates the formulation and solution of a fixed-charge problem.

Remington Manufacturing is planning its next production cycle. The company can produce three products, each of which must undergo machining, grinding, and assembly operations. The following table below summarizes the hours of machining, grinding, and assembly required by each unit of each product, and the total hours of capacity available for each operation.

Operation	Hours Required By			Total Hours Available
	Product 1	Product 2	Product 3	
Machining	2	3	6	600
Grinding	6	3	4	300
Assembly	5	6	2	400

The cost accounting department has estimated that each unit of product 1 manufactured and sold will contribute $48 to profit, and each unit of products 2 and 3 contributes $55 and $50, respectively. However, manufacturing a unit of product 1 requires a setup operation on the production line that costs $1,000. Similar setups are required for products 2 and 3 at costs of $800 and $900, respectively. The marketing department believes that it can sell all the products produced. Therefore, the management of Remington wants to determine the most profitable mix of products to produce.

6.13.1 DEFINING THE DECISION VARIABLES

Although only three products are under consideration in this problem, we need six variables to formulate the problem accurately. We can define these variables as:

$$X_i = \text{the amount of product } i \text{ to be produced, } i = 1, 2, 3$$

$$Y_i = \begin{cases} 1, \text{ if } X_i > 0 \\ 0, \text{ if } X_i = 0 \end{cases}, i = 1, 2, 3$$

We need three variables, X_1, X_2, and X_3, to correspond to the amount of products 1, 2, and 3 produced. Each of the X_i variables has a corresponding binary variable, Y_i, that will equal 1 if X_i assumes any positive value, or will equal 0 if X_i is 0. For now, do not be concerned about how this relationship between the X_i and Y_i is enforced. We will explore that soon.

6.13.2 DEFINING THE OBJECTIVE FUNCTION

Given our definition of the decision variables, the objective function for our model is stated as:

$$\text{MAX:} \quad 48X_1 + 55X_2 + 50X_3 - 1000Y_1 - 800Y_2 - 900Y_3$$

The first three terms in this function calculate the marginal profit generated by the number of products 1, 2, and 3 sold. The last three terms in this function subtract the fixed costs for the products produced. For example, if X_1 assumes a positive value, we know from our definition of the Y_i variables that Y_1 should equal 1. And if $Y_1 = 1$, the value of the objective function will be reduced by $1,000 to reflect payment of the setup cost. On the other hand, if $X_1 = 0$, we know that $Y_1 = 0$. Therefore, if no units of X_1 are produced, the setup cost for product 1 will not be incurred in the objective. Similar relationships exist between X_2 and Y_2 and between X_3 and Y_3.

6.13.3 DEFINING THE CONSTRAINTS

Several sets of constraints apply to this problem. Capacity constraints are needed to ensure that the number of machining, grinding, and assembly hours used does not exceed the number of hours available for each of these resources. These constraints are stated as:

$$2X_1 + 3X_2 + 6X_3 \le 600 \qquad \} \text{ machining constraint}$$
$$6X_1 + 3X_2 + 4X_3 \le 300 \qquad \} \text{ grinding constraint}$$
$$5X_1 + 6X_2 + 2X_3 \le 400 \qquad \} \text{ assembly constraint}$$

We also need to include nonnegativity conditions on the X_i variables as:

$$X_i \ge 0, i = 1, 2, 3$$

The following constraint on the Y_i variables is needed to ensure that they operate as binary variables:

$$\text{All } Y_i \text{ must be binary}$$

As mentioned earlier, we must ensure that the required relationship between the X_i and Y_i variables is enforced. In particular, the value of the Y_i variables can be determined from the X_i variables. Therefore, we need constraints to establish this *link* between the value of the Y_i variables and the X_i variables. These linking constraints are represented by:

$$X_1 \le M_1 Y_1$$
$$X_2 \le M_2 Y_2$$
$$X_3 \le M_3 Y_3$$

In each of these constraints, the M_i is a numeric constant that represents an upper bound on the optimal value of the X_i. Let's assume that all the M_i are arbitrarily large numbers; for example, $M_i = 10,000$. Then each constraint sets up a link between the value of the X_i and the Y_i. For example, if any X_i variables in the previous constraints assume a value greater than 0, the corresponding Y_i variable must assume the value 1 or the constraint will be violated. On the other hand, if any of the X_i variables are equal to 0, the corresponding Y_i variables could equal 0 or 1 and still satisfy the constraint. However, if we consider the objective function to this problem, we know that when given a choice, Solver will always set the Y_i equal to 0 (rather than 1) because this results in a better objective function value. Therefore, we can conclude that if any X_i variables are equal to 0, Solver will set the corresponding Y_i variable equal to 0 because this is feasible, and it results in a better objective function value.

6.13.4 DETERMINING VALUES FOR "BIG M"

The M_i values used in the linking constraints sometimes are referred to as "Big M" values because they can be assigned arbitrarily large values. However, for reasons that go beyond the scope of this text, these types of problems are much easier to solve if the M_i values are kept as small as possible. As indicated earlier, the M_i values impose upper bounds on the values of the X_i. So, if a problem indicates that a company could manufacture and sell no more than 60 units of X_1, for example, we could let $M_1 = 60$.

However, even if upper bounds for the X_i are not indicated explicitly, it is sometimes easy to derive implicit upper bounds for these variables.

Let's consider the variable X_1 in the Remington problem. What is the maximum number of units of X_1 that can be produced in this problem? Referring back to our capacity constraints, if the company produced 0 units of X_2 and X_3, it would run out of machining capacity after producing $600/2 = 300$ units of X_1. Similarly, it would run out of grinding capacity after producing $300/6 = 50$ units of X_1, and it would run out of assembly capacity after producing $400/5 = 80$ units of X_1. Therefore, the maximum number of units of X_1 that the company can produce is 50. Using similar logic, we can determine that the maximum units of X_2 the company can produce is $\text{MIN}(600/3, 300/3, 400/6) = 66.67$, and the maximum units of X_3 is $\text{MIN}(600/6, 300/4, 400/2) = 75$. Thus, for this problem, reasonable upper bounds for X_1, X_2, and X_3 are represented by $M_1 = 50$, $M_2 = 67$, and $M_3 = 75$, respectively. (Note that the method illustrated here for obtaining reasonable values for the M_i does not apply if any of the coefficients in the machining, grinding, or assembly constraints are negative. Why is this?) When possible, you should determine reasonable values for the M_i in this type of problem. However, if this is not possible, you can assign arbitrarily large values to the M_i.

6.13.5 IMPLEMENTING THE MODEL

Using the values for the M_i calculated earlier, our ILP formulation of Remington's production planning model is summarized as:

$$
\begin{array}{lll}
\text{MAX:} & 48X_1 + 55X_2 + 50X_3 - 1000Y_1 - 800Y_2 - 900Y_3 & \\
\text{Subject to:} & 2X_1 + 3X_2 + 6X_3 \leq 600 & \} \text{ machining constraint} \\
& 6X_1 + 3X_2 + 4X_3 \leq 300 & \} \text{ grinding constraint} \\
& 5X_1 + 6X_2 + 2X_3 \leq 400 & \} \text{ assembly constraint} \\
& X_1 - 50Y_1 \leq 0 & \} \text{ linking constraint} \\
& X_2 - 67Y_2 \leq 0 & \} \text{ linking constraint} \\
& X_3 - 75Y_3 \leq 0 & \} \text{ linking constraint} \\
& \text{All } Y_i \text{ must be binary} & \} \text{ binary constraints} \\
& X_i \geq 0,\ i = 1, 2, 3 & \} \text{ nonnegativity conditions}
\end{array}
$$

This model expresses the linking constraints in a slightly different (but algebraically equivalent) manner, to follow our convention of having all the variables on the LHS of the inequality and a constant on the RHS. This model is implemented in the spreadsheet shown in Figure 6.21 (and in the file Fig6-21.xls on your data disk).

In the spreadsheet in Figure 6.21, cells B5, C5, and D5 represent the variables X_1, X_2, and X_3, and cells B15, C15, and D15 represent Y_1, Y_2, and Y_3. The coefficients for the objective function are in cells B7 through D8. The objective function is implemented in cell F8 with the formula:

Formula for cell F8: =SUMPRODUCT(B7:D7,B5:D5)−
SUMPRODUCT(B8:D8,B15:D15)

Cells B11 through D13 contain the coefficients for the machining, grinding, and assembly constraints. The LHS formulas for these constraints are implemented in cells E11 through E13, and cells F11 through F13 contain the RHS values for these constraints. Finally, the LHS formulas for the linking constraints are entered in cells B16 through D16 as:

Formula for cell B16:   =B5 − MIN($F$11/B11,$F$12/B12,$F$13/B13)*B15

(Copy to cells C16 through D16.)

FIGURE 6.21

Spreadsheet model for Remington's fixed-charge problem

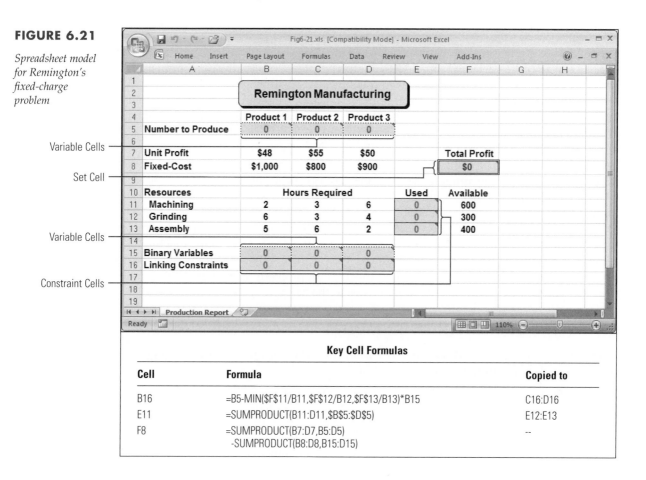

Key Cell Formulas

Cell	Formula	Copied to
B16	=B5-MIN($F$11/B11,$F$12/B12,$F$13/B13)*B15	C16:D16
E11	=SUMPRODUCT(B11:D11,$B$5:$D$5)	E12:E13
F8	=SUMPRODUCT(B7:D7,B5:D5) -SUMPRODUCT(B8:D8,B15:D15)	--

Instead of entering the values for M_i in these constraints, we implemented formulas that would calculate correct M_i values automatically if the user of this spreadsheet changed any of the coefficients or RHS values in the capacity constraints.

Potential Pitfall

Note that we are treating cells B15, C15, and D15, which represent the binary variables Y_1, Y_2, and Y_3, just like any other cells representing decision variables. We simply entered values of 0 into these cells to indicate that they represent decision variables. Ultimately, Solver will determine what values should be placed in these cells so that all the constraints are satisfied and the objective function is maximized. Some people try to make Solver's job "easier" by placing IF( ) functions in these cells to determine whether the values should be 0 or 1 depending on the values of cells B5, C5, and D5, which correspond to the variables X_1, X_2, and X_3. Although this approach seems to make sense, it can produce unwanted results. Using IF( ) functions in this way introduces *nonlinearities* in the spreadsheet model that can prevent Solver from finding the optimal solution to the problem. In Chapter 8, Nonlinear Programming, we will see that nonlinear programming problems can be very difficult to solve optimally. Thus, it is best to create a model so that it can be solved using linear optimization methods.

6.13.6 SOLVING THE MODEL

The Solver Parameters dialog box shown in Figure 6.22 indicates the settings required to solve this problem. Notice that the ranges B5 through D5 and B15 through D15, which correspond to the X_i and Y_i variables, are both listed as ranges of cells that can be changed. Also, notice that the necessary binary constraint is imposed on cells B15 through D15.

Because so few integer variables exist in this problem, we should be able to obtain an optimal integer solution easily. If we set the suboptimality tolerance to 0 in the Integer Options dialog box and instruct Solver to assume a linear model, we obtain the optimal solution to this problem, as shown in Figure 6.23.

FIGURE 6.22

Solver parameters for Remington's fixed-charge problem

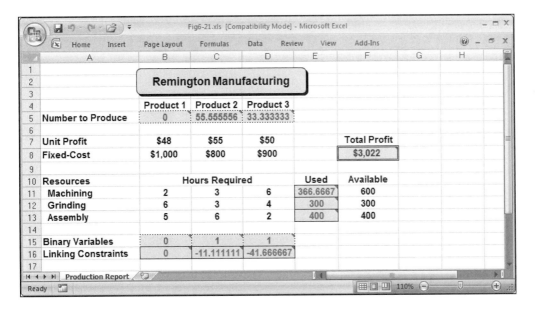

FIGURE 6.23

Optimal mixed-integer solution to Remington's fixed-charge problem

6.13.7 ANALYZING THE SOLUTION

The solution shown in Figure 6.23 indicates that the company should produce 0 units of product 1, 55.55 units of product 2, and 33.33 units of product 3 ($X_1 = 0$, $X_2 = 55.55$, and $X_3 = 33.33$). Solver assigned values of 0, 1, and 1 to cells B15, C15, and D15 ($Y_1 = 0$, $Y_2 = 1$, and $Y_3 = 1$). Thus, Solver maintained the proper relationship between the X_i and Y_i because the linking constraints were specified for this problem.

The values in B16, C16, and D16 indicate the amounts by which the values for X_1, X_2, and X_3 (in cells B5, C5, and D5) fall below the upper bounds imposed by their respective linking constraints. Thus, the optimal value of X_2 is approximately 11.11 units below its upper bound of 66.67 and the optimal value of X_3 is approximately 41.67 units below its upper bound of 75. Because the optimal value of Y_1 is zero, the linking constraint for X_1 and Y_1 imposes an upper bound of zero on X_1. Thus, the value in cell B16 indicates that the optimal value of X_1 is zero units below its upper bound of zero.

Because our formulation of this model did not specify that the X_i must be integers, we should not be surprised by the fractional values obtained for these variables in this solution. If we round the values of X_2 and X_3 down to 55 and 33, we obtain an integer feasible solution with an objective function value of $2,975. If we want to find the optimal all-integer solution, we can add the appropriate integrality condition for the X_i to the constraint set and then re-solve the problem. This optimal all-integer solution is shown in Figure 6.24.

Note that more computational effort is required to obtain the all-integer solution shown in Figure 6.24 versus the effort required to obtain the mixed-integer solution shown in Figure 6.23. This additional work resulted in only a $5 improvement in the objective function over the all-integer solution we obtained from rounding down the solution in Figure 6.23. This highlights two important points. First, problems involving binary integer variables are often easier to solve than problems involving general integer variables. Second, good near-optimal solutions often can be obtained by rounding, so this approach is not necessarily ineffective—and could be the only practical solution available for large ILPs that are difficult to solve.

FIGURE 6.24

Optimal all-integer solution to Remington's fixed-charge problem

6.14 Minimum Order/Purchase Size

Many investment, production, and distribution problems have minimum purchase amounts or minimum production lot size requirements that must be met. For example, a particular investment opportunity might require a minimum investment of $25,000. Or, a supplier of a given part used in a production process might require a minimum order of 10 units. Similarly, many manufacturing companies have a policy of not producing any units of a given item unless a certain minimum lot size will be produced.

To see how these types of minimum order/purchase requirements can be modeled, suppose that in the previous problem, Remington Manufacturing did not want to produce any units of product 3 (X_3) unless it produced at least 40 units of this product. This type of restriction is modeled as:

$$X_3 \leq M_3Y_3$$
$$X_3 \geq 40Y_3$$

The first constraint is the same type of linking constraint described earlier, in which M_3 represents an upper bound on X_3 (or an arbitrarily large number) and Y_3 represents a binary variable. If X_3 assumes any positive value, Y_3 must equal 1 (if $X_3 > 0$, then $Y_3 = 1$). However, according to the second constraint, if Y_3 equals 1, then X_3 must be greater than or equal to 40 (if $Y_3 = 1$, then $X_3 \geq 40$). On the other hand, if X_3 equals 0, Y_3 also must equal 0 to satisfy both constraints. Together, these two constraints ensure that if X_3 assumes any positive value, that value must be at least 40. This example illustrates how binary variables can be used to model a practical condition that is likely to occur in a variety of decision problems.

6.15 Quantity Discounts

In all the LP problems considered to this point, we have assumed that the profit or cost coefficients in the objective function were constant. For example, consider our revised Blue Ridge Hot Tubs problem, which is represented by:

MAX:	$350X_1 + 300X_2$	} profit
Subject to:	$1X_1 + 1X_2 \leq 200$	} pump constraint
	$9X_1 + 6X_2 \leq 1,520$	} labor constraint
	$12X_1 + 16X_2 \leq 2,650$	} tubing constraint
	$X_1, X_2 \geq 0$	} nonnegativity conditions
	X_1, X_2 must be integers	} integrality conditions

This model assumes that *every* additional Aqua-Spa (X_1) manufactured and sold results in a $350 increase in profit. It also assumes that every additional Hydro-Lux (X_2) manufactured and sold results in a $300 increase in profit. However, as the production of these products increases, quantity discounts might be obtained on component parts that would cause the profit margin on these items to increase.

For example, suppose that if the company produces more than 75 Aqua-Spas, it will be able to obtain quantity discounts and other economies of scale that would increase the profit margin to $375 per unit for each unit produced in excess of 75. Similarly, suppose that if the company produces more than 50 Hydro-Luxes, it will be able to increase its profit margin to $325 for each unit produced in excess of 50. That is, each of the first 75 units of X_1 and the first 50 units of X_2 would produce profits of $350 and $300 per unit, respectively, and each additional unit of X_1 and X_2 would produce profits of $375 and $325 per unit, respectively. How do we model this type of problem?

6.15.1 FORMULATING THE MODEL

To accommodate the different profit rates that can be generated by producing Aqua-Spas and Hydro-Luxes, we need to define new variables for the problem, where

X_{11} = the number of Aqua-Spas produced at \$350 profit per unit
X_{12} = the number of Aqua-Spas produced at \$375 profit per unit
X_{21} = the number of Hydro-Luxes produced at \$300 profit per unit
X_{22} = the number of Hydro-Luxes produced at \$325 profit per unit

Using these variables, we can begin to reformulate our problem as:

MAX: $350X_{11} + 375X_{12} + 300X_{21} + 325X_{22}$

Subject to:
$$1X_{11} + 1X_{12} + 1X_{21} + 1X_{22} \leq 200 \quad \text{\} pump constraint}$$
$$9X_{11} + 9X_{12} + 6X_{21} + 6X_{22} \leq 1{,}520 \quad \text{\} labor constraint}$$
$$12X_{11} + 12X_{12} + 16X_{21} + 16X_{22} \leq 2{,}650 \quad \text{\} tubing constraint}$$
$$\text{All } X_{ij} \geq 0 \quad \text{\} simple lower bounds}$$
$$\text{All } X_{ij} \text{ must be integers} \quad \text{\} integrality conditions}$$

This formulation is not complete. Notice that the variable X_{12} would always be preferred over X_{11} because X_{12} requires exactly the same resources as X_{11} and generates a larger per-unit profit. The same relationship holds between X_{22} and X_{21}. Thus, the optimal solution to the problem is $X_{11} = 0$, $X_{12} = 118$, $X_{21} = 0$, and $X_{22} = 76$. However, this solution is not allowable because we cannot produce any units of X_{12} until we have produced 75 units of X_{11}; and we cannot produce any units of X_{22} until we have produced 50 units of X_{21}. Therefore, we must identify some additional constraints to ensure that these conditions are met.

6.15.2 THE MISSING CONSTRAINTS

To ensure that the model does not allow any units of X_{12} to be produced unless we have produced 75 units of X_{11}, consider the constraints:

$$X_{12} \leq M_{12}Y_1$$
$$X_{11} \geq 75Y_1$$

In the first constraint, M_{12} represents some arbitrarily large numeric constant and Y_1 represents a binary variable. The first constraint requires that $Y_1 = 1$ if any units of X_{12} are produced (if $X_{12} > 0$, then $Y_1 = 1$). However, if $Y_1 = 1$, then the second constraint would require X_{11} to be at least 75. According to the second constraint, the only way that fewer than 75 units of X_{11} can be produced is if $Y_1 = 0$, which, by the first constraint, implies $X_{12} = 0$. These two constraints do not allow any units of X_{12} to be produced unless at least 75 units of X_{11} have been produced. The following constraints ensure that the model does not allow any units of X_{22} to be produced unless we have produced 50 units of X_{21}:

$$X_{22} \leq M_{22}Y_2$$
$$X_{21} \geq 50Y_2$$

If we include these new constraints in our previous formulation (along with the constraints necessary to make Y_1 and Y_2 operate as binary variables), we would have an accurate formulation of the decision problem. The optimal solution to this problem is $X_{11} = 75$, $X_{12} = 43$, $X_{21} = 50$, $X_{22} = 26$.

6.16 A Contract Award Problem

Other conditions often arise in decision problems that can be modeled effectively using binary variables. The following example, which involves awarding contracts, illustrates some of these conditions.

B&G Construction is a commercial building company located in Tampa, Florida. The company has recently signed contracts to construct four buildings in different locations throughout southern Florida. Each building project requires large amounts of cement to be delivered to the building sites. At B&G's request, three cement companies have submitted bids for supplying the cement for these jobs. The following table summarizes the prices the three companies charge per delivered ton of cement and the maximum amount of cement that each company can provide.

	Cost per Delivered Ton of Cement				
	Project 1	Project 2	Project 3	Project 4	Max. Supply
Company 1	$120	$115	$130	$125	525
Company 2	$100	$150	$110	$105	450
Company 3	$140	$ 95	$145	$165	550
Total Tons Needed	450	275	300	350	

For example, Company 1 can supply a maximum of 525 tons of cement, and each ton delivered to projects 1, 2, 3, and 4 will cost $120, $115, $130, and $125, respectively. The costs vary primarily because of the different distances between the cement plants and the construction sites. The numbers in the last row of the table indicate the total amount of cement (in tons) required for each project.

In addition to the maximum supplies listed, each cement company placed special conditions on its bid. Specifically, Company 1 indicated that it will not supply orders of less than 150 tons for any of the construction projects. Company 2 indicated that it can supply more than 200 tons to no more than one of the projects. Company 3 indicated that it will only accept orders that total 200 tons, 400 tons, or 550 tons.

B&G can contract with more than one supplier to meet the cement requirements for a given project. The problem is to determine what amounts to purchase from each supplier to meet the demands for each project at the least total cost.

This problem seems like a transportation problem in which we want to determine how much cement should be shipped from each cement company to each construction project to meet the demands of the projects at a minimum cost. However, the special conditions imposed by each supplier require side constraints, which usually are not found in a standard transportation problem. First, we'll discuss the formulation of the objective function and the transportation constraints. Then, we'll consider how to implement the side constraints required by the special conditions in the problem.

6.16.1 FORMULATING THE MODEL: THE OBJECTIVE FUNCTION AND TRANSPORTATION CONSTRAINTS

To begin formulating this problem, we need to define our decision variables as:

X_{ij} = tons of cement purchased from company i for construction project j

The objective function to minimize total cost is represented by:

$$\text{MIN:}\quad 120X_{11} + 115X_{12} + 130X_{13} + 125X_{14}$$
$$+ 100X_{21} + 150X_{22} + 110X_{23} + 105X_{24}$$
$$+ 140X_{31} + 95X_{32} + 145X_{33} + 165X_{34}$$

To ensure that the maximum supply of cement from each company is not exceeded, we need the following constraints:

$$X_{11} + X_{12} + X_{13} + X_{14} \leq 525 \quad \} \text{ supply from company 1}$$
$$X_{21} + X_{22} + X_{23} + X_{24} \leq 450 \quad \} \text{ supply from company 2}$$
$$X_{31} + X_{32} + X_{33} + X_{34} \leq 550 \quad \} \text{ supply from company 3}$$

To ensure that the requirement for cement at each construction project is met, we need the following constraints:

$$X_{11} + X_{21} + X_{31} = 450 \quad \} \text{ demand for cement at project 1}$$
$$X_{12} + X_{22} + X_{32} = 275 \quad \} \text{ demand for cement at project 2}$$
$$X_{13} + X_{23} + X_{33} = 300 \quad \} \text{ demand for cement at project 3}$$
$$X_{14} + X_{24} + X_{34} = 350 \quad \} \text{ demand for cement at project 4}$$

6.16.2 IMPLEMENTING THE TRANSPORTATION CONSTRAINTS

The objective function and the constraints of this problem are implemented in the spreadsheet model shown in Figure 6.25 (and in the file Fig6-25.xls on your data disk).

In this spreadsheet, the costs per delivered ton of cement are shown in cells B6 through E8. Cells B12 through E14 represent the decision variables in the model. The objective function is entered in cell G17 as:

Formula for cell G17:   =SUMPRODUCT(B6:E8,B12:E14)

FIGURE 6.25

Spreadsheet model for the transportation portion of B&G's contract award problem

The LHS formulas of the supply constraints are entered in cells F12 through F14 as:

$$\text{Formula for cell F12:} \qquad =\text{SUM(B12:E12)}$$

(Copy to F13 through F14.)

Cells G12 through G14 contain the RHS values for these constraints. The LHS formulas for the demand constraints are entered in cells B15 through E15 as:

$$\text{Formula for cell B15:} \qquad =\text{SUM(B12:B14)}$$

(Copy to C15 through E15.)

Cells B16 through E16 contain the RHS values for these constraints.

6.16.3 FORMULATING THE MODEL: THE SIDE CONSTRAINTS

Company 1 indicated that it will not accept orders for less than 150 tons for any of the construction projects. This minimum-size order restriction is modeled by the following eight constraints, where the Y_{ij} represent binary variables:

$$X_{11} \le 525Y_{11} \qquad \text{(implement as } X_{11} - 525Y_{11} \le 0)$$
$$X_{12} \le 525Y_{12} \qquad \text{(implement as } X_{12} - 525Y_{12} \le 0)$$
$$X_{13} \le 525Y_{13} \qquad \text{(implement as } X_{13} - 525Y_{13} \le 0)$$
$$X_{14} \le 525Y_{14} \qquad \text{(implement as } X_{14} - 525Y_{14} \le 0)$$
$$X_{11} \ge 150Y_{11} \qquad \text{(implement as } X_{11} - 150Y_{11} \ge 0)$$
$$X_{12} \ge 150Y_{12} \qquad \text{(implement as } X_{12} - 150Y_{12} \ge 0)$$
$$X_{13} \ge 150Y_{13} \qquad \text{(implement as } X_{13} - 150Y_{13} \ge 0)$$
$$X_{14} \ge 150Y_{14} \qquad \text{(implement as } X_{14} - 150Y_{14} \ge 0)$$

Each constraint has an algebraically equivalent constraint, which ultimately will be used in implementing the constraint in the spreadsheet. The first four constraints represent linking constraints that ensure that if X_{11}, X_{12}, X_{13}, or X_{14} is greater than 0, then its associated binary variable (Y_{11}, Y_{12}, Y_{13}, or Y_{14}) must equal 1. (These constraints also indicate that 525 is the maximum value that can be assumed by X_{11}, X_{12}, X_{13}, and X_{14}.) The next four constraints ensure that if X_{11}, X_{12}, X_{13}, or X_{14} is greater than 0, it must be at least 150. We include these constraints in the formulation of this model to ensure that any order given to Company 1 is for at least 150 tons of cement.

Company 2 indicated that it can supply more than 200 tons to no more than one of the projects. This type of restriction is represented by the following set of constraints where, again, the Y_{ij} represent binary variables:

$$X_{21} \le 200 + 250Y_{21} \qquad \text{(implement as } X_{21} - 200 - 250Y_{21} \le 0)$$
$$X_{22} \le 200 + 250Y_{22} \qquad \text{(implement as } X_{22} - 200 - 250Y_{22} \le 0)$$
$$X_{23} \le 200 + 250Y_{23} \qquad \text{(implement as } X_{23} - 200 - 250Y_{23} \le 0)$$
$$X_{24} \le 200 + 250Y_{24} \qquad \text{(implement as } X_{24} - 200 - 250Y_{24} \le 0)$$
$$Y_{21} + Y_{22} + Y_{23} + Y_{24} \le 1 \qquad \text{(implement as is)}$$

The first constraint indicates that the amount supplied from Company 2 for Project 1 must be less than 200 if $Y_{21} = 0$, or less than 450 (the maximum supply from company 2) if $Y_{21} = 1$. The next three constraints have similar interpretations for the amount supplied from Company 2 to Projects 2, 3, and 4, respectively. The last constraint indicates that at most, one of Y_{21}, Y_{22}, Y_{23}, and Y_{24} can equal 1. Therefore, only one of the projects can receive more than 200 tons of cement from Company 2.

The final set of constraints for this problem addresses Company 3's stipulation that it will accept only orders totaling 200, 400, or 550 tons. This type of condition is modeled using binary Y_{ij} variables as:

$$X_{31} + X_{32} + X_{33} + X_{34} = 200Y_{31} + 400Y_{32} + 550Y_{33}$$

$$\text{(implement as } X_{31} + X_{32} + X_{33} + X_{34} - 200Y_{31} - 400Y_{32} - 550Y_{33} = 0)$$

$$Y_{31} + Y_{32} + Y_{33} \le 1 \quad \text{(implement as is)}$$

These constraints allow for the total amount ordered from Company 3 to assume four distinct values. If $Y_{31} = Y_{32} = Y_{33} = 0$, then no cement will be ordered from Company 3. If $Y_{31} = 1$, then 200 tons must be ordered. If $Y_{32} = 1$ then 400 tons must be ordered. Finally, if $Y_{33} = 1$, then 550 tons must be ordered from Company 3. These two constraints enforce the special condition imposed by Company 3.

6.16.4 IMPLEMENTING THE SIDE CONSTRAINTS

Although the side constraints in this problem allow us to impose important restrictions on the feasible solutions that can be considered, these constraints serve more of a "mechanical" purpose—to make the model work—but are not of primary interest to management. Thus, it is often convenient to implement side constraints in an out-of-the-way area of the spreadsheet so that they do not detract from the primary purpose of the spreadsheet, in this case, to determine how much cement to order from each potential supplier. Figure 6.26 shows how the side constraints for the current problem can be implemented in a spreadsheet.

To implement the side constraints for Company 1, we enter the batch-size restriction of 150 in cell B20 and reserve cells B21 through E21 to represent the binary variables Y_{11}, Y_{12}, Y_{13}, and Y_{14}. The LHS formulas for the linking constraints for Company 1 are implemented in cells B22 through E22 as:

Formula for cell B22:   =B12–$G$12*B21
(Copy to C22 through E22.)

Cell F22 contains a reminder for us to tell Solver that these cells must be less than or equal to 0. The LHS formulas for the batch-size constraints for Company 1 are implemented in cells B23 through E23 as:

Formula for cell B23:   =B12–$B$20*B21
(Copy to C23 through E23.)

Cell F23 contains a reminder for us to tell Solver that these cells must be greater than or equal to 0.

To implement the side constraints for Company 2, we enter the maximum supply value of 200 in cell B25 and reserve cells B26 through E26 to represent the binary variables Y_{21}, Y_{22}, Y_{23}, and Y_{24}. The LHS formulas for the maximum supply constraints are implemented in cells B27 through E27 as:

Formula for cell B27:   =B13–$B$25–($G$13–$B$25)*B26
(Copy to C27 through E27.)

Cell F27 reminds us to tell Solver that these cells must be less than or equal to 0. As discussed earlier, to ensure that no more than one order from Company 2 exceeds 200 tons, the sum of the binary variables for Company 2 cannot exceed 1. The LHS formula for this constraint is entered in cell E28 as:

Formula for cell E28:   =SUM(B26:E26)

Cell F28 reminds us to tell Solver that this cell must be less than or equal to 1.

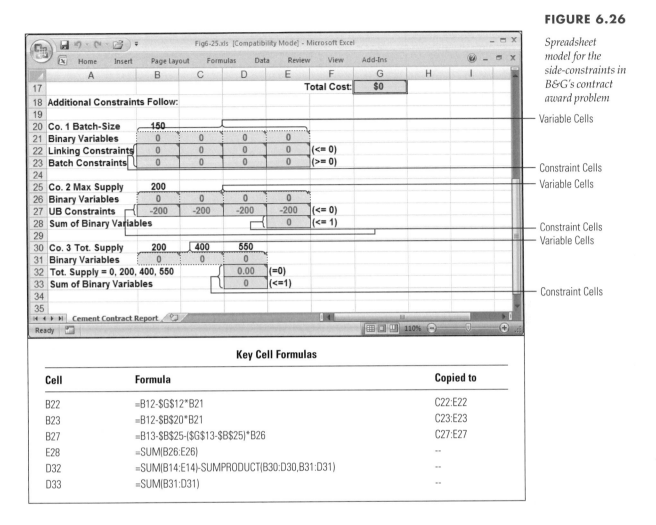

Key Cell Formulas

Cell	Formula	Copied to
B22	=B12-$G$12*B21	C22:E22
B23	=B12-$B$20*B21	C23:E23
B27	=B13-$B$25-($G$13-$B$25)*B26	C27:E27
E28	=SUM(B26:E26)	--
D32	=SUM(B14:E14)-SUMPRODUCT(B30:D30,B31:D31)	--
D33	=SUM(B31:D31)	--

To implement the side constraints for Company 3, the three possible total order amounts are entered in cells B30 through D30. Cells B31 through D31 are reserved to represent the binary variables Y_{31}, Y_{32}, and Y_{33}. The LHS formula for Company 3's total supply side constraint is entered in cell D32 as:

Formula for cell D32:   =SUM(B14:E14)–SUMPRODUCT(B30:D30,B31:D31)

Cell E32 reminds us to tell Solver that cell D32 must equal 0. Finally, to ensure that no more than one of the binary variables for company 3 is set equal to 1, we enter the sum of these variables in cell D33 as:

Formula for cell D33:   =SUM(B31:D31)

Cell E33 reminds us to tell Solver that this cell must be less than or equal to 1.

6.16.5 SOLVING THE MODEL

Because of the large number of variables and constraints in this problem, we summarized the Solver parameters required for this problem in Figure 6.27. Note that all of the cells representing binary variables must be identified as variable cells and must be constrained to assume only integer values between 0 and 1.

FIGURE 6.27

*Solver parameters
and options for
B&G's contract
award problem*

Solver Parameters:

Set Target Cell: G17

Equal to: Min

By Changing Cells: B12:E14,B21:E21,B26:E26,B31:D31

Subject to the Constraints:

$\qquad$ B12:E14 $\geq$ 0

$\qquad$ B21:E21 = binary

$\qquad$ B26:E26 = binary

$\qquad$ B31:D31 = binary

$\qquad$ F12:F14 $\geq$ G12:G14

$\qquad$ B15:E15 = B16:E16

$\qquad$ B22:E22 $\leq$ 0

$\qquad$ B23:E23 $\geq$ 0

$\qquad$ B27:E27 $\leq$ 0

$\qquad$ E28 $\leq$ 1

$\qquad$ D32 = 0

$\qquad$ D33 $\leq$ 1

Solver Options:

Standard Simplex LP $\qquad$ Integer Tolerance = 0

Use Automatic Scaling $\qquad$ Iterations = 100

6.16.6 ANALYZING THE SOLUTION

An optimal solution to this problem is shown in Figure 6.28 (there are alternate optimal solutions to this problem). In this solution, the amounts of cement required by each construction project are met exactly. Also, each condition imposed by the side constraints for each company is met. Specifically, the orders awarded to Company 1 are for at least 150 tons; no more than one of the orders awarded to Company 2 exceeds 200 tons; and the sum of the orders awarded to Company 3 is exactly equal to 400 tons.

6.17 The Branch-and-Bound Algorithm (Optional)

As mentioned earlier, a special procedure, known as the branch-and-bound (B&B) algorithm, is required to solve ILPs. Although we can easily indicate the presence of integer variables in a model, it usually requires quite a bit of effort on Solver's part to actually solve an ILP problem using the B&B algorithm. To better appreciate and understand what is involved in the B&B algorithm, let's consider how it works.

The B&B algorithm starts by relaxing all the integrality conditions in an ILP and solving the resulting LP problem. As noted earlier, if we are lucky, the optimal solution to the relaxed LP problem might happen to satisfy the original integrality conditions. If

FIGURE 6.28

Optimal solution to B&G's contract award problem

this occurs, then we are done—the optimal solution to the LP relaxation is also the optimal solution to the ILP. However, it is more likely that the optimal solution to the LP will violate one or more of the original integrality conditions. For example, consider the problem for which the integer and relaxed feasible regions were shown in Figure 6.1 and are repeated in Figure 6.29:

$$\text{MAX:} \qquad 2X_1 + 3X_2$$
$$\text{Subject to:} \qquad X_1 + 3X_2 \leq 8.25$$
$$2.5X_1 + X_2 \leq 8.75$$
$$X_1, X_2 \geq 0$$
$$X_1, X_2 \text{ must be integers}$$

If we relax the integrality conditions in this problem and solve the resulting LP problem, we obtain the solution $X_1 = 2.769$, $X_2 = 1.826$ shown in Figure 6.29. This solution clearly violates the integrality conditions stated in the original problem. Part of the difficulty here is that none of the corner points of the relaxed feasible region are integer feasible (other than the origin). We know that the optimal solution to an LP problem will occur at a corner point of its feasible region but, in this case, none of those corner points (except the origin) correspond to integer solutions. Thus, we need to modify the problem so that the integer feasible solutions to the problem occur at corner points of the relaxed feasible region. This is accomplished by branching.

6.17.1 BRANCHING

Any integer variable in an ILP that assumes a fractional value in the optimal solution to the relaxed problem can be designated as a **branching variable**. For example, the

FIGURE 6.29

Solution to LP relaxation at noninteger corner point

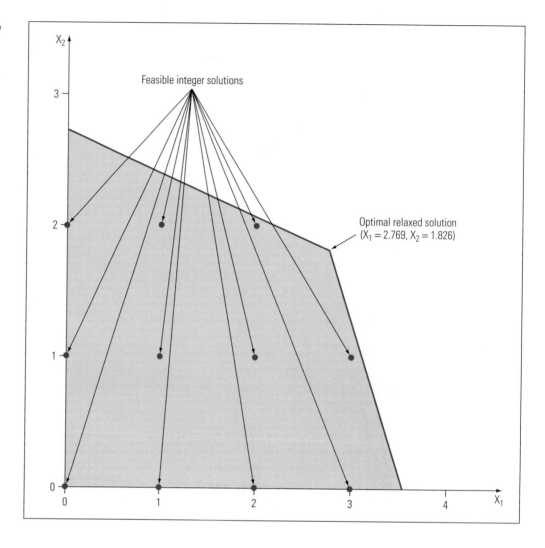

variables X_1 and X_2 in the previous problem should assume only integer values, but were assigned the values $X_1 = 2.769$ and $X_2 = 1.826$ in the optimal-solution to the LP relaxation of the problem. Either of these variables could be selected as branching variables.

Let's arbitrarily choose X_1 as our branching variable. Because the current value of X_1 is not integer feasible, we want to eliminate this solution from further consideration. Many other solutions in this same vicinity of the relaxed feasible region also can be eliminated. That is, X_1 must assume a value less than or equal to 2 ($X_1 \leq 2$) or greater than or equal to 3 ($X_1 \geq 3$) in the optimal integer solution to the ILP. Therefore, all other possible solutions where X_1 assumes values between 2 and 3 (such as the current solution where $X_1 = 2.769$) can be eliminated from consideration. By branching on X_1, our original ILP problem can be subdivided into the following two candidate problems:

Problem I: MAX: $2X_1 + 3X_2$

Subject to: $X_1 + 3X_2 \leq 8.25$

$2.5X_1 + X_2 \leq 8.75$

$X_1 \leq 2$

$X_1, X_2 \geq 0$

X_1, X_2 must be integers

Problem II: MAX: $2X_1 + 3X_2$

Subject to: $X_1 + 3X_2 \leq 8.25$

$2.5X_1 + X_2 \leq 8.75$

$X_1 \geq 3$

$X_1, X_2 \geq 0$

X_1, X_2 must be integers

The integer and relaxed feasible regions for each candidate problem are shown in Figure 6.30. Notice that a portion of the relaxed feasible region shown in Figure 6.29 has been eliminated in Figure 6.30, but none of the feasible integer solutions shown in Figure 6.29 have been eliminated. This is a general property of the branching operation in the B&B algorithm. Also notice that several feasible integer solutions now occur on the boundary lines of the feasible regions shown in Figure 6.30. More important, one of these feasible integer solutions occurs at an extreme point of the relaxed feasible region for problem I (at the point $X_1 = 2$, $X_2 = 0$). If we relax the integrality conditions in problem I and solve the resulting LP, we could obtain an integer solution because one of the corner points of the relaxed feasible region corresponds to such a point. (However, this integer feasible extreme point still might not be the optimal solution to the relaxed LP problem.)

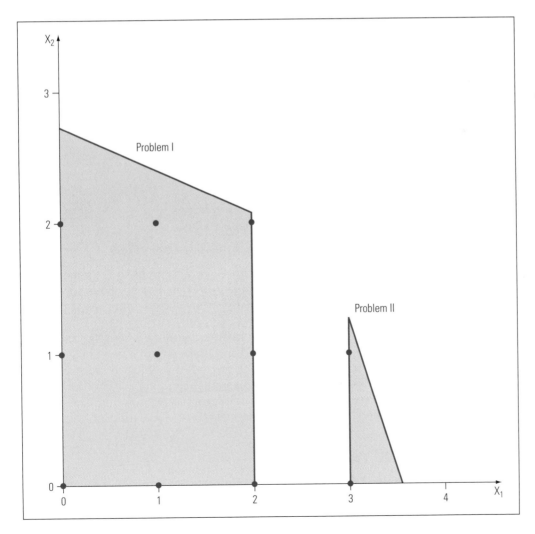

FIGURE 6.30

Feasible solutions to the candidate problems after the first branch

6.17.2 BOUNDING

The next step in the B&B algorithm is to select one of the existing candidate problems for further analysis. Let's arbitrarily select problem I. If we relax the integrality conditions in problem I and solve the resulting LP, we obtain the solution $X_1 = 2$, $X_2 = 2.083$ and an objective function value of 10.25. This value represents an upper bound on the best possible integer solution that can be obtained from problem I. That is, because the relaxed solution to problem I is not integer feasible, we have not yet found the best possible integer solution for this problem. However, we do know that the objective function value of the best possible integer solution that can be obtained from problem I can be no greater than 10.25. As we shall see, this information can be useful in reducing the amount of work required to locate the optimal integer solution to an ILP problem.

6.17.3 BRANCHING AGAIN

Because the relaxed solution to problem I is not entirely integer feasible, the B&B algorithm proceeds by selecting X_2 as a branching variable and creating two additional candidate problems from problem I. These problems are represented as:

$$
\begin{array}{lll}
\text{Problem III:} & \text{MAX:} & 2X_1 + 3X_2 \\
& \text{Subject to:} & X_1 + 3X_2 \leq 8.25 \\
& & 2.5X_1 + X_2 \leq 8.75 \\
& & X_1 \leq 2 \\
& & X_2 \leq 2 \\
& & X_1, X_2 \geq 0 \\
& & X_1, X_2 \text{ must be integers} \\
\text{Problem IV:} & \text{MAX:} & 2X_1 + 3X_2 \\
& \text{Subject to:} & X_1 + 3X_2 \leq 8.25 \\
& & 2.5X_1 + X_2 \leq 8.75 \\
& & X_1 \leq 2 \\
& & X_2 \geq 3 \\
& & X_1, X_2 \geq 0 \\
& & X_1, X_2 \text{ must be integers}
\end{array}
$$

Problem III is created by adding the constraint $X_2 \leq 2$ to problem I. Problem IV is created by adding the constraint $X_2 \geq 3$ to problem I. Thus, our previous solution to problem I (where $X_2 = 2.083$) will be eliminated from consideration as a possible solution to the LP relaxations of problems III and IV.

Problem IV is infeasible because there are no feasible solutions where $X_2 \geq 3$. The integer and relaxed feasible regions for problems II and III are summarized in Figure 6.31.

All of the corner points to the relaxed feasible region of problem III correspond to integer feasible solutions. Thus, if we relax the integrality conditions in problem III and solve the resulting LP problem, we must obtain an integer feasible solution. The solution to problem III is represented by $X_1 = 2$, $X_2 = 2$ and has an objective function value of 10.

6.17.4 BOUNDING AGAIN

Although we have obtained an integer feasible solution to our problem, we won't know if it is the *optimal* integer solution until we evaluate the remaining candidate problem

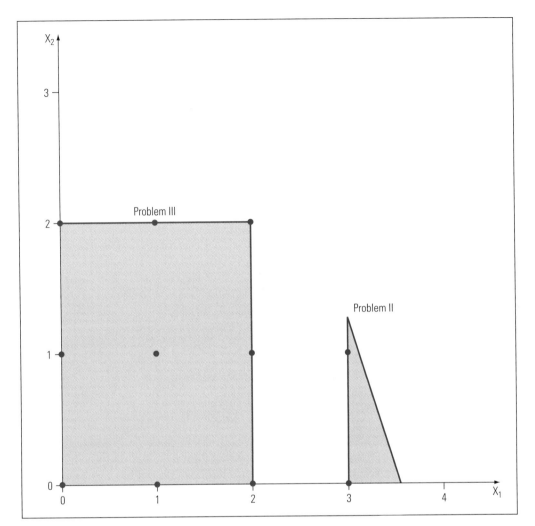

FIGURE 6.31

Feasible solutions to the candidate problems after the second branch

(that is, problem II). If we relax the integrality conditions in problem II and solve the resulting LP problem, we obtain the solution $X_1 = 3$, $X_2 = 1.25$ with an objective function value of 9.75.

Because the solution to problem II is not integer feasible, we might be inclined to branch on X_2 in a further attempt to determine the best possible integer solution for problem II. However, this is not necessary. Earlier we noted that for *maximization* ILP problems, the objective function value at the optimal solution to the LP relaxation of the problem represents an *upper bound* on the optimal objective function value of the original ILP problem. This means that even though we do not yet know the optimal integer solution to problem II, we do know that its objective function value cannot be greater than 9.75. And because 9.75 is worse than the objective function value for the integer solution obtained from problem III, we cannot find a better integer solution by continuing to branch problem II. Therefore, problem II can be eliminated from further consideration. Because we have no more candidate problems to consider, we can conclude that the optimal integer solution to our problem is $X_1 = 2$, $X_2 = 2$ with an optimal objective function value of 10.

FIGURE 6.32

Branch-and-bound tree for the example problem

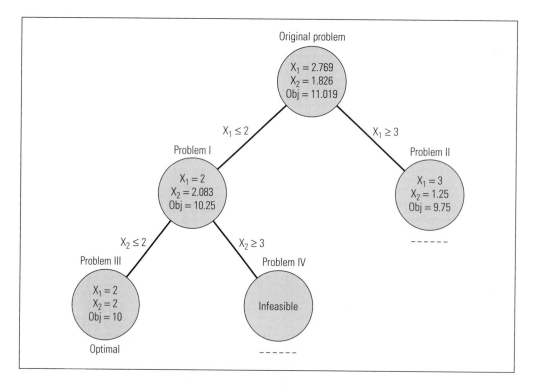

6.17.5 SUMMARY OF B&B EXAMPLE

The steps involved in the solution to our example problem can be represented graphically in the form of a *branch-and-bound tree*, as shown in Figure 6.32. Although Figure 6.29 indicates that 11 integer solutions exist for this problem, we do not have to locate all of them to prove that the integer solution we found is the optimal solution. The bounding operation of the B&B algorithm eliminated the need to explicitly enumerate all the integer feasible solutions and select the best of those as the optimal solution.

If the relaxed solution to problem II was greater than 10 (say 12.5), then the B&B algorithm would have continued branching from this problem in an attempt to find a better integer solution (an integer solution with an objective function value greater than 10). Similarly, if problem IV had a feasible noninteger solution, we would have needed to perform further branching from that problem if its relaxed objective value was better than that of the best known integer feasible solution. Thus, the first integer solution obtained using B&B will not always be the optimal integer solution. A more detailed description of the operations of the B&B algorithm is given in Figure 6.33.

6.18 Summary

This chapter discussed the issues involved in formulating and solving ILP problems. In some cases, acceptable integer solutions to ILP problems can be obtained by rounding the solution to the LP relaxation of the problem. However, this procedure can lead to suboptimal solutions, which still might be viable if you can show that the solution obtained by rounding is within an acceptable distance from the optimal integer solution. This approach might be the only practical way to obtain integer solutions for some ILP problems.

FIGURE 6.33

Detailed description of the B&B algorithm for solving ILP problems

THE BRANCH-AND-BOUND ALGORITHM

1. Relax all the integrality conditions in ILP and solve the resulting LP problem. If the optimal solution to the relaxed LP problem happens to satisfy the original integrality conditions, stop—this is the optimal integer solution. Otherwise, proceed to step 2.
2. If the problem being solved is a maximization problem let $Z_{best} = -$infinity. If it is a minimization problem, let $Z_{best} = +$infinity. (In general Z_{best} represents the objective function value of the best known integer solution as the algorithm proceeds.)
3. Let X_j represent one of the variables that violated the integrality conditions in the solution to the problem that was solved most recently and let b_j represent its noninteger value. Let $INT(b_j)$ represent the largest integer that is less than b_j. Create two new candidate problems: one by appending the constraint $X_j \leq INT(b_j)$ to the most recently solved LP problem, and the other by appending the constraint $X_j \geq INT(b_j) + 1$ to the most recently solved LP problem. Place both of these new LP problems in a list of candidate problems to be solved.
4. If the list of candidate problems is empty, proceed to step 9. Otherwise, remove a candidate problem from the list, relax any integrality conditions in the problem, and solve it.
5. If there is not a solution to the current candidate problem (that is, it is infeasible), proceed to step 4. Otherwise, let Z_{cp} denote the optimal objective function value for the current candidate problem.
6. If Z_{cp} is not better than Z_{best} (for a maximization problem $Z_{cp} \leq Z_{best}$ or for a minimization problem $Z_{cp} \geq Z_{best}$), proceed to step 4.
7. If the solution to the current candidate problem *does not* satisfy the original integrality conditions, proceed to step 3.
8. If the solution to the current candidate problem *does* satisfy the original integrality conditions, a better integer solution has been found. Thus, let $Z_{best} = Z_{cp}$ and save the solution obtained for this candidate problem. Then go back to step 4.
9. Stop. The optimal solution has been found and has an objective function value given by the current value of Z_{best}.

The B&B algorithm is a powerful technique for solving ILP problems. A great deal of skill and creativity is involved in formulating ILPs so that they can be solved efficiently using the B&B technique. Binary variables can be useful in overcoming a number of the simplifying assumptions often made in the formulation of LP models. Here again, quite a bit of creativity might be required on the part of the model builder to identify the constraints to implement various logical conditions in a given problem.

6.19 References

Bean, J., et al. "Selecting Tenants in a Shopping Mall. *Interfaces*, vol. 18, no. 2, 1988.

Blake, J. and J. Donald. "Mount Sinai Hospital Uses Integer Programming to Allocate Operating Room Time." *Interfaces*, vol. 32, no. 2, 2002.

Calloway, R., M. Cummins, and J. Freeland. "Solving Spreadsheet-Based Integer Programming Models: An Example From the Telecommunications Industry." *Decision Sciences*, vol. 21, 1990.

Nauss, R. and R. Markland. "Theory and Application of an Optimizing Procedure for the Lock Box Location Analysis." *Management Science*, vol. 27, no. 8, 1981.

Nemhauser, G. and L. Wolsey. *Integer and Combinatorial Optimization*. New York: Wiley, 1988.

Peiser, R. and S. Andrus. "Phasing of Income-Producing Real Estate." *Interfaces*, vol. 13, no. 1, 1983.

Schindler, S. and T. Semmel, "Station Staffing at Pan American World Airways." *Interfaces*, vol. 23, no. 3, 1993.

Stowe, J. "An Integer Programming Solution for the Optimal Credit Investigation/Credit Granting Sequence." *Financial Management*, vol. 14, Summer 1985.

Tavakoli, A. and C. Lightner. "Implementing a Mathematical Model for Locating EMS Vehicles in Fayetteville, NC." *Computers & Operations Research*, vol. 31, 2004.

THE WORLD OF MANAGEMENT SCIENCE

Who Eats the Float?—Maryland National Improves Check Clearing Operations and Cuts Costs

Maryland National Bank (MNB) of Baltimore typically processes about 500,000 checks worth over $250,000,000 each day. Those checks not drawn on MNB or a local bank must be cleared via the Federal Reserve System, a private clearing bank, or a "direct send" by courier service to the bank on which they were drawn.

Because funds are not available until the check clears, banks try to maximize the availability of current funds by reducing the float—the time interval required for a check to clear. Banks publish an availability schedule listing the number of days before funds from a deposited check are available to the customer. If clearing time is longer than the schedule, the bank must "eat the float." If the check is cleared through the Federal Reserve and clearing takes longer than the Federal Reserve availability schedule, then the Federal Reserve "eats the float." If clearing time is actually less than the local bank's availability schedule, the customer "eats the float." The cost of float is related to the daily cost of capital.

MNB uses a system based on binary integer LP to decide the timing and method to be used for each bundle of checks of a certain type (called a cash letter). Total clearing costs (the objective function) include float costs, clearing charges from the Federal Reserve or private clearing banks, and transportation costs for direct sends. Constraints ensure that exactly one method is chosen for each check type and that a method can be used only at a time that method is available. Use of this system saves the bank $100,000 annually.

Source: Markland, Robert E., and Robert M. Nauss, "Improving Transit Check Clearing Operations at Maryland National Bank," *Interfaces*, vol. 13, no. 1, February 1983, pp. 1–9.

Questions and Problems

1. As shown in Figure 6.1, the feasible region for an ILP consists of a relatively small, *finite* number of points, whereas the feasible region of its LP relaxation consists of an *infinite* number of points. Why, then, are ILPs so much harder to solve than LPs?

2. Identify reasonable values for M_{12} and M_{22} in the example on quantity discounts presented in section 6.15.2 of this chapter.

3. The following questions refer to the CRT Technologies project selection example presented in this chapter. Formulate a constraint to implement the conditions described in each of the following statements.

    a. Out of projects 1, 2, 4, and 6, CRT's management wants to select exactly two projects.

    b. Project 2 can be selected only if project 3 is selected and vice versa.

    c. Project 5 cannot be undertaken unless both projects 3 and 4 are also undertaken.

    d. If projects 2 and 4 are undertaken, then project 5 must also be undertaken.

4. In the CRT Technologies project selection example in this chapter, the problem indicates that surplus funds in any year are reappropriated and cannot be carried over to the next year. Suppose that this is no longer the case and surplus funds may be carried over to future years.

    a. Modify the spreadsheet model given for this problem to reflect this change in assumptions.

    b. What is the optimal solution to the revised problem?

5. The following questions refers to the Blue Ridge Hot Tubs example discussed in this chapter.

    a. Suppose Howie Jones has to purchase a single piece of equipment for $1,000 to produce any Aqua-Spas or Hydro-Luxes. How will this affect the formulation of the model of his decision problem?

    b. Suppose Howie must buy one piece of equipment that costs $900 to produce any Aqua-Spas and a different piece of equipment that costs $800 to produce any Hydro-Luxes. How will this affect the formulation of the model for his problem?

6. Garden City Beach is a popular summer vacation destination for thousands of people. Each summer, the city hires temporary lifeguards to ensure the safety of the vacationing public. Garden City's lifeguards are assigned to work five consecutive days each week and then have two days off. However, the city's insurance company requires that the city have at least the following number of lifeguards on duty each day of the week:

Minimum Number of Lifeguards Required Each Day						
Sunday	Monday	Tuesday	Wednesday	Thursday	Friday	Saturday

	Sunday	Monday	Tuesday	Wednesday	Thursday	Friday	Saturday
Lifeguards	18	17	16	16	16	14	19

The city manager would like to determine the minimum number of lifeguards that will have to be hired.

    a. Formulate an ILP for this problem.

    b. Implement your model in a spreadsheet and solve it.

    c. What is the optimal solution?

    d. Several lifeguards have expressed a preference to be off on Saturdays and Sundays. What is the maximum number of lifeguards that can be off on the weekend without increasing the total number of lifeguards required?

7. Snookers Restaurant is open from 8:00 am to 10:00 pm daily. Besides the hours that they are open for business, workers are needed an hour before opening and an hour after closing for setup and cleanup activities. The restaurant operates with both full-time and part-time workers on the following shifts:

Shift	Daily Pay Rate
7:00 am–11:00 am	$32
7:00 am–3:00 pm	$80
11:00 am–3:00 pm	$32
11:00 am–7:00 pm	$80
3:00 pm–7:00 pm	$32
3:00 pm–11:00 pm	$80
7:00 pm–11:00 pm	$32

The following numbers of workers are needed during each of the indicated time blocks.

Hours	Workers Needed
7:00 am–11:00 am	11
11:00 am–1:00 pm	24
1:00 pm–3:00 pm	16
3:00 pm–5:00 pm	10
5:00 pm–7:00 pm	22
7:00 pm–9:00 pm	17
9:00 pm–11:00 pm	6

At least one full-time worker must be available during the hour before opening and after closing. Additionally, at least 30% of the employees should be full-time (8-hour) workers during the restaurant's busy periods from 11:00 am–1:00 pm and 5:00 pm–7:00 pm.

a. Formulate an ILP for this problem with the objective of minimizing total daily labor costs.

b. Implement your model in a spreadsheet and solve it.

c. What is the optimal solution?

8. A power company is considering how to increase its generating capacity to meet expected demand in its growing service area. Currently, the company has 750 megawatts (MW) of generating capacity but projects that it will need the following minimum generating capacities in each of the next five years:

	Year				
	1	2	3	4	5
Minimum Capacity in Megawatts (MW)	780	860	950	1060	1180

The company can increase its generating capacity by purchasing four different types of generators: 10 MW, 25 MW, 50 MW, and/or 100 MW. The cost of acquiring and installing each of the four types of generators in each of the next five years is summarized in the following table:

Generator Size	Cost of Generator (in $1,000s) in Year				
	1	2	3	4	5
10 MW	$300	$250	$200	$170	$145
25 MW	$460	$375	$350	$280	$235
50 MW	$670	$558	$465	$380	$320
100 MW	$950	$790	$670	$550	$460

a. Formulate a mathematical programming model to determine the least costly way of expanding the company's generating assets to the minimum required levels.

b. Implement your model in a spreadsheet and solve it.

c. What is the optimal solution?

9. Health Care Systems of Florida (HCSF) is planning to build a number of new emergency-care clinics in central Florida. HCSF management has divided a map of the area into seven regions. They want to locate the emergency centers so that all seven regions will be conveniently served by at least one facility. Five possible sites

are available for constructing the new facilities. The regions that can be served conveniently by each site are indicated by X in the following table:

Possible Building Sites

Region	Sanford	Altamonte	Apopka	Casselberry	Maitland
1	X		X		
2	X	X		X	X
3		X		X	
4			X		X
5	X	X			
6			X		X
7				X	X
Cost ($1,000s)	$450	$650	$550	$500	$525

a. Formulate an ILP problem to determine which sites should be selected so as to provide convenient service to all locations in the least costly manner.
b. Implement your model in a spreadsheet and solve it.
c. What is the optimal solution?

10. Kentwood Electronics manufactures three components for stereo systems: CD players, tape decks, and stereo tuners. The wholesale price and manufacturing cost of each item are:

Component	Wholesale Price	Manufacturing Cost
CD Player	$150	$75
Tape Deck	$ 85	$35
Stereo Tuner	$ 70	$30

Each CD player produced requires three hours of assembly; each tape deck requires two hours of assembly; and each tuner requires one hour of assembly. However, the company manufactures these products only in batches of 150—partial batches are not allowed. The marketing department believes that it can sell no more than 150,000 CD players, 100,000 tape decks, and 90,000 stereo tuners. It expects a demand for at least 50,000 units of each item and wants to be able to meet this demand. If Kentwood has 400,000 hours of assembly time available, how many batches of CD players, tape decks, and stereo tuners should it produce to maximize profits while meeting the minimum demand figures supplied by marketing?

a. Formulate an ILP model for this problem. (*Hint:* Let your decision variables represent the number of batches of each item to produce.)
b. Create a spreadsheet model for this problem and solve it.
c. What is the optimal solution?

11. Radford Castings can produce brake shoes on six different machines. The following table summarizes the manufacturing costs associated with producing the brake shoes on each machine along with the available capacity on each machine. If the company has received an order for 1,800 brake shoes, how should it schedule these machines?

Machine	Fixed Cost	Variable Cost	Capacity
1	$1000	$21	500
2	$ 950	$23	600
3	$ 875	$25	750
4	$ 850	$24	400
5	$ 800	$20	600
6	$ 700	$26	800

a. Formulate an ILP model for this problem.
b. Create a spreadsheet model for this problem and solve it.
c. What is the optimal solution?

12. The teenage daughter of a recently deceased movie star inherited a number of items from her famous father's estate. Rather than convert these assets to cash immediately, her financial advisor has recommended that she let some of these assets appreciate in value before disposing of them. An appraiser has given the following estimates of the assets' worth (in $1,000s) for each of the next five years.

	Year 1	Year 2	Year 3	Year 4	Year 5
Car	$ 35	$ 37	$ 39	$ 42	$ 45
Piano	$ 16	$ 17	$ 18	$ 19	$ 20
Necklace	$125	$130	$136	$139	$144
Desk	$ 25	$ 27	$ 29	$ 30	$ 33
Golf Clubs	$ 40	$ 43	$ 46	$ 50	$ 52
Humidor	$ 5	$ 7	$ 8	$ 10	$ 11

Knowing this teenager's propensity to spend money, her financial advisor would like to develop a plan to dispose of these assets that will maximize the amount of money received and ensure that at least $30,000 of new funds become available each year to pay her college tuition.
a. Formulate an ILP model for this problem.
b. Create a spreadsheet model for this problem and solve it.
c. What is the optimal solution?

13. A developer of video game software has seven proposals for new games. Unfortunately, the company cannot develop all the proposals because its budget for new projects is limited to $950,000 and it has only 20 programmers to assign to new projects. The financial requirements, returns, and the number of programmers required by each project are summarized below. Projects 2 and 6 require specialized programming knowledge that only one of the programmers has. Both of these projects cannot be selected because the programmer with the necessary skills can be assigned to only one of the projects. (Note: All dollar amounts represent thousands.)

Project	Programmers Required	Capital Required	Estimated NPV
1	7	$250	$650
2	6	$175	$550
3	9	$300	$600
4	5	$150	$450
5	6	$145	$375
6	4	$160	$525
7	8	$325	$750

a. Formulate an ILP model for this problem.
b. Create a spreadsheet model for this problem and solve it.
c. What is the optimal solution?

14. Tropicsun is a leading grower and distributor of fresh citrus products with three large citrus groves scattered around central Florida in the cities of Mt. Dora, Eustis, and Clermont. Tropicsun currently has 275,000 bushels of citrus at the grove in Mt. Dora, 400,000 bushels at the grove in Eustis, and 300,000 at the grove in Clermont. Tropicsun has citrus processing plants in Ocala, Orlando, and Leesburg with processing capacities to handle 200,000, 600,000, and 225,000 bushels, respectively.

Tropicsun contracts with a local trucking company to transport its fruit from the groves to the processing plants. The trucking company charges a flat rate of $8 per mile regardless of how many bushels of fruit are transported. The following table summarizes the distances (in miles) between each grove and processing plant:

Distances (in Miles) Between Groves and Plants

Grove	Processing Plant		
	Ocala	Orlando	Leesburg
Mt. Dora	21	50	40
Eustis	35	30	22
Clermont	55	20	25

Tropicsun wants to determine how many bushels to ship from each grove to each processing plant to minimize the total transportation cost.

a. Formulate an ILP model for this problem.
b. Create a spreadsheet model for this problem and solve it.
c. What is the optimal solution?

15. A real estate developer is planning to build an apartment building specifically for graduate students on a parcel of land adjacent to a major university. Four types of apartments can be included in the building: efficiencies, and one-, two-, or three-bedroom units. Each efficiency requires 500 square feet; each one-bedroom apartment requires 700 square feet; each two-bedroom apartment requires 800 square feet; and each three-bedroom unit requires 1,000 square feet. The developer believes that the building should include no more than 15 one-bedroom units, 22 two-bedroom units, and 10 three-bedroom units. Local zoning ordinances do not allow the developer to build more than 40 units in this particular building location. They restrict the building to a maximum of 40,000 square feet. The developer already has agreed to lease 5 one-bedroom units and 8 two-bedroom units to a local rental agency that is a "silent partner" in this endeavor. Market studies indicate that efficiencies can be rented for $350 per month, one-bedrooms for $450 per month, two-bedrooms for $550 per month, and three-bedrooms for $750 per month. How many rental units of each type should the developer include in the building plans to maximize the potential rental income from the building?

a. Formulate an LP model for this problem.
b. Create a spreadsheet model for this problem and solve it using Solver.
c. What is the optimal solution?
d. Which constraint in this model limits the builder's potential rental income from increasing any further?

16. Bellows Lumber Yard, Inc. stocks standard length 25-foot boards, which it cuts to custom lengths to fill individual customer orders. An order has just come in for 5,000 7-foot boards, 1,200 9-foot boards, and 300 11-foot boards. The lumber yard manager has identified six ways to cut the 25-foot boards to fill this order. The six cutting patterns are summarized in the following table.

Number of Boards Produced

Cutting Pattern	7 ft	9 ft	11 ft
1	3	0	0
2	2	1	0
3	2	0	1
4	1	2	0
5	0	1	1
6	0	0	2

One possibility (cutting pattern 1) is to cut a 25-foot board into three 7-foot boards, and not to cut any 9- or 11-foot boards. Note that cutting pattern 1 uses a total of 21 feet of board and leaves a 4-foot piece of scrap. Another possibility (cutting pattern 4) is to cut a 25-foot board into one 7-foot board and two 9-foot boards (using all 25 feet of the board). The remaining cutting patterns have similar interpretations. The lumber yard manager wants to fill this order using the fewest number of 25-foot boards as possible. To do this, the manager needs to determine how many 25-foot boards to run through each cutting pattern.

a. Formulate an LP model for this problem.
b. Create a spreadsheet model for this problem and solve it using Solver.
c. What is the optimal solution?
d. Suppose the manager wants to minimize waste. Would the solution change?

17. Howie's Carpet World has just received an order for carpets for a new office building. The order is for 4,000 yards of carpet 4 feet wide, 20,000 yards of carpet 9 feet wide, and 9,000 yards of carpet 12 feet wide. Howie can order two kinds of carpet rolls, which he will then have to cut to fill this order. One type of roll is 14 feet wide, 100 yards long, and costs $1,000 per roll; the other is 18 feet wide, 100 yards long, and costs $1,400 per roll. Howie needs to determine how many of the two types of carpet rolls to order and how they should be cut. He wants to do this in the least costly way possible.

a. Formulate an LP model for this problem.
b. Create a spreadsheet model for this problem and solve it using Solver.
c. What is the optimal solution?
d. Suppose Howie wants to minimize waste. Would the solution change?

18. A manufacturer is considering alternatives for building new plants, to be located closer to three of its primary customers with whom it intends to develop long-term, sole-supplier relationships. The net cost of manufacturing and transporting each unit of the product to its customers will vary depending on where the plant is built and the production capacity of the plant. These costs are summarized in the table below:

Plant	Net Cost per Unit to Supply Customer		
	X	Y	Z
1	35	30	45
2	45	40	50
3	70	65	50
4	20	45	25
5	65	45	45

The annual demand for products from customers X, Y, and Z is expected to be 40,000, 25,000, and 35,000 units, respectively. The annual production capacity and construction costs for each plant are:

Plant	Production Capacity	Construction Cost (in $1000s)
1	40,000	$1,325
2	30,000	$1,100
3	50,000	$1,500
4	20,000	$1,200
5	40,000	$1,400

The company wants to determine which plant to build to satisfy customer demand at a minimum total cost.

a. Formulate an ILP model for this problem.
b. Create a spreadsheet model for this problem and solve it.
c. What is the optimal solution?

19. Refer to the previous question. Suppose plants 1 and 2 represent different building alternatives for the same site (that is, only one of these plants can be built). Similarly, suppose plants 4 and 5 represent different building alternatives for another site.
   a. What additional constraints are required to model these new conditions?
   b. Revise the spreadsheet to reflect these additional constraints and solve the resulting problem.
   c. What is the optimal solution?

20. A company manufactures three products: A, B, and C. The company currently has an order for three units of product A, 7 units of product B, and 4 units of product C. There is no inventory for any of these products. All three products require special processing that can be done on one of two machines. The cost of producing each product on each machine is summarized below:

Cost of Producing a Unit of Product

Machine	A	B	C
1	$13	$ 9	$10
2	$11	$12	$ 8

The time required to produce each product on each machine is summarized below:

Time (Hours) Needed to Produced a Unit of Product

Machine	A	B	C
1	0.4	1.1	0.9
2	0.5	1.2	1.3

Assume that machine 1 can be used for eight hours and machine 2 can be used for six hours. Each machine must undergo a special setup operation to prepare it to produce each product. After completing this setup for a product, any number of that product type can be produced. The setup costs for producing each product on each machine are summarized below.

Setup Costs for Producing

Machine	A	B	C
1	$55	$93	$60
2	$65	$58	$75

a. Formulate an ILP model to determine how many units of each product to produce on each machine to meet demand at a minimum cost.
b. Implement your model in a spreadsheet and solve it.
c. What is the optimal solution?

21. Clampett Oil purchases crude oil products from suppliers in Texas (TX), Oklahoma (OK), Pennsylvania (PA), and Alabama (AL), from which it refines four end-products: gasoline, kerosene, heating oil, and asphalt. Because of differences in the quality and chemical characteristics of the oil from the different suppliers, the amount of each end product that can be refined from a barrel of crude oil varies depending on the source of the crude. Additionally, the amount of crude available from each source varies, as does the cost of a barrel of crude from each supplier. These values

are summarized below. For example, the first line of this table indicates that a barrel of crude oil from Texas can be refined into 2 barrels of gasoline, 2.8 barrels of kerosene, 1.7 barrels of heating oil, or 2.4 barrels of asphalt. Each supplier requires a minimum purchase of at least 500 barrels.

Raw Material Characteristics

Crude Oils	Barrels Available	Possible Production Per Barrel				Cost Per Barrel	Trucking Cost
		Gas	Kero.	Heat	Asphalt		
TX	1,500	2.00	2.80	1.70	2.40	$22	$1,500
OK	2,000	1.80	2.30	1.75	1.90	$21	$1,700
PA	1,500	2.30	2.20	1.60	2.60	$22	$1,500
AL	1,800	2.10	2.60	1.90	2.40	$23	$1,400

The company owns a tanker truck that picks up whatever crude oil it purchases. This truck can hold 2,000 barrels of crude. The cost of sending the truck to pick up oil from the various locations is shown in the column labeled "Trucking Cost." The company's plans for its next production cycle specify 750 barrels of gasoline, 800 barrels of kerosene, 1,000 barrels of heating oil, and 300 barrels of asphalt to be produced.

   a. Formulate an ILP model that can be solved to determine the purchasing plan that will allow the company to implement its production plan at the least cost.

   b. Implement this model in a spreadsheet and solve it.

   c. What is the optimal solution?

22. The Clampett Oil Company has a tanker truck that it uses to deliver fuel to customers. The tanker has five different storage compartments with capacities to hold 2,500, 2,000, 1,500, 1,800 and 2,300 gallons, respectively. The company has an order to deliver 2,700 gallons of diesel fuel; 3,500 gallons of regular unleaded gasoline; and 4,200 gallons of premium unleaded gasoline. If each storage compartment can hold only one type of fuel, how should Clampett Oil load the tanker? If it is impossible to load the truck with the full order, the company wants to minimize the total number of gallons by which the order is short. (*Hint:* Consider using slack variables to represent shortage amounts.)

   a. Formulate an ILP model for this problem.

   b. Implement this model in a spreadsheet and solve it.

   c. What is the optimal solution?

23. Dan Boyd is a financial planner trying to determine how to invest $100,000 for one of his clients. The cash flows for the five investments under consideration are summarized in the following table:

**Summary of Cash In-Flows and Out-Flows
(at Beginning of Year)**

	A	B	C	D	E
Year 1	−1.00	0.00	−1.00	0.00	−1.00
Year 2	+0.45	−1.00	0.00	0.00	0.00
Year 3	+1.05	0.00	0.00	−1.00	1.25
Year 4	0.00	+1.30	+1.65	+1.30	0.00

For example, if Dan invests $1 in investment A at the beginning of year 1, he will receive $0.45 at the beginning of year 2 and another $1.05 at the beginning of year 3.

Alternatively, he can invest $1 in investment B at the beginning of year 2 and receive $1.30 at the beginning of year 4. Entries of "0.00" in the above table indicate times when no cash inflows or outflows can occur. The minimum required investment for each of the possible investments is $50,000. Also, at the beginning of each year, Dan may also place any or all of the available money in a money market account that is expected to yield 5% per year. How should Dan plan his investments if he wants to maximize the amount of money available to his client at the end of year 4?

  a. Formulate an ILP model for this problem.
  b. Create a spreadsheet model for this problem and solve it using Solver.
  c. What is the optimal solution?

24. The Mega-Bucks Corporation is planning its production schedule for the next four weeks and is forecasting the following demand for compound X—a key raw material used in its production process:

Forecasted Demand of Compound X

Week	1	2	3	4
Demand	400 lbs.	150 lbs.	200 lbs.	350 lbs.

The company currently has no compound X on hand. The supplier of this product delivers only in batch sizes that are multiples of 100 pounds (0, 100, 200, 300, and so on). The price of this material is $125 per 100 pounds. Deliveries can be arranged weekly, but there is a delivery charge of $50. Mega-Bucks estimates that it costs $15 for each 100 pounds of compound X held in inventory from one week to the next. Assuming that Mega-Bucks does not want more than 50 pounds of compound X in inventory at the end of week 4, how much should it order each week so that the demand for this product will be met in the least costly manner?

  a. Formulate an ILP model for this problem.
  b. Create a spreadsheet model for this problem and solve it using Solver.
  c. What is the optimal solution?

25. An automobile manufacturer is considering mechanical design changes in one of its top-selling cars to reduce the weight of the car by at least 400 pounds to improve its fuel efficiency. Design engineers have identified ten changes that could be made in the car to make it lighter (for example, using composite body pieces rather than metal). The weight saved by each design change and the estimated costs of implementing each change are summarized below:

Design Change

	1	2	3	4	5	6	7	8	9	10
Weight Saved (lbs)	50	75	25	150	60	95	200	40	80	30
Cost (in $1,000s)	$150	$350	$50	$450	$90	$35	$650	$75	$110	$30

Changes 4 and 7 represent alternate ways of modifying the engine block and, therefore, only one of these options could be selected. The company wants to determine which changes to make to reduce the total weight of the car by at least 400 pounds in the least costly manner.

  a. Formulate an ILP model for this problem.
  b. Create a spreadsheet model for this problem and solve it.
  c. What is the optimal solution?

26. Darten Restaurants owns and operates several different restaurant chains including Red Snapper and the Olive Grove. The company is considering opening a number of new units in Ohio. There are ten different sites available for the company to build

new restaurants, and the company can build either type of restaurant at a given site. The following table summarizes the estimated net present value (NPV) of the cash flows (in millions) resulting from locating each type of restaurant at each of the sites and also indicates which sites are within 15 miles of each other.

Site	Red Snapper NPV	Olive Grove NPV	Other Sites within 15 Miles
1	$11.8	$16.2	2, 3, 4
2	13.3	13.8	1, 3, 5
3	19.0	14.6	1, 2, 4, 5
4	17.8	12.4	1, 3
5	10.0	13.7	2, 3, 9
6	16.1	19.0	7
7	13.3	10.8	6, 8
8	18.8	15.2	7
9	17.2	15.9	5, 10
10	14.4	16.8	9

a. Suppose the company does not want to build two units from the same chain within 15 miles of each other (for example, it does not want to build two Red Snappers within 15 miles of each other, nor is it willing to build two Olive Groves within 15 miles of each other). Create a spreadsheet model to determine which (if any) restaurant it should build at each site to maximize total NPV.

b. What is the optimal solution?

c. Now suppose also that the company does not want to build a Red Snapper unless it also builds an Olive Grove at another site within 15 miles. Modify your spreadsheet model to determine which (if any) restaurant it should build at each site to maximize total NPV.

d. What is the optimal solution?

27. Paul Bergey is in charge of loading cargo ships for International Cargo Company (ICC) at the port in Newport News, Virginia. Paul is preparing a loading plan for an ICC freighter destined for Ghana. An agricultural commodities dealer would like to transport the following products aboard this ship.

Commodity	Amount Available (tons)	Volume per Ton (cubic feet)	Profit per Ton ($)
1	4,800	40	70
2	2,500	25	50
3	1,200	60	60
4	1,700	55	80

Paul can elect to load any and/or all of the available commodities. However, the ship has three cargo holds with the following capacity restrictions:

Cargo Hold	Weight Capacity (tons)	Volume Capacity (cubic feet)
Forward	3,000	145,000
Center	6,000	180,000
Rear	4,000	155,000

Only one type of commodity can be placed into any cargo hold. However, because of balance considerations, the weight in the forward cargo hold must be within 10%

of the weight in the rear cargo hold and the center cargo hold must be between 40% to 60% of the total weight on board.

a. Formulate an ILP model for this problem.

b. Create a spreadsheet model for this problem and solve it using Solver.

c. What is the optimal solution?

28. KPS Communications is planning to bring wireless internet access to the town of Ames, Iowa. Using a geographic information system, KPS has divided Ames into the following 5 by 5 grid. The values in each block of the grid indicate the expected annual revenue (in $1,000s) KPS will receive if wireless internet service is provided to the geographic area represented by each block.

Expected Annual Revenue by Area (in $1,000s)

$34	$43	$62	$42	$34
$64	$43	$71	$48	$65
$57	$57	$51	$61	$30
$32	$38	$70	$56	$40
$68	$73	$30	$56	$44

KPS can build wireless towers in any block in the grid at a cost of $150,000 per tower. Each tower can provide wireless service to the block it is in and to all adjacent blocks. (Blocks are considered to be adjacent if they share a side. Blocks touching only at cornerpoints are not considered adjacent.) KPS would like to determine how many towers to build and where to build them to maximize profits in the first year of operations. (*Note:* If a block can receive wireless service from two different towers, the revenue for that block should be counted only once.)

a. Create a spreadsheet model for this problem and solve it.

b. What is the optimal solution and how much money will KPS make in the first year?

c. Suppose KPS is required to provide wireless service to all of the blocks. What is the optimal solution and how much money will KPS make in the first year?

29. The emergency services coordinator for Clarke County is interested in locating the county's two ambulances to maximize the number of residents that can be reached within four minutes in emergency situations. The county is divided into five regions, and the average times required to travel from one region to the next are summarized below:

	To Region				
From Region	**1**	**2**	**3**	**4**	**5**
1	0	4	6	3	2
2	4	0	2	3	6
3	6	2	0	5	3
4	3	3	5	0	7
5	2	6	3	7	0

The population in regions 1, 2, 3, 4, and 5 are estimated as 45,000, 65,000, 28,000, 52,000, and 43,000, respectively. In which two regions should the ambulances be placed?

a. Formulate an ILP model for this problem.

b. Implement your model in a spreadsheet and solve it.

c. What is the optimal solution?

30. Ken Stark is an operations analyst for an insurance company in Muncie, Indiana. Over the next 6 weeks the company needs to send 2,028,415 pieces of marketing literature to customers in the 16 states shown below.

State	Mailing Pieces
AZ	82,380
CA	212,954
CT	63,796
GA	136,562
IL	296,479
MA	99,070
ME	38,848
MN	86,207
MT	33,309
NC	170,997
NJ	104,974
NV	29,608
OH	260,858
OR	63,605
TX	214,076
VA	134,692
TOTAL	**2,028,415**

To coordinate with other marketing efforts, all the mailings for a given state must go out in the same week (i.e., if Ken decides to schedule mailings for Georgia in week 2, then all of the 136,562 pieces of mail for Georgia must be sent that week). Ken would like to balance the work load in each week as much as possible and, in particular, would like to minimize the maximum amount of mail to be processed in any given week during the 6-week period.

a. Create a spreadsheet model to determine which states should be processed each week to achieve Ken's objective.

b. What is the optimal solution?

31. The CoolAire Company manufactures air conditioners that are sold to five different retail customers across the United States. The company is evaluating its manufacturing and logistics strategy to ensure that it is operating in the most efficient manner possible. The company can produce air conditioners at six plants across the country and stock these units in any of four different warehouses. The cost of manufacturing and shipping a unit between each plant and warehouse is summarized in the following table along with the monthly capacity and fixed cost of operating each plant.

	Warehouse 1	Warehouse 2	Warehouse 3	Warehouse 4	Fixed Cost	Capacity
Plant 1	$700	$1,000	$900	$1,200	$55,000	300
Plant 2	$800	$ 500	$600	$ 700	$40,000	200
Plant 3	$850	$ 600	$700	$ 500	$45,000	300
Plant 4	$600	$ 800	$500	$ 600	$50,000	250
Plant 5	$500	$ 600	$450	$ 700	$42,000	350
Plant 6	$700	$ 600	$750	$ 500	$40,000	400

Similarly, the per-unit cost of shipping units from each warehouse to each customer is given below, along with the monthly fixed cost of operating each warehouse.

	Customer 1	Customer 2	Customer 3	Customer 4	Customer 5	Fixed Cost
Warehouse 1	$40	$80	$60	$90	$50	$40,000
Warehouse 2	$60	$50	$75	$40	$35	$50,000
Warehouse 3	$55	$40	$65	$60	$80	$35,000
Warehouse 4	$80	$30	$80	$50	$60	$60,000

The monthly demand from each customer is summarized below.

	Customer 1	Customer 2	Customer 3	Customer 4	Customer 5
Demand	200	300	200	150	250

CoolAire would like to determine which plants and warehouses it should operate to meet demand in the most cost-effective manner.
a. Create a spreadsheet model for this problem and solve it.
b. Which plants and warehouses should CoolAire operate?
c. What is the optimal shipping plan?

32. A blood bank wants to determine the least expensive way to transport available blood donations from Pittsburg and Staunton to hospitals in Charleston, Roanoke, Richmond, Norfolk, and Suffolk. Figure 6.34 shows the possible shipping paths between cities along with the per unit cost of shipping along each possible arc. Additionally, the courier service used by the blood bank charges a flat rate of $125 any time it makes a trip across any of these arcs, regardless of how many units of blood are transported. The van used by the courier service can carry a maximum of 200 units of blood. Assume that Pittsburg has 600 units of blood type O positive (O+) and 800 units of blood type AB available. Assume that Staunton has 500 units of O+ and 600 units of AB available. The following table summarizes the number of units of each blood type needed at the various hospitals:

	Units Needed	
Hospital	O+	AB
Charleston	100	200
Roanoke	100	100
Richmond	500	300
Norfolk	200	500
Suffolk	150	250

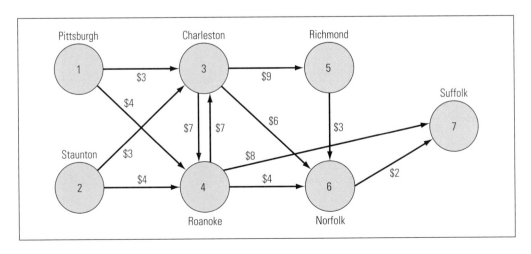

FIGURE 6.34

Possible shipping routes for the blood bank problem

a. Create a spreadsheet model for this problem.

b. What is the optimal solution?

c. Suppose that the courier service switches to a new type of van that can carry no more than 1000 units of blood between any two cities. What is the optimal solution to this revised problem?

33. CaroliNet is an Internet service provider for residential consumers in North Carolina. The company is planning to expand and offer Internet service in South Carolina. The company wants to establish a set of hubs throughout the state to ensure that all residents of the state can access at least one of their hubs via a local phone call. Local phone service is available between all adjacent counties throughout the state. Figure 6.35 (and the file FIG6-35.xls on your data disk) show an Excel spreadsheet with a matrix indicating county adjacencies throughout the state. That is, values of 1 in the matrix indicate counties that are adjacent to one another while values of 0 indicate counties that are not adjacent to one another. (Note that a county is also considered to be adjacent to itself.)

a. Assume CaroliNet wants to minimize the number of hubs it must install. In what counties should the hubs be installed?

b. Suppose CaroliNet is willing to install hubs in exactly ten different counties. In what counties should the hubs be installed if the company wants to maximize its service coverage?

34. Solve the following problem manually using the B&B algorithm. You can use the computer to solve the individual problems generated. Create a branch-and-bound tree to display the steps you complete.

FIGURE 6.35

County adjacency matrix for the CaroliNet ISP location problem

County Adjacency Matrix (1=adjacent counties)

	Abbeville	Aiken	Allendale	Anderson	Bamberg	Barnwell	Beaufort	Berkeley	Calhoun	Charleston	Cherokee	Chester	Cheste
Abbeville	1	0	0	1	0	0	0	0	0	0	0	0	0
Aiken	0	1	0	0	0	1	0	0	0	0	0	0	0
Allendale	0	0	1	0	1	1	0	0	0	0	0	0	0
Anderson	1	0	0	1	0	0	0	0	0	0	0	0	0
Bamberg	0	0	1	0	1	1	0	0	0	0	0	0	0
Barnwell	0	1	1	0	1	1	0	0	0	0	0	0	0
Beaufort	0	0	0	0	0	0	1	0	0	0	0	0	0
Berkeley	0	0	0	0	0	0	0	1	0	1	0	0	0
Calhoun	0	0	0	0	0	0	0	0	1	0	0	0	0
Charleston	0	0	0	0	0	0	0	1	0	1	0	0	0
Cherokee	0	0	0	0	0	0	0	0	0	0	1	0	0
Chester	0	0	0	0	0	0	0	0	0	0	0	1	0
Chesterfield	0	0	0	0	0	0	0	0	0	0	0	0	1
Claredon	0	0	0	0	0	0	0	1	1	0	0	0	0
Colleton	0	0	1	0	1	0	1	0	0	1	0	0	0
Darlington	0	0	0	0	0	0	0	0	0	0	0	0	1
Dillon	0	0	0	0	0	0	0	0	0	0	0	0	0
Dorchester	0	0	0	0	1	0	0	1	0	1	0	0	0
Edgefield	0	1	0	0	0	0	0	0	0	0	0	0	0
Fairfield	0	0	0	0	0	0	0	0	0	0	0	1	0
Florence	0	0	0	0	0	0	0	0	0	0	0	0	0
Georgetown	0	0	0	0	0	0	0	1	0	0	0	0	0
Greenville	1	0	0	1	0	0	0	0	0	0	0	0	0
Greenwood	1	0	0	0	0	0	0	0	0	0	0	0	0
Hampton	0	0	1	0	1	0	1	0	0	0	0	0	0
Horry	0	0	0	0	0	0	0	0	0	0	0	0	0
Jasper	0	0	0	0	0	0	1	0	0	0	0	0	0
Kershaw	0	0	0	0	0	0	0	0	0	0	0	0	1
Lancaster	0	0	0	0	0	0	0	0	0	0	0	1	1
Laurens	1	0	0	1	0	0	0	0	0	0	0	0	0

$$\text{MAX:} \qquad 6X_1 + 8X_2$$

$$\text{Subject to:} \qquad 6X_1 + 3X_2 \leq 18$$

$$2X_1 + 3X_2 \leq 9$$

$$X_1, X_2 \leq 0$$

$$X_1, X_2 \text{ must be integers}$$

34. During the execution of the B&B algorithm, many candidate problems are likely to be generated and awaiting further analysis. In the B&B example in this chapter, we chose the next candidate problem to analyze in a rather arbitrary way. What other, more structured ways might we use to select the next candidate problem? What are the pros and cons of these techniques?

Optimizing a Timber Harvest

CASE 6.1

The state of Virginia is one of the largest producers of wood furniture in the United States, with the furniture industry accounting for 50% of value added to wood materials. Over the past 40 years the inventory volume of wood in Virginia's forests has increased by 81 percent. Today, 15.4 million acres, which is well over half of the state, are covered in forest. Private owners hold 77% of this land. When making decisions about which trees to harvest, forestry professionals consider many factors and must follow numerous laws and regulations.

Figure 6.36 depicts a tract of forested land that has been sectioned off into 12 harvestable areas, indicated by dashed lines. Area 2 provides the only access to the forest via a paved road, so any timber cut ultimately must be transported out of the forest through area 2. Currently, there are no roads through this forest. So to harvest the timber, forest roads must be built. The allowable routes for these roads are also shown in Figure 6.36. They are determined largely by the geography of the land and by the location of streams and wildlife habitat.

Not all areas of the forest have to be harvested. However, to harvest any area, a forest road must be built to that area. The cost of building each section of forest road (in

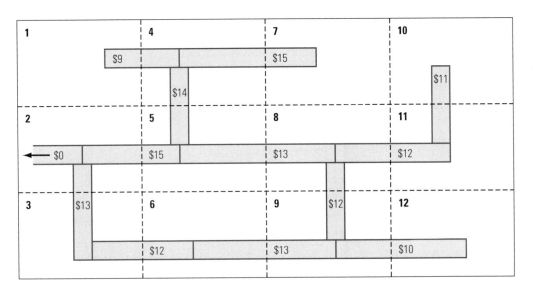

FIGURE 6.36

Forest diagram for the timber harvesting problem

$1000s) is indicated in the figure. Finally, the net value of the harvestable timber in each area is estimated as follows:

Harvested Value (in $1000s)

Area	1	2	3	4	5	6	7	8	9	10	11	12
Value	$15	$7	$10	$12	$8	$17	$14	$18	$13	$12	$10	$11

Which areas should be harvested and what roads should be built to make the most profitable use of this forest?

a. Create a spreadsheet model for this problem.
b. What is the optimal solution?
c. Suppose the cost of building the road connecting areas 4 and 5 dropped to $12,000. What impact does this have on the optimal solution?

CASE 6.2   Power Dispatching at Old Dominion

The demand for electricity varies greatly during the day. Because large amounts of electricity cannot be stored economically, electric power companies cannot manufacture electricity and hold it in inventory until it is needed. Instead, power companies must balance the production of power with the demand for power in real time. One of the greatest uncertainties in forecasting the demand for electricity is the weather. Most power companies employ meteorologists who constantly monitor weather patterns and update computer models that predict the demand for power over a rolling, seven-day planning horizon. This forecasted seven-day window of demand is referred to as the company's load profile. Typically it is updated every hour.

Every power company has a baseload demand that is relatively constant. To satisfy this baseload demand, a power company uses its most economical, low-cost power generating assets and keeps them running continuously. To meet additional demands for power above the baseload, a power company must dispatch (or turn on) other generators. These other generators are sometimes called "peakers," as they help the power company meet the highest demands or peak loads. It costs differing amounts of money to bring different types of peakers online. And because different peakers use different types of fuel (e.g., coal, gas, biomass), their operating costs per megawatt (MW) generated also differ. Thus, dispatchers for a power company continually have to decide which generator to bring online or turn off to meet their load profile with the least cost.

The Old Dominion Power (ODP) Company provides electrical power throughout Virginia and the Carolinas. Suppose ODP's peak-load profile (that is the estimated load above baseload) in MWs is currently estimated as follows:

	Day						
	1	2	3	4	5	6	7
Load (in MWs)	4,300	3,700	3,900	4,000	4,700	4,800	3,600

ODP currently has three peaking generators offline that are available to help meet this load. The generators have the following operating characteristics:

Generator Location	Startup Cost	Cost per Day	Maximum MW Capacity per Day
New River	$ 800	$200 + $5 per MW	2,100
Galax	$1,000	$300 + $4 per MW	1,900
James River	$ 700	$250 + $7 per MW	3,000

To get an offline generator up and running, a startup cost must be paid. Once a generator is running, it can continue to run indefinitely without having to pay this startup cost again. However, if the generator is turned off at any point, the setup cost must be paid again to get it back up and running. Each day that a generator runs, there is both a fixed and variable cost that must be paid. For example, any day that the New River generator is online, it incurs a fixed cost of $200 plus $5 per MW generated. So even if this generator is not producing any MWs, it still costs $200 per day to keep it running (so as to avoid a restart). When they are running, each generator can supply up to the maximum daily MWs listed in the final column of the table.

a. Formulate a mathematical programming model for ODP's power dispatching problem.
b. Implement your model in a spreadsheet and solve it.
c. What is the optimal solution?
d. Suppose ODP can buy power sometimes from a competitor. How much should ODP be willing to pay to acquire 300 MW of power on day 1? Explain your answer.
e. What concerns, if any, would you have about implementing this plan?

The MasterDebt Lockbox Problem   CASE 6.3

MasterDebt is a national credit card company with thousands of card holders located across the United States. Every day throughout the month, MasterDebt sends out statements to different customers summarizing their charges for the previous month. Customers then have 30 days to remit a payment for their bills. MasterDebt includes a pre-addressed envelope with each statement for customers to use in making their payments.

One of the critical problems facing MasterDebt involves determining what address to put on the pre-addressed envelopes sent to various parts of the country. The amount of time that elapses between when a customer writes his check and when MasterDebt receives the cash for the check is referred to as *float*. Checks can spend several days floating in the mail and in processing before being cashed. This float time represents lost revenue to MasterDebt because if they could receive and cash these checks immediately, they could earn additional interest on these funds.

To reduce the interest being lost from floating checks, MasterDebt would like to implement a lockbox system to speed the processing of checks. Under such a system, MasterDebt might have all their customers on the West Coast send their payments to a bank in Sacramento which, for a fee, processes the checks and deposits the proceeds in a MasterDebt account. Similarly, MasterDebt might arrange for a similar service with a bank on the East Coast for their customers there. Such lockbox systems are a common method that companies use to improve their cash flows.

MasterDebt has identified six different cities as possible lockbox sites. The annual fixed cost of operating a lockbox in each of the possible locations is given below.

Annual Lockbox Operating Costs (in $1,000s)					
Sacramento	Denver	Chicago	Dallas	New York	Atlanta
$25	$30	$35	$35	$30	$35

An analysis was done to determine the average number of days that a check floats when sent from seven different regions of the country to each of these six cities. The results of this analysis are summarized below. This table indicates, for instance, that a check sent from the central region of the country to New York spends an average of three days in the mail and in processing before MasterDebt actually receives the cash for the check.

Average Days of Float Between Regions and Possible Lockbox Locations

	Sacramento	Denver	Chicago	Dallas	New York	Atlanta
Central	4	2	2	2	3	3
Mid-Atlantic	6	4	3	4	2	2
Midwest	3	2	3	2	5	4
Northeast	6	4	2	5	2	3
Northwest	2	3	5	4	6	7
Southeast	7	4	3	2	4	2
Southwest	2	3	6	2	7	6

Further analysis was done to determine the average amount of payments being sent from each region of the country. These results are given below.

Average Daily Payments (in $1,000s) by Region

	Payments
Central	$45
Mid-Atlantic	$65
Midwest	$50
Northeast	$90
Northwest	$70
Southeast	$80
Southwest	$60

Thus, if payments from the Central Region are sent to New York, on any given day there is an average of $135,000 in undeposited checks from the Central Region. Because MasterDebt can earn 15% on cash deposits, it would be losing $20,250 per year in potential interest on these checks alone.

a. Which of the six potential lockbox locations should MasterDebt use and to which lockbox location should each region be assigned?

b. How would your solution change if a maximum of four regions could be assigned to any lockbox location?

CASE 6.4   Removing Snow in Montreal

Based on: Campbell, J. and Langevin, A. "The Snow Disposal Assignment Problem." *Journal of the Operational Research Society,* 1995, pp. 919–929.

CASE 6.4   Removing Snow in Montreal

Snow removal and disposal are important and expensive activities in Montreal and many northern cities. Even though snow can be cleared from streets and sidewalks by plowing and shoveling, in prolonged sub-freezing temperatures, the resulting banks of accumulated snow can impede pedestrian and vehicular traffic and must be removed.

To allow timely removal and disposal of snow, a city is divided into several sectors and snow removal operations are carried out concurrently in each sector. In Montreal, accumulated snow is loaded onto trucks and hauled away to disposal sites (e.g., rivers, quarries, sewer chutes, surface holding areas). For contractual reasons, each sector may be assigned to only a *single* disposal site. (However, each disposal site may receive snow from multiple sectors.) The different types of disposal sites can accommodate different amounts of snow either because of the physical size of the disposal facility or environmental restrictions on the amount of snow (often contaminated by salt and de-icing chemicals) that can be dumped into rivers. The annual capacities for five different snow disposal sites are given below (in 1,000s of cubic meters).

	Disposal Site				
	1	2	3	4	5
Capacity	350	250	500	400	200

The cost of removing and disposing of snow depends mainly on the distance it must be trucked. For planning purposes, the city of Montreal uses the straight-line distance between the center of each sector to each of the various disposal sites as an approximation of the cost involved in transporting snow between these locations. The following table summarizes these distances (in kilometers) for ten sectors in the city.

	Disposal Site				
Sector	1	2	3	4	5
1	3.4	1.4	4.9	7.4	9.3
2	2.4	2.1	8.3	9.1	8.8
3	1.4	2.9	3.7	9.4	8.6
4	2.6	3.6	4.5	8.2	8.9
5	1.5	3.1	2.1	7.9	8.8
6	4.2	4.9	6.5	7.7	6.1
7	4.8	6.2	9.9	6.2	5.7
8	5.4	6.0	5.2	7.6	4.9
9	3.1	4.1	6.6	7.5	7.2
10	3.2	6.5	7.1	6.0	8.3

Using historical snowfall data, the city can estimate the annual volume of snow requiring removal in each sector as four times the length of streets in the sectors in meters (i.e., it is assumed that each linear meter of street generates four cubic meters of snow to remove over an entire year). The following table estimates the snow removal requirements (in 1,000s of cubic meters) for each sector in the coming year.

Estimated Annual Snow Removal Requirements									
1	2	3	4	5	6	7	8	9	10
153	152	154	138	127	129	111	110	130	135

Questions

1. Create a spreadsheet that Montreal could use to determine the most efficient snow removal plan for the coming year. Assume it costs $0.10 to transport one cubic meter of snow one kilometer.
2. What is the optimal solution?
3. How much will it cost Montreal to implement your snow disposal plan?
4. Ignoring the capacity restrictions at the disposal sites, how many different assignments of sectors to disposal sites are possible?
5. Suppose Montreal can increase the capacity of a single disposal site by 100,000 cubic meters. Which disposal site's capacity (if any) should be increased and how much should the city be willing to pay to obtain this extra disposal capacity?

Chapter 12

Introduction to Simulation Using Crystal Ball

12.0 Introduction

Chapter 1 discussed how the calculations in a spreadsheet can be viewed as a mathematical model that defines a functional relationship between various input variables (or independent variables) and one or more bottom-line performance measures (or dependent variables). The following equation expresses this relationship:

$$Y = f(X_1, X_2, \ldots, X_k)$$

In many spreadsheets, the values of various input cells are determined by the person using the spreadsheet. These input cells correspond to the independent variables $X_1, X_2, \ldots, X_k$ in the previous equation. Various formulas (represented by $f(\cdot)$ above) are entered in other cells of the spreadsheet to transform the values of the input cells into some bottom-line output (denoted by Y above). Simulation is a technique that is helpful in analyzing models in which the value to be assumed by one or more independent variables is uncertain.

This chapter discusses how to perform simulation using a popular commercial spreadsheet add-in called Crystal Ball, created and distributed by Decisioneering, Inc. A limited-life (140-day) version of Crystal Ball and related products can be accessed via the bind-in card accompanying this book. Decisioneering offers students one- and two-year extensions of this software at very affordable prices. You can find additional information about Crystal Ball and these extension options at http://www.decisioneering.com.

12.1 Random Variables and Risk

To compute a value for the bottom-line performance measure of a spreadsheet model, each input cell must be assigned a specific value so that all the related calculations can be performed. However, some uncertainty often exists regarding the value that should be assumed by one or more independent variables (or input cells) in the spreadsheet. This is particularly true in spreadsheet models that represent future conditions. A **random variable** is any variable whose value cannot be predicted or set with certainty. Thus, many input variables in a spreadsheet model represent random variables whose actual values cannot be determined with certainty.

For example, projections of the cost of raw materials, future interest rates, future numbers of employees, and expected product demand are random variables because their true values are unknown and will be determined in the future. If we cannot say with certainty what value one or more input variables in a model will assume, we also cannot say with certainty what value the dependent variable will assume. This uncertainty associated with the value of the dependent variable introduces an element of risk to the decision-making problem. Specifically, if the dependent variable represents some bottom-line performance measure that managers use to make decisions, and its value is uncertain, any decisions made on the basis of this value are based on uncertain (or incomplete) information. When such a decision is made, some chance exists that the decision will not produce the intended results. This chance, or uncertainty, represents an element of **risk** in the decision-making problem.

The term "risk" also implies the *potential* for loss. The fact that a decision's outcome is uncertain does not mean that the decision is particularly risky. For example, whenever we put money into a soft-drink machine, there is a chance that the machine will take our money and not deliver the product. However, most of us would not consider this risk to be particularly great. From past experience, we know that the chance of not receiving the product is small. But even if the machine takes our money and does not deliver the product, most of us would not consider this to be a tremendous loss. Thus, the amount of risk involved in a given decision-making situation is a function of the uncertainty in the outcome of the decision and the magnitude of the potential loss. A proper assessment of the risk present in a decision-making situation should address both of these issues, as the examples in this chapter will demonstrate.

12.2 Why Analyze Risk?

Many spreadsheets built by business people contain *estimated* values for the uncertain input variables in their models. If a manager cannot say with certainty what value a particular cell in a spreadsheet will assume, this cell most likely represents a random variable. Ordinarily, the manager will attempt to make an informed guess about the values such cells will assume. The manager hopes that inserting the expected, or most likely, values for all the uncertain cells in a spreadsheet will provide the most likely value for the cell containing the bottom-line performance measure (Y). The problem with this type of analysis is that it tells the decision maker nothing about the variability of the performance measure.

For example, in analyzing a particular investment opportunity, we might determine that the expected return on a $1,000 investment is $10,000 within two years. But how much variability exists in the possible outcomes? If all the potential outcomes are scattered closely around $10,000 (say from $9,000 to $11,000), then the investment opportunity still might be attractive. If, on the other hand, the potential outcomes are scattered widely around $10,000 (say from −$30,000 up to +$50,000), then the investment opportunity might be unattractive. Although these two scenarios might have the same expected or average value, the risks involved are quite different. Thus, even if we can determine the expected outcome of a decision using a spreadsheet, it is just as important, if not more so, to consider the risk involved in the decision.

12.3 Methods of Risk Analysis

Several techniques are available to help managers analyze risk. Three of the most common are best-case/worst-case analysis, what-if analysis, and simulation. Of these methods, simulation is the most powerful and, therefore, is the technique that we will focus on in this chapter. Although the other techniques might not be completely effective in risk analysis, they probably are used more often than simulation by most managers in business today. This is largely because most managers are unaware of the spreadsheet's ability to perform simulation and of the benefits provided by this technique. So before discussing simulation, let's first look briefly at the other methods of risk analysis to understand their strengths and weaknesses.

12.3.1 BEST-CASE/WORST-CASE ANALYSIS

If we don't know what value a particular cell in a spreadsheet will assume, we could enter a number that we think is the most likely value for the uncertain cell. If we enter such numbers for all the uncertain cells in the spreadsheet, we can easily calculate the most likely value of the bottom-line performance measure. This is also called the **base-case** scenario. However, this scenario gives us no information about how far away the actual outcome might be from this expected, or most likely, value.

One simple solution to this problem is to calculate the value of the bottom-line performance measure using the **best-case**, or most optimistic, and **worst-case**, or most pessimistic, values for the uncertain input cells. These additional scenarios show the range of possible values that might be assumed by the bottom-line performance measure. As indicated in the earlier example about the $1,000 investment, knowing the range of possible outcomes helps us assess the risk involved in different alternatives. However, simply knowing the best-case and worst-case outcomes tells us nothing about the distribution of possible values within this range, nor does it tell us the probability of either scenario occurring.

Figure 12.1 displays several probability distributions that might be associated with the value of a bottom-line performance measure within a given range. Each of these distributions describes variables that have identical ranges and similar average values. But each distribution is very different in terms of the risk it represents to the decision maker. The appeal of best-case/worst-case analysis is that it is easy to do. Its weakness is that it tells us nothing about the shape of the distribution associated with the bottom-line

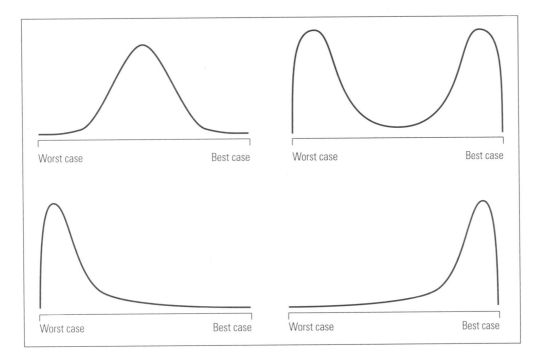

FIGURE 12.1

Possible distributions of performance measure values within a given range

performance measure. As we will see later, knowing the shape of the distribution of the bottom-line performance measure can be critically important in helping us answer several managerial questions.

12.3.2 WHAT-IF ANALYSIS

Before the introduction of electronic spreadsheets in the early 1980s, the use of best-case/worst-case analysis often was the only feasible way for a manager to analyze the risk associated with a decision. This process was extremely time-consuming, error prone, and tedious, using only paper, pencil, and calculator to recalculate the performance measure of a model using different values for the uncertain inputs. The arrival of personal computers and electronic spreadsheets made it much easier for a manager to play out a large number of scenarios in addition to the best and worst cases—which is the essence of what-if analysis.

In **what-if analysis**, a manager changes the values of the uncertain input variables to see what happens to the bottom-line performance measure. By making a series of such changes, a manager can gain some insight into how sensitive the performance measure is to changes to the input variables. Although many managers perform this type of manual what-if analysis, it has three major flaws.

First, if the values selected for the independent variables are based only on the manager's judgment, the resulting sample values of the performance measure are likely to be biased. That is, if several uncertain variables can each assume some range of values, it would be difficult to ensure that the manager tests a fair, or representative, sample of all possible combinations of these values. To select values for the uncertain variables that correctly reflect their random variations, the values must be randomly selected from a distribution, or pool, of values that reflects the appropriate range of possible values, and the appropriate relative frequencies of these variables.

Second, hundreds or thousands of what-if scenarios might be required to create a valid representation of the underlying variability in the bottom-line performance measure. No one would want to perform these scenarios manually, nor could anyone make sense of the resulting stream of numbers that would flash on the screen.

The third problem with what-if analysis is that the insight that the manager might gain from playing out various scenarios is of little value when recommending a decision to top management. What-if analysis simply does not supply the manager with the tangible evidence (facts and figures) needed to justify why a given decision was made or recommended. Additionally, what-if analysis does not address the problem identified in our earlier discussion of best-case/worst-case analysis—it does not allow us to estimate the distribution of the performance measure in a formal enough manner. Thus, what-if analysis is a step in the right direction, but it is not quite a large enough step to allow managers to analyze risk effectively in the decisions they face.

12.3.3 SIMULATION

Simulation is a technique that measures and describes various characteristics of the bottom-line performance measure of a model when one or more values for the independent variables are uncertain. If any independent variables in a model are random variables, the dependent variable (Y) also represents a random variable. The objective in simulation is to describe the distribution and characteristics of the possible values of the bottom-line performance measure Y, given the possible values and behavior of the independent variables $X_1, X_2, \ldots, X_k$.

The idea behind simulation is similar to the notion of playing out many what-if scenarios. The difference is that the process of assigning values to the cells in the spreadsheet that represent random variables is automated so that: (1) the values are assigned in a non-biased way, and (2) the spreadsheet user is relieved of the burden of determining these values. With simulation, we repeatedly and randomly generate sample values for each uncertain input variable $(X_1, X_2, \ldots, X_k)$ in our model and then compute the resulting value of our bottom-line performance measure (Y). We can then use the sample values of Y to estimate the true distribution and other characteristics of the performance measure Y. For example, we can use the sample observations to construct a frequency distribution of the performance measure, to estimate the range of values over which the performance measure might vary, to estimate its mean and variance, and to estimate the probability that the actual value of the performance measure will be greater than (or less than) a particular value. All these measures provide greater insight into the risk associated with a given decision than a single value calculated based on the expected values for the uncertain independent variables.

On Uncertainty and Decision-Making...

"Uncertainty is the most difficult thing about decision-making. In the face of uncertainty, some people react with paralysis, or they do exhaustive research to avoid making a decision. The best decision-making happens when the mental environment is focused. In a physical environment, you focus on something physical. In tennis, that might be the spinning seams of the ball. In a mental environment, you focus on the facts at hand. That fine-tuned focus doesn't leave room for fears and doubts to enter. Doubts knock at the door of our consciousness, but you don't have to have them in for tea and crumpets."—Timothy Gallwey, author of *The Inner Game of Tennis* and *The Inner Game of Work*.

12.4 A Corporate Health Insurance Example

The following example demonstrates the mechanics of preparing a spreadsheet model for risk analysis using simulation. The example presents a fairly simple model to illustrate the process and give a sense of the amount of effort involved. However, the process for performing simulation is basically the same regardless of the size of the model.

Lisa Pon has just been hired as an analyst in the corporate planning department of Hungry Dawg Restaurants. Her first assignment is to determine how much money the company needs to accrue in the coming year to pay for its employees' health insurance claims. Hungry Dawg is a large, growing chain of restaurants that specializes in traditional southern foods. The company has become large enough that it no longer buys insurance from a private insurance company. The company is now self-insured, meaning that it pays health insurance claims with its own money (although it contracts with an outside company to handle the administrative details of processing claims and writing checks).

FIGURE 12.2

Original corporate health insurance model with expected values for uncertain variables

The money the company uses to pay claims comes from two sources: employee contributions (or premiums deducted from employees' paychecks), and company funds (the company must pay whatever costs are not covered by employee contributions). Each employee covered by the health plan contributes $125 per month. However, the number of employees covered by the plan changes from month to month as employees are hired and fired, quit, or simply add or drop health insurance coverage. A total of 18,533 employees were covered by the plan last month. The average monthly health claim per covered employee was $250 last month.

An example of how most analysts would model this problem is shown in Figure 12.2 (and in the file Fig12-2.xls on your data disk). The spreadsheet begins with a listing of the initial conditions and assumptions for the problem. For example, cell D5 indicates that 18,533 employees currently are covered by the health plan, and cell D6 indicates that the average monthly claim per covered employee is $250. The average monthly contribution per employee is $125, as shown in cell D7. The values in cells D5 and D6 are unlikely to stay the same for the entire year. Thus, we need to make some assumptions about the rate at which these values are likely to increase during the year. For example, we might assume that the number of covered employees will increase by about 2% per month, and that the average claim per employee will increase at a rate of 1% per month. These assumptions are reflected in cells F5 and F6. The average contribution per employee is assumed to be constant over the coming year.

Using the assumed rate of increase in the number of covered employees (cell F5), we can create formulas for cells B11 through B22 that cause the number of covered employees to increase by the assumed amount each month. (The details of these formulas are covered later.) The expected monthly employee contributions shown in column C are calculated as $125 times the number of employees in each month. We can use the assumed rate of increase in average monthly claims (cell F6) to create formulas for cells D11 through D22 that cause the average claim per employee to increase at the assumed rate.

The total claims for each month (shown in column E) are calculated as the average claim figures in column D times the number of employees for each month in column B. Because the company must pay for any claims that are not covered by the employee contributions, the company cost figures in column G are calculated as the total claims minus the employee contributions (column E minus column C). Finally, cell G23 sums the company cost figures listed in column G, and shows that the company can expect to contribute $36,126,069 of its revenues toward paying the health insurance claims of its employees in the coming year.

12.4.1 A CRITIQUE OF THE BASE CASE MODEL

Now, let's consider the model we just described. The example model assumes that the number of covered employees will increase by *exactly* 2% each month and that the average claim per covered employee will increase by *exactly* 1% each month. Although these values might be reasonable approximations of what might happen, they are unlikely to reflect exactly what will happen. In fact, the number of employees covered by the health plan each month is likely to vary randomly around the average increase per month—that is, the number might decrease in some months and increase by more than 2% in others. Similarly, the average claim per covered employee might be lower than expected in certain months and higher than expected in others.

Both of these figures are likely to exhibit some uncertainty or random behavior, even if they do move in the general upward direction assumed throughout the year. So, we cannot say with certainty that the total cost figure of $36,126,069 is exactly what the company will have to contribute toward health claims in the coming year. It is simply a prediction of what might happen. The actual outcome could be smaller or larger than this estimate. Using the original model, we have no idea how much larger or smaller the actual result could be—nor do we have any idea of how the actual values are distributed around this estimate. We do not know if there is a 10%, 50%, or 90% chance of the actual total costs exceeding this estimate. To determine the variability or risk inherent in the bottom-line performance measure of total company costs, we will apply the technique of simulation to our model.

12.5 Spreadsheet Simulation Using Crystal Ball

To perform simulation in a spreadsheet, we must first place a **random number generator** (RNG) in each cell that represents a random, or uncertain, independent variable. Each RNG provides a sample observation from an appropriate distribution that represents the range and frequency of possible values for the variable. After the RNGs are in place, a new value of the bottom-line performance measure is computed every time new sample values are generated for the uncertain input cells. We can sample the spreadsheet *n* times, where *n* is the desired number of replications or scenarios, and the value of the bottom-line performance measure will be stored after each replication. We then analyze these stored observations to gain insights into the behavior and characteristics of the performance measure.

The process of simulation involves a lot of work but, fortunately, the spreadsheet can do most of the work for us fairly easily. In particular, the spreadsheet add-in package Crystal Ball is designed specifically to make spreadsheet simulation a simple process. The Crystal Ball software provides the following capabilities, which are not otherwise available while working in Excel: additional tools that are helpful in generating the

FIGURE 12.3

Crystal Ball Commands in Excel

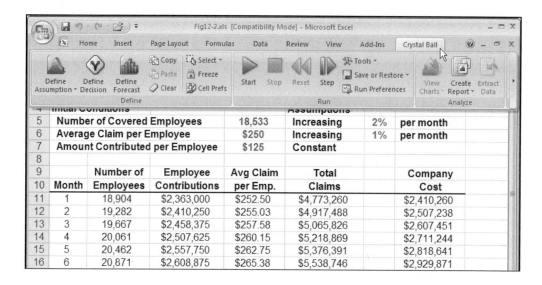

		Number of	Employee	Avg Claim	Total		Company
10	Month	Employees	Contributions	per Emp.	Claims		Cost
11	1	18,904	$2,363,000	$252.50	$4,773,260		$2,410,260
12	2	19,282	$2,410,250	$255.03	$4,917,488		$2,507,238
13	3	19,667	$2,458,375	$257.58	$5,065,826		$2,607,451
14	4	20,061	$2,507,625	$260.15	$5,218,869		$2,711,244
15	5	20,462	$2,557,750	$262.75	$5,376,391		$2,818,641
16	6	20,871	$2,608,875	$265.38	$5,538,746		$2,929,871

random numbers needed in simulation; additional commands that are helpful in setting up and running the simulation; and graphical and statistical summaries of the simulation data. As we shall see, these capabilities make simulation a relatively easy technique to apply in spreadsheets.

12.5.1 STARTING CRYSTAL BALL

If you are running Crystal Ball from a local area network (LAN) or in a computer lab, your instructor or LAN coordinator should give you directions on how to access this software. If you have installed Crystal Ball on your own computer, you can load Crystal Ball in Windows as follows:

1. Click Start.
2. Click Programs.
3. Click Crystal Ball 7.
4. Click Crystal Ball.

This loads Crystal Ball in a new instance of Excel and causes the Crystal Ball commands shown in Figure 12.3 to appear. We will refer to the various commands in Figure 12.3 throughout this chapter.

12.6 Random Number Generators

As mentioned earlier, the first step in spreadsheet simulation is to place an RNG in each cell that contains an uncertain value. Each RNG will generate (or return) a number that represents a randomly selected value from a distribution, or pool, of values. The distributions that these samples are taken from should be representative of the underlying pool of values expected to occur in each uncertain cell. Crystal Ball refers to such cells as *assumption cells.* To create the RNGs required for simulating a spreadsheet model,

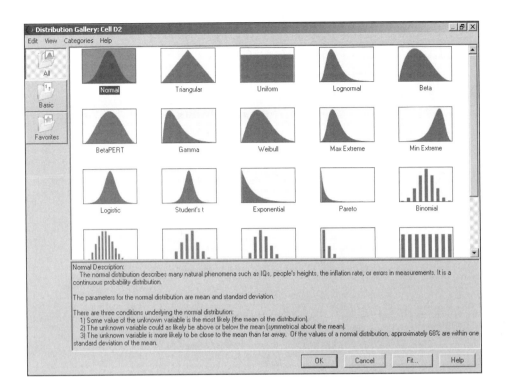

FIGURE 12.4

The Crystal Ball Distribution Gallery

Crystal Ball provides the Distribution Gallery tool shown in Figure 12.4. (The Distribution Gallery is launched by clicking the Define Assumption button on the Crystal Ball tab.)

The distributions shown in Figure 12.4 allow us to generate a variety of random numbers easily. For example, if we think that the behavior of a particular uncertain cell (perhaps representing the average health insurance claim per employee in a given month) could be modeled as a normally distributed random variable with a mean of $250 and standard deviation of $3, we could double-click the Normal distribution button in Figure 12.4. This launches the dialog in Figure 12.5 that allows us to indicate the mean and standard deviation for the assumption (or uncertain) cell in question. (The entries for the mean and standard deviation also could be formulas that refer to other cells in the spreadsheet.) Whenever Crystal Ball creates a new replication of the spreadsheet, the value in this assumption cell would be a randomly selected value from a normal distribution with a mean of 250 and standard deviation of 3.

As a different example, suppose that an assumption cell in a spreadsheet (perhaps representing the number of gallons of white ceiling paint sold on a given day at a paint store) has a 30% chance of assuming the value 10, a 50% chance of assuming the value 15, and a 20% chance of assuming the value 20. We could model the behavior of this random variable using the Custom distribution from Crystal Ball's distribution gallery as shown in Figure 12.6. If we used Crystal Ball to replicate this spreadsheet many times, it would randomly choose the value 10 for this assumption cell approximately 30% of the time, the value 15 approximately 50% of the time, and the value 20 approximately 20% of the time.

Each of the RNGs in Figure 12.4 require different parameters that allow us to generate random numbers from probability distributions with a wide variety of shapes. Figures 12.7 and 12.8 illustrate some example distributions. Additional information about each distribution is available by clicking the Help button on any of the Crystal Ball dialogs.

FIGURE 12.5

Example of creating a normally distributed assumption cell

FIGURE 12.6

Example of creating a custom distribution for an assumption cell

FIGURE 12.7

Examples of selected discrete distributions

12.6.1 DISCRETE VS. CONTINUOUS RANDOM VARIABLES

An important distinction exists between the graphs in Figures 12.7 and 12.8. In particular, the RNGs depicted in Figure 12.7 generate *discrete* outcomes, whereas those represented in Figure 12.8 generate *continuous* outcomes. That is, some of the RNGs displayed in Figure 12.4 can return only a distinct set of individual values, whereas the other RNGs can return any value from an infinite set of values. The distinction between discrete and continuous random variables is very important.

For example, the number of defective tires on a new car is a discrete random variable because it can assume only one of five distinct values: 0, 1, 2, 3, or 4. On the other hand, the amount of fuel in a new car is a continuous random variable because it can assume any value between 0 and the maximum capacity of the fuel tank. Thus, when selecting

FIGURE 12.8

Examples of selected continuous distributions

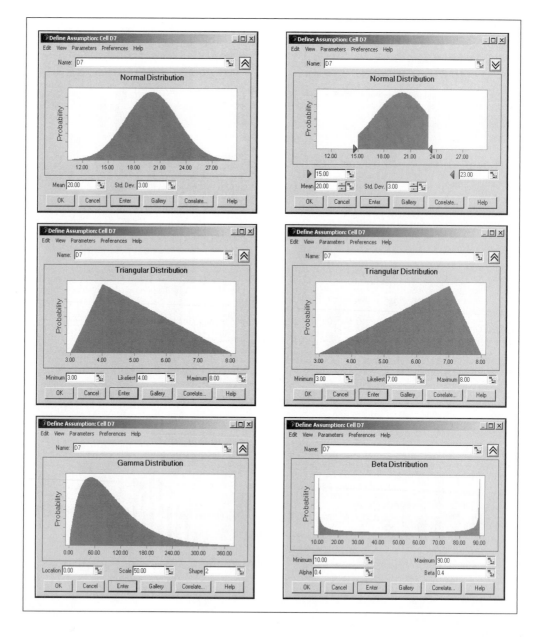

an RNG for an uncertain variable in a model, it is important to consider whether the variable can assume discrete or continuous values.

12.7 Preparing the Model for Simulation

To apply simulation to the model for Hungry Dawg Restaurants described earlier, first we must select appropriate RNGs for the uncertain variables in the model. If available, historical data on the uncertain variables could be analyzed to determine appropriate RNGs for these variables. (Crystal Ball's Batch Fit tool can be used for this purpose.) If past data are not available, or if we have some reason to expect the future behavior of a variable to be significantly different from the past, then we must use judgment in selecting appropriate RNGs to model the random behavior of the uncertain variables.

For our example problem, let's assume that by analyzing historical data, we determined that the change in the number of covered employees from one month to the next is expected to vary uniformly between a 3% decrease and a 7% increase. (Note that this should cause the *average* change in the number of employees to be a 2% increase, because 0.02 is the midpoint between −0.03 and +0.07.) Further, assume that we can model the average monthly claim per covered employee as a normally distributed random variable with the mean increasing by 1% per month and a standard deviation of approximately $3. (Note that this will cause the *average* increase in claims per covered employee from one month to the next to be approximately 1%.) These assumptions are reflected in cells F5 through H6 at the top of Figure 12.9 (and in the file Fig12-9.xls on your data disk).

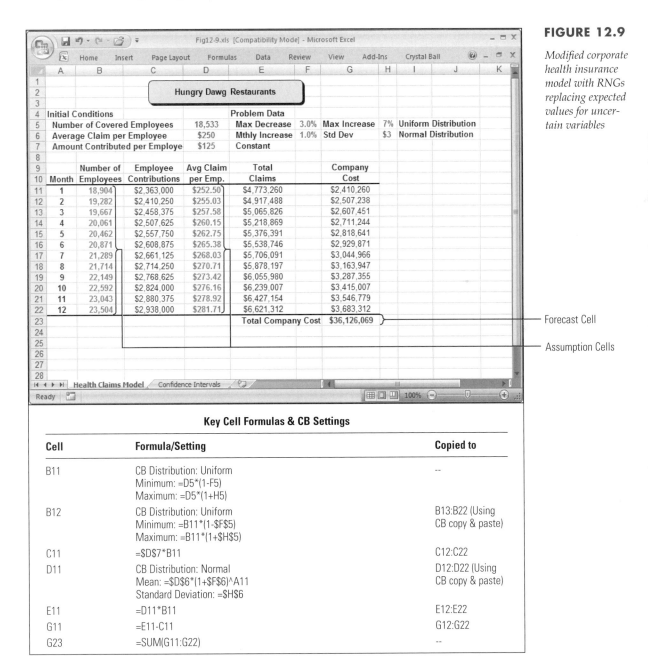

FIGURE 12.9

Modified corporate health insurance model with RNGs replacing expected values for uncertain variables

12.7.1 DEFINING ASSUMPTIONS FOR THE NUMBER OF COVERED EMPLOYEES

To randomly generate the appropriate number of employees covered by the health plan each month, we will use the Uniform distribution shown in Figure 12.4. Because the change in the number of employees from one month to the next can vary between a 3% decrease and a 7% increase, the number of employees in any month should be between a minimum of 97% and a maximum of 107% of the number of employees in the previous month. Thus, the number of employees in month 1 (represented by cell B11) should vary uniformly between 97% and 107% of the number of employees given in cell D5. Using Crystal Ball, we place this assumption on cell B11 as follows:

1. Select cell B11.
2. Click Crystall Ball, Define Assumption.
3. Select the Uniform distribution.
4. In the Name text box type: Employees in Month 1
5. For the Minimum parameter type the formula: =D5*(1-F5)
6. For the Minimum parameter type the formula: =D5*(1+H5)

The resulting Define Assumption dialog box is shown in Figure 12.10. Notice that we are instructing Crystal Ball to treat cell B11 as an assumption (or uncertain) cell whose value is a uniformly distributed random variable between a minimum of 97% (or 1-F5) of the value in D5 and a maximum of 107% (or 1+H5) of the value in cell D5. So when we run the simulation, Crystal Ball will randomly select values between 17,977 and 19,830 for cell B11.

FIGURE 12.10

Defining the assumptions cell for cell B11

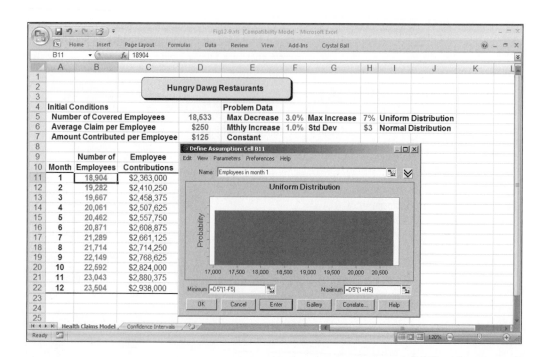

Preparing the Model for Simulation   **573**

Do You Want to See the Formulas or the Numbers?

Using the Define Assumption dialog as shown in Figure 12.10, you can use the Parameters, Show Cell References command (or Ctrl+ ~) to instruct Crystal Ball to show either the formulas that define the minimum and maximum values or the values produced by the formulas.

When you click OK on the Define Assumption dialog shown in Figure 12.10, Crystal Ball automatically changes the background color of cell B11 to green to indicate that it is now an assumption cell. If you want assumption cells to be indicated by a different color you may indicate your preference using the Define, Cell Preferences command.

Next, we need to place similar assumptions on the number of employees in months 2 through 12 (cells B12 through B22). Again, the number of employees in each month should be between a minimum of 97% and a maximum of 107% of the number of employees in the previous month. We could define the assumptions for each cell individually, just as we did for month 1 (cell B11). However, it is also possible to copy and paste assumption definitions from one cell to other cells when the formulas that describe the distribution follow a common pattern. So if we are careful about how we create the formulas that define the minimum and maximum values for number of employees in month 2 (for cell B12), we can copy the assumptions about that cell to the remaining cells for months 3 through 12 (cells B13 through B22).

Figure 12.11 shows the Define Assumptions dialog box for cell B12. Notice that the formulas for the minimum and maximum number of employees are =B11*(1-$F$5) and

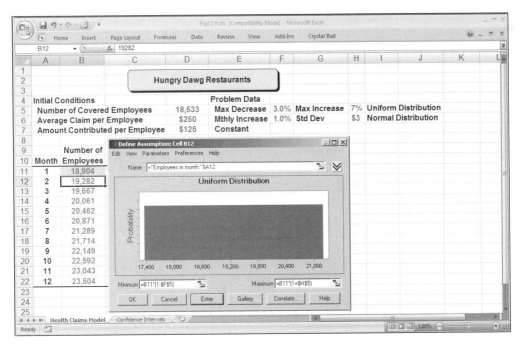

FIGURE 12.11

Defining the assumptions for cell B12

=B11*(1+$H$5), respectively. The dollar signs embedded in the references to cells F5 and H5 indicate that these are absolute cell references that should not change if the definition for this assumption cell is ever copied to another cell. The reference to B11 lacks the dollar signs and will change in the customary relative fashion if the definition for this assumption cell is copied elsewhere. Also notice that the name being defined for cell B12 is given by the formula: ="Employees in month "&A12. (Because the value in cell A12 is two (2), this formula evaluates to the text string "Employees in month 2".) When defining cells whose definitions will be copied, it is good practice to use formulas like this (when possible) for creating names so that these items are identified clearly in subsequent Crystal Ball reports and charts.

Once our assumptions about cell B12 are properly recorded, we can copy its assumption cell definition to cells B13 through B22. However, it is ***critical*** that we use Crystal Ball's copy and paste commands to do this. Excel's copy and paste command *will not work* on assumption cell definitions. Thus, to copy the assumption cell definitions from cell B12 to cells B13 through B22:

1. Select cell B12.
2. Click Crystal Ball, Copy.
3. Select cells B13 through B22.
4. Click Crystal Ball, Paste.

I m p o r t a n t   S o f t w a r e   I s s u e

To copy assumption cell definitions, you must use Crystal Ball's copy data and paste data commands. Excel's copy and paste commands do not work on assumption cell definitions.

12.7.2 DEFINING ASSUMPTIONS FOR THE AVERAGE MONTHLY CLAIM PER EMPLOYEE

To randomly generate the appropriate average claims per covered employee in each month, we will use the Normal distribution shown in Figure 12.4. This distribution requires that we supply the value of the mean and standard deviation of the distribution from which we want to sample. The assumed $3 standard deviation for the average monthly claim, shown in cell H6 in Figure 12.11, is constant from month to month. Thus, we need only to determine the proper mean value for each month.

In this case, the mean for any given month should be 1% larger than the mean in the previous month. For example, the mean for month 1 is:

$$\text{Mean in month 1} = (\text{original mean}) \times 1.01$$

and the mean for month 2 is:

$$\text{Mean in month 2} = (\text{mean in month 1}) \times 1.01$$

If we substitute the previous definition of the mean in month 1 into the previous equation, we obtain,

$$\text{Mean in month 2} = (\text{original mean}) \times (1.01)^2$$

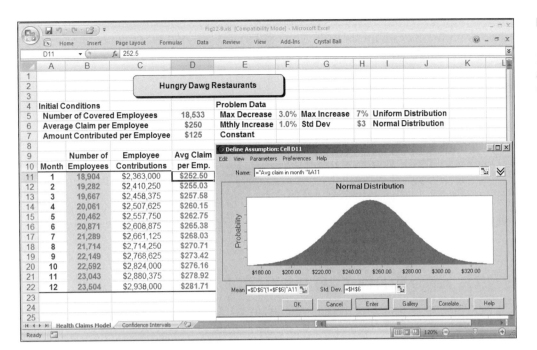

FIGURE 12.12

Defining the assumptions for cell D11

Similarly, the mean in month 3 is:

$$\text{Mean in month 3} = (\text{mean in month 2}) \times 1.01 = (\text{original mean}) \times (1.01)^3$$

So in general, the mean for month n is:

$$\text{Mean in month } n = (\text{original mean}) \times (1.01)^n$$

Thus, to generate the average claim per covered employee for month 1, we use the assumption cell definition for cell D11 shown in Figure 12.12.

Notice that the mean for cell D11 is defined by the formula: =$D$6*(1+$F$6)^A11. This formula implements the general definition of the mean in month n. Similarly, the standard deviation, which is assumed to be constant in all months, is defined by the formula: =$H$6. So after entering our assumptions for cell D11, we can copy this definition to cells D11 through D22 to complete the assumption cell specifications related to the average claim per employee each month. Again, it is **_critical_** that we use Crystal Ball's copy and paste commands to do this because Excel's copy and paste command *will not work* on assumption cell definitions.

12.7.3 DEFINING ASSUMPTIONS FOR THE AVERAGE MONTHLY CLAIM PER EMPLOYEE

After entering the appropriate RNGs via our assumption cell definitions, you can use Crystal Ball's Run, Single Step command to automatically select new values for all the cells in the spreadsheet that represent uncertain (or random) values. Similarly, with each replication, a new value for the bottom-line performance measure (total company cost) appears in cell G23. Thus, by executing the Single Step command several times, we can observe representative values of the company's total cost for health claims. This also helps to verify that we implemented the RNGs correctly and that they are generating appropriate values for each uncertain cell.

W h y   D o n ' t   Y o u r   N u m b e r s   C h a n g e ?

By default, Crystal Ball displays the mean (or average) value of the distribution for cells containing RNG functions. To make Crystal Ball display new values for your RNG cells whenever you click the Single Step button, click Crystal Ball, Cell Prefs, and deselect the check box labeled "Set cell value to distribution mean."

12.8 Running the Simulation

The next step in performing the simulation involves recalculating the spreadsheet several hundred or several thousand times and recording the resulting values generated for the output cell, or bottom-line performance measure. Fortunately, Crystal Ball can do this for us if we indicate: 1) which cell(s) in the spreadsheet we want to track, and 2) how many times we want it to replicate the model.

12.8.1 SELECTING THE OUTPUT CELLS TO TRACK

We can use the Define Forecast button on the Crystal Ball tab (see Figure 12.3) to indicate the output cell (or cells) that we want Crystal Ball to track during the simulation. In the current example, cell G23 represents the output cell we want Crystal Ball to track. To indicate this:

1. Click cell G23.
2. Click the Define Forecast button on the Crystal Ball tab.
   (This causes the dialog box in Figure 12.13 to appear. If you see a button labeled More, click it.)
3. Make the indicated selections.
4. Click OK.

In some simulations, we might want to analyze several performance measures. In such a case, we can follow the preceding procedure repeatedly to select additional output cells to track.

S o f t w a r e   N o t e . . .

When you define assumption, decision, or forecast cells, Crystal Ball automatically changes the background color of the cells to distinguish these cells from others on the spreadsheet. You can change the default colors Crystal Ball uses (or suppress this behavior entirely) by clicking Crystal Ball, Cell Prefs.

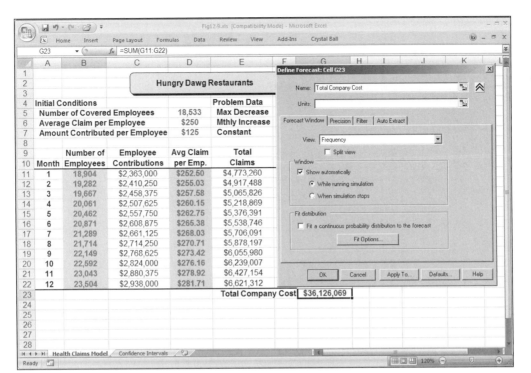

FIGURE 12.13

Defining the forecast cell

12.8.2 SELECTING THE NUMBER OF ITERATIONS

Figure 12.14 shows the Trials card in the Run Preferences dialog box for Crystal Ball. The "Maximum Number of Trials" option in this dialog box allows us to specify the number of iterations (or replications) to include in our simulation. Thus, to indicate that we want to perform 5000 replications of our model:

1. Click the Run Preferences button on the Crystal Ball tab.
2. Type 5000 in the box labeled "Number of trials to run."
3. Click OK.

12.8.3 DETERMINING THE SAMPLE SIZE

You might wonder why we selected 5000 replications. Why not 500, or 8000? Unfortunately, there is no easy answer to this question. Remember that the goal in simulation is to estimate various characteristics about the bottom-line performance measure(s) under consideration. For example, we might want to estimate the mean value of the performance measure and the shape of its probability distribution. However, a different value of the bottom-line performance measure occurs each time we manually recalculate the model in Figure 12.8. Thus, there is an infinite number of possibilities—or an **infinite population**—of total company cost values associated with this model.

We cannot analyze all of these infinite possibilities. But by taking a large enough sample from this infinite population, we can make reasonably accurate estimates about the characteristics of the underlying infinite population of values. The larger the sample we

FIGURE 12.14

Trials options in the Run Prefer-ences dialog box

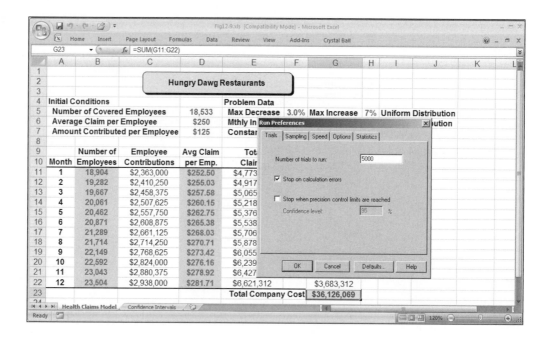

take (that is, the more replications we do), the more accurate our final results will be. But, performing many replications takes time, so we must make a trade-off in terms of estimation accuracy versus convenience. Thus, there is no simple answer to the question of how many replications to perform, but, as a bare minimum you should always per-form at least 1000 replications, and more as time permits or accuracy demands.

12.8.4 RUNNING THE SIMULATION

Having identified the output cells to track and the number of replications to perform, we now need to instruct Crystal Ball to perform the simulation by clicking the Start Simula-tion button on the Crystal Ball tab in Figure 12.3. Crystal Ball then begins to perform the specified number of replications. Depending on the number of iterations selected, the size of the model, and the speed of your computer, it could take anywhere from several sec-onds to several minutes for these computations to be carried out.

For our example problem, Crystal Ball performs 5000 recalculations of the model, keeping track of the value in cell G23 for each replication. By default, Crystal Ball updates the computer screen after each replication, which can be very time-consuming. If you select the "When simulation stops" option shown in Figure 12.13, Crystal Ball will not update the screen after each replication and will perform the replications more quickly.

12.9 Data Analysis

As mentioned earlier, the objective of performing simulation is to estimate various char-acteristics of the performance measure resulting from uncertainty in some or all of the input variables. After performing the replications, Crystal Ball summarizes the output data, as shown in Figure 12.15. (Click Crystal Ball, View Charts, Forecast Charts, Total Company Cost, Open.) The summary statistics and frequency chart are shown simulta-neously by clicking View, Split View.

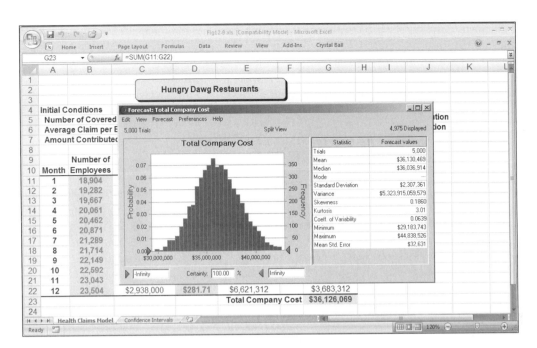

FIGURE 12.15

Summary statistics and histogram for simulation results

12.9.1 THE BEST CASE AND THE WORST CASE

As shown in Figure 12.15, the average (or mean) value for cell G23 is approximately $36.1 million. (If you are working through this example on a computer, the graphs and statistics you generate might be somewhat different from the results shown here because you might be working with a different sample of 5000 observations.) However, decision makers usually want to know the best-case and worst-case scenarios to get an idea of the range of possible outcomes they might face. This information is available from the simulation results, as shown by the Minimum and Maximum values listed in Figure 12.15.

Although the average total cost value observed in the 5000 replications is $36.1 million, in one case the total cost is approximately $29.1 million (representing the best case) and in another case the total cost is approximately $44.8 million (representing the worst case). These figures should give the decision maker a good idea about the range of possible cost values that might occur. Note that these values might be difficult to determine manually in a complex model with many uncertain independent variables.

12.9.2 THE DISTRIBUTION OF THE OUTPUT CELL

The best- and worst-case scenarios are the most extreme outcomes, and might not be likely to occur. To determine the likelihood of these outcomes requires that we know something about the shape of the distribution of our bottom-line performance measure. A histogram of the simulation data for cell G23 also appears in Figure 12.15. This graph provides a visual summary of the approximate shape of the probability distribution associated with the output cell tracked by Crystal Ball during the simulation.

As shown in Figure 12.15, the shape of the distribution associated with the total cost variable is fairly bell-shaped, with a maximum value around $44 million and a minimum value around \$29 million. Thus, we now have a clear idea of the shape of the distribution associated with our bottom-line performance measure—one of the goals in simulation.

If we tracked more than one output cell during the simulation, we could display histograms of the values occurring in these other cells in a similar fashion.

12.9.3 VIEWING THE CUMULATIVE DISTRIBUTION OF THE OUTPUT CELLS

At times, we might want to view a graph of the cumulative probability distribution associated with one of the output cells tracked during a simulation. For example, suppose that the chief financial officer (CFO) for Hungry Dawg would prefer to accrue an excess amount of money to pay health claims rather than not accrue enough money. The CFO might want to know what amount the company should accrue so that there is only a 10% chance of coming up short of funds at the end of the year. So, how much money would you recommend be accrued?

Figure 12.16 shows a graph of the cumulative probability distribution of the values that occurred in cell G23 during the simulation. This graph could help us answer the preceding question. To change the graph shown in Figure 12.15 to the graph and statistics shown in Figure 12.16:

1.   Click View.
2.   De-select Frequency.
3.   Select Cumulative Frequency.
4.   De-select Statistics.
5.   Select Percentiles.
6.   Click and drag the right-hand arrowhead on the X-axis until the certainty level is 90%.

FIGURE 12.16

Cumulative frequency distribution and percentiles of possible total costs

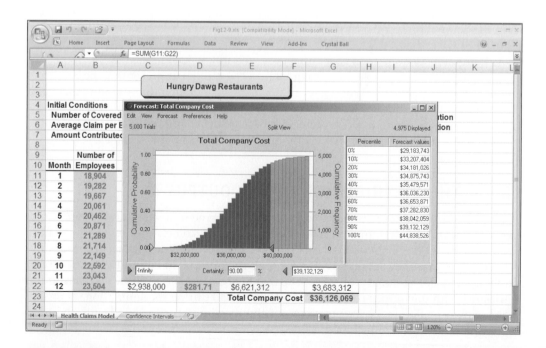

This graph displays the probability of the selected output cell taking on a value smaller than each value on the X-axis. For example, this graph indicates that approximately a 25% chance exists of the output cell (Total Company Cost) assuming a value smaller than approximately $34.5 million. Similarly, this graph indicates that roughly a 75% chance exists of total costs being less than approximately $37.6 million (or a 25% chance of total costs exceeding approximately $37.6 million). Thus, from this graph, we would estimate that roughly a 10% chance exists of the company's costs exceeding approximately $39.1 million.

12.9.4 OBTAINING OTHER CUMULATIVE PROBABILITIES

We also can answer the CFO's question from information in the Percentiles window shown in Figure 12.16. This window reveals several percentile values for the output cell G23. For example, the 10th percentile of the values generated for the output cell is approximately $33.2 million—or 10% of the 5000 values generated for cell G23 are less than or equal to this value. Similarly, the 90th percentile of the distribution of values is approximately $39.1 million. Thus, based on these results, if the company accrues $39.1 million, we would expect that only a 10% chance exists of the actual company costs exceeding this amount.

The ability to perform this type of analysis demonstrates the power and value of simulation and Crystal Ball. For example, how could we have answered the CFO's question about how much money to accrue using best-case/worst-case analysis or what-if analysis? The fact is, we could not have answered the question with any degree of accuracy without using simulation.

12.10 Incorporating Graphs and Statistics into a Spreadsheet

At times, you will want to save some of the graphs or statistics created by Crystal Ball. You can do so by selecting the Create Report option found on the Crystal Ball tab. This option displays the dialog box shown in Figure 12.17. This dialog box provides options for saving different results to Excel. Crystal Ball automatically saves all the selected graphs and statistics in a worksheet in a new workbook.

Similarly, you might want to save the individual trial or replication data generated during the simulation to a separate file for further analysis. You can do so by selecting the Extract Data option from the Crystal Ball tab. This option displays the dialog box shown in Figure 12.18. Here again, Crystal Ball automatically saves all the selected data items in a worksheet in a new workbook.

12.11 The Uncertainty of Sampling

To this point, we have used simulation to generate 5000 observations on our bottom-line performance measure and then calculated various statistics to describe the characteristics and behavior of the performance measure. For example, Figure 12.15 indicates that the mean company cost value in our sample is $36,130,469, and Figure 12.16 shows that a 90% chance exists of this performance measure assuming a value less than $39,132,129. But what if we repeat this process and generate another 5000 observations? Would the

FIGURE 12.17

Saving charts and statistics from the simulation

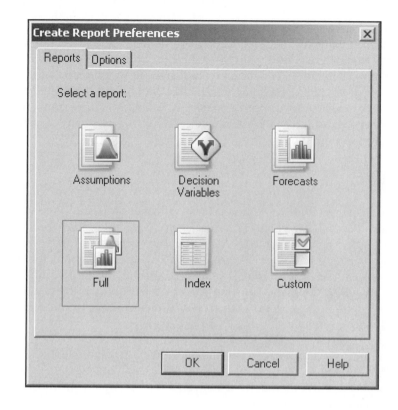

FIGURE 12.18

Saving data from the simulation

sample mean for the new 5000 observations also be exactly $36,130,469? Or would exactly 90% of the observations in the new sample be less than $39,132,129?

The answer to both these questions is "probably not." The sample of 5000 observations used in our analysis was taken from a population of values that theoretically is infinite in size. That is, if we had enough time and our computer had enough memory, we could generate an infinite number of values for our bottom-line performance measure. Theoretically, we then could analyze this infinite population of values to determine its true mean value, its true standard deviation, and the true probability of the performance measure being less than $39,132,129. Unfortunately, we do not have the time or computer resources to determine these true characteristics (or parameters) of the population. The best we can do is take a sample from this population and, based on our sample, make estimates about the true characteristics of the underlying population. Our estimates will differ depending on the sample we choose and the size of the sample.

So, the mean of the sample we take probably is not equal to the true mean we would observe if we could analyze the entire population of values for our performance measure. The sample mean we calculate is just an estimate of the true population mean. In our example problem, we estimated that a 90% chance exists for our output variable to assume a value less than $39,132,129. However, this most likely is not equal to the true probability we would calculate if we could analyze the entire population. Thus, there is some element of uncertainty surrounding the statistical estimates resulting from simulation because we are using a sample to make inferences about the population. Fortunately, there are ways of measuring and describing the amount of uncertainty present in some of the estimates we make about the population under study. Typically this is done by constructing confidence intervals for the population parameters being estimated.

12.11.1 CONSTRUCTING A CONFIDENCE INTERVAL FOR THE TRUE POPULATION MEAN

Constructing a confidence interval for the true population mean is a simple process. If $\bar{y}$ and s represent, respectively, the mean and standard deviation of a sample of size n from any population, then assuming n is sufficiently large ($n \geq 30$), the Central Limit Theorem tells us that the lower and upper limits of a 95% confidence interval for the true mean of the population are represented by:

$$95\% \text{ Lower Confidence Limit} = \bar{y} - 1.96 \times \frac{s}{\sqrt{n}}$$

$$95\% \text{ Upper Confidence Limit} = \bar{y} + 1.96 \times \frac{s}{\sqrt{n}}$$

Although we can be fairly certain that the sample mean we calculate from our sample data is not equal to the true population mean, we can be 95% confident that the true mean of the population falls somewhere between the lower and upper limits given previously. If we want a 90% or 99% confidence interval, we must change the value 1.96 in the previous equation to 1.645 or 2.575, respectively. The values 1.645, 1.96, and 2.575 represent the 95, 97.5, and 99.5 percentiles of the standard normal distribution. Any percentile of the standard normal distribution can be obtained easily using Excel's NORMSINV( ) function.

For our example, the lower and upper limits of a 95% confidence interval for the true mean of the population of total company cost values can be calculated easily, as shown

FIGURE 12.19

Confidence intervals for the population mean and population proportion

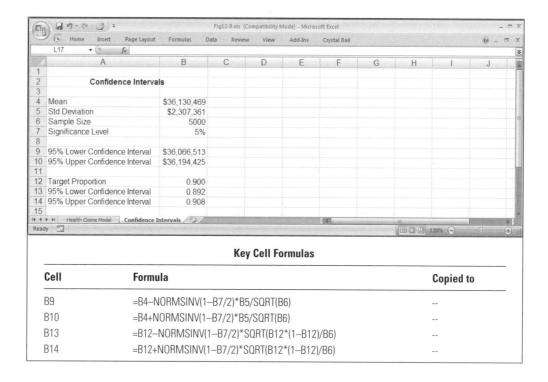

Key Cell Formulas		
Cell	**Formula**	**Copied to**
B9	=B4−NORMSINV(1−B7/2)*B5/SQRT(B6)	--
B10	=B4+NORMSINV(1−B7/2)*B5/SQRT(B6)	--
B13	=B12−NORMSINV(1−B7/2)*SQRT(B12*(1−B12)/B6)	--
B14	=B12+NORMSINV(1−B7/2)*SQRT(B12*(1−B12)/B6)	--

in cells B9 and B10 in Figure 12.19. (The sample mean and standard deviation shown in Figure 12.19 were obtained from Figure 12.15.) The formulas for these cells are:

Formula for cell B9:   =B4−NORMSINV(1−B7/2)*B5/SQRT(B6)

Formula for cell B10:   =B4+NORMSINV(1−B7/2)*B5/SQRT(B6)

Thus, we can be 95% confident that the true mean of the population of total company cost values falls somewhere in the interval from $36,066,513 to $36,194,425.

12.11.2 CONSTRUCTING A CONFIDENCE INTERVAL FOR A POPULATION PROPORTION

In our example, we estimated that 90% of the population of total company cost values fall below $39,132,129 based on our sample of 5000 observations. However, if we could evaluate the entire population of total cost values, we might find that only 80% of these values fall below $39,132,129. Or, we might find that 99% of the entire population falls below this mark. It would be helpful to determine how accurate the 90% value is. So, at times, we might want to construct a confidence interval for the true proportion of a population that falls below (or above) some value, for example Y_p.

To see how this is done, let $\bar{p}$ denote the proportion of observations in a sample of size n that falls below some value Y_p. Assuming that n is sufficiently large ($n \geq 30$), the Central Limit Theorem tells us that the lower and upper limits of a 95% confidence interval for the true proportion of the population falling below Y_p are represented by:

$$95\% \text{ Lower Confidence Limit} = \bar{p} - 1.96 \times \sqrt{\frac{\bar{p}(1 - \bar{p})}{n}}$$

$$95\% \text{ Upper Confidence Limit} = \bar{p} + 1.96 \times \sqrt{\frac{\bar{p}(1 - \bar{p})}{n}}$$

Although we can be fairly certain that the proportion of observations falling below Y_p in our sample is not equal to the true proportion of the population falling below Y_p, we can be 95% confident that the true proportion of the population falling below Y_p is contained within the lower and upper limits given previously. Again, if we want a 90% or 99% confidence interval, we must change the value 1.96 in the previous equations to 1.645 or 2.575, respectively.

Using these formulas, we can calculate the lower and upper limits of a 95% confidence interval for the true proportion of the population falling below \$39,132,129. From our simulation results, we know that 90% of the observations in our sample are less than \$39,132,129. Thus, our estimated value of $\bar{p}$ is 0.90. This value was entered into cell B12 in Figure 12.19. The upper and lower limits of a 95% confidence interval for the true proportion of the population falling below \$39,132,129 are calculated in cells B13 and B14 of Figure 12.19 using the following formulas:

Formula for cell B13:   =B12−NORMSINV(1−B7/2)*SQRT(B12*(1−B12)/B6)

Formula for cell B14:   =B12+NORMSINV(1−B7/2)*SQRT(B12*(1−B12)/B6)

We can be 95% confident that the true proportion of the population of total cost values falling below \$39,132,129 is between 0.892 and 0.908. Because this interval is fairly tight around the value 0.90, we can be reasonably certain that the \$39.1 million figure quoted to the CFO has approximately a 10% chance of being exceeded.

12.11.3 SAMPLE SIZES AND CONFIDENCE INTERVAL WIDTHS

The formulas for the confidence intervals in the previous section depend directly on the number of replications (n) in the simulation. As the number of replications (n) increases, the width of the confidence interval decreases (or becomes more precise). Thus, for a given level of confidence (for example, 95%), the only way to make the upper and lower limits of the interval closer together (or tighter) is to make n larger—that is, use a larger sample size. A larger sample should provide more information about the population and, therefore, allow us to be more accurate in estimating the true parameters of the population.

12.12 The Benefits of Simulation

What have we accomplished through simulation? Are we really better off than if we had just used the results of the original model proposed in Figure 12.2? The estimated value for the expected total cost to the company in Figure 12.2 is comparable to that obtained through simulation (although this might not always be the case). But remember that the goal of modeling is to give us greater insight into a problem to help us make more informed decisions.

The results of our simulation analysis do give us greater insight into the example problem. In particular, we now have some idea of the best- and worst-case total cost outcomes for the company. We have a better idea of the distribution and variability of the possible outcomes, and a more precise idea about where the mean of the distribution is located. We also now have a way of determining how likely it is for the actual outcome to fall above or below some value. Thus, in addition to our greater insight and understanding of the problem, we also have solid empirical evidence (the facts and figures) to support our recommendations.

Applying Simulation in Personal Financial Planning

A recent article in the *Wall Street Journal* highlighted the importance of simulation in evaluating the risk in personal financial investments. "Many people are taking a lot more risk than they realize. They are walking around with a false sense of security," said Christopher Cordaro, an investment adviser at Bugen Stuart Korn & Cordaro of Chatham, N.J. Using one online retirement calculator, after entering information about your finances and assumptions about investment gains, the screen shows a green or red light indicating whether you have saved enough to retire. What is doesn't tell you is whether there is a 95% chance or just a 60% chance that your plan will succeed. "How certain are you about the green light— is it just about to turn yellow and you're just sneaking by?" Mr. Cordaro asked.

Although any planning is better than nothing, traditional planning models spit out answers that create "the illusion that the number is a certainty, when it isn't," said Ross Levin, a Minneapolis investment adviser who uses simulation. Mutual-fund firm T. Rowe Price applied simulation to its recently launched Retirement Income Manager, a personalized consultation service that helps retirees understand how much income they can afford without outliving their assets or depleting funds they want to leave to heirs. A number of independent financial planning companies are now also using simulation software (see the Advisor Tools section of http://www.financeware.com).

In the face of widely divergent possibilities, the number crunching involved in simulation can bring some peace of mind. Steven Haas of Randolph, N.J., was not sure whether he had saved enough to accept an early retirement package from AT&T at age 53. After his financial advisor used simulation to determine he had a 95% probability that his money would last until he reached age 110, Mr. Haas took the package and retired. Mr. Haas reported that by using simulation, "I found that even under significantly negative scenarios we could live comfortably. It relieved a lot of anxiety."

Adapted from "Monte Carlo Financial Simulator May Be A Good Bet For Planning," *Wall Street Journal*, Section C1, April 27, 2000 by Karen Hube.

12.13 Additional Uses of Simulation

Earlier, we indicated that simulation is a technique that *describes* the behavior or characteristics of a bottom-line performance measure. The next several examples show how describing the behavior of a performance measure gives a manager a useful tool in determining the optimal value for one or more controllable parameters in a decision problem. These examples reinforce the mechanics of using simulation, and also demonstrate some additional capabilities of Crystal Ball.

12.14 A Reservation Management Example

Businesses that allow customers to make reservations for services (such as airlines, hotels, and car rental companies) know that some percentage of the reservations made will not be used for one reason or another, leaving these companies with a difficult decision problem. If they accept reservations for only the number of customers that actually can be served, then a portion of the company's assets will be underutilized when some customers with reservations fail to arrive. On the other hand, if they over-book (or accept more reservations than can be handled), then at times, more customers will arrive than can be served. This typically results in additional financial costs to the company and often generates ill-will among those customers who cannot be served. The following example illustrates how simulation might be used to help a company deter-mine the optimal number of reservations to accept.

Marty Ford is an operations analyst for Piedmont Commuter Airlines (PCA). Re-cently, Marty was asked to make a recommendation on how many reservations PCA should book on Flight 343—a flight from a small regional airport in New England to a major hub at Boston's Logan airport. The plane used on Flight 343 is a small twin-engine turbo-prop with 19 passenger seats available. PCA sells nonrefundable tick-ets for Flight 343 for $150 per seat.

Industry statistics show that for every ticket sold for a commuter flight, a 0.10 probability exists that the ticket holder will not be on the flight. Thus, if PCA sells 19 tickets for this flight, there is a fairly good chance that one or more seats on the plane will be empty. Of course, empty seats represent lost potential revenue to the company. On the other hand, if PCA overbooks this flight and more than 19 passen-gers show up, some of them will have to be bumped to a later flight.

To compensate for the inconvenience of being bumped, PCA gives these pas-sengers vouchers for a free meal, a free flight at a later date, and sometimes also pays for them to stay overnight in a hotel near the airport. PCA pays an average of $325 (including the cost of lost goodwill) for each passenger that gets bumped. Marty wants to determine if PCA can increase profits by overbooking this flight and, if so, how many reservations should be accepted to produce the maximum average profit. To assist in the analysis, Marty analyzed market research data for this flight that reveals the following probability distribution of demand for this flight:

Seats Demanded	14	15	16	17	18	19	20	21	22	23	24	25
Probability	0.03	0.05	0.07	0.09	0.11	0.15	0.18	0.14	0.08	0.05	0.03	0.02

12.14.1 IMPLEMENTING THE MODEL

A spreadsheet model for this problem is shown in Figure 12.20 (and in the file Fig12-20.xls on your data disk). The spreadsheet begins by listing the relevant data from the problem, including the number of seats available on the plane, the price PCA charges for each seat, the probability of a no-show (a ticketed passenger not arriving in time for the flight), the cost of bumping passengers, and the number of reservations that will be accepted.

The distribution of demand for seats on the flight is summarized in columns E and F. With this data, cell C10 is defined as an assumption cell representing the random num-ber of seats demanded for a particular flight using Crystal Ball's Custom distribution with the settings shown in Figure 21.21.

FIGURE 12.20

Spreadsheet model for the overbooking problem

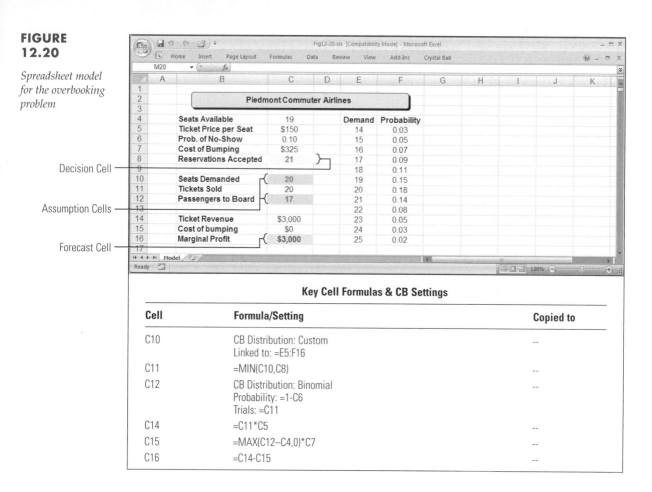

Key Cell Formulas & CB Settings

Cell	Formula/Setting	Copied to
C10	CB Distribution: Custom Linked to: =E5:F16	--
C11	=MIN(C10,C8)	--
C12	CB Distribution: Binomial Probability: =1-C6 Trials: =C11	--
C14	=C11*C5	--
C15	=MAX(C12–C4,0)*C7	--
C16	=C14-C15	--

The number of tickets actually sold for a flight cannot exceed the number of reservations the company is willing to accept. Thus, the number of tickets sold is calculated in cell C11 as follows:

Formula for cell C11:   =MIN(C10,C8)

Because each ticketed passenger has a 0.10 probability of being a no-show, a 0.9 probability exists that each ticketed passenger will arrive in time to board the flight. So the number of passengers present to board the flight can be modeled as a Binomial random variable. The Binomial RNG returns the number of "successes" in a sample of size n where each trial has a probability p of "success." In this case, the sample size is the number of tickets sold (cell C11) and the probability of "success" is 0.9 – the probability that each ticketed passenger will arrive in time to board the flight (or 1-C6). Thus, Crystal Ball's Binomial distribution is used to define cell C12 as an assumption cell that models the number of ticketed passengers that actually arrive for a flight as shown in Figure 12.22.

Cell C14 represents the ticket revenue that PCA earns based on the number of tickets it sells for each flight. The formula for this cell is:

Formula for cell C14:   =C11*C5

**FIGURE
12.21**

*Defining the
assumptions for
cell C10*

Cell C15 computes the costs PCA incurs when passengers must be bumped (i.e., when the number of passengers wanting to board exceeds the number of available seats).

> Formula for cell C15:   =MAX(C12−C4,0)*C7

Finally, cell C16 computes the marginal profit PCA earns on each flight.

> Formula for cell C16:   =C14-C15

12.14.2 USING THE DECISION TABLE TOOL

Marty wants to determine the number of reservations to accept that, on average, will result in the highest marginal profit. To do so, he needs to simulate what would happen to the marginal profit cell (C16) if 19, 20, 21, . . . , 25 reservations were accepted. Fortunately, Crystal Ball includes a tool called Decision Table that simplifies this type of

FIGURE 12.22

Defining the assumptions for cell C12

analysis. To use Decision Table, first indicate the marginal profit cell (C16) to be a forecast cell in the usual way:

1. Select C16.
2. Click the Define Forecast button on the Crystal Ball tab.

Next, define cell C8 (number of reservations accepted) to be a decision variable that may assume integer values from 19 to 25. To do this:

1. Select cell C8.
2. Click Crystal Ball, Define Decision.
3. Fill in the values shown in Figure 12.23.
4. Click OK.

When comparing different values for one or more decision variables (*i.e.*, different solutions), it is best if each possible solution is evaluated using exactly the same series of random numbers. In this way, any difference in the performance of two possible solutions can be attributed to the decision variables' values and not the result of a more favorable set of random numbers for one of the solutions. You can ensure that Crystal Ball uses the same set of random numbers for each simulation by selecting the "Use Same Sequence of Random Numbers" option and supplying an "Initial Seed Value" under the Sampling option on Crystal Ball's Run Preferences dialog box shown in Figure 12.24.

The Sampling Method options shown in Figure 12.21 also affect the accuracy of the results of a simulation run. Using the Monte Carlo option, Crystal Ball is free to select any value for a particular RNG during each replication of the model. For example,

FIGURE 12.23

Defining reservations accepted as a decision variable

FIGURE 12.24

Crystal Ball's Run Preferences dialog

Crystal Ball might repeatedly generate several very extreme (and rare!) values from the upper tail of a normal distribution. The Latin Hypercube option guards against this by ensuring that a fair representation of values is generated from the entire distribution for each RNG. As you might imagine, the Latin Hypercube sampling option requires a bit more work during each replication of the model, but it tends to generate more accurate simulation results in a fewer number of trials.

After setting a random number seed as shown in Figure 12.24, we are ready to use the Decision Table tool. To invoke the Decision Table tool:

1. Click Crystal Ball, Tools.
2. Click Decision Table.

**FIGURE
12.25**

*Specifying the
target cell for the
Decision Table tool*

The dialog box shown in Figure 12.25 appears prompting us to select the forecast (or target) cell we want to track. Here, we select the "Marginal Profit" option and click the Next button.

In the next dialog box, shown in Figure 12.26, we select the decision variable we want to evaluate. In this case there is only one variable (Reservations Accepted). However, the Decision Table tool allows you to select up to two decision variables to analyze simultaneously.

The next dialog box, shown in Figure 12.27, allows us to specify the number of values to test for each decision variable and the number of iterations (trials) to use for each resulting simulation run. In our case, there are seven possible discrete values for Reservations Accepted (i.e., 19, 20, 21, . . . , 25) and we want to test them all. However, for continuous decision variables that can assume any value within some interval, it is impossible to test all the possible values, and we must tell the Decision Table tool the number of possible values to try.

When you click the Start button in Figure 12.27, the Decision Table tool runs a separate simulation for each of the seven possible values we indicated for the decision variable. When it is finished, the Decision Table tool creates a new workbook like the one shown in Figure 12.28 summarizing the average value of the forecast cell (Marginal Profit) for each of the seven simulations. These values indicate that the average marginal profit reaches a maximum value of $2,834 when PCA accepts 22 reservations. We can easily create a bar chart from this data to graphically represent the differences in the average profits under each scenario.

You can also select one or more of the average profit values on row 2 in Figure 12.28 and display a Trend Chart, Overlay Chart, or Forecast Chart for the selected values.

FIGURE 12.26

Choosing the decision variable with the Decision Table tool

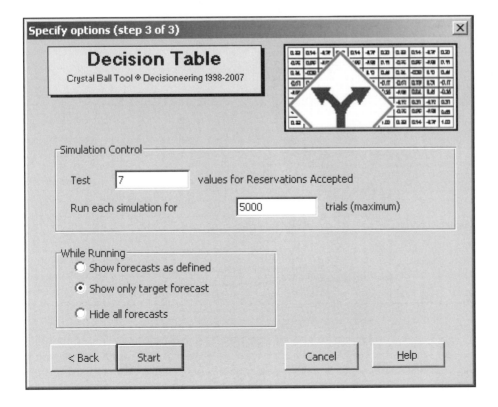

FIGURE 12.27

Setting options with the Decision Table tool

FIGURE 12.28

Results of the Decision Table tool

FIGURE 12.29

Overlay chart comparing outcome distributions for 21 and 25 reservations accepted

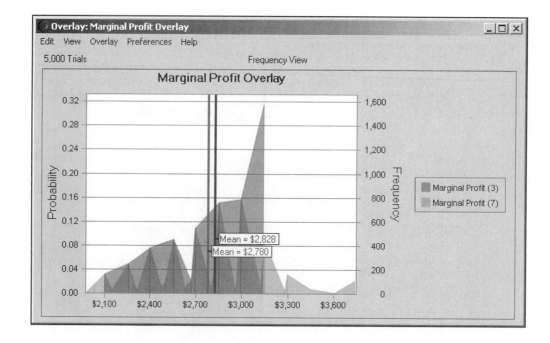

Figure 12.29 shows an Overlay Chart comparing the distributions of values generated in simulation 3 (where up to 21 reservations were accepted) and simulation 7 (where up to 25 reservations were accepted). This type of chart is often helpful in comparing the risk-iness of different decision alternatives.

12.15 An Inventory Control Example

According to the *Wall Street Journal*, U.S. businesses recently had a combined inventory worth $884.77 billion. Because so much money is tied up in inventories, businesses face many important decisions regarding the management of these assets. Frequently asked questions regarding inventory include:

* What's the best level of inventory for a business to maintain?
* When should goods be reordered (or manufactured)?
* How much safety stock should be held in inventory?

The study of inventory control principles is split into two distinct areas—one assumes that demand is known (or deterministic), and the other assumes that demand is random (or stochastic). If demand is known, various formulas can be derived that provide answers to the previous questions (an example of one such formula is given in the discussion of the EOQ model in Chapter 8.) However, when demand for a product is uncertain or random, answers to the previous questions cannot be expressed in terms of a simple formula. In these situations, the technique of simulation proves to be a useful tool, as illustrated in the following example.

Laura Tanner is the owner of Millennium Computer Corporation (MCC), a retail computer store in Austin, Texas. Competition in retail computer sales is fierce—both in terms of price and service. Laura is concerned about the number of stockouts occurring on a popular type of computer monitor. Stockouts are very costly to the business because when customers cannot buy this item at MCC, they simply buy it from a competing store and MCC loses the sale (there are no back orders). Laura measures the effects of stockouts on her business in terms of service level, or the percentage of total demand that can be satisfied from inventory.

Laura has been following the policy of ordering 50 monitors whenever her daily ending inventory position (defined as ending inventory on hand plus outstanding orders) falls below her reorder point of 28 units. Laura places the order at the beginning of the next day. Orders are delivered at the beginning of the day and, therefore, can be used to satisfy demand on that day. For example, if the ending inventory position on day 2 is less than 28, Laura places the order at the beginning of day 3. If the actual time between order and delivery, or lead time, turns out to be four days, then the order arrives at the start of day 7.

The current level of on-hand inventory is 50 units and no orders are pending. MCC sells an average of six monitors per day. However, the actual number sold on any given day can vary. By reviewing her sales records for the past several months, Laura determined that the actual daily demand for this monitor is a random variable that can be described by the following probability distribution:

Units Demanded	0	1	2	3	4	5	6	7	8	9	10
Probability	0.01	0.02	0.04	0.06	0.09	0.14	0.18	0.22	0.16	0.06	0.02

The manufacturer of this computer monitor is located in California. Although it takes an average of four days for MCC to receive an order from this company, Laura has determined that the lead time of a shipment of monitors is also a random variable that can be described by the following probability distribution:

Lead Time (days)	3	4	5
Probability	0.2	0.6	0.2

One way to guard against stockouts and improve the service level is to increase the reorder point for the item so that more inventory is on hand to meet the demand occurring during the lead time. However, there are holding costs associated with keeping more inventory on hand. Laura wants to evaluate her current ordering policy for this item and determine if it might be possible to improve the service level without increasing the average amount of inventory on hand.

12.15.1 IMPLEMENTING THE MODEL

To solve this problem, we need to build a model to represent the inventory of computer monitors during an average month of 30 days. This model must account for the random daily demands that can occur and the random lead times encountered when orders are placed. To facilitate this, we first entered the data for these variables as shown in Figure 12.30 (and in the file Fig12-30.xls on your data disk). We will use this data in conjunction with Crystal Ball's Custom distribution to create assumption cells representing the random order lead times and daily demand values needed for this problem.

Figure 12.31 shows a model representing 30 days of inventory activity. Notice that cells M5 and M6 have been reserved to represent, respectively, the reorder point and order quantity for the model.

The inventory on hand at the beginning of each day is calculated in column B in Figure 12.31. The beginning inventory for each day is simply the ending inventory from the previous day. The formulas in column B are:

Formula for cell B6:	=50
Formula for cell B7:	=F6

(Copy to B8 through B35.)

Column C represents the number of units scheduled to be received each day. We will discuss the formulas in column C after we discuss columns H, I, and J, which relate to ordering and order lead times.

FIGURE 12.30

RNG data for MCC's inventory problem

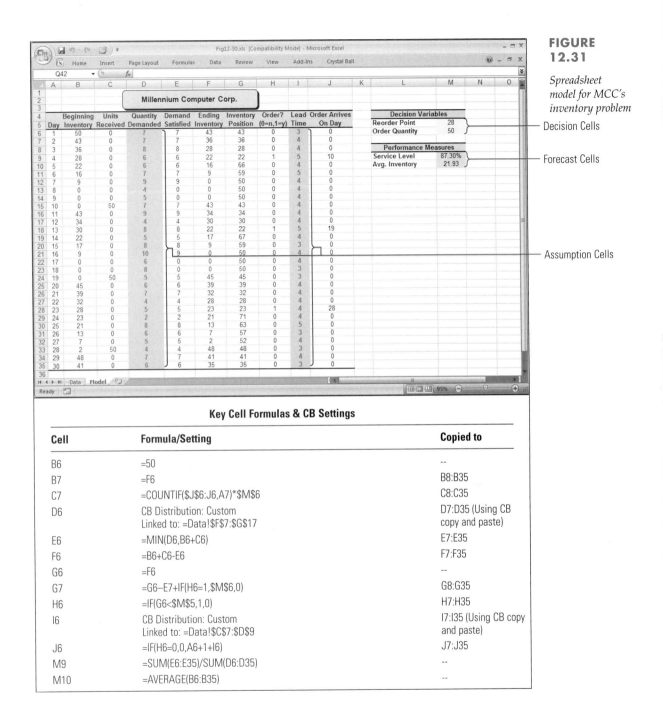

FIGURE 12.31

Spreadsheet model for MCC's inventory problem

— Decision Cells

— Forecast Cells

— Assumption Cells

Key Cell Formulas & CB Settings

Cell	Formula/Setting	Copied to
B6	=50	--
B7	=F6	B8:B35
C7	=COUNTIF($J$6:J6,A7)*$M$6	C8:C35
D6	CB Distribution: Custom Linked to: =Data!$F$7:$G$17	D7:D35 (Using CB copy and paste)
E6	=MIN(D6,B6+C6)	E7:E35
F6	=B6+C6-E6	F7:F35
G6	=F6	--
G7	=G6−E7+IF(H6=1,$M$6,0)	G8:G35
H6	=IF(G6<$M$5,1,0)	H7:H35
I6	CB Distribution: Custom Linked to: =Data!$C$7:$D$9	I7:I35 (Using CB copy and paste)
J6	=IF(H6=0,0,A6+1+I6)	J7:J35
M9	=SUM(E6:E35)/SUM(D6:D35)	--
M10	=AVERAGE(B6:B35)	--

In column D, we use Crystal Ball's Custom distribution to define our assumptions about the random behavior of daily demand for monitors. Figure 12.32 shows the Define Assumption dialog box for cell D6. This definition was also copied to cells D7 through D35 (using Crystal Ball's copy data and paste data commands).

Because it is possible for demand to exceed the available supply, column E indicates how much of the daily demand can be met. If the beginning inventory (in column B)

FIGURE 12.32

Defining the assumptions for cell D6

plus the ordered units received (in column C) is greater than or equal to the actual demand, then all the demand can be satisfied; otherwise, MCC can sell only as many units as are available. This condition is modeled as:

Formula for cell E6:   =MIN(D6,B6+C6)

(Copy to E7 through E35.)

The values in column F represent the on-hand inventory at the end of each day, and are calculated as:

Formula for cell F6:   =B6+C6−E6

(Copy to F7 through F35.)

To determine whether to place an order, we first must calculate the inventory position, which was defined earlier as the ending inventory plus any outstanding orders. This is implemented in column G as:

Formula for cell G6:   =F6

Formula for cell G7:   =G6−E7+IF(H6=1,$M$6,0)

(Copy to G8 through G35.)

Column H indicates if an order should be placed based on inventory position and the reorder point, as:

Formula for cell H6: =IF(G6<$M$5,1,0)

(Copy to H7 through H35.)

In column I, we use Crystal Ball's Custom distribution to define our assumptions about the random behavior of order lead times. Figure 12.33 shows the Define Assumption dialog box for cell I6. This definition was also copied to cells I7 through I35 (using Crystal Ball's copy data and paste data commands). Note that column I generates an order lead time for each day, irrespective of if an order is actually placed on a given day. If no order is placed on a given day, the associated lead time value in Column I is ignored.

If an order is placed (as indicated by column H), column J indicates the day on which the order will be received based on its random lead time in column I. This is done as:

Formula for cell J6: =IF(H6=0,0,A6+1+I6)

(Copy to J7 through J35.)

The values in column C are coordinated with those in column J. The nonzero values in column J indicate the days on which orders will be received. For example, cell J9 indicates that an order will be received on day 10. The actual receipt of this order is reflected by the value of 50 in cell C15, which represents the receipt of an order at the beginning of day 10. The formula in cell C15 that achieves this is:

Formula for cell C15: =COUNTIF($J$6:J14,A15)*$M$6

This formula counts how many times the value in cell A15 (representing day 10) appears as a scheduled receipt day between days 1 through 9 in column J. This represents

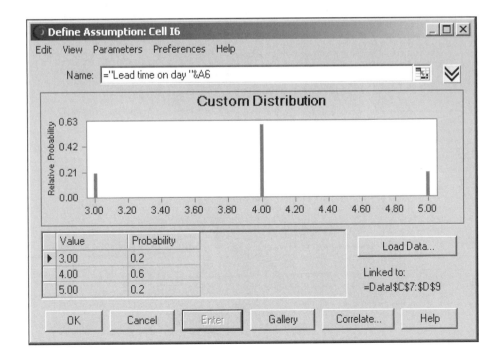

FIGURE 12.33

Defining the assumptions for cell I6

the number of orders scheduled to be received on day 10. We then multiply this by the order quantity (50), given in cell M6 to determine the total units to be received on day 10. Thus, the values in column C are generated as:

Formula for cell C6:   =0

Formula for cell C7:   =COUNTIF($J$6:J6,A7)*$M$6
(Copy to C8 through C35.)

The service level for the model is calculated in cell M9 using the values in columns D and E as:

Formula for cell M9:   =SUM(E6:E35)/SUM(D6:D35)

Again, the service level represents the proportion of total demand that can be satisfied from inventory. The value in cell M9 indicates that in the scenario shown, 87.30% of the total demand is satisfied.

The average inventory level is calculated in cell M10 by averaging the values in column B. This is accomplished as follows:

Formula for cell M10:   =AVERAGE(B6:B35)

12.15.2 REPLICATING THE MODEL

The model in Figure 12.31 indicates one possible scenario that could occur if Laura uses a reorder point of 28 units for the computer monitor. Figure 12.34 shows the results of using Crystal Ball to replicate this model 5000 times, tracking the values in cells M9 (service level) and M10 (average inventory) as forecast cells.

Figure 12.34 indicates that MCC's current reorder point (28 units) and order quantity (50 units) results in an average service level of approximately 96.2% (with a minimum

FIGURE 12.34

Results of 5000 replications of the MCC model

value of 79.8% and a maximum value of 100%) and an average inventory level of almost 26 monitors (with a minimum value of 19.7 and a maximum value of 34.07).

12.15.3 OPTIMIZING THE MODEL

Suppose Laura wants to determine a reorder point and order quantity that provides an average service level of 98% while keeping the average inventory level as low as possible. One way to do this is to run additional simulations at various reorder point and inventory level combinations trying to find the combination of settings that produce the desired behavior. However, as you might imagine, this could be very time-consuming.

Fortunately, Crystal Ball Professional includes a product called OptQuest that is designed to solve this type of problem. To use OptQuest, first we must use Crystal Ball to define cells M5 (reorder point) and M6 (order quantity) to be decision variable cells. We will assume that Laura wants to consider discrete reorder points in the range from 20 and 50 and discrete order quantity values in the range from 20 to 70. To do this:

1. Select cells M5 and M6.
2. Click the Define Decision button on the Crystal Ball tab.
3. Enter lower and upper bounds for each cell and a discrete step size of 1.
4. Click OK.

Note that cells M9 (service level) and M10 (average inventory level) should already be selected as forecast cells from our earlier simulation run.

Again, when comparing different values for one or more decision variables, it is best if each possible solution is evaluated using exactly the same series of random numbers. We can ensure that Crystal Ball uses the same set of random numbers for each simulation by selecting the "Use same sequence of random numbers" option and supplying an "Initial seed value" under the Sampling option on Crystal Ball's Run Preferences dialog box (shown earlier in Figure 12.24).

After the decision variable cells, forecast cells, random number seed, and an Assumption cell are specified using Crystal Ball, you may start an OptQuest session for the model as follows:

1. Click Crystal Ball, Tools, OptQuest.
2. In OptQuest, click File, New.

The resulting OptQuest screen is shown in Figure 12.35. This screen shows the decision variables for the current problem along with the bounds and restrictions we have placed on these variables. Click the OK button on this screen to accept these selections.

FIGURE 12.35

OptQuest's Decision Variable Selection screen

**FIGURE
12.36**

*OptQuest's
Forecast Selection
screen*

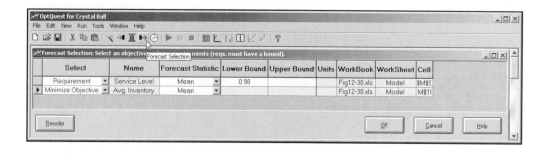

**FIGURE
12.37**

*OptQuest's
Options screen*

The next step is to tell OptQuest about the objectives we want it to pursue. This is done using the Forecast Selection window shown in Figure 12.36.

In the window shown in Figure 12.36, we indicated that we want OptQuest to minimize the value of the "Avg. Inventory" cell. We also placed a lower bound of 0.98 on the "Service Level" cell and indicated that this is a requirement that must be enforced. (Note that you can make changes to the various cells in the Forecast Selection window by clicking on the appropriate cell.) Click the OK button on this screen to accept these selections.

Next, we use the Options window shown in Figure 12.37 to indicate the amount of time we want OptQuest to search for solutions to the problem. Remember that a separate simulation must be run for each combination of the decision variables that OptQuest chooses. OptQuest uses several heuristics to search intelligently for the best combination of decision variables. However, this is still inherently a very computationally intensive and time-consuming process and complicated models may take hours (or days) of solution time. Note that we are giving OptQuest ten minutes to search for a solution to the MCC problem.

With all the appropriate options set, click the Start button (or click Run, Start). OptQuest then runs multiple simulations using different combinations of values for the decision variables. The Performance Graph and Status and Solutions windows shown in Figure 12.38 provide a summary of OptQuest's efforts on the problem. Ultimately, OptQuest found that a reorder point of 34 and order quantity of 20 resulted in an average service level of 98.4% while requiring an average inventory of approximately 18.3 units per month. Thus, MCC can simultaneously increase its service level and reduce its average inventory level by using the new ordering policy identified by OptQuest.

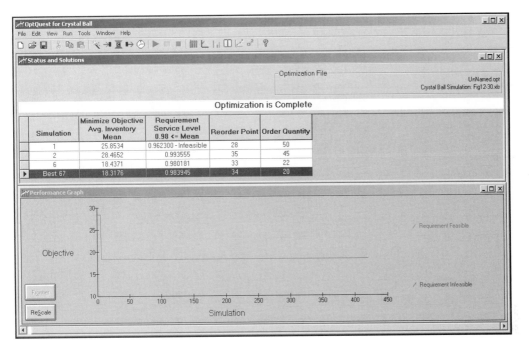

FIGURE 12.38

OptQuest results

A Tip on Using OptQuest...

When using OptQuest to solve a problem, it is often a good idea to reduce the number of trials that Crystal Ball performs during each simulation. This allows OptQuest to explore more possible combinations of decision variable values (solutions) in the allotted amount of time. Then after OptQuest identifies a solution for the problem, you can implement that solution in your model (click Edit, Copy to Excel in OptQuest) and rerun Crystal Ball with a higher number of trials to get a better idea of how well the suggested solution actually performs.

12.15.4 COMPARING THE ORIGINAL AND OPTIMAL ORDERING POLICIES

MCC's manager should be pleased with the new ordering policy OptQuest identified, but she may have other questions about how the reorder point and order quantity will affect the physical storage requirements for this inventory item. Figure 12.39 shows two separate charts illustrating the variability in daily ending inventory under the original and optimal ordering policies. Clearly, in addition to its other benefits, the new ordering policy also requires a more consistent and smaller amount of storage space for this inventory item.

The charts in Figure 12.39 were created using Crystal Ball's Analyze, Trend Charts command. To collect the data for these charts, each of the ending inventory cells shown in column F of Figure 12.31 were defined to be Crystal Ball forecast cells. Two separate simulations then were run: one with the original reorder point and order

FIGURE 12.39

Comparison of original and optimal inventory policies

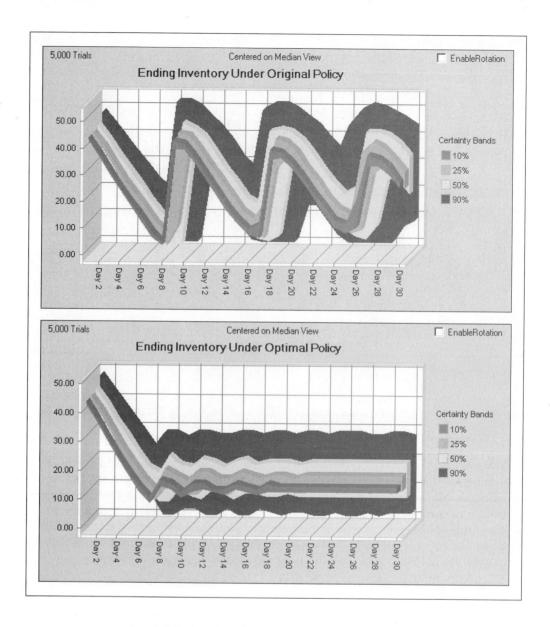

quantity values (in cells M5 and M6, respectively), and the other with the optimal reorder point and order quantity values identified by OptQuest. After each simulation, a trend chart was created from the forecast cells representing the daily ending inventory values.

12.16 A Project Selection Example

In Chapter 6, we saw how Solver can be used in project selection problems in which the payoff for each project is assumed to be known with certainty. In many cases, a great deal of uncertainty exists with respect to the ultimate payoff that will be received if a particular project is undertaken. In these situations, Crystal Ball and OptQuest offer an alternate means for deciding which project(s) to undertake. Consider the following example.

> TRC Technologies has $2 million to invest in new R&D projects. The following table summarizes the initial cost, probability of success, and revenue potential for each of the projects.

Project	Initial Cost ($1000s)	Probability of Success	Revenue Potential ($1000s)		
			Min.	Most Likely	Max.
1	$250.0	90%	$ 600	$ 750	$ 900
2	$650.0	70%	$1,250	$1,500	$1,600
3	$250.0	60%	$ 500	$ 600	$ 750
4	$500.0	40%	$1,600	$1,800	$1,900
5	$700.0	80%	$1,150	$1,200	$1,400
6	$ 30.0	60%	$ 150	$ 180	$ 250
7	$350.0	70%	$ 750	$ 900	$1,000
8	$ 70.0	90%	$ 220	$ 250	$ 320

> TRC's management wants to determine the set of projects that will maximize the firm's expected profit.

12.16.1 A SPREADSHEET MODEL

A spreadsheet model for this problem is shown in Figure 12.40 (and the file Fig12-40.xls on your data disk). Cells C6 through C13 in this spreadsheet indicate which projects will be selected. Using Crystal Ball, we can define these cells to be decision variables that must take on discrete values between zero and one—or operate as binary variables. The values shown in cells C6 though C13 were assigned arbitrarily. We will use OptQuest to determine the optimal values for these variables.

In cell D14, we compute the total initial investment required by the selected projects as follows:

Formula for cell D14:   =SUMPRODUCT(D6:D13,C6:C13)

In cell D16, we calculate the amount of unused or surplus investment funds. Using Crystal Ball, we will define this to be a forecast cell. Using OptQuest, we can place a lower bound requirement of zero on the value of this cell to ensure that the projects selected do not require more than $2 million in initial investment funds.

Formula for cell D16:   =D15−D14

The potential success or failure of each project may be modeled using Crystal Ball's Yes-No distribution. This distribution randomly returns a value of either 1 (representing "Yes" or success) or 0 (representing "No" or failure) according to a specified probability of success. The probability of success for each project is given in column E. Thus, we model the potential success of project 1 in cell F6 using the Crystal Ball Define Assumption settings shown in Figure 12.41. This definition also was copied to cells F7 through F13 (using Crystal Ball's copy data and paste data commands).

There is also uncertainty about the revenue that each project might generate. Because we have estimates of the minimum, most likely, and maximum possible revenue for

FIGURE 12.40

Spreadsheet model for TRC Technologies' project selection problem

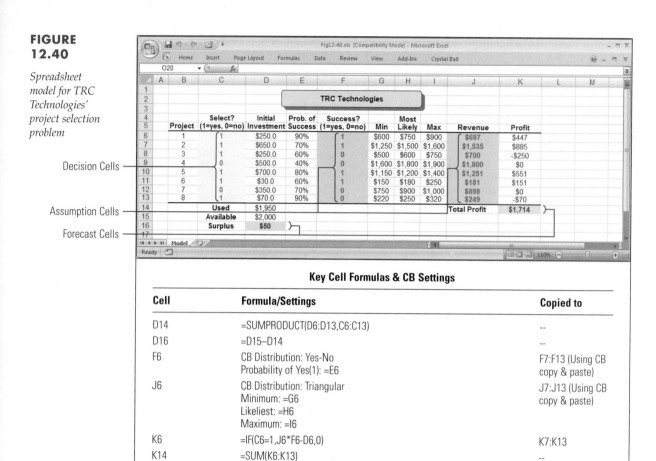

Decision Cells

Assumption Cells

Forecast Cells

Key Cell Formulas & CB Settings

Cell	Formula/Settings	Copied to
D14	=SUMPRODUCT(D6:D13,C6:C13)	--
D16	=D15–D14	--
F6	CB Distribution: Yes-No Probability of Yes(1): =E6	F7:F13 (Using CB copy & paste)
J6	CB Distribution: Triangular Minimum: =G6 Likeliest: =H6 Maximum: =I6	J7:J13 (Using CB copy & paste)
K6	=IF(C6=1,J6*F6-D6,0)	K7:K13
K14	=SUM(K6:K13)	--

each project, we will model the revenues for selected, successful projects using a triangular distribution. We accomplish this for project 1 in cell J6 as shown in Figure 12.42. This definition also was copied to cells J7 through J13 (using Crystal Ball's copy data and paste data commands).

Note that each project's potential success or failure must be generated independently of whether or not the project is selected (even though only selected projects have the potential to be successful). Similarly, each project's potential revenue must be generated independently of whether or the not the project is successful (even though only successful projects generate revenue). Thus, in column K we must compute the profit for each project carefully based on whether the project is selected and, if selected, whether it is also successful. This is accomplished in column K as follows:

Formula for cell K6:   =IF(C6=1,J6*F6-D6,0)

(Copy to cells K7 through K13.)

Finally, cell K14 computes the total profit for each replication of the model. We will define this as a forecast cell using Crystal Ball and attempt to maximize its value using OptQuest.

Formula for cell K14:   =SUM(K6:K13)

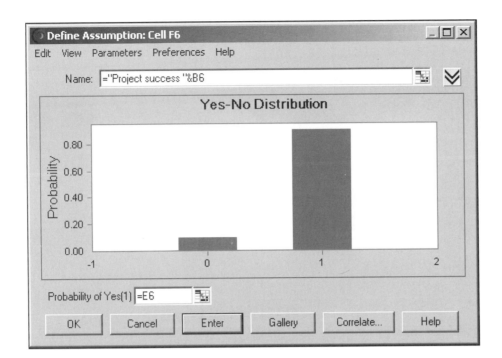

FIGURE 12.41

Defining the assumptions for cell F6

FIGURE 12.42

Defining the assumptions for cell J6

12.16.2 SOLVING THE PROBLEM WITH OptQUEST

The OptQuest settings used to solve this problem are shown in Figure 12.43 and the optimal solution is shown in Figure 12.44. This solution involves selecting projects 1, 2, 4, 6, 7, and 8, requiring an initial investment of $1.85 million and resulting in an expected profit of approximately $1.5 million.

FIGURE 12.43

OptQuest settings for the project selection problem

FIGURE 12.44

Optimal solution to the project selection problem

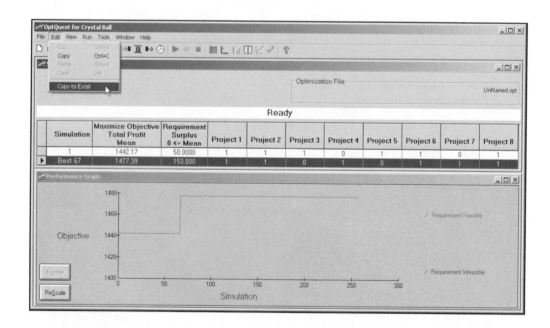

To investigate this solution in a bit more detail, we can copy it back into Crystal Ball (click Edit, Copy to Excel in OptQuest), and view the statistics and frequency distribution associated with the solution. These results are shown in Figures 12.45.

Although the expected (mean) profit associated with this solution is approximately $1.5 million, the range of the possible outcomes is fairly wide (approximately $5.5 million). The worst-case outcome observed with this solution resulted in approximately a $1.6 million loss, whereas the best-case outcome resulted in approximately a $3.86 million profit. Because each of the projects is a one-time occurrence that either can succeed or fail, the decision makers in this problem do not have the luxury of selecting this set of projects over and over and realizing the average profit level of $1.5 million over time. Also, we see that there is about a 10% chance of losing money if this solution

**FIGURE
12.45**

*Results for the
project selection
problem*

is implemented, but about a 64% chance of making at least $1 million. Thus, there is a significant risk associated with this solution that is not apparent if one simply looks at its expected profit level of $1.5 million.

12.16.3 CONSIDERING OTHER SOLUTIONS

The decision makers in this problem might be interested in considering other alternatives. Because each of the projects has the potential to fail and lose money, the only way to completely avoid the possibility of a loss is not to invest in any of the projects. Unfortunately, this also completely avoids the possibility of earning profit! In most situations, greater levels of risk are required to achieve higher levels of return.

After considering the earlier solution and their attitudes toward risk and return, suppose the decision makers at TRC decide that they are comfortable with a 10% chance of losing money. But while assuming this risk, they want to ensure that they maximize the chance of earning a profit of at least $1 million. The OptQuest Forecast Selections settings required to solve this revised problem are shown in Figure 12.46. Notice that now

**FIGURE
12.46**

*OptQuest settings
for the revised
project selection
problem*

we are attempting to maximize the number of times that the forecasted profit value (in cell K14 in Figure 12.40) falls above $1 million (as opposed to maximizing the average profit value). We have implemented a requirement that the 10th percentile of the distribution of forecasted profit values be greater than zero (or have a lower bound of 0). This should ensure that the resulting solution will have at most a 10% chance of losing money. To place more than one requirement on the same forecast cell (as was done for cell K14 in Figure 12.46), in OptQuest's Forecast Selection window,

1. Click anywhere on the row corresponding to the forecast cell you want to duplicate.
2. Click Edit, Duplicate.

Placing Multiple Requirements on the Same Forecast Cell...

To place more than one requirement on the same forecast cell (as done in Figure 12.46), in OptQuest's Forecast Selection window, click anywhere on the row corresponding to the forecast cell you want to duplicate. Then click Edit, Duplicate.

OptQuest's solution to this problem is shown in Figure 12.47. This solution indicates that TRC should accept projects 1, 2, 3, 5, 6, and 8, consuming $1.95 million in initial capital. To investigate this solution in more detail, we copy this solution back into our spreadsheet (in OptQuest click Edit, Copy to Excel) and generate the solution statistics and frequency distribution shown in Figure 12.48.

In Figure 12.48, notice that the expected (mean) profit for this solution is about $1.44 million, representing a decrease of approximately $35,000 from the earlier solution.

FIGURE 12.47

OptQuest solution for the revised project selection problem

**FIGURE
12.48**

*Statistics for the
revised project
selection problem*

The range of possible outcomes also has decreased to about $4.6 million, with a worst-case outcome of a $1.7 million loss, and a best-case outcome of approximately a $2.9 million profit. This solution *reduces* the chances of realizing a loss to approximately 8.5% and *increases* the chances of making at least $1 million to approximately 70.2%. Thus, although the best possible outcome realized under this solution ($2.9 million) is not as large as that of the earlier solution ($3.86 million), it reduces the downside risk in the problem and makes it more likely for the company to earn at least $1 million—but it also requires a slightly larger initial investment. It is also interesting to note that the probability of *all* the selected projects being successful under this solution is 0.1633 (i.e., $0.1633 = .9 \times .7 \times .6 \times .8 \times .6 \times .9$), whereas the probability of all selected projects being successful under the first solution is only 0.0953 (i.e., $0.0953 = .9 \times .7 \times .4 \times .6 \times .7 \times .9$).

So, what is the best solution to this problem? It depends on the risk attitudes and preferences of the decision makers at TRC. However, the simulation techniques that we have described clearly provide valuable insights into the risks associated with various solutions.

12.17 A Portfolio Optimization Example

In Chapter 8, we saw how Solver can be used to analyze potential tradeoffs between risk and return for a given set of stocks using the idea of an *efficient frontier*. The efficient frontier represents the highest level of return a portfolio can achieve for any given level of risk. Whereas portfolio optimization and efficient frontier analysis is most commonly associated with financial instruments such as stocks and bonds, it also can be applied to physical assets. OptQuest contains an efficient frontier calculation process that makes identifying the efficient frontier a relatively simple process. This will be illustrated using the following example.

> In recent years, a fundamental shift occurred in power plant asset ownership. Traditionally, a single regulated utility would own a given power plant. Today, more and more power plants are owned by merchant generators that provide power to a competitive wholesale marketplace. This makes is possible for an investor to buy, for example, 10% of ten different generating assets rather than 100% of a single power plant. As a result, non-traditional power plant owners have emerged in the form of investment groups, private equity funds, and energy hedge funds.

The McDaniel Group is a private investment company in Richmond, VA, that currently has a total of $1 billion that it wants to invest in power generation assets. Five different types of investments are possible: natural gas, oil, coal, nuclear, and wind-powered plants. The following table summarizes the megawatts (MW) of generation capacity that can be purchased per each $1 million investment in the various types of power plants.

Generation Capacity per Million $ Invested				
Fuel Type	Gas	Coal	Oil	Nuclear	Wind
MWs	2.0	1.2	3.5	1.0	0.5

The return on each type of investment varies randomly and is determined primarily by fluctuations in fuel prices and the spot price (or current market value) of electricity. Assume that the McDaniel Group analyzed historical data to determine that the return per MW produced by each type of plant can be modeled as normally distributed random variables with the following means and standard deviations.

Normal Distribution Return Parameters by Fuel Type					
	Gas	Coal	Oil	Nuclear	Wind
Mean	16%	12%	10%	9%	8%
Std Dev	12%	6%	4%	3%	1%

Additionally, while analyzing the historical data on operating costs, it was observed that many of the returns are correlated. For example, when the returns from plants fueled by natural gas are high (due to low gas prices), returns from plants fueled by coal and oil tend to be low. So there is a negative correlation between the returns from gas plants and the returns from coal and oil plants. The following table summarizes all the pairwise correlations between the returns from different types of power plants.

Correlations Between Returns by Fuel Type					
	Gas	Coal	Oil	Nuclear	Wind
Gas	1	−0.49	−0.31	0.16	0.12
Coal		1	−0.41	0.11	0.07
Oil			1	0.13	0.09
Nuclear				1	0.04
Wind					1

The McDaniel Group would like to determine the efficient frontier for its investment options in power generation assets.

12.17.1 A SPREADSHEET MODEL

A spreadsheet model for this problem is shown in Figure 12.49 (and the file Fig12-49.xls on your data disk). Cells D5 through D9 in this spreadsheet indicate how much money (in millions) will be invested in each type of generation asset. Using Crystal Ball, we can define these cells to be decision variables that must take on values between zero and $1,000. The values shown in cells D5 though D19 were assigned arbitrarily. We will use OptQuest to determine the optimal values for these variables. In OptQuest, we also will create a constraint that requires these values to sum to $1,000 (or $1 billion).

FIGURE
12.49

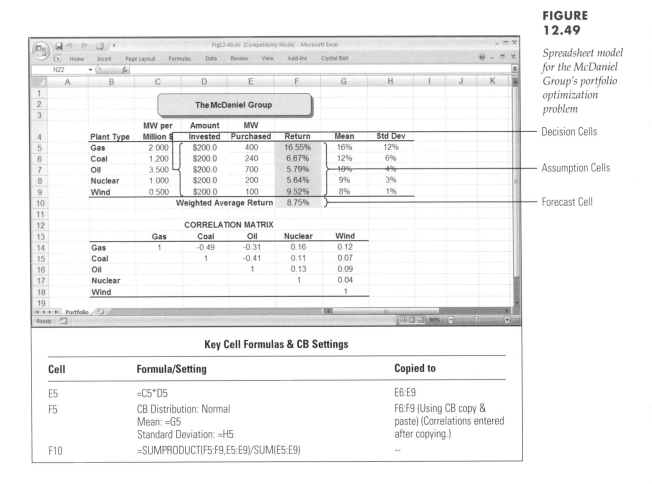

*Spreadsheet model
for the McDaniel
Group's portfolio
optimization
problem*

Decision Cells

Assumption Cells

Forecast Cell

Key Cell Formulas & CB Settings

Cell	Formula/Setting	Copied to
E5	=C5*D5	E6:E9
F5	CB Distribution: Normal Mean: =G5 Standard Deviation: =H5	F6:F9 (Using CB copy & paste) (Correlations entered after copying.)
F10	=SUMPRODUCT(F5:F9,E5:E9)/SUM(E5:E9)	--

In column E we compute the number of MW of generation capacity purchased in each asset category as follows:

Formula for cell E5:   =C5*D5

(Copy to cells E6 through E9.)

The assumption cells representing the random return for each asset category are implemented in column F using Crystal Ball's Normal distribution with the means and standard deviations specified in columns G and H, respectively. We accomplish this for investments in gas-fueled plants in cell F5 as shown in Figure 12.50. This definition also was copied to cells F6 through F9 (using Crystal Ball's copy data and paste data commands).

The "Correlate . . ." button on Crystal Ball's Define Assumption dialog box (shown in Figure 12.50) allows us to define correlations among the random variables (or assumption cells) in our spreadsheet models. However, there is not an accurate way to copy correlations from one assumption cell to another assumption cell. So first we must define all our assumption cells and then go back and individually specify any correlations between them. The Define Correlation dialog box for cell F5 is shown in Figure 12.51. The "Choose . . ." button on this dialog box allows you to select any assumption cells on the spreadsheet and individually specify their correlations to the assumption cell being

**FIGURE
12.50**

*Defining the
assumptions for
cell F5*

defined. In Figure 12.51 we indicated that the return on gas-fueled plants (represented by cell F5) is correlated with the returns on the other types of plants as indicated by the values in cells D14 through G14 on our spreadsheet model (shown in Figure 12.49). The graph in Figure 12.51 shows an example of the assumed negative correlation between the return of gas assets (assumption cell F5) and the return on coal assets (assumption cell F6). Again, using Crystal Ball's Define Correlation dialog, we have to enter the correlations repeatedly for each individual assumption cell.

Finally, in cell F10, we calculate the weighted average return on investments. Using Crystal Ball, we will define this to be a forecast cell:

Formula for cell F10:   =SUMPRODUCT(F5:F9,E5:E9)/SUM(E5:E9)

**FIGURE
12.51**

*Defining
correlations
for cell F5*

Another Way of Specifying Correlations...

Crystal Ball also offers a Correlation Matrix tool (launched via Crystal Ball, Tools, Correlation Matrix) that allows you to upload an entire correlation matrix in a small number of steps. The Correlation Matrix tool is especially useful if you have many correlated assumption cells.

12.17.2 SOLVING THE PROBLEM WITH OptQUEST

The OptQuest settings used to solve this problem are shown in Figure 12.52. The Decision Variable Selection window indicates that we are asking OptQuest to determine the optimal amounts (in millions) to invest in gas, coal, oil, nuclear and wind generation assets, represented by cells D5 through D9, respectively, on our spreadsheet. The Constraints window indicates that the sum of the decision variables must equal 1000 (which is equivalent to $1 billion).

Recall that the McDaniel Group is interested in examining solutions on the efficient frontier of its possible investment options, these power generation assets. This requires determining the portfolios that provide the maximum expected (or average) return at a variety of different risk levels. In this case, we will define risk to be the standard deviation of a portfolio's weighted average return. Thus, in the Forecast Selection window, we indicate that our objective is to maximize the mean value of the weighted average return calculated in cell F10 in our spreadsheet. Finally, we also specify a variable requirement on the allowable upper bound of the standard deviation of the weighted

FIGURE 12.52

OptQuest settings for the portfolio optimization problem

FIGURE 12.53

Efficient frontier for the portfolio optimization problem

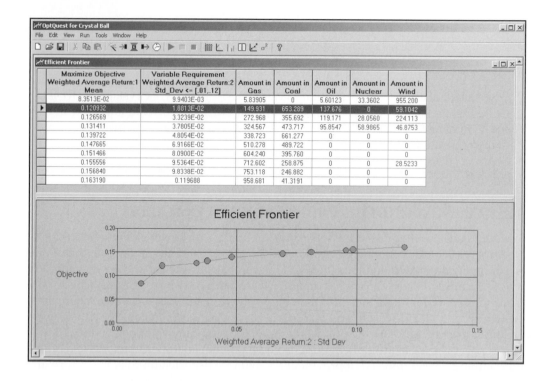

Maximize Objective Weighted Average Return:1 Mean	Variable Requirement Weighted Average Return:2 Std_Dev <= [.01..12]	Amount in Gas	Amount in Coal	Amount in Oil	Amount in Nuclear	Amount in Wind
8.3513E-02	9.9403E-03	5.83905	0	5.60123	33.3602	955.200
0.120932	1.8813E-02	149.931	653.289	137.676	0	59.1042
0.126569	3.3239E-02	272.968	355.692	119.171	28.0560	224.113
0.131411	3.7805E-02	324.567	473.717	95.8547	58.9865	46.8753
0.139722	4.8054E-02	338.723	661.277	0	0	0
0.147665	6.9166E-02	510.278	489.722	0	0	0
0.151466	8.0900E-02	604.240	395.760	0	0	0
0.155556	9.5364E-02	712.602	258.875	0	0	28.5233
0.156840	9.8338E-02	753.118	246.882	0	0	0
0.163190	0.119688	958.681	41.3191	0	0	0

average return via the forecast selection labeled "Variable Req. Upper Bound (10)." When you select a variable required upper (or lower) bound on a forecast cell statistic, OptQuest will prompt you to indicate the number of possible upper (or lower) bounds you want to consider. In this case, we indicated we want to investigate 10 different upper bound values for the standard deviation of the forecast cell. The indicated lower and upper bounds of 1% and 12%, respectively, defined the range over which the standard deviation's upper bound will be allowed to vary. (Note that 1% and 12% were selected since they correspond, respectively, to the standard deviations on the returns for the least risky and most risky individual assets available in our portfolio). With these forecast selection settings, OptQuest will automatically identify portfolios that provide the maximum expected return for 10 different levels of risk as measured by portfolio return standard deviations between 1% and 12%.

Figure 12.53 displays OptQuest's Efficient Frontier window summarizing the ten portfolios it found and their relative trade-offs in terms of risk and return. The expected returns on these portfolios vary from 8.3% to 16.3% with standard deviations varying from approximately 1% to 12% with higher expected returns being associated with higher levels of risk. Determining the portfolio that is optimal for the McDaniel Group depends on the firm's preferences for risk versus return. But this analysis should help the firm identify a portfolio that provides the maximum return for the desired level of risk—or the minimum level of risk for the desired level of return.

12.18 Summary

This chapter introduced the concept of risk analysis and simulation. Many of the input cells in a spreadsheet represent random variables whose values cannot be determined with certainty. Any uncertainty in the input cells flows through the spreadsheet model to create a related uncertainty in the value of the output cell(s). Decisions made on the basis of these uncertain values involve some degree of risk.

Various methods of risk analysis are available, including best-case/worst-case analysis, what-if analysis, and simulation. Of these three methods, simulation is the only technique that provides hard evidence (facts and figures) that can be used objectively in making decisions. This chapter introduced the use of the Crystal Ball add-in to perform spreadsheet simulation. To simulate a model, RNGs are used to select representative values for each uncertain independent variable in the model. This process is repeated over and over to generate a sample of representative values for the dependent variable(s) in the model. The variability and distribution of the sample values for the dependent variable(s) can then be analyzed to gain insight into the possible outcomes that might occur. We also illustrated the use of OptQuest in determining the optimal value of controllable parameters or decision variables in simulation models.

12.19 References

Banks, J. and J. Carson. *Discrete-Event Simulation*. Englewood Cliffs, NJ: Prentice Hall, 1984. *Crystal Ball 2000 User Manual*. Decisioneering, Inc., Denver, CO, 2001.

Evans, J. and D. Olson. *Introduction to Simulation and Risk Analysis*. Upper Saddle River, NJ: Prentice Hall, 1998.

Hamzawi, S. "Management and Planning of Airport Gate Capacity: A Microcomputer-Based Gate Assignment Simulation Model." *Transportation Planning and Technology*, vol. 11, 1986.

Kaplan, A. and S. Frazza. "Empirical Inventory Simulation: A Case Study." *Decision Sciences*, vol. 14, January 1983.

Khoshnevis, B. *Discrete Systems Simulation*. New York: McGraw-Hill, 1994.

Law, A. and W. Kelton. *Simulation Modeling and Analysis*. New York: McGraw-Hill, 1990.

Marcus, A. "The Magellan Fund and Market Efficiency." *Journal of Portfolio Management*, Fall 1990. *OptQuest for Crystal Ball 2000 User Manual*. Decisioneering Inc., Denver, CO, 2001.

Russell, R. and R. Hickle. "Simulation of a CD Portfolio." *Interfaces*, vol. 16, no. 3, 1986.

Vollman, T., W. Berry and C. Whybark. *Manufacturing Planning and Control Systems*. Homewood, IL: Irwin, 1987.

Watson, H. *Computer Simulation in Business*. New York: Wiley, 1981.

THE WORLD OF MANAGEMENT SCIENCE

The U.S. Postal Service Moves to the Fast Lane

Mail flows into the U.S. Postal Service at the rate of 500 million pieces per day, and it comes in many forms. There are standard-sized letters with 9-digit ZIP codes (with or without imprinted bar codes), 5-digit ZIP codes, typed addresses that can be read by optical character readers, handwritten addresses that are barely decipherable, Christmas cards in red envelopes addressed in red ink, and so on. The enormous task of sorting all these pieces at the sending post office and at the destination has caused postal management to consider and adopt many new forms of technology. These include operator-assisted mechanized sorters, optical character readers (last-line and multiple-line), and bar code sorters. Implementation of new technology brings with it associated policy decisions, such as rate discounts for bar coding by the customer, finer sorting at the origin, and so on.

(Continued)

A simulation model called META (model for evaluating technology alternatives) assists management in evaluating new technologies, configurations, and operating plans. Using distributions based on experience or projections of the effects of new policies, META simulates a random stream of mail of different types; routes the mail through the system configuration being tested; and prints reports detailing total pieces handled, capacity utilization, work hours required, space requirements, and cost.

META has been used on several projects associated with the Postal Service corporate automation plan. These include facilities planning, benefits of alternative sorting plans, justification of efforts to enhance address readability, planning studies for reducing the time that carriers spend sorting vs. delivering, and identification of mail types that offer the greatest potential for cost savings.

According to the Associate Postmaster General, ". . . META became the vehicle to help steer our organization on an entirely new course at a speed we had never before experienced."

Source: Cebry, Michael E., Anura H. deSilva and Fred J. DiLisio. "Management Science in Automating Postal Operations: Facility and Equipment Planning in the United States Postal Service." *Interfaces*, vol. 22, no. 1, January–February 1992, pages 110–130.

Questions and Problems

1. Under what condition(s) is it appropriate to use simulation to analyze a model? That is, what characteristics should a model possess for simulation to be used?
2. The graph of the probability distribution of a normally distributed random variable with a mean of 20 and standard deviation of 3 is shown in Figure 12.8. The Excel function =NORMINV(Rand( ),20,3) also returns randomly generated observations from this distribution.
   a. Use Excel's NORMINV( ) function to generate 100 sample values from this distribution.
   b. Produce a histogram of the 100 sample values that you generated. Does your histogram look like the graph for this distribution in Figure 12.8?
   c. Repeat this experiment, with 1,000 sample values.
   d. Produce a histogram for the 1,000 sample values you generated. Does the histogram now more closely resemble the graph in Figure 12.8 for this distribution?
   e. Why does your second histogram look more "normal" than the first one?
3. Refer to the Hungry Dawg Restaurant example presented in this chapter. Health claim costs actually tend to be seasonal, with higher levels of claims occurring during the summer months (when kids are out of school and more likely to injure themselves) and during December (when people schedule elective procedures before the next year's deductible must be paid). The following table summarizes the seasonal adjustment factors that apply to RNGs for average claims in the Hungry Dawg problem. For instance, the average claim for month 6 should be multiplied by 115% and claims for month 1 should be multiplied by 80%.

Month	1	2	3	4	5	6	7	8	9	10	11	12
Seasonal Factor	0.80	0.85	0.87	0.92	0.93	1.15	1.20	1.18	1.03	0.95	0.98	1.14

Suppose that the company maintains an account from which it pays health insurance claims. Assume that there is $2.5 million in the account at the beginning of month 1. Each month, employee contributions are deposited into this account and claims are paid from the account.

a. Modify the spreadsheet shown in Figure 12.9 to include the cash flows in this account. If the company deposits $3 million into this account every month, what is the probability that the account will have insufficient funds to pay claims at some point during the year? Use 5000 replications. (*Hint*: You can use the COUNTIF( ) function to count the number of months in a year in which the ending balance in the account is below 0.)

b. If the company wants to deposit an equal amount of money in this account each month, what should this amount be if they want there to only be a 5% chance of having insufficient funds?

4. One of the examples in this chapter dealt with determining the optimal reorder point for a computer monitor sold by Millennium Computer Corp. Suppose that it costs MCC $0.30 per day in holding costs for each monitor in beginning inventory, and it costs $20 to place an order. Each monitor sold generates a profit of $45, and each lost sale results in an opportunity cost of $65 (including the lost profit of $45 and $20 in lost goodwill). Modify the spreadsheet shown in Figure 12.31 to determine the reorder point and order quantity that maximize the average monthly profit associated with this monitor.

5. A debate recently erupted about the optimal strategy for playing a game on the TV show called "Let's Make a Deal." In one of the games on this show, the contestant would be given the choice of prizes behind three closed doors. A valuable prize was behind one door and worthless prizes were behind the other two doors. After the contestant selected a door, the host would open one of the two remaining doors to reveal one of the worthless prizes. Then, before opening the selected door, the host would give the contestant the opportunity to switch the selection to the other door that had not been opened. The question is, should the contestant switch?

a. Suppose a contestant is allowed to play this game 500 times, always picks door number 1, and never switches when given the option. If the valuable prize is equally likely to be behind each door at the beginning of each play, how many times would the contestant win the valuable prize? Use simulation to answer this question.

b. Now suppose the contestant is allowed to play this game another 500 times. This time the player always selects door number 1 initially and switches when given the option. Using simulation, how many times would the contestant win the valuable prize?

c. If you were a contestant on this show, what would you do if given the option of switching doors?

6. Suppose that a product must go through an assembly line that consists of five sequential operations. The time it takes to complete each operation is normally distributed with a mean of 180 seconds and standard deviation of 5 seconds. Let X denote the cycle time for the line, so that after X seconds each operation is supposed to be finished and ready to pass the product to the next operation in the assembly line.

a. If the cycle time $X = 180$ seconds, what is the probability that all five operations will be completed?

b. What cycle time will ensure that all operations are finished 98% of the time?

7. Suppose that a product must go through an assembly line that consists of five sequential operations. The time it takes to complete each operation is normally

distributed with a mean of 180 seconds and standard deviation of 5 seconds. Define the flow time to be the total time it takes a product to go through the assembly line from start to finish.

a. What is the mean and standard deviation of the flow time? What is the probability that the total time will be less than 920 seconds?

b. Now assume that the time required to complete each operation has a 0.40 correlation with the operation time immediately preceding it. What is the mean and standard deviation of the flow time? What is the probability that the total time will be less than 920 seconds?

c. Now assume that the time required to complete each operation has a −0.40 correlation with the operation time immediately preceding it. What is the mean and standard deviation of the flow time? What is the probability that the total time will be less than 920 seconds?

d. Explain the effects of positive and negative correlations on the previous results.

8. WVTU is a television station that has 20 thirty-second advertising slots during its regularly scheduled programming each evening. The station is now selling advertising for the first few days in November. It could sell all the slots immediately for $4,500 each, but because November 7 will be Election Day, the station manager knows she might be able to sell slots at the last minute to political candidates in tight races for $8,000 each. The demand for these last minute slots is estimated as follows:

	Demand											
	8	9	10	11	12	13	14	15	16	17	18	19
Probability	0.03	0.05	0.10	0.15	0.20	0.15	0.10	0.05	0.05	0.05	0.05	0.02

Slots not sold in advance and not sold to political candidates at the last minute can be sold to local advertisers for $2,000.

a. If the station manager sells all the advertising slots in advance, how much revenue will the station receive?

b. How many advertising slots should be sold in advance if the station manager wants to maximize expected revenue?

c. If the station manager sells in advance the number of slots identified in the previous question, what is the probability that the total revenue received will exceed the amount identified in part a where all slots are sold in advance?

9. The owner of a ski apparel store in Winter Park, CO, must decide in July how many ski jackets to order for the following ski season. Each ski jacket costs $54 each and can be sold during the ski season for $145. Any unsold jackets at the end of the season are sold for $45. The demand for jackets is expected to follow a Poisson distribution with a average rate of 80. The store owner can order jackets in lot sizes of 10 units.

a. How many jackets should the store owner order if she wants to maximize her expected profit?

b. What are the best-case and worst-case outcomes the owner might face for this product if she implements your suggestion?

c. How likely is it that the store owner will make at least $7,000 if she implements your suggestion?

d. How likely is it that the store owner will make between $6,000 to $7,000 if she implements your suggestion?

10. The owner of a golf shop in Myrtle Beach, SC, must decide how many sets of beginner golf clubs to order for the coming tourist season. Demand for golf clubs is random but follows a Poisson distribution with the average demand rates indicated in

the following table for each month. The expected selling price of the clubs also is shown for each month.

	May	June	July	August	September	October
Average Demand	60	90	70	50	30	40
Selling Price	$145	$140	$130	$110	$80	$60

In May, each set of clubs can be ordered at a cost of $75. This price is expected to drop 5% a month during the remainder of the season. Each month, the owner of the shop also gives away a free set of clubs to anyone who makes a hole-in-one from a short practice tee next to the shop. The number of people making a hole-in-one on this tee each month follows a Poisson distribution with a mean of 3. Any sets of clubs left over at the end of October are sold for $45 per set.

a. How many sets of clubs should the shop owner order if he wants to maximize the expected profit on this product?

b. What are the best-case and worst-case outcomes the owner might face on this product if he implements your suggestion?

c. How likely is it that the store owner will make at least $17,000 if he implements your suggestion?

d. How likely is it that the store owner will make between $12,000 to $14,000 if he implements your suggestion?

e. What percentage of the total demand for this product (excluding the free give-aways) will the owner be able to meet if he implements your suggestion?

11. Large Lots is planning a seven-day promotion on a discontinued model of 31" color television sets. At a price of $575 per set, the daily demand for this type of TV has been estimated as follows:

	Units Demanded per Day					
	0	**1**	**2**	**3**	**4**	**5**
Probability	0.15	0.20	0.30	0.20	0.10	0.05

Large Lots can order up to 50 of these TVs from a surplus dealer at a cost of $325. This dealer has offered to buy back any unsold sets at the end of the promotion for $250 each.

a. How many TVs should Large Lots order if it wants to maximize the expected profit on this promotion?

b. What is the expected level of profit?

c. Suppose the surplus dealer will buy back a maximum of only four sets at the end of the promotion. Would this change your answer? If so, how?

12. The monthly demand for the latest computer at Newland Computers follows a normal distribution with a mean of 350 and standard deviation of 75. Newland purchases these computers for $1,200 and sells them for $2,300. It costs the company $100 to place an order and $12 for every computer held in inventory at the end of each month. Currently, the company places an order for 1000 computers whenever the inventory at the end of a month falls below 100 units. Assume that the beginning inventory is 400 units, unmet demand in any month is lost to competitors, and orders placed at the end of one month arrive at the beginning of the next month.

a. Create a spreadsheet model to simulate the profit that the company will earn on this product over the next two years. Use 5000 replications. What is the average level of profit the company will earn?

b. Suppose that the company wants to determine the optimum reorder point and order quantity. Which combination of reorder point and order quantity will provide the highest average profit over the next two years?

13. The manager of Moore's Catalog Showroom is trying to predict how much revenue will be generated by each major department in the store during 2006. The manager has estimated the minimum and maximum growth rates possible for revenues in each department. The manager believes that any of the possible growth rates between the minimum and maximum values are equally likely to occur. These estimates are summarized in the following table:

| | | Growth Rates | |
Department	2005 Revenues	Minimum	Maximum
Electronics	$6,342,213	2%	10%
Garden Supplies	$1,203,231	−4%	5%
Jewelry	$4,367,342	−2%	6%
Sporting Goods	$3,543,532	−1%	8%
Toys	$4,342,132	4%	15%

Create a spreadsheet to simulate the total revenues that could occur in the coming year. Run 5000 replications of the model and do the following:
a. Construct a 95% confidence interval for the average level of revenues that the manager could expect for 2006.
b. According to your model, what are the chances that total revenues in 2006 will be more than 5% larger than those in 2005?

14. The Harriet Hotel in downtown Boston has 100 rooms that rent for $150 per night. It costs the hotel $30 per room in variable costs (cleaning, bathroom items, etc.) each night a room is occupied. For each reservation accepted, there is a 5% chance that the guest will not arrive. If the hotel overbooks, it costs $200 to compensate guests whose reservations cannot be honored.
a. How many reservations should the hotel accept if it wants to maximize the average daily profit? Use 1000 replications for each reservation level that you consider.

15. Lynn Price recently completed her MBA and accepted a job with an electronics manufacturing company. Although she likes her job, she also is looking forward to retiring one day. To ensure that her retirement is comfortable, Lynn intends to invest $3,000 of her salary into a tax-sheltered retirement fund at the end of each year. Lynn is not certain what rate of return this investment will earn each year, but she expects that each year's rate of return could be modeled appropriately as a normally distributed random variable with a mean of 12.5% and standard deviation of 2%.
a. If Lynn is 30 years old, how much money should she expect to have in her retirement fund at age 60? (Use 5000 replications.)
b. Construct a 95% confidence interval for the average amount that Lynn will have at age 60.
c. What is the probability that Lynn will have more than $1 million in her retirement fund when she reaches age 60?
d. How much should Lynn invest each year if she wants there to be a 90% chance of having at least $1 million in her retirement fund at age 60?
e. Suppose that Lynn contributes $3,000 annually to her retirement fund for eight years and then terminates these annual contributions. How much of her salary would she have contributed to this retirement plan and how much money could she expect to have accumulated at age 60?

f. Now suppose that Lynn contributes nothing to her retirement fund for eight years and then begins contributing $3,000 annually until age 60. How much of her salary would she have contributed to this retirement plan and how much money could she expect to have accumulated at age 60?

g. What should Lynn (and you) learn from the answers to questions e and f?

16. Employees of Georgia-Atlantic are permitted to contribute a portion of their earnings (in increments of $500) to a flexible spending account from which they can pay medical expenses not covered by the company's health insurance program. Contributions to an employee's "flex" account are not subject to income taxes. However, the employee forfeits any amount contributed to the "flex" account that is not spent during the year. Suppose Greg Davis makes $60,000 per year from Georgia-Atlantic and pays a marginal tax rate of 33%. Greg and his wife estimate that in the coming year their normal medical expenses not covered by the health insurance program could be as small as $500, as large as $5,000, and most likely about $1,300. However, Greg also believes there is a 5% chance that an abnormal medical event could occur which might add $10,000 to the normal expenses paid from their flex account. If their uncovered medical claims exceed their contribution to their "flex" account, they will have to cover these expenses with the after-tax money Greg brings home.

a. Use simulation to determine the amount of money Greg should contribute to his flexible spending account in the coming year if he wants to maximize his disposable income (after taxes and all medical expenses are paid). Use 5000 replications for each level of "flex" account contribution you consider.

17. Acme Equipment Company is considering the development of a new machine that would be marketed to tire manufacturers. Research and development costs for the project are expected to be about $4 million but could vary between $3 and $6 million. The market life for the product is estimated to be 3 to 8 years with all intervening possibilities being equally likely. The company thinks it will sell 250 units per year, but acknowledges that this figure could be as low as 50 or as high as 350. The company will sell the machine for about $23,000. Finally, the cost of manufacturing the machine is expected to be $14,000 but could be as low as $12,000 or as high as $18,000. The company's cost of capital is 15%.

a. Use appropriate RNGs to create a spreadsheet to calculate the possible net present values (NPVs) that could result from taking on this project.

b. Replicate the model 5000 times. What is the expected NPV for this project?

c. What is the probability of this project generating a positive NPV for the company?

18. Representatives from the American Heart Association are planning to go door-to-door throughout a community, soliciting contributions. From past experience, they know that when someone answers the door, 80% of the time it is a female and 20% of the time it is a male. They also know that 70% of the females who answer the door make a donation, whereas only 40% of the males who answer the door make donations. The amount of money that females contribute follows a normal distribution with a mean of $20 and standard deviation of $3. The amount of money that males contribute follows a normal distribution with a mean of $10 and standard deviation of $2.

a. Create a spreadsheet model that simulates what might happen whenever a representative of the American Heart Association knocks on a door and someone answers.

b. Replicate your model 5000 times. What is the average contribution the Heart Association can expect to receive when someone answers the door?

   c. Suppose that the Heart Association plans to visit 300 homes on a given Saturday. If no one is home at 25% of the residences, what is the total amount that the Heart Association can expect to receive in donations?

19. Techsburg, Inc. uses a stamping machine to manufacture aluminum bodies for light-weight miniature aircraft used for military reconnaissance. Currently, forms in the stamping machine are changed after every 60 hours of operation or whenever a form breaks, whichever happens first. The lifetime of each form follows a Weibull distribution with location, scale, and shape parameters of 50, 25, and 2, respectively. The machine is operated 5840 hours per year. It costs $800 to replace the stamping forms. If a form breaks before its scheduled replacement time (or in less than 60 hours of use), the shop loses 8 hours of production time. However, if a form lasts until its scheduled replacement after 60 hours of use, the shop only loses 2 hours of production time. The company estimates that each hour of lost production time costs $1200.

   a. On average, how much does Techsburg spend maintaining this stamping machine per year?

   b. Suppose Techsburg wanted to minimize its total maintenance cost for the stamping machine. How often should the company plan on changing the stamping forms and how much money would it save?

   c. Suppose the cost to replace the stamping forms is expected to increase. What impact should this have on the optimal planned replacement time of the forms? Explain.

   d. Suppose the cost of lost production time is increased. What effect should this have on the optimal planned replacement time of the forms? Explain.

20. After spending ten years as an assistant manager for a large restaurant chain, Ray Clark has decided to become his own boss. The owner of a local submarine sandwich store wants to sell the store to Ray for $65,000, to be paid in installments of $13,000 in each of the next five years. According to the current owner, the store brings in revenue of about $110,000 per year and incurs operating costs of about 63% of sales. Thus, once the store is paid for, Ray should make about $35,000–$40,000 per year before taxes. Until the store is paid for, he will make substantially less—but he will be his own boss. Realizing that some uncertainty is involved in this decision, Ray wants to simulate what level of net income he can expect to earn during the next five years as he operates and pays for the store. In particular, he wants to see what could happen if sales are allowed to vary uniformly between $90,000 and $120,000, and if operating costs are allowed to vary uniformly between 60% and 65% of sales. Assume that Ray's payments for the store are not deductible for tax purposes and that he is in the 28% tax bracket.

   a. Create a spreadsheet model to simulate the annual net income Ray would receive during each of the next five years if he decides to buy the store.

   b. Given the money he has in savings, Ray thinks he can get by for the next five years if he can make at least $12,000 from the store each year. Replicate the model 5000 times and track: 1) the minimum amount of money Ray makes over the five-year period represented by each replication, and 2) the total amount Ray makes during the five-year period represented by each replication.

   c. What is the probability that Ray will make at least $12,000 in each of the next five years?

   d. What is the probability that Ray will make at least $60,000 total over the next five years?

21. Road Racer Sports, Inc. is a mail-order business dedicated to the running enthusiast. The company sends out full-color catalogs several times a year to several hundred

thousand people on its mailing list. Production and mailing costs are fairly expensive for direct mail advertising, averaging about $3.25 per catalog. As a result, management does not want to continue sending catalogs to persons who do not buy enough to cover the costs of the catalogs they receive. Currently, the company removes customers from their mailing list if they receive six consecutive catalogs without placing an order. The following table summarizes the probability of a customer placing an order.

Last Order	Prob. of Order
1 catalog ago	0.40
2 catalogs ago	0.34
3 catalogs ago	0.25
4 catalogs ago	0.17
5 catalogs ago	0.09
6 catalogs ago	0.03

According to the first row in this table, if customers receive a catalog and place an order, there is a 40% chance they will place another order when they receive their next catalog. The second row indicates there is a 34% chance that customers will receive a catalog, place an order, and then not order again until they receive two more catalogs. The remaining rows in this table have similar interpretations.

a. How much profit must the company earn on an average order in order to cover the cost of printing and distributing the catalogs?

b. Approximately what percentage of the names on the mailing list will be purged before each catalog mailing?

22. Sammy Slick works for a company that allows him to contribute up to 10% of his earnings into a tax-deferred savings plan. The company matches a portion of the contributions its employees make based on the organization's financial performance. Although the minimum match is 25% of the employee's contributions and the maximum match is 100%, in most years the company match is about 50%. Sammy is currently 30 years old and makes $35,000. He wants to retire at age 60. He expects his salary to increase in any given year to be at least 2% per year, at most 6%, and most likely 3%. The funds contributed by Sammy and his employer are invested in mutual funds. Sammy expects the annual return on his investments to vary according to a normal distribution with a mean of 12.5% and standard deviation of 2%.

a. If Sammy contributes 10% of his income to this plan, how much money could he expect to have at age 60?

b. Suppose Sammy makes 10% contributions to this plan for eight years, from age 30 to 37, and then stops contributing. How much of his own money would he have invested and how much money could he expect to have at age 60?

c. Now suppose Sammy contributes nothing to the plan his first eight years and then contributes 10% for 23 years from age 38 to age 60. How much of his own money would he have invested and how much money could he expect to have at age 60?

d. What do you learn from Sammy's example?

23. Podcessories manufactures several accessories for a popular digital music player. The company is trying to decide whether to discontinue one of the items in this product line. Discontinuing the item would save the company $600,000 in fixed costs (consisting of leases on building and machinery) during the coming year. However, the company is anticipating that it might receive an order for 60,000 units from a large discount retailer that could be very profitable. Unfortunately, the company is

being forced to decide about renewing the leases required to continue this item before knowing if it will receive the large order from the discount retailer. The variable cost per unit for this item is $6. The regular selling price of the item is $12 per unit. However, the company has offered the discount retailer a price of $10.50 per unit due to the size of its potential order. Podcessories believes there is a 60% chance it will receive the order from the discount retailer. Additionally, it believes general demand for this product (apart from the discount retailer's order) will vary between 45,000 to 115,000 units with a most likely outcome of 75,000 units.

a. Create a spreadsheet model for this problem.
b. How much money might the company lose next year (worst case) if it continues this line?
c. How much money might the company make next year (best case) if it continues this line?
d. If the company loses money, on average how much could it expect to lose? (*Hint*: Use the filter option under the forecast window's preferences command.)
e. If the company makes money, on average how much could it expect to make? (*Hint*: Use the filter option under the forecast window's preferences command.)
f. What other actions might you suggest this company take to improve its chance of making a decision with a good outcome?

24. Bob Davidson owns a newsstand outside the Waterstone office building complex in Atlanta, near Hartsfield International Airport. He buys his papers wholesale at $0.50 per paper and sells them for $0.75. Bob wonders what is the optimal number of papers to order each day. Based on history, he has found that demand (even though it is discrete) can be modeled by a normal distribution with a mean of 50 and standard deviation of 5. When he has more papers than customers, he can recycle all the extra papers the next day and receive $0.05 per paper. On the other hand, if he has more customers than papers, he loses some goodwill in addition to the lost profit on the potential sale of $0.25. Bob estimates the incremental lost goodwill costs five days' worth of business (that is, dissatisfied customers will go to a competitor the next week, but come back to him the week after that).

a. Create a spreadsheet model to determine the optimal number of papers to order each day. Use 5000 replications and round the demand values generated by the normal RNG to the closest integer value.
b. Construct a 95% confidence interval for the expected payoff from the optimal decision.

25. Vinton Auto Insurance is trying to decide how much money to keep in liquid assets to cover insurance claims. In the past, the company held some of the premiums it received in interest-bearing checking accounts and put the rest into investments that are not quite as liquid, but tend to generate a higher investment return. The company wants to study cash flows to determine how much money it should keep in liquid assets to pay claims. After reviewing historical data, the company determined that the average repair bill per claim is normally distributed with a mean of $1,700 and standard deviation of $400. It also determined that the number of repair claims filed each week is a random variable that follows the probability distribution shown in the following table:

Number of Claims	1	2	3	4	5	6	7	8	9
Probability	0.1	0.1	0	0.2	0.3	0.1	0.1	0.1	0.1

In addition to repair claims, the company also receives claims for cars that have been "totaled" and cannot be repaired. A 20% chance of receiving this type of claim exists in any week. These claims for "totaled" cars typically cost anywhere from $2,000 to $35,000, with $13,000 being the most common cost.

a. Create a spreadsheet model of the total claims cost incurred by the company in any week.

b. Replicate the model 5000 times and create a histogram of the distribution of total cost values that were generated.

c. What is the average cost that the company should expect to pay each week?

d. Suppose that the company decides to keep $20,000 cash on hand to pay claims. What is the probability that this amount would not be adequate to cover claims in any week?

e. Create a 95% confidence interval for the true probability of claims exceeding $20,000 in a given week.

26. Executives at Meds-R-Us have decided to build a new production facility for the company's best-selling high-blood-pressure drug. The problem they now face is determining the size of the facility (in terms of production capacity). Last year, the company sold 1,085,000 units of this drug at a price of $13 per unit. They estimate the demand for the drug to be normally distributed with a mean increasing by approximately 59,000 units per year over the next 10 years with a standard deviation of 30,000 units. They expect the price of the drug to increase with inflation at a rate of 3% per year. Variable production costs currently are $9 per unit and are expected to increase in future years at the rate of inflation. Other operating costs are expected to be $1.50 per unit of capacity in the first year of operation, increasing at the rate of inflation in subsequent years. The plant construction cost is expected to be $18 million for 1 million units of annual production capacity. The company can increase the annual production capacity above this level at a cost of $12 per unit of additional capacity. Assume that the company must pay for the plant when it is completed and all other cash flows occur at the end of each year. The company uses a 10% discount rate on cash flows for financial decisions.

a. Create a spreadsheet model to compute the net present value (NPV) for this decision.

b. What is the expected NPV for a plant with a production capacity of 1.2 million units per year?

c. What is the expected NPV for a plant with a production capacity of 1.4 million units per year?

d. How large a plant should the company build if they want to be 90% certain of obtaining a positive NPV for this project?

27. The owner of a local car dealership has just received a call from a regional distributor stating that a $5,000 bonus will be awarded if the owner's dealership sells at least 10 new cars next Saturday. On an average Saturday, this dealership has 75 potential customers look at new cars, but there is no way to determine exactly how many customers will come this particular Saturday. The owner is fairly certain that the number would not be less than 40, but also thinks it would be unrealistic to expect more than 120 (which is the largest number of customers ever to show up in one day). The owner determined that, on average, about one out of ten customers who look at cars at the dealership actually purchases a car—or, a 0.10 probability (or 10% chance) exists that any given customer will buy a new car.

a. Create a spreadsheet model for this problem and generate 5000 random outcomes for the number of cars the dealership might sell next Saturday.

b. What is the probability that the dealership will earn the $5,000 bonus?

c. If you were this dealer, what is the maximum amount of money you would be willing to spend on sales incentives to try to earn this bonus?

28. Dr. Sarah Benson is an ophthalmologist who, in addition to prescribing glasses and contact lenses, performs optical laser surgery to correct nearsightedness. This surgery is fairly easy and inexpensive to perform. Thus, it represents a potential gold mine for her practice. To inform the public about this procedure, Dr. Benson advertises in the local paper and holds information sessions in her office one night a week at which she shows a videotape about the procedure and answers any questions that potential patients might have. The room where these meetings are held can seat ten people, and reservations are required. The number of people attending each session varies from week to week. Dr. Benson cancels the meeting if two or fewer people have made reservations. Using data from the previous year, Dr. Benson determined that the distribution of reservations is as follows:

Number of Reservations	0	1	2	3	4	5	6	7	8	9	10
Probability	0.02	0.05	0.08	0.16	0.26	0.18	0.11	0.07	0.05	0.01	0.01

Using data from the past year, Dr. Benson determined that each person who attends an information session has a 0.25 probability of electing to have the surgery. Of those who do not, most cite the cost of the procedure—$2,000—as their major concern.

a. On average, how much revenue does Dr. Benson's practice in laser surgery generate each week? (Use 5000 replications.)

b. On average, how much revenue would the laser surgery generate each week if Dr. Benson did not cancel sessions with two or fewer reservations?

c. Dr. Benson believes that 40% of the people attending the information sessions would have the surgery if she reduced the price to $1,500. Under this scenario, how much revenue could Dr. Benson expect to realize per week from laser surgery?

29. Calls to the 24-hour customer support line for Richman Financial Services occur randomly following a Poisson distribution with the following average rates during different hours of the day:

Time Period	Avg Calls Per Hour	Time Period	Avg Calls Per Hour
Midnight–1 A.M.	2	Noon–1 P.M.	35
1 A.M.–2 A.M.	2	1 P.M.–2 P.M.	20
2 A.M.–3 A.M.	2	2 P.M.–3 P.M.	20
3 A.M.–4 A.M.	4	3 P.M.–4 P.M.	20
4 A.M.–5 A.M.	4	4 P.M.–5 P.M.	18
5 A.M.–6 A.M.	8	5 P.M.–6 P.M.	18
6 A.M.–7 A.M.	12	6 P.M.–7 P.M.	15
7 A.M.–8 A.M.	18	7 P.M.–8 P.M.	10
8 A.M.–9 A.M.	25	8 P.M.–9 P.M.	6
9 A.M.–10 A.M.	30	9 P.M.–10 P.M.	5
10 A.M.–11 A.M.	25	10 P.M.–11 P.M.	4
11 A.M.–Noon	20	11 P.M.–Midnight	2

The Richman customer service representatives spend approximately seven minutes on each call and are assigned to work eight-hour shifts that begin at the top of each hour. Richman wants to ensure that, on average, they can provide a 98% service level.

a. Determine the customer service schedule that allows Richman to achieve its service level objective using the fewest number of employees.

b. According to your solution, how many customer service representatives should Richman employ and how should they be scheduled?

30. A European call option gives a person the right to buy a particular stock at a given price (the strike price) on a specific date in the future (the expiration date). This type of call option typically is sold at the net present value of the expected value of the option on its expiration date. Suppose you own a call option with a strike price of $54. If the stock is worth $59 on the expiration date, you would exercise your option and buy the stock, making a $5 profit. On the other hand, if the stock is worth $47 on the expiration date, you would not exercise your option and make $0 profit. Researchers have suggested the following model for simulating the movement of stock prices:

$$P_{k+1} = P_k \left(1 + (\mu t + z\sigma\sqrt{t})\right)$$

where:

P_k = price of the stock at time period k

$\mu = v + 0.5\sigma^2$

v = the stock's expected annual growth rate

σ = the standard deviation on the stock's annual growth rate

t = time period interval (expressed in years)

z = a random observation from a normal distribution with mean 0 and standard deviation of 1.

Suppose that a stock has an initial price (P_0) of $80, an expected annual growth rate (v) of 15%, and a standard deviation (σ) of 25%.

a. Create a spreadsheet model to simulate this stock's price behavior for the next 13 weeks (note $t = 1/52$ because the time period is weekly).

b. Suppose you are interested in purchasing a call option with a strike price of $75 and an expiration date at week 13. On average, how much profit would you earn with this option? (Use 5000 replications.)

c. Assume that a risk-free discount rate is 6%. How much should you be willing to pay for this option today? (*Hint*: Use Excel's NPV function.)

d. If you purchase the option, what is the probability that you will make a profit?

31. Refer to the previous question. Another type of option is the Asian option. Its payoff is not based on the price of the stock on the expiration date but, instead, on the average price of the stock over the lifetime of the option.

Suppose a stock has an initial price (P_0) of $80, an expected annual growth rate (v) of 15%, and a standard deviation (σ) of 25%.

a. Create a spreadsheet model to simulate this stock's price behavior for the next 13 weeks (note $t = 1/52$ because the time period is weekly).

b. Suppose you are interested in purchasing a call option with a strike price of $75 and an expiration date at week 13. On average, how much profit would you earn with this option? (Use 5000 replications.)

c. Assume a risk-free discount rate is 6%. How much should you be willing to pay for this option today? (*Hint*: Use Excel's NPV function.)

d. If you purchase the option, what is the probability that you will make a profit?

32. Amanda Green is interested in investing in the following set of mutual funds whose returns are all normally distributed with the indicated means and standard deviations:

	Windsor	Columbus	Vanguard	Integrity	Nottingham
Mean	17.0%	14.0%	11.0%	8.0%	5.0%
Std Dev	9.0%	6.5%	5.0%	3.5%	2.0%

The correlations between the mutual funds are as follows:

	Windsor	Columbus	Vanguard	Integrity	Nottingham
Windsor	1	0.1	0.05	0.3	0.6
Columbus		1	0.2	0.15	0.1
Vanguard			1	0.1	0.2
Integrity				1	0.4
Nottingham					1

a. What is the expected return and standard deviation on a portfolio where Amanda invests her money equally in all five mutual funds?
b. Suppose Amanda is willing to assume the risk associated with a 5% standard deviation in returns on her portfolio. What portfolio will give her the greatest expected return for this level of risk?
c. Construct the efficient frontier for this portfolio. How would you explain this graph to Amanda?

33. Martin manufacturing company uses a piece of machinery that has three different bushings that periodically fail in service. The probability distribution of the life of each bushing is identical and is summarized by the following table.

Bushing Life (operating hours)									
1000	1100	1200	1300	1400	1500	1600	1700	1800	1900
Probability 0.08	0.13	0.25	0.15	0.12	0.09	0.07	0.05	0.04	0.02

When a bushing fails, the machine stops, a repair person is called, and a new bushing is installed. Each bushing costs $35. Downtime for the machine costs the company an estimated $15 per minute. The direct on-site cost for the repair person is $50 per hour. The amount of time required for the repair person to arrive after a bushing fails is approximately normally distributed with a mean of 10 minutes and standard deviation of 2 minutes. The amount of time required to change a bushing follows a triangular distribution with minimum, most likely, and maximum values of 15, 20, and 30 minutes, respectively.

a. On average, what is the total bushing-related cost that Martin incurs to operate this machine for 20,000 hours?
b. Martin is considering implementing another repair policy: if any of the bushings fail, all three are replaced. What is the total bushing-related cost that Martin incurs to operate this machine for 20,000 hours under this policy?
c. Should Martin implement the new policy?

34. Michael Abrams runs a specialty clothing store that sells collegiate sports apparel. One of his primary business opportunities involves selling custom screenprinted sweatshirts for college football bowl games. He is trying to determine how many sweatshirts to produce for the upcoming Tangerine Bowl game. During the month before the game, Michael plans to sell his sweatshirts for $25 apiece. At this price, he believes the demand for sweatshirts will be triangularly distributed with a minimum demand of 10,000, maximum demand of 30,000 and a most likely demand of 18,000. During the month after the game, Michael plans to sell any remaining sweatshirts for $12 apiece. At this price, he believes the demand for sweatshirts will be triangularly distributed with a minimum demand of 2,000, maximum demand of 7,000, and a most likely demand of 5,000. Two months after the game, Michael plans to sell any remaining sweatshirts to a surplus store that has agreed to buy up to 2,000

sweatshirts for a price of $3 per shirt. Michael can order custom screenprinted sweatshirts for $8 apiece in lot sizes of 3,000.

a. On average, how much profit would Michael earn if he orders 18,000 sweatshirts? Use 5000 replications.

b. How many sweatshirts should he order if he wants to maximize his expected profit? Again use 5000 replications in each simulation you perform.

35. The Major Motors Corporation is trying to decide whether to introduce a new midsize car. The directors of the company only want to produce the car if it has at least an 80% chance of generating a positive net present value over the next ten years. If the company decides to produce the car, it will have to pay an uncertain initial startup cost that is estimated to follow a triangular distribution with a minimum value of $2 billion, maximum value of $2.4 billion, and a most likely value of $2.1 billion. In the first year, the company would produce 100,000 units. Demand during the first year is uncertain but expected to be normally distributed with a mean of 95,000 and standard deviation of 7,000. For any year in which the demand exceeds production, production will be increased by 5% in the following year. For any year in which the production exceeds demand, production will be decreased by 5% in the next year, and the excess cars will be sold to a rental car company at a 20% discount. After the first year, the demand in any year will be modeled as a normally distributed random variable with a mean equal to the actual demand in the previous year and standard deviation of 7,000. In the first year, the sales price of the car will be $13,000 and the total variable cost per car is expected to be $9,500. Both the selling price and variable cost is expected to increase each year at the rate of inflation, which is assumed to be uniformly distributed between 2% and 7%. The company uses a discount rate of 9% to discount future cash flows.

a. Create a spreadsheet model for this problem and replicate it 5000 times. What is the minimum, average, and maximum NPV Major Motors can expect if it decides to produce this car? (*Hint*: Consider using the NPV( ) function to discount the profits Major Motors would earn each year.)

b. What is the probability of Major Motors earning a positive NPV over the next ten years?

c. Should Major Motors produce this car?

36. Each year, the Schriber Corporation must determine how much to contribute to the company's pension plan. The company uses a ten-year planning horizon to determine the contribution which, if made annually in each of the next ten years, would allow for only a 10% chance of the fund running short of money. The company then makes that contribution in the current year and repeats this process in each subsequent year to determine the specific amount to contribute each year. (Last year, the company contributed $23 million to the plan.) The pension plan covers two types of employees: hourly and salaried. In the current year, there will be 6,000 former hourly employees and 3,000 former salaried employees receiving benefits from the plan. The change in the number of retired hourly employees from one year to the next is expected to vary according to a normal distribution with a mean of 4% and standard deviation of 1%. The change in the number of retired salaried employees from one year to the next is expected to vary between 1% and 4% according to a truncated normal distribution with a mean of 2% and standard deviation of 1%. Currently, hourly retirees receive an average benefit of $15,000 per year, whereas salaried retirees receive an average annual benefit of $40,000. Both of these averages are expected to increase annually with the rate of inflation, which is assumed to vary between 2% and 7% according to a triangular distribution with a most likely value of 3.5%. The current balance in the company's pension fund is $1.5 billion. Investments in this

fund earn an annual return that is assumed to be normally distributed with a mean of 12% and standard deviation of 2%. Create a spreadsheet model for this problem and use simulation to determine the pension fund contribution that the company should make in the current year. What is your recommendation?

CASE 12.1   Live Well, Die Broke

(Inspired by a presentation given by Dr. John Charnes, University of Kansas, at the 2005 Crystal Ball Users Group meeting.)

For investment advisors, a major consideration in planning for a client in retirement is the determination of a withdrawal amount that will provide the client with the funds necessary to maintain a desired standard of living throughout the client's remaining lifetime. If a client withdraws too much or if investment returns fall below expectations, there is a danger of either running out of funds or reducing the desired standard of living. A sustainable retirement withdrawal is the inflation-adjusted monetary amount a client can withdraw periodically from retirement funds for an assumed planning horizon. This amount cannot be determined with complete certainty because of the random nature of investment returns. Usually, the sustainable retirement withdrawal is determined by limiting the probability of running out of funds to some specified level, such as 5%. The sustainable retirement withdrawal amount typically is expressed as a percentage of the initial value of the assets in the retirement portfolio, but is actually the inflation-adjusted monetary amount that the client would like each year for living expenses.

Assume that an investment advisor, Roy Dodson, is assisting a widowed client in determining a sustainable retirement withdrawal. The client is a 59 year-old woman who will turn 60 in two months. She has $1,000,000 in a tax-deferred retirement account that will be the primary source of her retirement income. Roy has designed a portfolio for his client with returns that he expects to be normally distributed with a mean of 8% and a standard deviation of 2%. Withdrawals will be made at the beginning of each year on the client's birthday.

Roy assumes that the inflation rate will be 3%, based on long-term historic data. So if her withdrawal at the beginning of the first year is $40,000, her inflation-adjusted withdrawal at the beginning of the second year will be $41,200, and third year's withdrawal will be $42,436, etc.

For his initial analysis, Roy wants to assume that his client will live until age 90. In consultation with his client, he also wants to limit the chance that she will run out of money before her death to a maximum of 5%.

a. What is the maximum amount that Roy should advise his client to withdraw on her 60th birthday? If she lives until age 90, how much should the client expect to leave to her heirs?

b. Roy is now concerned about basing his analysis on the assumption that his client will live to age 90. After all, she is healthy and might live to be 110, or she could be in a car accident and die at age 62. To account for this uncertainty in the client's age at death, Roy would like to model the client's remaining life expectancy as a random variable between 0 and 50 years that follows a lognormal distribution with a mean of 20 and standard deviation of 10 (rounded to the nearest integer). Under this assumption, what is the maximum amount that Roy should advise his client to withdraw on her 60th birthday and how much should the client expect to leave to her heirs? *Hint:* Modify your spreadsheet to accommodate ages up to 110 and use a VLOOKUP( ) function to return the client's ending balance in her randomly determined year of death.)

c. Roy is pleased to now be modeling the uncertainty in his client's life expectancy. But he is now curious about limiting to 5% the chance that his client will run out of money before her death. In particular, he is wondering how sensitive the sustainable withdrawal amount is to changes in this 5% assumption. To answer this question, create an efficient frontier showing the maximum sustainable withdrawal amount as the chance of running out of money is varied from 1% to 10%. How should Roy explain the meaning of this chart to his client?

d. Suppose that Roy's client has three children and wants there to be a 95% chance that they will each inherit at least $250,000 when she dies. Under this assumption, what is the maximum amount that Roy should advise his client to withdraw on her 60th birthday and how much should the client expect to leave to her heirs?

Death and Taxes

Benjamin Franklin once said, "In this world nothing is certain but death and taxes." Although that might be true, there is often great uncertainty involved in when one will encounter death and how much one must pay in taxes before arriving there. Another Benjamin made a very significant contribution toward assessing the uncertainty associated with both death and taxes. Benjamin Gompertz (1779–1865) was a British mathematician who, by studying Mediterranean fruit flies, theorized that mortality rates increase at an exponential rate as age increases (*i.e.*, as an organism gets older, its chance of dying per unit of time increases exponentially). Gompertz's Law of Mortality has since become a cornerstone of actuarial and financial planning activities.

In a group of people of a given age (for example, 65), some proportion of those people will not live another year. Let q_x represent the proportion of people of age x who will die before reaching age $x + 1$. The value q_x is sometimes referred to as the *mortality rate* at age x. The following formula, based on Gompertz's Law, is sometimes used to model mortality rates.

$$q_x = 1 - \text{EXP}\left(\frac{(\text{LN}(1-q_{x-1}))^2}{\text{LN}(1-q_{x-2})}\right)$$

Mortality rates play an important role in numerous financial planning and retirement decisions. For instance, most individuals do not want to retire unless they are reasonably certain that they have enough assets to sustain themselves financially for the rest of their life. The uncertainties associated with this sort of decision create a perfect application for spreadsheet simulation.

The following questions give you the opportunity to explore several issues that actuaries and financial planners face on a daily basis. Assume the mortality rates for males at ages 63 and 64 are $q_{63} = 0.0235$ and $q_{64} = 0.0262$, respectively, and those of females at ages 63 and 64 are $q_{63} = 0.0208$ and $q_{64} = 0.0225$, respectively.

a. On average, to what age should a 65-year-old male expect to live?
b. What is the probability of a 65-year-old male living to at least age 80?
c. What is the probability of a 65-year-old male living to exactly age 80?
d. On average, to what age should a 70-year-old male expect to live?
e. What is the probability of a 70-year-old male living to at least age 80?
f. What is the probability of a 70-year-old male living to exactly age 80?
g. Suppose a 65-year-old male has $1,200,000 in retirement investments earning an 8% interest rate. Assume he intends to withdraw $100,000 in his first year of retirement and 3% more in subsequent years to adjust for inflation. Annual interest earnings are credited on the beginning balance minus one half the amount withdrawn. For

example, in the first year interest earnings would be $0.08 \times (\$1,200,000 - \$100,000/2) = \$92,000$. What is the probability that this individual would outlive his retirement assets (assuming he spends all that he withdraws each year)?

h. Refer to the previous question. Suppose the interest rate each year can be modeled as a normally distributed random variable with a mean of 8% and standard deviation of 1.5%. Further suppose that the rate of inflation each year can be described as a random variable following a triangular distribution with minimum, most likely, and maximum values of 2%, 3%, and 5%, respectively. Under these conditions, what is the probability that this individual would outlive his retirement assets (assuming that he spends all he withdraws each year)?

i. Suppose that the person described in the previous question has a 65-year-old wife who is joint owner of the retirement assets described earlier. What is the probability that the retirement assets would be depleted before both spouses die (assuming they spend all they withdraw each year)?

j. Refer to the previous question. How much money should this couple plan on withdrawing in the first year if they want there to be a maximum of a 5% chance of depleting their retirement assets before they both die?

CASE 12.3   The Sound's Alive Company

(Contributed by Dr. Jack Yurkiewicz, Lubin School of Business, Pace University.)

Marissa Jones is the president and CEO of Sound's Alive, a company that manufactures and sells a line of speakers, CD players, receivers, high-definition televisions, and other items geared for the home entertainment market. Respected throughout the industry for bringing many high-quality, innovative products to market, Marissa is considering adding a speaker system to her product line.

The speaker market has changed dramatically during the last several years. Originally, high-fidelity aficionados knew that to reproduce sound covering the fullest range of frequencies—from the lowest kettle drum to the highest violin—a speaker system had to be large and heavy. The speaker had various drivers: a woofer to reproduce the low notes, a tweeter for the high notes, and a mid-range driver for the broad spectrum of frequencies in between. Many speaker systems had a minimum of three drivers, but some had even more. The trouble was that such a system was too large for anything but the biggest rooms, and consumers were reluctant to spend thousands of dollars and give up valuable wall space to get the excellent sound these speakers could reproduce.

The trend has changed during the past several years. Consumers still want good sound, but they want it from smaller boxes. Therefore, the satellite system became popular. Consisting of two small boxes that house either one driver (to cover the mid-range and high frequencies) or two (a mid-range and tweeter), a satellite system can be mounted easily on walls or shelves. To reproduce the low notes, a separate subwoofer that is approximately the size of a cube 18 inches on a side also is needed. This subwoofer can be placed anywhere in the room. Taking up less space than a typical large speaker system and sounding almost as good, yet costing hundreds of dollars less, these satellite systems are hot items in the high-fidelity market.

Recently, the separate wings of home entertainment—high fidelity (receivers, speakers, CD players, CDs, cassettes, and so on), television (large screen monitors, video cassette recorders, laser players), and computers (games with sounds, virtual reality software, and so on)—have merged into the home theater concept. To simulate the movie environment, a home theater system requires the traditional stereo speaker system plus additional speakers placed in the rear of the room so that viewers are literally surrounded with sound. Although the rear speakers do not have to match the high quality of the front speakers and, therefore, can be less expensive, most consumers choose a system in which the front and rear speakers are of equal quality, reproducing the full range of frequencies with equal fidelity.

This is the speaker market that Marissa wants to enter. She is considering having Sound's Alive manufacture and sell a home theater system that consists of seven speakers. Three small speakers—each with one dome tweeter that could reproduce the frequency range of 200 Hertz to 20,000 Hertz (upper-low frequencies to the highest frequencies)—would be placed in front, and three similar speakers would be placed strategically around the sides and back of the room. To reproduce the lowest frequencies (from 35 Hertz to 200 Hertz), a single subwoofer also would be part of the system. This subwoofer is revolutionary because it is smaller than the ordinary subwoofer, only 10 inches per side, and it has a built-in amplifier to power it. Consumers and critics are thrilled with the music from early prototype systems, claiming that these speakers have the best balance of sound and size. Marissa is extremely encouraged by these early reviews, and although her company has never produced a product with its house label on it (having always sold systems from established high-fidelity companies), she believes that Sound's Alive should enter the home theater market with this product.

Phase One: Projecting Profits

Marissa decides to create a spreadsheet that will project profits over the next several years. After consulting with economists, market analysts, employees in her own company, and employees from other companies that sell house brand components, Marissa is confident that the gross revenues for these speakers in 2007 would be around $6 million. She also must figure that a small percentage of speakers will be damaged in transit, or some will be returned by dissatisfied customers shortly after the sales. These returns and allowances (R&As) usually are calculated as 2% of the gross revenues. Hence, the net revenues are simply the gross revenues minus the R&As. Marissa believes that the 2007 labor costs for these speakers will be $995,100. The cost of materials (including boxes to ship the speakers) should be $915,350 for 2007. Finally, her overhead costs (rent, lighting, heating in winter, air conditioning in summer, security, and so on) for 2007 should be $1,536,120. Thus, the cost of goods sold is the sum of labor, material, and overhead costs. Marissa figures the gross profit as the difference between the net revenues and the cost of goods sold. In addition, she must consider the selling, general, and administrative (SG&A) expenses. These expenses are more difficult to estimate, but the standard industry practice is to use 18% of the net revenues as the nominal percentage value for these expenses. Therefore, Marissa's profit *before taxes* is the gross profit minus the SG&A value. To calculate taxes, Marissa multiplies her profits before taxes times the tax rate, currently 30%. If her company is operating at a loss, however, no taxes would have to be paid. Finally, Marissa's net (or after tax) profit is simply the difference between the profit before taxes and the actual taxes paid.

To determine the numbers for 2008 through 2010, Marissa assumes that gross revenues, labor costs, material costs, and overhead costs will increase over the years. Although the rates of increase for these items are difficult to estimate, Marissa figures that gross revenues will increase by 9% per year, labor costs will increase by 4% per year, material costs will increase by 6% per year, and overhead costs will increase by 3% per year. She figures that the tax rate will not change from the 30% mark, and she assumes that the SG&A value will remain at 18%.

**FIGURE
12.54**

*Spreadsheet
template for the
Sound's Alive case*

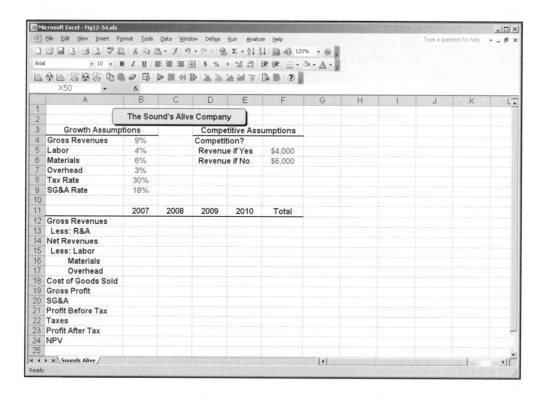

The basic layout of the spreadsheet that Marissa creates is shown in Figure 12-54 (and in the file Fig12-54.xls on your data disk). (Ignore the Competitive Assumptions section for now; we will consider it later.) Construct the spreadsheet, determine the values for the years 2007 through 2010, and then determine the totals for the four years.

Marissa not only wants to determine her net profits for 2007 through 2010, she also must justify her decisions to the company's Board of Trustees. Should she even consider entering this market, from a financial point of view? One way to answer this question is to find the net present value (NPV) of the net profits for 2007 through 2010. Use Excel's NPV capability to find the NPV, at the current interest rate of 5%, of the profit values for 2007 through 2010.

To avoid large values in the spreadsheet, enter all dollar calculations in thousands. For example, enter labor costs as 995.10 and overhead costs as 1536.12.

Phase Two: Bringing Competition into the Model

With her spreadsheet complete, Marissa is confident that entering the home theater speaker market would be lucrative for Sound's Alive. However, she has not considered one factor in her calculations—competition. The current market leader and company she is most concerned about is the Bose Corporation. Bose pioneered the concept of a satellite speaker system, and its AMT series is very successful. Marissa is concerned that Bose will enter the home market, cutting into her gross revenues. If Bose does enter the market, Marissa believes that Sound's Alive still would make money; however, she would have to revise her gross revenues estimate from $6 million to $4 million for 2007.

To account for the competition factor, Marissa revises her spreadsheet by adding a Competitive Assumptions section. Cell F4 will contain either a 0 (no competition) or a 1 (if Bose enters the market). Cells F5 and F6 provide the gross revenue estimates (in thousands of dollars) for the two possibilities. Modify your spreadsheet to take these options into account. Use the IF( ) function for the gross revenues for 2007 (cell B12). If Bose does enter the market, not only would Marissa's gross revenues be lower, but the labor, materials, and overhead costs also would be lower because Sound's Alive would be making and selling fewer speakers. Marissa thinks that if Bose enters the market, her 2007 labor costs would be $859,170; 2007 material costs would be $702,950; and 2007 overhead costs would be $1,288,750. She believes that her growth rate assumptions would stay the same whether or not Bose enters the market. Add these possible values to your spreadsheet using the IF( ) function in the appropriate cells.

Look at the net profits for 2007 through 2010. In particular, examine the NPV for the two scenarios: Bose does or does not enter the home theater speaker market.

Phase Three: Bringing Uncertainty into the Model

Jim Allison, the chief of operations at Sound's Alive and a quantitative methods specialist, plays a key role in providing Marissa with estimates for the various revenues and costs. He is uneasy about the basic estimates for the growth rates. For example, although market research indicates that a 9% gross revenue increase per year is reasonable, Jim knows that if this value is 7%, for example, the profit values and the NPV would be quite different. Even more troublesome is a potential tax increase, which would hit Sound's Alive hard. Jim believes that the tax rate could vary around the expected 30% figure. Finally, Jim is uncomfortable with the industry's standard estimate of 18% for the SG&A rate. Jim thinks that this value could be higher or even lower.

The Sound's Alive problem is too complicated for solving with what-if analysis because seven assumed values could change: the growth rates for gross revenues, labor, materials, overhead costs, tax rate, SG&A percent, and whether or not Bose enters the market. Jim believes that a Monte Carlo simulation would be a better approach. Jim thinks that the behavior of these variables can be modeled as follows:

Gross Revenues (%): normally distributed, mean = 9.9, std dev = 1.4

Labor Growth (%): normally distributed, mean = 3.45, std dev = 1.0

Materials (%)	Probability		Overhead (%)	Probability
4	0.10		2	0.20
5	0.15		3	0.35
6	0.15		4	0.25
7	0.25		5	0.20
8	0.25			
9	0.10			

Tax Rate (%)	Probability		SG&A (%)	Probability
30	0.15		15	0.05
32	0.30		16	0.10
34	0.30		17	0.20
36	0.25		18	0.25
			19	0.20
			20	0.20

Finally, Jim and Marissa agree that there is a 50/50 chance that Bose will enter the market.

a. Use simulation to analyze the Sound's Alive problem. Based on your results, what is the expected net profit for the years 2007 through 2010, and what is the expected NPV for this business venture?

b. The Board of Trustees told Marissa that the stockholders would feel comfortable with this business venture if its NPV is at least $5 million. What are the chances that Sound's Alive home theater venture will result in an NPV of $5 million or more?

CASE 12.4 ## The Foxridge Investment Group

(Inspired by a case written by MBA students Fred Hirsch and Ray Rogers for Professor Larry Weatherford at the University of Wyoming.)

The Foxridge Investment Group buys and sells rental income properties in Southwest Virginia. Bill Hunter, president of Foxridge, has asked for your assistance in analyzing a small apartment building the group is interested in purchasing.

The property in question is a small two-story structure with three rental units on each floor. The purchase price of the property is $170,000 representing $30,000 in land value and $140,000 in buildings and improvements. Foxridge will depreciate the buildings and improvements value on a straight-line basis over 27.5 years. The Foxridge Group will make a down payment of $40,000 to acquire the property and finance the remainder of the purchase price over 20 years with an 11% fixed-rate loan with payments due annually. Figure 12.55 (and the file Fig12-55.xls on your data disk) summarizes this and other pertinent information.

FIGURE 12.55

Assumptions for the Foxridge Investment Group

If all units are fully occupied, Mr. Hunter expects the property to generate rental income of $35,000 in the first year and expects to increase the rent at the rate of inflation (currently 4%). Because vacancies occur and some residents might not always be able to pay their rent, Mr. Hunter factors in a 3% vacancy & collection (V&C) allowance against rental income. Operating expenses are expected to be approximately 45% of rental income. The group's marginal tax rate is 28%.

If the group decides to purchase this property, their plan is to hold it for five years and then sell it to another investor. Presently, property values in this area are increasing at a rate of approximately 2.5% per year. The group will have to pay a sales commission of 5% of the gross selling price when they sell the property.

Figure 12.56 shows a spreadsheet model that Mr. Hunter developed to analyze this problem. This model first uses the data and assumptions given in Figure 12.55 to generate the expected net cash flows in each of the next five years. It then provides a final summary of the proceeds expected from selling the property at the end of five years. The total net present value (NPV) of the project is then calculated in cell I18 using the discount rate of 12% in cell C24 of Figure 12.55. Thus, after discounting all the future cash flows associated with this investment by 12% per year, the investment still generates an NPV of $2,007.

Although the group has been using this type of analysis for many years to make investment decisions, one of Mr. Hunter's investment partners recently read an article in the *Wall Street Journal* about risk analysis and simulation using spreadsheets. As a result, the partner realizes that there is quite a bit of uncertainty associated with many of the economic assumptions shown in Figure 12.55. After explaining the potential problem to Mr. Hunter, the two have decided to apply simulation to this model before making a decision. Because neither of them know how to do simulation, they have asked for your assistance.

FIGURE 12.56

Cash flow and financial summary for the Foxridge Investment Group

	1	2	3	4	5		Financial Summary	
	Cash Flows in Year							
Gross Income	$35,000	$36,400	$37,856	$39,370	$40,945		Sales price @ year 5	$192,339
Less:							Less:	
V&C Allowance	$1,050	$1,092	$1,136	$1,181	$1,228		Selling expense	$9,617
Operating Exp.	$15,750	$16,380	$17,035	$17,717	$18,425		Tax basis	$144,545
Net Operating Income	$18,200	$18,928	$19,685	$20,473	$21,291		Taxable gain	$38,177
Less:								
Depreciation	$5,091	$5,091	$5,091	$5,091	$5,091		Proceeds from sale	$182,722
Interest	$14,300	$14,077	$13,830	$13,556	$13,251		Less:	
Taxable Income	($1,191)	($240)	$764	$1,826	$2,950		Taxes	$10,690
							Loan payoff	$117,390
Taxes Paid (Saved)	($333)	($67)	$214	$511	$826		Net cash from sale	$54,643
Principal Paid	$2,025	$2,248	$2,495	$2,769	$3,074		PV of sale proceeds	$31,006
							PV of cash flows	$11,001
Net Cash Flow	$2,209	$2,670	$3,146	$3,636	$4,141		Less: Original Equity	$40,000
							Total NPV	$2,007

To model the uncertainty in this decision problem, Mr. Hunter and his partner have decided that the growth in rental income from one year to the next could vary uniformly from 2% to 6% in years 2 through 5. Similarly, they believe that the V&C allowance in any year could be as low as 1% and as high as 5%, with 3% being the most likely outcome. They think that the operating expenses in each year should be normally distributed with a mean of 45% and standard deviation of 2% but never should be less than 40% and never greater than 50% of gross income. Finally, they believe that the property value growth rate could be as small as 1% or as large as 5%, with 2.5% being the most likely outcome.

a. Revise the spreadsheets shown in Figures 12.55 and 12.56 to reflect the uncertainties outlined.

b. Construct a 95% confidence interval for the average total NPV that the Foxridge Investment Group can expect if they undertake this project. (Use 500 replications.) Interpret this confidence interval.

c. Based on your analysis, what is the probability of this project generating a positive total NPV if the group uses a 12% discount rate?

d. Suppose the investors are willing to buy the property if the expected total NPV is greater than zero. Based on your analysis, should they buy this property?

e. Assume that the investors decide to increase the discount rate to 14% and repeat questions 2, 3, and 4.

f. What discount rate results in a 90% chance of the project generating a positive total NPV?

Chapter 13

Queuing Theory

13.0 Introduction

Sometimes it seems as if we spend most of our lives waiting in lines. We wait in lines at grocery stores, banks, airports, hotels, restaurants, theaters, theme parks, post offices, and traffic lights. At home, we are likely to spend time waiting in an "electronic line" if we use the telephone to order merchandise from mail-order firms, or to call the customer service number of most computer hardware or software companies.

Some reports indicate that Americans spend 37 *billion* hours a year waiting in lines. Much of this time represents a loss of a limited resource (time) that can never be recovered. Add the frustration and irritation that many people experience while waiting in lines, and it is easy to see why businesses should be interested in reducing or eliminating the amount of time their customers spend waiting in lines.

Waiting lines do not always contain people. In a manufacturing company, subassemblies often wait in a line at machining centers to have the next operation performed on them. At a video rental store, returned videos often wait to be placed on shelves so they can be rented again. Electronic messages on the Internet sometimes wait at intermediate computing centers before they are sent to their final destinations. Costs could be reduced, or customer service improved, by reducing the amount of time that the subassemblies, videos, or electronic messages spend waiting in line.

In management science terminology, the term **queuing theory** represents the body of knowledge dealing with waiting lines. Queuing theory was conceived in the early 1900s when a Danish telephone engineer named A. K. Erlang began studying the congestion and waiting times occurring in the completion of telephone calls. Since then, several quantitative models have been developed to help business people understand waiting lines and make better decisions about how to manage them. This chapter introduces some of these models and discusses other issues involved in queuing theory.

13.1 The Purpose of Queuing Models

Most queuing problems focus on determining the level of service that a company should provide. For example, grocery stores must determine how many cash registers to operate at a given time of day so that customers do not have to wait too long to check out. Banks must determine how many tellers to schedule at various times of day to maintain an acceptable level of service. Companies that lease copying machines must determine the number of technicians to employ so that repairs can be made in a timely manner.

In many queuing problems, management has some control over the level of service provided. In the examples just mentioned, customer waiting times could be kept to a

FIGURE 13.1

Trade-off between costs of providing service and customer satisfaction

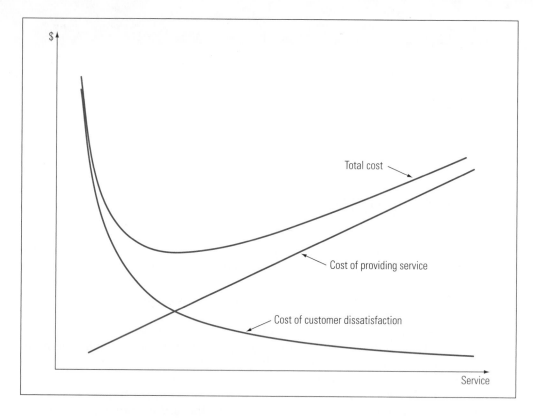

minimum by employing a large number of servers (in the form of cashiers, tellers, and technicians). However, this can be expensive, or actually wasteful, if an excessive number of idle servers is maintained. On the other hand, employing a small number of servers keeps the cost of providing service low, but is likely to result in longer customer waiting times and greater customer dissatisfaction. Thus, a trade-off exists between the cost of providing service and the cost of having dissatisfied customers if service is lacking. The nature of this trade-off is illustrated in Figure 13.1.

Figure 13.1 indicates that as service levels increase, the cost of providing service also increases, but the cost of customer dissatisfaction decreases (as does the length of time customers must wait for service). As service levels decrease, the cost of providing service also decreases, but the cost of customer dissatisfaction increases. The objective in many queuing problems is to find the optimal service level that achieves an acceptable balance between the cost of providing service and customer satisfaction.

13.2 Queuing System Configurations

The queuing systems we encounter in everyday life are configured in a variety of ways. Three typical configurations are illustrated in Figure 13.2.

The first configuration in Figure 13.2 represents a single-queue, single-server system. In this configuration, customers enter the system and wait in line on a first-in, first-out (FIFO) basis until they receive service; then they exit the system. This type of queuing system is employed at most Wendy's and Taco Bell restaurants. You also might encounter this type of queuing system at some automatic teller machines (ATMs).

The second configuration in Figure 13.2 represents a single-queue, multi-server system. Here again, customers enter the system and join a FIFO queue. Upon reaching the

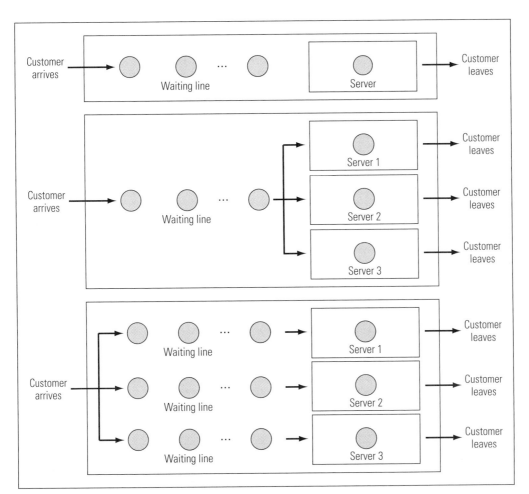

FIGURE 13.2

*Examples of
different queuing
system
configurations*

front of the line, a customer is serviced by the next available server. The example shows three servers, but there could be more or fewer servers depending on the problem at hand. This type of queuing system is found at most airport check-in counters, post offices, and banks.

The third configuration in Figure 13.2 represents a collection of single-queue, single-server systems. In this type of arrangement, when customers arrive, they must choose one of the queues and then wait in that line to receive service. This type of system is found at most grocery stores and most Burger King and McDonald's restaurants.

This chapter discusses queuing models that can be used to analyze the first two types of configurations shown in Figure 13.2. In some cases, the individual queues in the third configuration in Figure 13.2 can be analyzed as independent, single-queue, single-server systems. Thus, the results presented for the first type of configuration can sometimes be generalized to analyze the third configuration also.

13.3 Characteristics of Queuing Systems

To create and analyze mathematical models of the queuing configurations shown in Figure 13.2, we must make some assumptions about the way in which customers arrive to the system and the amount of time it takes for them to receive service.

13.3.1 ARRIVAL RATE

In most queuing systems, customers (or jobs in a manufacturing environment) arrive in a somewhat random fashion. That is, the number of arrivals that occurs in a given time period represents a random variable. It is often appropriate to model the arrival process in a queuing system as a Poisson random variable. To use the Poisson probability distribution, we must specify a value for the **arrival rate**, denoted as λ, representing the average number of arrivals per time period. (For a Poisson random variable, the variance of the number of arrivals per time period is also λ.) The probability of x arrivals in a specific time period is represented by:

$$P(x) = \frac{\lambda^x e^{-\lambda}}{x!} \quad \text{for } x = 0, 1, 2, \ldots \tag{13.1}$$

where e represents the base of the natural logarithm ($e = 2.71828$) and $x! = (x)(x-1)$ $(x-2)\ldots(2)(1)$. ($x!$ is referred to as x factorial and can be calculated using the FACT( ) function in Excel.)

For example, suppose that calls to the customer service hotline of a computer retailer occur at a rate of five per hour and follow a Poisson probability distribution ($\lambda = 5$). The probability distribution associated with the number of calls arriving in a given hour is illustrated in Figure 13.3 (and in the file Fig13-3.xls on your data disk).

In Figure 13.3, the values in column B represent the probabilities associated with each value in column A. For example, the value in cell B5 indicates that a 0.0067 probability exists of 0 calls arriving in a given hour; cell B6 indicates that a 0.0337 probability exists of one call arriving, and so on. The histogram of the probability distribution indicates that, on average, we can expect approximately five calls to arrive in one hour. However,

FIGURE 13.3

Example of a Poisson probability distribution with mean $\lambda = 5$

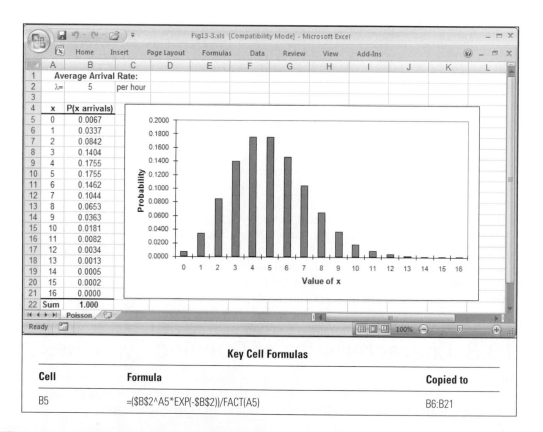

Cell	Formula	Copied to
B5	=($B$2^A5*EXP(-$B$2))/FACT(A5)	B6:B21

because the Poisson distribution is skewed to the right, a significantly larger number of calls (in this case, 13 or more) could arrive in some one-hour time periods.

Figure 13.3 indicates that the probability of six calls occurring in a given hour is 0.1462. However, the six calls probably will not occur all at the same time. Some random amount of time is likely to transpire between arriving calls. This time between arrivals is known as the **interarrival time**. If the number of arrivals in a given period of time follows a Poisson distribution with mean λ, it can be shown that the interarrival times follow an exponential probability distribution with mean $1/\lambda$.

For example, if calls to the computer retailer's hotline follow a Poisson distribution and occur at an average rate of $\lambda = 5$ per hour, the interarrival times follow an exponential distribution with an average interarrival time of $1/5 = 0.2$ hours. That is, calls occur once every 12 minutes on average (because there are 60 minutes in an hour and 0.2×60 minutes $= 12$ minutes).

The exponential distribution plays a key role in queuing models. It is one of the few probability distributions that exhibits the **memoryless** (or lack of memory) property. An arrival process is memoryless if the time until the next arrival occurs does not depend on how much time has elapsed since the last arrival. The Russian mathematician Markov was the first to recognize the memoryless property of certain random variables. Therefore, the memoryless property is also sometimes referred to as the Markov or Markovian property.

All the queuing models presented in this chapter assume that arrivals follow a Poisson distribution (or, equivalently, that interarrival times follow an exponential distribution). To use these models, it is important to verify that this assumption is valid for the queuing system being modeled. One way to verify that arrivals can be approximated by the Poisson distribution is to collect data on the number of arrivals occurring per time period for several hours, days, or weeks. The average number of arrivals per time period can be calculated from these data and used as an estimate of λ. A histogram of the actual data can be constructed and compared to a histogram of the actual probabilities expected of a Poisson random variable with mean λ. If the histograms are similar, it is reasonable to assume that the arrival process is approximately Poisson. (Additional goodness-of-fit tests can be found in most texts on queuing and simulation.)

13.3.2 SERVICE RATE

A customer who arrives at a service facility spends some amount of time (possibly 0) waiting in line for service to begin. We refer to this time as **queue time**. **Service time** is the amount of time a customer spends at a service facility once the actual performance of service begins. (So service time *does not* include queue time.)

It is often appropriate to model the service times in a queuing system as an exponential random variable. To use the exponential probability distribution for this purpose, we must specify a value for the **service rate**, denoted by μ, representing the average number of customers (or jobs) that can be served per time period. The average service time per customer is $1/\mu$ time periods (and the variance of the service time per customer is $(1/\mu)^2$ time periods). Because the exponential distribution is continuous, the probability of an exponential random variable equaling any specific value is zero. Thus, probabilities associated with an exponential random variable must be defined in terms of intervals. If the distribution of service times follows an exponential distribution, the probability that the service time T of a given customer will be between t_1 and t_2 time periods is defined by:

$$P(t_1 \leq T \leq t_2) = \int_{t_1}^{t_2} \mu e^{-\mu x} dx = e^{-\mu t_1} - e^{-\mu t_2}, \quad \text{for } t_1 \leq t_2 \qquad \textbf{13.2}$$

FIGURE 13.4

*Example of an
exponential
distribution with
$\mu = 7$*

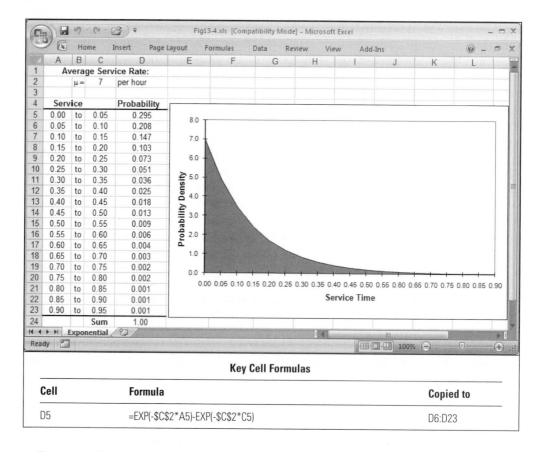

Cell	Formula	Copied to
D5	=EXP(-$C$2*A5)-EXP(-$C$2*C5)	D6:D23

For example, suppose that the operator on the customer service hotline can service calls at a rate of seven per hour, on average, and that the service times follow an exponential distribution ($\mu = 7$). Figure 13.4 (and the file Fig13-4.xls on your data disk) shows the probability of the service time falling within several time intervals.

In Figure 13.4, the value in cell D5 indicates that a 0.295 probability exists that it will take from 0 to 0.05 hours (or 3 minutes) to service any call. Similarly, the value in cell D9 indicates that a 0.073 probability exists that it will take between 0.2 and 0.25 hours (or from 12 to 15 minutes) to service any call.

The data and graph in Figure 13.4 indicate that for exponential distributions, shorter service times have the largest relative probability of occurring. In reality, some minimal amount of time is usually required to provide most services. This might lead us to believe that the exponential distribution would tend to underestimate the actual service time required by most customers. However, the exponential distribution also assumes that some very long service times will occur (though very infrequently). The possibility of these very long (but infrequent) service times provides a balance to the very short (but frequent) service times so that, on average, the exponential distribution provides a reasonably accurate description of the behavior of service times in many real-world problems. But keep in mind that the exponential distribution is not an adequate model of service times in all applications.

One way to verify that the service rate can be modeled using the exponential distribution is to collect data on the service times occurring per time period for several hours, days, or weeks. The average number of customers serviced per time period can be calculated from these data and used as an estimate of the service rate μ. Using actual data, a relative frequency distribution of the service times falling within various intervals can be constructed and compared to the distribution of the actual probabilities expected for each interval for an exponential random variable with a service rate of μ (like the one shown in Figure 13.4). If the distributions are similar, it is reasonable to assume that the distribution of service times is approximately exponential. (Again, additional goodness-of-fit tests can be found in most texts on queuing and simulation.)

13.4 Kendall Notation

Given the variety of queuing models that exist, a system known as **Kendall notation** was developed to allow the key characteristics of a specific queuing model to be described in an efficient manner. With Kendall notation, simple queuing models can be described by three characteristics in the following general format:

$$1/2/3$$

The first characteristic identifies the nature of the arrival process using the following standard abbreviations:

M = Markovian interarrival times (following an exponential distribution)

D = deterministic interarrival times (not random)

The second characteristic identifies the nature of the service times using the following standard abbreviations:

M = Markovian service times (following an exponential distribution)

G = general service times (following a nonexponential distribution)

D = deterministic service times (not random)

Finally, the third characteristic indicates the number of servers available. So, using Kendall notation, an M/M/1 queue refers to a queuing model in which the time between arrivals follows an exponential distribution, the service times follow an exponential distribution, and there is one server. An M/G/3 queue refers to a model in which the interarrival times are assumed to be exponential, the service times follow some general distribution, and three servers are present.

An expanded version of Kendall notation involves specifying six (rather than three) queue characteristics. A more complete description of this notation can be found in advanced management science or queuing texts.

13.5 Queuing Models

Numerous queuing models are available to evaluate different combinations of arrival distributions, service time distributions, and other queuing characteristics. This chapter discusses only a few of these models. Typical operating characteristics of interest include:

Characteristic	Description
U	Utilization factor, or the percentage of time that all servers are busy
P_0	Probability that there are no units in the system
L_q	Average number of units in line waiting for service
L	Average number of units in the system (in line and being served)
W_q	Average time a unit spends in line waiting for service
W	Average time a unit spends in the system (in line and being served)
P_w	Probability that an arriving unit has to wait for service
P_n	Probability of n units in the system

Information about these operating characteristics can be helpful to managers who need to make decisions about the trade-offs between the costs of providing different levels of service and the associated impact on customers' experiences in the queuing system. Where possible, researchers have derived closed-form equations to calculate various operating characteristics of a particular queuing model. For instance, for the M/M/1 queuing model it can be shown that:

$$W = \frac{1}{\mu - \lambda}$$

$$L = \lambda W$$

$$W_q = W - \frac{1}{\mu}$$

$$L_q = \lambda W_q$$

This chapter does not show the derivation of the equations used to calculate operating characteristics. Rather, it simply states the equations for several common queuing models and shows how they can be used. The equations for the queuing models we will consider are implemented in spreadsheet templates in the file Q.xls on your data disk. Figure 13.5 shows the introduction screen for these templates.

As Figure 13.5 indicates, the templates in this file can be used to analyze four types of queuing models: the M/M/s model, the M/M/s model with finite queue length, the M/M/s model with finite arrival population, and the M/G/1 model.

13.6 The M/M/s Model

The M/M/s model is appropriate for analyzing queuing problems where the following assumptions are met:

- There are *s* servers, where *s* is a positive integer.
- Arrivals follow a Poisson distribution and occur at an average rate of λ per time period.

FIGURE 13.5

Introductory screen for Q.xls queuing template file

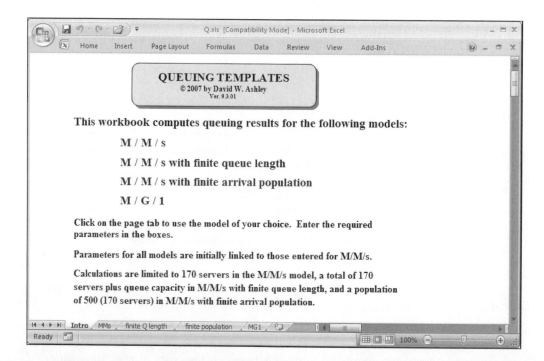

- Each server provides service at an average rate of μ per time period, and actual service times follow an exponential distribution.
- Arrivals wait in a single FIFO queue and are serviced by the first available server.
- $\lambda < s\mu$

The final assumption indicates that the total service capacity of the system, $s\mu$, must be strictly greater than the rate at which arrivals occur λ. If the arrival rate exceeds the system's total service capacity, the system would fill up over time and the queue would become infinitely long. In fact, the queue becomes infinitely long even if the average arrival rate λ is equal to the average service rate $s\mu$. To see why, note that individual arrival times and service times vary in an unpredictable manner (even though their averages may be constant). So there will be times when the servers are idle. This idle time is lost forever and the servers will not be able to make up for this at other times when the demand for service is heavy. (Note that demand is never lost forever but is assumed to wait patiently in the queue.) This causes the servers to fall hopelessly behind if $\lambda \geq s\mu$.

The formulas describing the operating characteristics of the M/M/s model are given in Figure 13.6. Although these formulas might seem somewhat daunting, they are easy to use when implemented in a spreadsheet template.

13.6.1 AN EXAMPLE

The following example illustrates how the M/M/s model might be used.

The customer support hotline for Bitway Computers is currently staffed by a single technician. Calls arrive randomly at a rate of five per hour and follow a Poisson distribution. The technician can service calls at an average rate of seven per hour, but

FIGURE 13.6

Formulas describing the operating characteristics of an M/M/s queue

$$U = \lambda/(s\mu)$$

$$P_0 = \left(\sum_{n=0}^{s-1} \frac{(\lambda/\mu)^n}{n!} + \frac{(\lambda/\mu)^s}{s!} \left(\frac{s\mu}{s\mu - \lambda} \right) \right)^{-1}$$

$$L_q = \frac{P_0(\lambda/\mu)^{s+1}}{(s-1)!(s - \lambda/\mu)^2}$$

$$L = L_q + \frac{\lambda}{\mu}$$

$$W_q = \frac{L_q}{\lambda}$$

$$W = W_q + \frac{1}{\mu}$$

$$P_w = \frac{1}{s!} \left(\frac{\lambda}{\mu} \right)^s \left(\frac{s\mu}{s\mu - \lambda} \right) P_0$$

$$P_n = \begin{cases} \dfrac{(\lambda/\mu)^n}{n!} P_0, & \text{for } n \leq s \\ \dfrac{(\lambda/\mu)^n}{s!s^{(n-s)}} P_0, & \text{for } n > s \end{cases}$$

the actual time required to handle a given call is an exponential random variable. The president of Bitway, Rod Taylor, has received numerous complaints from customers about the length of time they must wait "on hold" for service when calling the hotline. Rod wants to determine the average length of time that customers currently wait before the technician answers their calls. If the average waiting time is more than five minutes, he wants to determine how many technicians would be required to reduce the average waiting time to two minutes or less.

13.6.2 THE CURRENT SITUATION

Because only one technician (or server) currently staffs Bitway's customer service hotline, we can calculate the operating characteristics for the hotline using an M/M/1 queuing model. Figure 13.7 shows the results of this model for Bitway's current configuration.

Cells E2, E3, and E4 contain the values for the arrival rate, service rate, and number of servers in our example problem, respectively. The various operating characteristics of this model are calculated automatically in column F.

The value in cell F12 indicates that a 0.7143 probability exists that callers to Bitway's customer service hotline must wait on hold before receiving service from the technician. The value in cell F10 indicates that the average length of this wait is 0.3571 hours (or approximately 21.42 minutes). The value in cell F11 indicates that, on average, a caller spends a total of 0.5 hours (or 30 minutes) waiting for service and being served under Bitway's current hotline configuration. Thus, it appears that the customer complaints to Bitway's president are justifiable.

13.6.3 ADDING A SERVER

To improve the level of service on the hotline, Bitway could investigate how the operating characteristics of the system would change if two technicians were assigned to

FIGURE 13.7

Results of the M/M/1 model for Bitway's customer service model

FIGURE 13.8

*Results of the
M/M/2 model for
Bitway's customer
service hotline*

answer calls. That is, incoming calls could be handled by either one of two equally capable technicians. We can calculate the operating characteristics for this configuration using an M/M/2 queuing model, as shown in Figure 13.8.

The value in cell F12 indicates that, with two servers, the probability that a caller must wait before receiving service drops significantly from 0.7143 to 0.1880. Similarly, cell F10 indicates that the average amount of time a caller must wait before service begins drops to 0.0209 hours (or approximately 1.25 minutes). Thus, it seems that adding a second technician to the customer service hotline would achieve the two-minute average waiting time objective Rod wants.

Although the addition of a second server greatly reduces the average time hotline callers spend waiting for service to begin, it does not reduce the expected *service time*. For the M/M/1 model in Figure 13.7, which includes only one server, the expected total time in the system is 0.5 hours and the expected queue time is 0.3571 hours. This implies that the expected service time is $0.5 - 0.3571 = 0.1429$ hours. For the M/M/2 model in Figure 13.8, which includes two servers, the expected total time in the system is 0.1637 hours and the expected queue time is 0.0209 hours. This implies an expected service time of $0.1637 - 0.0209 = 0.1429$ hours (allowing for a slight rounding error). The M/M/2 model assumes that both servers can provide service at the same rate—in this case, an average of seven calls per hour. Therefore, the average service time per call should be $1/7 = 0.1429$ hours, which is consistent with the observed results.

13.6.4 ECONOMIC ANALYSIS

Bitway undoubtedly will incur some additional costs in going from one to two customer support technicians. This might include the cost of salary and benefits for the additional technician and perhaps an additional telephone line. However, the improved service level provided by the two-server system should reduce the number of customer complaints and perhaps lead to favorable word-of-mouth advertising and increased business for the company. Rod could attempt to quantify these benefits and compare them to the cost of adding a customer support technician. Alternatively, Rod simply might view the addition of the customer support technician as a competitive necessity.

13.7 The M/M/s Model with Finite Queue Length

The results for the M/M/s models in Figures 13.7 and 13.8 assume that the size or capacity of the waiting area is infinite, so that all arrivals to the system join the queue and wait for service. In some situations, however, the size or capacity of the waiting area might be restricted—in other words, there might be a finite queue length. The formulas describing the operating characteristics of an M/M/s queue with a finite queue length of K are summarized in Figure 13.9.

To see how this queuing model might be used, suppose that Bitway's telephone system can keep a maximum of five calls on hold at any point in time. If a new call is made to the hotline when five calls are already in the queue, the new call receives a busy signal. One way to reduce the number of calls encountering busy signals is to increase the number of calls that can be put on hold. However, if a call is answered only to be put on hold for a long time, the caller might find this more annoying than receiving a busy signal. Thus, Rod might want to investigate what effect adding a second technician to answer hotline calls would have on the number of calls receiving busy signals and on the average time callers must wait before receiving service.

FIGURE 13.9

Formulas describing the operating characteristics of an M/M/s queue with a finite queue length of K

$$U = (L - L_q)/s$$

$$P_0 = \left(1 + \sum_{n=1}^{s} \frac{(\lambda/\mu)^n}{n!} + \frac{(\lambda/\mu)^s}{s!} \sum_{n=s+1}^{K} \left(\frac{\lambda}{s\mu}\right)^{n-s}\right)^{-1}$$

$$P_n = \frac{(\lambda/\mu)^n}{n!} P_0, \text{ for } n = 1, 2, \ldots, s$$

$$P_n = \frac{(\lambda/\mu)^n}{s!s^{n-s}} P_0, \text{ for } n = s+1, s+2, \ldots, K$$

$$P_n = 0, \text{ for } n > K$$

$$L_q = \frac{P_0(\lambda/\mu)^s \rho}{s!(1-\rho)^2} (1 - \rho^{K-s} - (K-s)\rho^{K-s}(1-\rho)), \text{ where } \rho = \lambda/(s\mu)$$

$$L = \sum_{n=0}^{s-1} nP_n + L_q + s\left(1 - \sum_{n=0}^{s-1} P_n\right)$$

$$W_q = \frac{L_q}{\lambda(1 - P_K)}$$

$$W = \frac{L}{\lambda(1 - P_K)}$$

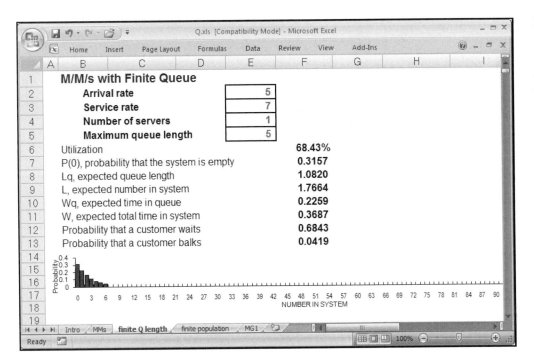

FIGURE 13.10

Results of the M/M/1 model with a finite queue length of five for Bitway's customer service hotline

13.7.1 THE CURRENT SITUATION

Because only one technician (or server) currently staffs Bitway's customer service hotline, we can calculate the current operating characteristics for the hotline using an M/M/1 queuing model with a finite queue length of 5. Figure 13.10 shows the results of this model for Bitway's current configuration.

Cells E2, E3, and E4 contain the values for the arrival rate, service rate, and number of servers in our example problem, respectively. Cell E5 contains the maximum queue length of five.

The value in cell F13 indicates that a 0.0419 probability exists that callers to Bitway's customer service hotline will balk (or, in this case, receive a busy signal). A **balk** refers to an arrival that does not join the queue because the queue is full or too long. The value in cell F10 indicates that the average length of this wait is 0.2259 hours (or approximately 13.55 minutes). The value in cell F11 indicates that, on average, a caller spends a total of 0.3687 hours (or 22.12 minutes) either waiting for service or being served under Bitway's current hotline configuration.

13.7.2 ADDING A SERVER

To improve the level of service on the hotline, Bitway could investigate how the operating characteristics of the system would change if two technicians were assigned to answer calls. We can calculate the operating characteristics for this configuration using an M/M/2 queuing model with a finite queue length of five, as shown in Figure 13.11.

The value in cell F13 indicates that, with two servers, the probability that a caller receives a busy signal drops to 0.0007. Similarly, cell F10 indicates that the average amount of time a caller must wait before service begins drops to 0.0204 hours (or approximately 1.22 minutes). Thus, it seems that adding a second technician to the customer service hotline would achieve the two-minute average waiting time objective Rod wants and

**FIGURE
13.11**

*Results of the
M/M/2 model with
a finite queue
length of five for
Bitway's customer
service hotline*

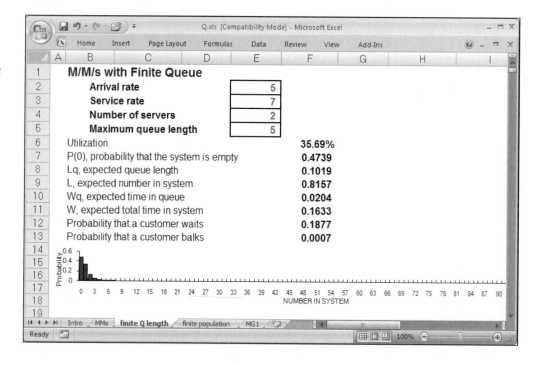

would virtually eliminate any chance of a customer receiving a busy signal. Here again, Rod should consider weighing the costs of adding the additional support technician against the benefits of eliminating the chances of customers receiving busy signals when they call the customer support hotline.

13.8 The M/M/s Model with Finite Population

The previous queuing models assume that the customers (or calls) arriving at the queuing system come from a population of potential customers that is infinite, or extremely large. Under this assumption, the mean arrival rate, λ, remains constant regardless of the number of calls in the system.

In some queuing problems, however, the possible number of arriving customers is finite. In other words, these queuing models have a finite arrival (or calling) population. In such a model, the average arrival rate for the system changes depending on the number of customers in the queue. The M/M/s model for finite arrival populations is appropriate for analyzing queuing problems where the following assumptions are met:

- There are s servers, where s is a positive integer.
- There are N potential customers in the arrival population.
- The arrival pattern of *each customer* follows a Poisson distribution with a mean arrival rate of λ per time period.
- Each server provides service at an average rate of μ per time period, and actual service times follow an exponential distribution.
- Arrivals wait in a single FIFO queue and are serviced by the first available server.

FIGURE
13.12

*Formulas
describing the
operating
characteristics of
an M/M/s queue
with a finite
arrival population
of size N*

$$P_0 = \left(\sum_{n=0}^{s-1} \frac{N!}{(N-n)!n!} \left(\frac{\lambda}{\mu}\right)^n + \sum_{n=s}^{N} \frac{N!}{(N-n)!s!s^{n-s}} \left(\frac{\lambda}{\mu}\right)^n \right)^{-1}$$

$$P_n = \frac{N!}{(N-n)!n!} \left(\frac{\lambda}{\mu}\right)^n P_0, \text{ if } 0 < n \leq s$$

$$P_n = \frac{N!}{(N-n)!s!s^{n-s}} \left(\frac{\lambda}{\mu}\right)^n P_0, \text{ if } s < n \leq N$$

$$P_n = 0, \text{ if } n > N$$

$$L_q = \sum_{n=s}^{N} (n-s)P_n$$

$$L = \sum_{n=0}^{s-1} nP_n + L_q + s\left(1 - \sum_{n=0}^{s-1} P_n\right)$$

$$W_q = \frac{L_q}{\lambda(N-L)}$$

$$W = \frac{L}{\lambda(N-L)}$$

Note that the average arrival rate for this model (λ) is defined in terms of the rate at which *each customer* arrives. The formulas describing the operating characteristics for an M/M/s queue with a finite arrival population of size N are summarized in Figure 13.12.

13.8.1 AN EXAMPLE

One of the most common applications for the M/M/s model with a finite arrival population is the machine repair problem, as illustrated in the following example.

The Miller Manufacturing Company owns 10 identical machines that it uses in the production of colored nylon thread for the textile industry. Machine breakdowns occur following a Poisson distribution with an average of 0.01 breakdowns occurring per operating hour per machine. The company loses $100 each hour while a machine is inoperable. The company employs one technician to fix these machines when they break down. Service times to repair the machines are exponentially distributed with an average of eight hours per repair. Thus, service is performed at a rate of 1/8 machines per hour. Management wants to analyze what impact adding another service technician would have on the average length of time required to fix a machine when it breaks down. Service technicians are paid $20 per hour.

13.8.2 THE CURRENT SITUATION

The 10 machines in this problem represent a finite set of objects that can break down. Therefore, the M/M/s model for a finite calling operation is appropriate to use for

FIGURE 13.13

Results of an M/M/1 model with a finite population of 10 machines for Miller Manufacturing's machine repair problem

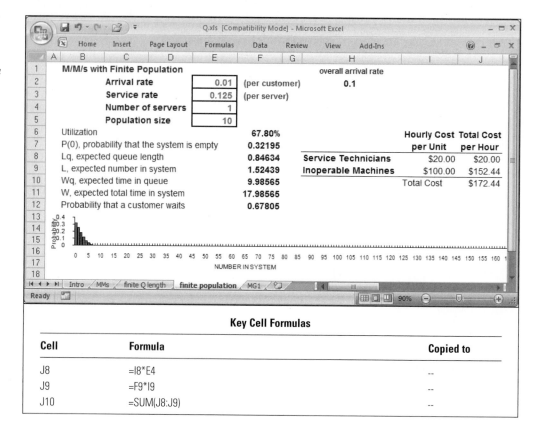

Key Cell Formulas

Cell	Formula	Copied to
J8	=I8*E4	--
J9	=F9*I9	--
J10	=SUM(J8:J9)	--

analyzing this problem. The current operating characteristics for Miller Manufacturing's machine repair problem are summarized in Figure 13.13.

Because the individual machines break down at a rate of 0.01 per hour, this is the rate at which individual machines "arrive" for repair. Thus, cell E2 contains the value 0.01 to represent the arrival rate per customer (machine). The technician can service broken machines at an average rate of $1/8 = 0.125$ machines per hour, as indicated in cell E3. The number of servers (or technicians) is shown in cell E4. Because there are 10 machines that can break down, cell E5 contains a population size of 10. The spreadsheet calculates the overall arrival rate shown in cell H2. Because there are 10 machines, each with a 0.01 probability of breaking down each hour, the overall arrival rate of broken machines is 10 $\times$ 0.01 = 0.1, as indicated in cell H2.

The operating characteristics for this system are calculated in cells F6 through F12. According to cell F11, whenever a machine breaks down, it is out of operation for an average of 17.98 hours. Of this total down time, cell F10 indicates that the machine spends approximately 10 hours waiting for service to begin. Cell F9 indicates that approximately 1.524 machines are out of operation at any point in time.

We used columns H through J of the worksheet to calculate the economic consequences of the current situation. There is one server (or service technician) in this problem who is paid $20 per hour. According to cell F9, an average of approximately 1.524 machines are broken in any given hour. Because the company loses $100 each hour a machine is inoperable, cell J9 indicates the company is presently losing about $152.44 per hour due to machine down time. Thus, with a single service technician, the company is incurring costs at the rate of $172.44 per hour.

Software Note

The Q.xls file comes "protected" so that you will not inadvertently write over or delete important formulas in this template. Sometimes, you might want to turn off this protection on a sheet so you can do your own calculations off to the side or format your results (as shown in Figure 13.13). To do this,

1. Click Review.
2. Click Unprotect.

If you unprotect a sheet, you should take special care not to alter any of the formulas on the sheet.

13.8.3 ADDING SERVERS

Figure 13.14 shows the expected operation of this system if Miller Manufacturing adds another service technician.

Cell F10 indicates that when a machine breaks down, repairs start, on average, in only 0.82 hours (or approximately 49 minutes), in comparison to the 10-hour waiting time with only one technician. Similarly, cell F9 indicates that with two technicians, an average of only 0.81 machines are out of operation at any point in time. Thus, by adding another repair technician, Miller Manufacturing can keep approximately one more machine in operation at all times. Thus, while the additional service technician increases the total hourly cost to $40, the decrease in the average number of machines in the system saves the company $71.32 per hour (i.e., $152.44 - 81.12 = 71.32$). The net effect is a cost savings of $51.32 as the total hourly cost in cell J10 drops to $121.12.

Figure 13.15 shows the results of adding a third service technician for this problem. Notice that this has the effect of increasing labor costs by $20 per hour over the solution shown in Figure 13.14 while reducing the losses due to idle machines by only $6.36. So, as we go from two to three service technicians, the total hourly cost increases from

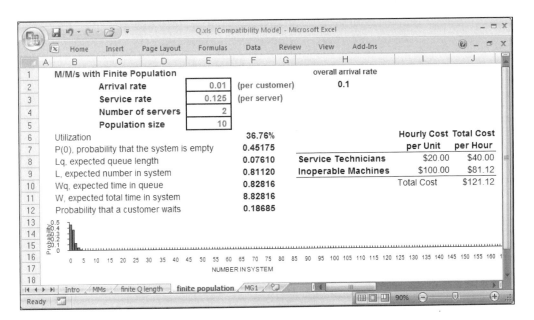

FIGURE 13.14

Results of an M/M/2 model with a finite population of 10 machines for Miller Manufacturing's machine repair problem

FIGURE 13.15

Results of an M/M/3 model with a finite population of 10 machines for Miller Manufacturing's machine repair problem

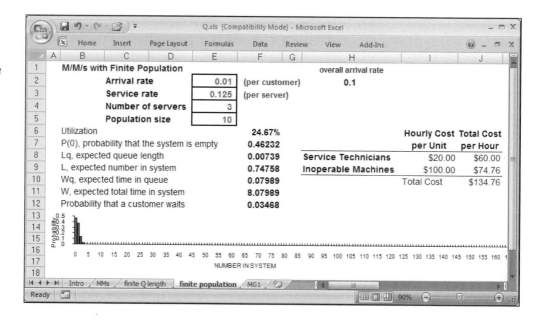

$121.12 to $134.76 per hour. Thus, the optimal solution is for Miller Manufacturing to employ two service technicians because this results in the smallest total hourly cost.

13.9 The M/G/1 Model

All the models presented so far assume that service times follow an exponential distribution. As noted earlier in Figure 13.4, random service times from an exponential distribution can assume *any* positive value. However, in some situations, this assumption is unrealistic. For example, consider the time required to change the oil in a car at an auto service center. This service probably requires *at least* 10 minutes and might require up to 30, 45, or even 60 minutes, depending on the service being performed. The M/G/1 queuing model enables us to analyze queuing problems in which service times cannot be modeled accurately using an exponential distribution. The formulas describing the operating characteristics of an M/G/1 queue are summarized in Figure 13.16.

The M/G/1 queuing model is quite remarkable because it can be used to compute the operating characteristics for *any* one-server queuing system where arrivals follow a Poisson distribution and the mean μ and standard deviation σ of the service times are

FIGURE 13.16

Formulas describing the operating characteristics of an M/G/1 queue

$$P_0 = 1 - \lambda/\mu$$

$$L_q = \frac{\lambda^2\sigma^2 + (\lambda/\mu)^2}{2(1 - \lambda/\mu)}$$

$$L = L_q + \lambda/\mu$$

$$W_q = L_q/\lambda$$

$$W = W_q + 1/\mu$$

$$P_w = \lambda/\mu$$

known. That is, the formulas in Figure 13.16 do not require that service times follow one specific probability distribution. The following example illustrates the use of the M/G/1 queuing model.

> Zippy-Lube is a drive-through automotive oil change business that operates 10 hours a day, 6 days a week. The profit margin on an oil change at Zippy-Lube is $15. Cars arrive randomly at the Zippy-Lube oil change center following a Poisson distribution at an average rate of 3.5 cars per hour. After reviewing the historical data on operations at this business, the owner of Zippy-Lube, Olie Boe, has determined that the average service time per car is 15 minutes (or 0.25 hours) with a standard deviation of 2 minutes (or 0.0333 hours). Olie has the opportunity to purchase a new automated oil dispensing device that costs $5,000. The manufacturer's representative claims this device will reduce the average service time by 3 minutes per car. (Currently, Olie's employees manually open and pour individual cans of oil.) Olie wants to analyze the impact the new automated device would have on his business and determine the payback period for this device.

13.9.1 THE CURRENT SITUATION

We can model Olie's current service facility as an M/G/1 queue. The operating characteristics of this facility are shown in Figure 13.17.

Cell E3 contains the average arrival rate of 3.5 cars per hour. The average service time per car (also in hours) is indicated in cell E4, and the standard deviation of the service time (in hours) is indicated in cell E5. Cell F11 shows that an average of about 3.12 cars wait for service at any given point in time. Cell F14 indicates that, on average, 1.14 hours (or about 68 minutes) elapse between the time a car arrives and leaves the system.

13.9.2 ADDING THE AUTOMATED DISPENSING DEVICE

If Olie purchases the automated oil dispensing device, the average service time per car should drop to 12 minutes (or 0.20 hours). Figure 13.18 shows the impact this would have if the arrival rate remained constant at 3.5 cars per hour.

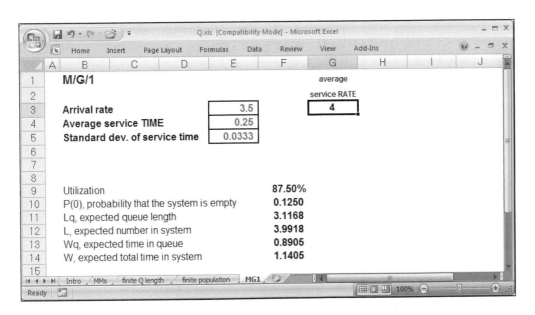

FIGURE 13.17

Results of an M/G/1 model for the original Zippy-Lube problem

FIGURE 13.18

Results of an M/G/1 model for the Zippy-Lube problem after purchasing the automatic oil dispensing machine and assuming an increase in arrivals

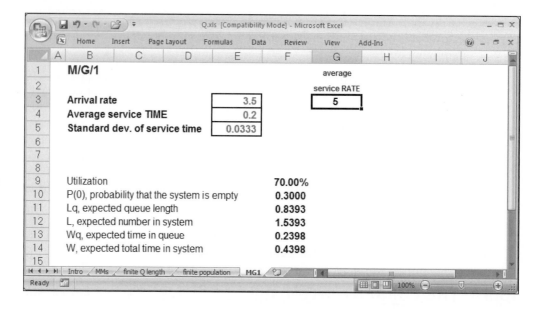

The value in cell F14 indicates that going to the automated oil dispensing device reduces the amount of time a car spends in the system from 1.14 hours to 0.4398 hours (or about 26 minutes). Cell F11 indicates that the expected queue in front of the service bay consists of only 0.8393 cars, on average. Thus, the addition of a new oil dispensing device would improve customer service significantly.

The shorter queue at Zippy-Lube resulting from the acquisition of the automated dispensing device would likely result in an increase in the arrival rate, because customers who previously balked when confronted with a lengthy queue might now consider stopping for service. Thus, Olie might be interested in determining just how much the arrival rate could increase before the average queue length returned to its original level of about 3.12 shown in Figure 13.17. We can use the Goal Seek tool to answer this question. To do this,

1. Click Data, Data Tools.
2. Click the What-If Analysis icon and select Goal Seek.
3. Fill in the Goal Seek dialog box as shown in Figure 13.19.
4. Click OK.

The results of this Goal Seek analysis are shown in Figure 13.20. Here, we see that if the arrival rate increases to 4.37 cars per hour, the average length of the queue will return to approximately 3.12. Thus, by purchasing the automatic oil dispensing machine, it is reasonable to expect that the average number of cars arriving for service at Zippy-Lube might increase from 3.5 per hour to approximately 4.371.

FIGURE 13.19

Goal Seek settings to determine the arrival rate that produces an average queue length of 3.12 cars

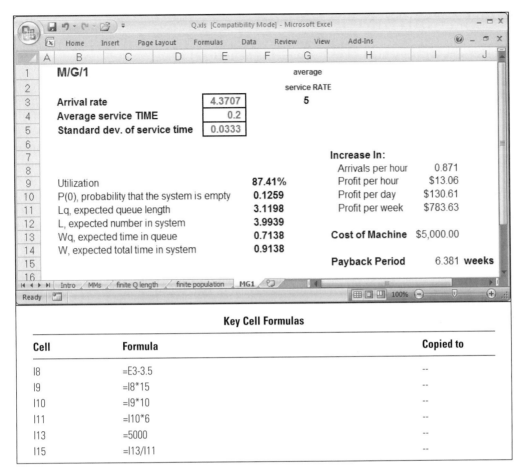

FIGURE 13.20

Results of an M/G/1 model for the Zippy-Lube problem after purchasing the automatic oil dispensing machine and assuming arrival rate will increase

Key Cell Formulas

Cell	Formula	Copied to
I8	=E3-3.5	--
I9	=I8*15	--
I10	=I9*10	--
I11	=I10*6	--
I13	=5000	--
I15	=I13/I11	--

Column I in Figure 13.20 summarizes the financial impact of purchasing the new oil dispensing machine. Because the arrival rate may be expected to increase by approximately 0.871 cars per hour, weekly profits should increase by approximately $783.63 per week. If this increase in profits occurs, the payback period for the new machine will be approximately 6.38 weeks.

13.10 The M/D/1 Model

The M/G/1 model can be used when service times are random with known mean and standard deviation. However, service times might not be random in some queuing systems. For example, in a manufacturing environment, it is not unusual to have a queue of material or subassemblies waiting to be serviced by a certain machine. The machine time required to perform the service might be very predictable—such as exactly 10 seconds of machine time per piece. Similarly, an automatic car wash might spend exactly the same amount of time on each car it services. The M/D/1 model can be used in these types of situations in which the service times are deterministic (not random).

The results for an M/D/1 model can be obtained using the M/G/1 model by setting the standard deviation of the service time to 0 ($\sigma = 0$). Setting $\sigma = 0$ indicates that no variability exists in the service times and, therefore, the service time for each unit is equal to the average service time μ.

13.11 Simulating Queues and the Steady-state Assumption

Queuing theory is one of the oldest and most well-researched areas of management science. Discussions of other types of queuing models can be found in advanced texts on management science and in texts devoted solely to queuing theory. However, keep in mind that the technique of simulation can also be used to analyze virtually any queuing problem you might encounter. Indeed, not all queuing models have closed-form equations to describe their operating characteristics. So, simulation is often the only means available for analyzing complex queuing systems where customers **balk** (don't join a queue upon arrival), **renege** (leave a queue before being served), or **jockey** (switch from one queue to another).

The formulas used in this chapter describe the *steady-state* operations of the various queuing systems presented. At the beginning of each day, most queuing systems start in an "empty and idle" condition and go through a **transient** period as business activity gradually builds up to reach the normal, or **steady-state**, level of operation. The queuing models presented describe only the behavior of the system in its steady-state level of operation. A queuing system can have different levels of steady-state operations at different times throughout the day. For example, a restaurant might have one steady-state level of operation for breakfast, and different steady-state levels at lunch and dinner. So, before using the models in this chapter, it is important to identify the arrival rate and service rate for the specific steady-state level of operation that you want to study. If an analysis of the transient phase is needed or if you want to model the operation of the system across different steady-state levels, you should use simulation.

Figure 13.21 (and the file Fig13-21.xls on your data disk) contains a spreadsheet model that simulates the operation of a single server (M/M/1) queue and plots several graphs associated with different operating characteristics of the system. (If you open

FIGURE 13.21

Graph of the average waiting time in the simulation of a single server queuing system

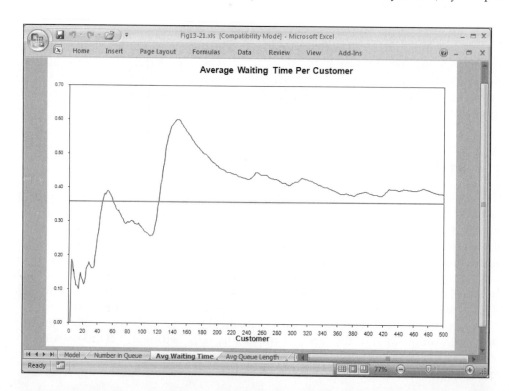

this file, your graph might not match the one in Figure 13.21 because the random numbers used in the simulation will change.) The graph in Figure 13.21 shows a plot of the average waiting time per customer (W_q) for 500 customers. The horizontal line indicates the steady-state value of W_q. Note that several hundred customers are processed in the system in this transient period before the observed average waiting time begins to converge on its steady-state value.

13.12 Summary

Waiting lines, or queues, are a common occurrence in many types of businesses. The study of the operating characteristics of waiting lines is known as queuing theory. Numerous mathematical models are available to represent and study the behavior of different types of queues. These models have different assumptions about the nature of the arrival process to the queuing system, the allowable size and nature of the queuing discipline, and the service process within the system. For many models, closed-form equations have been developed to describe various operating characteristics of the system. When closed-form solutions are not possible, the technique of simulation must be used to analyze the behavior of the system.

13.13 References

Gilliam, R. "An Application of Queueing Theory to Airport Passenger Security Screening." *Interfaces*, vol. 9, 1979.

Gross, D. and C. Harris. *Fundamentals of Queueing Theory*. New York: Wiley, 1985.

Hall, R. *Queueing Methods for Service and Manufacturing*. Englewood Cliffs, NJ: Prentice Hall, 1991.

Kolesar, P. "A Quick and Dirty Response to the Quick and Dirty Crowd: Particularly to Jack Byrd's 'The Value of Queueing Theory'." *Interfaces*, vol. 9, 1979.

Mann, L. "Queue Culture: The Waiting Line as a Social System." *American Journal of Sociology*, vol. 75, 1969.

Quinn, P., et al. "Allocating Telecommunications Resources at LL Bean, Inc." *Interfaces*, vol. 21, 1991.

THE WORLD OF MANAGEMENT SCIENCE

"Wait Watchers" Try to Take Stress Out of Standing in Line

Standing in line—at the bank, the market, the movies—is the time-waster everyone loves to hate. Stand in just one 15-minute line a day, every day, and kiss goodbye to four days of idle time by year's end.

While we've been waiting and grumbling, researchers have been analyzing lines with an eye to making them, if not shorter, at least less stressful.

The field of line analysis—more scientifically known as queuing theory—began in the early 1900s when a Danish telephone engineer devised a mathematical approach to help design phone switches. Researchers found that the principles developed through that system, which helped process calls more efficiently, could be applied to help move people through lines more efficiently.

The concept has spread from the communications and computer industries to other fields, helping modern researchers predict such things as how long customers might wait for a restaurant lunch or how many customers might visit a bank ATM

(Continued)

at noon on Saturday. Now, some researchers have gone beyond a mere mathematical analysis of lines, focusing as well on our psychological reactions.

In one recent study, Richard Larson, a professor of electrical engineering at the Massachusetts Institute of Technology, wanted to determine which of two approaches would be more tolerable to Bank of Boston customers. As Larson's researchers filmed the customers, one group watched an electronic news board while waiting in line; the other group was advised via an electric clock how long the wait would be before each one entered the line. About 300 customers, nearly a third of those filmed, were interviewed after they finished their transactions. The findings, published in the *Sloan Management Review*, an MIT publication circulated to corporate managers, showed that:

- Customers in both lines overestimated their waits by nearly a minute; those who watched the news board overestimated the most. On average, customers thought they had waited 5.1 minutes to see a teller but actually had waited 4.2 minutes.
- Watching the news board did not change customers' perceptions of their waiting time. But it did make the time spent more palatable, customers reported. (After the bank removed the news board, many customers asked that it be reinstalled.)
- The news board also seemed to make customers less fidgety. Without it, they touched their faces and played with their hair. With the news board in view, they stood still with their arms at their sides.
- Customers who were advised of the length of the line via an electronic clock at the entry did not find the experience less stressful than those not told the expected waiting time, much to Larson's surprise. Nor were they more satisfied than the other group with the service. The electronic clock's display of waiting time might backfire, Larson speculates, by making respondents even more aware of time wasted standing in line.
- Customers in the lines with the clock tended to play "beat the clock." They felt they had "won" if they spent less time in line than predicted. The clock also seemed to make more customers balk at joining the line if the predicted delay was lengthy.
- In both lines, customers altered their definition of a "reasonable" wait depending on their time of arrival. They were willing to wait longer during lunch time than during other times of day.

Larson's recent findings bear out a formula published in 1984 by David Maister, a former Harvard Business School faculty member and now a business consultant. When it comes to lines, Maister said, satisfaction is tied to both perception and expectation.

"Nowhere in that [equation] does reality appear," Maister said with a laugh during a telephone interview. Giving a personal example of how perception influences reaction, he said he would wait "40 minutes for a performance by a world-class musician but less than 30 seconds for a hamburger."

Larson, a professional "wait watcher" for 20 years, puts it a bit differently: "When it comes to customer satisfaction, perception is reality."

If those concepts are true, taming customer unrest does not necessarily mean a business must beef up its staff to eliminate lines, Larson and Maister contend. It's much more a matter of "perception management," they say. "People in the service

(Continued)

industries who think they have a line problem may be able to virtually erase customer dissatisfaction and customer complaints not by changing the statistic of the wait but by changing the environment of it," Larson said.

He points to a number of companies already actively wooing waiters. Some companies use a "queue delay guarantee," giving customers free dessert or money if the wait exceeds a preset time period.

Larson predicts customers can expect lines that segment them by personality type. Impatient souls may have the option of paying more to join an automated express line; "people watchers" could opt to wait for less expensive, friendlier human service.

© Kathleen Doheny, a Los Angeles journalist. Reprinted with permission from the *Los Angeles Times*, 7/15/91, vol. 110, p. B3, 14 col. in.

Questions and Problems

1. Consider the three queuing configurations shown in Figure 13.2. For each configuration, describe a situation (besides the examples mentioned in the chapter) in which you have encountered or observed the same type of queuing system.
2. Of the queuing configurations shown in Figure 13.2, which would you prefer to wait in? Explain your response.
3. This chapter implies that customers find waiting in line to be an unpleasant experience. In addition to reducing the length of the wait itself, what other steps could a business take to reduce the frustration that customers experience while waiting? Give specific examples.
4. Describe a situation in which a business might want customers to wait some amount of time before receiving service.
5. The day after a snowstorm, cars arrive at Mel's Auto-Wash at an average rate of 10 per hour according to a Poisson process. The automated car washing process takes exactly 5 minutes from start to finish.
   a. What is the probability that an arriving car will find the car wash empty?
   b. On average, how many cars are waiting for service?
   c. On average, what is the total length of time (from arrival to departure) that cars will spend at the car wash?
6. Tri-Cities Bank has a single drive-in teller window. On Friday mornings, customers arrive at the drive-in window randomly, following a Poisson distribution at an average rate of 30 per hour.
   a. How many customers arrive per minute, on average?
   b. How many customers would you expect to arrive in a 10-minute interval?
   c. Use equation 13.1 to determine the probability of exactly 0, 1, 2, and 3 arrivals in a 10-minute interval. (You can verify your answers using the POISSON( ) function in Excel.)
   d. What is the probability of more than three arrivals occurring in a 10-minute interval?
7. Refer to question 6. Suppose that service at the drive-in window is provided at a rate of 40 customers per hour and follows an exponential distribution.
   a. What is the expected service time per customer?
   b. Use equation 13.2 to determine the probability that a customer's service time is one minute or less. (Verify your answer using the EXPONDIST( ) function in Excel.)

c. Compute the probabilities that the customer's service time is: between two and five minutes, less than four minutes, and more than three minutes.

8. Refer to questions 6 and 7 and answer the following questions:
   a. What is the probability that the drive-in window is empty?
   b. What is the probability that a customer must wait for service?
   c. On average, how many cars wait for service?
   d. On average, what is the total length of time that a customer spends in the system?
   e. On average, what is the total length of time that a customer spends in the queue?
   f. What service rate would be required to reduce the average total time in the system to two minutes? (*Hint:* You can use Solver or simple what-if analysis to answer this question.)

9. On Friday nights, patients arrive at the emergency room at Mercy Hospital at an average rate of seven per hour, which follows a Poisson distribution. Assume that an emergency-room physician can treat an average of three patients per hour, and that the treatment times follow an exponential distribution. The board of directors for Mercy Hospital wants patients arriving at the emergency room to wait no more than five minutes before seeing a doctor.
   a. How many emergency-room doctors should be scheduled on Friday nights to achieve the hospital's objective?

10. Seabreeze Furniture in Orlando maintains a large central warehouse where it stores items until they are sold or needed by the company's many stores in the central Florida area. A four-person crew works at the warehouse to load or unload trucks that arrive at the warehouse at a rate of one per hour (with exponentially distributed interarrival times). The time that it takes the crew to unload each truck follows an exponential distribution with a mean service rate of 4 trucks per hour. Each worker costs the company $21 per hour in wages and benefits. Seabreeze's management is currently trying to cut costs and is considering reducing the number of workers on this warehouse crew. They believe that three workers could provide a service rate of 3 trucks per hour, two workers a service rate of 2 trucks per hour, and one worker a service rate of 1 truck per hour. The company estimates that it costs $35 for each hour a truck spends at the loading dock (whether it is waiting for service or being loaded or unloaded).
    a. Should Seabreeze ever consider having only one worker on the crew? Explain your answer.
    b. For each possible crew size, determine the expected queue length, expected total time in the system, the probability that a customer waits, and the total hourly cost.
    c. What crew size would you recommend?

11. The Madrid Mist outlet store at Chiswell Mills sells discount luggage and does most of its daily business between 6 pm and 9 pm. During this time, customers arrive at the checkout desk at a rate of one every two minutes following a Poisson distribution. The checkout operation takes an average of three minutes per customer and can be approximated well by an exponential distribution. Madrid Mist's corporate policy is that customers should not have to wait longer than one minute to begin the checkout operation.
    a. What is the average service rate per minute?
    b. What is the average arrival rate per minute?
    c. What would happen if the store operated a single checkout station during the time period in question?
    d. How many checkout stations should the store plan to operate during this time period to stay within the corporate policy on checkout operations?

12. Customers checking out at Food Tiger arrive in a single-line queue served by two cashiers at a rate of eight per hour according to a Poisson distribution. Each cashier processes customers at a rate of eight per hour according to an exponential distribution.
    a. If, on average, customers spend 30 minutes shopping before getting in the check-out line, what is the average time a customer spends in the store?
    b. What is the average number of customers waiting for service in the checkout line?
    c. What is the probability that a customer must wait?
    d. What assumption did you make to answer this question?

13. The manager of the Radford Credit Union (RCU) wants to determine how many part-time tellers to employ to cover the peak demand time in its lobby from 11:00 am to 2:00 pm. RCU currently has three full-time tellers that handle the demand during the rest of the day, but during this peak demand time, customers have been complaining that the wait time for service is too long. The manager at RCU has determined that customers arrive according to a Poisson distribution with an average of 60 arrivals per hour during the peak period. Each teller services customers at a rate of 24 per hour, with service times following an exponential distribution.
    a. On average, how long must customers wait in line before service begins?
    b. Once service begins for a customer, how long does it take to complete the transaction, on average?
    c. If one part-time teller is hired to work during the peak time period, what effect would this have on the average amount of time a customer spends waiting in the queue?
    d. If one part-time teller is hired to work during the peak time period, what effect would this have on the average amount of time it takes to serve a customer?

14. The Westland Title Insurance Company leases one copying machine for $45 per day that is used by all individuals at its office. An average of five persons per hour arrive to use this machine, with each person using it for an average of eight minutes. Assume that the interarrival times and copying times are exponentially distributed.
    a. What is the probability that a person arriving to use the machine will find it idle?
    b. On average, how long will a person have to wait before getting to use the machine?
    c. On average, how many people will be using or waiting to use the copy machine?
    d. Suppose that the people who use the copy machine are paid an average of $9 per hour. On average, how much does the company spend in wages during each eight-hour day paying the people who are using or waiting to use the copy machine?
    e. If the company can lease another copying machine for $45 per day, should they do it?

15. The Orange Blossom Marathon takes place in Orlando, Florida, each December. The organizers of this race are trying to solve a problem that occurs at the finish line each year. Thousands of runners take part in this race. The fastest runners finish the 26-mile course in just over two hours, but the majority of the runners finish about 1 1/2 hours later. After runners enter the finish area, they go through one of four finish chutes where their times and places are recorded. (Each chute has its own queue.) During the time in which the majority of the runners finish the race, the chutes become backlogged and significant delays occur. The race organizers want to determine how many chutes should be added to eliminate this problem. At the time in question, runners arrive at the finish area at a rate of 50 per minute according to a Poisson distribution, and they randomly select one of the four chutes. The time

required to record the necessary information for each finishing runner at any chute is an exponentially distributed random variable with a mean of four seconds.

   a. On average, how many runners arrive at each chute per minute?

   b. Under the current arrangement with four chutes, what is the expected length of the queue at each chute?

   c. Under the current arrangement, what is the average length of time a runner waits before being processed?

   d. How many chutes should be added if the race organizers want to reduce the queue time at each chute to an average of five seconds?

16. State University allows students and faculty to access its mainframe computer by modem. The university has 15 modem connections that can be used. When all of the modem connections are in use, the phone system can keep up to 10 callers on hold waiting for a modem connection to become available. If all 15 modem connections are in use and 10 calls are already holding, a new caller receives a busy signal. Calls to the modem pool follow a Poisson distribution and occur at an average rate of 60 per hour. The length of each session with the mainframe is an exponential random variable with a mean of 15 minutes—therefore, each modem services an average of four callers per hour.

   a. On average, how many callers are on hold waiting for a modem connection?

   b. On average, how long is a caller kept on hold before receiving a modem connection?

   c. What is the probability that a caller receives a busy signal?

   d. How many modem connections would the university need to add to its modem pool for there to be no more than a 1% chance of a caller receiving a busy signal?

17. During tax season, the IRS hires seasonal workers to help answer the questions of taxpayers who call a special 800 telephone number for tax information. Suppose that calls to this line occur at a rate of 60 per hour and follow a Poisson distribution. The IRS workers manning the phone lines can answer an average of five calls per hour with the actual service times following an exponential distribution. Assume that 10 IRS workers are available and, when they are all busy, the phone system can keep five additional callers on hold.

   a. What is the probability that a caller receives a busy signal?

   b. What is the probability that a caller is put on hold before receiving service?

   c. On average, how long must a caller wait before speaking with an IRS agent?

   d. How many additional workers would be required if the IRS wants no more than a 5% chance of a caller receiving a busy signal?

18. Road Rambler sells specialty running shoes and apparel through catalogs and the Web. Customers can phone in orders at any time day or night, seven days a week. During the 4 am to 8 am shift, a single sales rep handles all calls. During this time, calls arrive at a rate of 14 per hour following a Poisson distribution. It takes the sales rep an average of four minutes to process each call. The variability in service times is approximately exponentially distributed. All calls received while the sales rep is busy are placed in a queue.

   a. On average, how long (in minutes) must callers wait before talking to the sales rep?

   b. On average, how many customers are on hold?

   c. What is the probability that the customer will be placed on hold?

   d. What is the sales rep's utilization rate?

   e. Suppose Road Rambler wants there to be no more than a 10% chance that a customer will be placed on hold. How many sales reps should the company employ?

19. Refer to the previous question. Suppose that Road Rambler's phone system can keep only four calls on hold at any time, the average profit margin of each call is $55, and that sales reps cost the company $12 per hour.
    a. If callers who receive a busy signal take their business elsewhere, how much money is the company losing per hour (on average) if they employ a single sales rep?
    b. What is the net effect on average hourly profits if the company employs two sales reps instead of one?
    c. What is the net effect on average hourly profits if the company employs three sales reps instead of one?
    d. How many sales reps should the company employ if it wants to maximize profit?
20. Several hundred personal computers (PCs) are in use at the corporate headquarters for National Insurance Corporation. The pattern of breakdowns for these PCs follows a Poisson distribution with an average rate of 4.5 breakdowns per five-day work week. The company has a repair technician on staff to repair the PCs. The average time required to repair a PC varies somewhat, but takes an average of one day with a standard deviation of 0.5 days.
    a. What is the average service time in terms of a five-day work week?
    b. What is the standard deviation of the service times in terms of a five-day work week?
    c. On average, how many PCs are either being repaired or waiting to be repaired?
    d. On average, how much time transpires from the time a PC breaks down to the time it is repaired?
    e. Suppose that National Insurance estimates it loses $40 a day in productivity and efficiency for each PC that is out of service. How much should the company be willing to pay to increase service capacity to the point where an average of seven PCs a week could be repaired?
21. Interstate 81 through southwest Virginia is heavily traveled by long-distance truckers. To cut down on accidents, The Virginia State Patrol carries out random inspections of a truck's weight and the condition of its brakes. On Fridays, trucks approach the inspection station at a rate of one every 45 seconds following a Poisson process. The time required to check a truck's weight and brakes follows an exponential distribution with an average inspection time of 5 minutes. The state troopers only pull over trucks when at least one of their three portable inspection units is available.
    a. What is the probability that all three inspection units will be idle at the same time?
    b. What proportion of trucks traveling this section of Interstate 81 will be inspected?
    c. On average, how many trucks will be pulled over for inspection each hour?
22. The drive-thru window at Hokie Burger requires 2.5 minutes on average to process an order with a standard deviation of 3 minutes. Cars arrive at the window at a rate of 20 per hour.
    a. On average, how many cars are waiting to be served?
    b. On average, how long will a car spend in the service process?
    c. Suppose Hokie Burger can install an automated drink-dispensing device that would reduce the standard deviation of the service time to 1 minute. How would your answers to the previous questions change?
23. A manufacturer of engine belts uses multipurpose manufacturing equipment to produce a variety of products. A technician is employed to perform the setup operations needed to change the machines over from one product to the next. The amount of

time required to set up the machines is a random variable that follows an exponential distribution with a mean of 20 minutes. The number of machines requiring a new setup is a Poisson random variable with an average of two machines per hour requiring setup. The technician is responsible for setups on five machines.

a. What percentage of time is the technician idle, or not involved in setting up a machine?

b. What should the technician do during this idle time?

c. On average, how long is a machine out of operation while waiting for the next setup to be completed?

d. If the company hires another equally capable technician to perform setups on these machines, how long on average would a machine be out of operation while waiting for the next setup to be completed?

24. DeColores Paint Company owns ten trucks that it uses to deliver paint and decorating supplies to builders. On average, each truck returns to the company's single loading dock at a rate of three times per eight-hour day (or at a rate of $3/8 = 0.375$ times per hour). The times between arrivals at the dock follow an exponential distribution. The loading dock can service an average of four trucks per hour with actual service times following an exponential distribution.

a. What is the probability that a truck must wait for service to begin?

b. On average, how many trucks wait for service to begin at any point in time?

c. On average, how long must a truck wait before service begins?

d. If the company builds and staffs another loading dock, how would your answers to parts a, b, and c change?

e. The capitalized cost of adding a loading dock is $5.40 per hour. The hourly cost of having a truck idle is $50. What is the optimal number of loading docks that will minimize the sum of dock cost and idle truck cost?

25. Suppose that arrivals to a queuing system with one server follow a Poisson distribution with an average of $\lambda = 5$ per time period, and that service times follow an exponential distribution with an average service rate of $\mu = 6$ per time period.

a. Compute the operating characteristics for this system using the M/M/s model with $s = 1$.

b. Compute the operating characteristics for this system using the M/G/1 model. (Note that the average service time for the exponential random variable is $1/\mu$ and the standard deviation of the service time is also $1/\mu$.)

c. Compare the results obtained from the M/M/1 and M/G/1 models. (They should be the same.) Explain why they are the same.

26. Calls arrive at a rate of 150 per hour to the 800 number for the Land's Beginning mail-order catalog company. The company currently employs 20 operators who are paid $10 per hour in wages and benefits and can each handle an average of six calls per hour. Assume that interarrival times and service times follow the exponential distribution. A maximum of 20 calls can be placed on hold when all the operators are busy. The company estimates that it costs $25 in lost sales whenever a customer calls and receives a busy signal.

a. On average, how many customers are waiting on hold at any point in time?

b. What is the probability that a customer will receive a busy signal?

c. If the number of operators plus the number of calls placed on hold cannot exceed 40, how many operators should the company employ?

d. If the company implements your answer to part c, on average, how many customers will be waiting on hold at any point in time and what is the probability that a customer will receive a busy signal?

May the (Police) Force be with You

"I hope this goes better than last time," thought Craig Rooney as he thought about having to walk into the city council's chambers next week. Craig is the assistant chief of police in Newport, VA, and, each September he has to provide the city council with a report on the effectiveness of the city's police force. This report immediately precedes the council's discussion of the police department's budget. So Craig often feels like a tightrope artist trying to find the right balance in his presentation to both convince the council that the department is being run well and also persuade them to increase the department's budget for new officers.

The city of Newport has a total of 19 police officers assigned to five precincts. Currently, precinct A has three officers assigned to it while the others each have four officers. One of the town council's primary concerns each year is the amount of time it takes for an officer to begin responding when a 911 emergency call is received. Unfortunately, the city's information system does not track this data exactly, but it does keep track of the number of calls received in each precinct each hour and the amount of time that elapses between when officers first begin responding to call and the time they report being available again to respond to other calls (this is also known as the service time for each call).

A student intern from a local university worked for Craig last summer and collected data shown in the file named CallData.xls found on your data disk. One of the sheets in this workbook (named calls per hour) shows the number of 911 calls received during 500 randomly chosen hours of operation in each precinct. Another sheet (named service times) shows the services time required for each of these calls.

The student intern also set up a worksheet (based on the formulas in Figure 13.6) to calculate operating characteristics of an M/M/s queue for each of the Newport's five precincts. Unfortunately, the student intern had to return to school before finishing this project. But Craig believes that with a little work he can use the data collected to figure out appropriate arrival and service rates for each precinct and complete the analysis. More importantly, he feels sure the queuing model will allow him to quickly answer many of the questions he expects the city council to ask.

a. What are the arrival rate of 911 calls and the service rates for each precinct?
b. Does the arrival rate of calls for each precinct appear to follow a Poisson distribution?
c. Does the service rate for each precinct appear to follow an exponential distribution?
d. Using an M/M/s queue, on average, how many minutes must a 911 caller in each precinct wait before a police officer begins responding?
e. Suppose Craig wants to redistribute officers among precincts so as to reduce the maximum amount of time callers in any one precinct have to wait for a police response. What should he do and what effect would this have?
f. How many additional police officers would Newport have to hire for the average response time in each precinct to be less than two minutes?

Call Center Staffing at Vacations Inc.

Vacations Inc. (VI) markets time-share condominiums throughout North America. One way the company generates sales leads is by offering a chance to win a free mini-vacation to anyone who fills out an information card and places it in boxes that VI has distributed at various restaurants and shopping malls. All those who fill out the card and indicate an adequate income level subsequently receive a letter from VI indicating that they have indeed won the mini-vacation. To claim their prize, all the "winner" needs to do is call VI's toll free number. When the "winner" calls the number, they learn that their mini-vacation consists of a free dinner, entertainment, and two-night stay at one of VI's time-share properties; but they must agree to sit through a two hour property tour and sales presentation.

About half the people who call VI's toll free number to claim their prize wind up rejecting the offer after they learn about the two hour property tour. About 40% of those who call accept the mini-vacation and do the property tour but don't buy anything. The remaining 10% of those who call the toll free number accept the mini-vacation and ultimately purchase a time-share. Each mini-vacation that VI awards costs the company about $250. Each sale of a time-share generates a net profit of $7,000 for VI after all commissions and other costs (including the $250 for the buyer's mini-vacation) have been paid.

VI's call center operates from 10 am to 10 pm daily with four sales representatives and receives calls at a rate of 50 per hour following a Poisson distribution. It takes an average of 4 minutes to handle each call with actual times being exponentially distributed. The phone system VI uses can keep up to 10 callers on hold at any time. Assume those who receive a busy signal don't call back.

a. On average, how many customers per hour does each sales person process?
b. What is the expected value of each call to VI's toll free line?
c. Suppose VI pays it phone reps $12 per hour. How many phone reps should it employ if it wants to maximize profit?

CASE 13.3   Bullseye Department Store

Bullseye Department store is a discount retailer of general merchandise in the Southeastern United States. The company owns more than 50 stores in Florida, Georgia, South Carolina, and Tennessee that are serviced by the company's main warehouse near Statesboro, GA. Most of the merchandise received at the warehouse arrives in trucks from ports in Jacksonville, FL and Savannah, GA.

Trucks arrive at the warehouse following a Poisson process with a rate of once every seven minutes. Eight loading docks are available at the warehouse. A single worker mans each dock and can unload a truck in approximately 30 minutes on average. When all the docks are occupied, arriving trucks wait in a queue until one becomes available.

Bullseye has received complaints from some of the trucking firms that deliveries are taking too long at the warehouse. In response, Bullseye is considering several options to try to reduce the time that trucks must spend at the warehouse. One option is to hire an extra worker for each of the loading docks. This is expected to reduce the average time it takes to unload a truck to 18 minutes. It costs approximately $17 per hour in salary and fringe benefits to employ each additional worker.

Alternatively, the company can continue to use a single worker at each loading dock but upgrade the forklift equipment that workers use to unload trucks. The company can replace the existing forklift equipment with a new model that can be leased for $6 per hour and is expected to reduce the average time required to unload a truck to 23 minutes.

Finally, the company can build two new loading docks for a capitalized cost of $6 per hour and hire two additional workers at a rate of $17 per hour to man these locations. Bullseye estimates it costs $60 in goodwill for each hour a truck spends at the warehouse. Which, if any, of the three alternatives would you recommend that Bullseye implement?

Chapter 14

Project Management

14.0 Introduction

At some point, almost every manager assumes responsibility for the completion of some type of project. The project might be relatively simple—such as planning a company picnic or producing an employee newsletter—or it might be more complex—such as planning the launch of a space shuttle, designing and implementing a large computer information system, or constructing a multistory office building. Successfully completing a project of any size requires a thorough analysis of the physical and logical interdependencies among the tasks involved, and accurate estimates of the time and resources required to accomplish these tasks. Keeping track of all these details for even a relatively small project can be overwhelming.

This chapter presents two techniques that were developed to help managers plan, organize, and control projects: the **Critical Path Method** (CPM) and the **Program Evaluation and Review Technique** (PERT). Both techniques were developed concurrently but independently during the 1950s. CPM was developed by representatives of DuPont and Sperry-Rand to assist in the management of industrial projects in which the time required to perform each activity in the project could be estimated with a high degree of accuracy. The focus of CPM is to determine when a project should be completed and to schedule when each activity in the project must begin, to keep the project on schedule. PERT was developed jointly by representatives of the U.S. Navy, Lockheed, and the consulting firm of Booz, Allen and Hamilton working on the Polaris submarine. Because many of the tasks required in the development of the Polaris had never been done before, the time required to complete the tasks was uncertain. Thus, PERT was designed for projects in which the time required to perform each activity is essentially a random variable. PERT focuses on estimating the probability of completing a project by a given deadline.

Over the years, the two techniques have blended together, so that most practitioners today refer to them collectively as PERT/CPM or CPM/PERT. The fact that these techniques have stood the test of time and are still widely used is a tribute to their usefulness and simplicity. Indeed, the basic ideas behind PERT/CPM provide the underpinnings for a number of project management software tools. In this chapter, we explore some of the fundamental concepts of CPM and PERT using a spreadsheet. Then we will see how many of these concepts and techniques are implemented in Microsoft Project (see http://www.microsoft.com/office/project).

14.1 An Example

One of the key ideas in both CPM and PERT is that any project can be broken down into component activities that require different amounts of time and that must be accomplished in a specific order. The major difference between CPM and PERT involves how

FIGURE 14.1

Activities for the Lightner Construction home-building project

Activity	Description	Time Required (in days)	Immediate Predecessor Activity
A	Excavate	3	—
B	Lay foundation	4	A
C	Rough plumbing	3	B
D	Frame	10	B
E	Finish exterior	8	D
F	Install HVAC	4	D
G	Rough electric	6	D
H	Sheetrock	8	C, E, F, G
I	Install cabinets	5	H
J	Paint	5	H
K	Final plumbing	4	I
L	Final electric	2	J
M	Install flooring	4	K, L

the time element of the activities is determined. However, both CPM and PERT require a detailed network of the project that clearly indicates each of the main activities in the project and their precedence relationships. The following example illustrates how to create such a project network.

> Tom Lightner is the owner of Lightner Construction, a general contracting company that specializes in the construction of single-family residences and small office buildings. Tom frequently has numerous construction projects going on at the same time and needs a formal procedure for planning, monitoring, and controlling each project. He is aware of various project scheduling techniques but has never used them. He wants to see how he might apply such techniques to one of the home-building projects he will be undertaking in the near future. Tom has identified each of the major activities required for this project and has estimated how much time each activity will require. Figure 14.1 summarizes this information along with the precedence relationships among the activities.

14.2 Creating the Project Network

The activities in a project can be represented as a network in one of two ways. As noted in Chapter 5, a network is a set of nodes that are connected in various ways by directed arcs. Thus, if we let the nodes in a network represent the activities in a project, we are employing the **Activity-On-Node** (AON) network design. Figure 14.2 shows this type of network for our example problem.

The nodes in the network shown in Figure 14.2 correspond to each project activity in Figure 14.1. The arcs in this network indicate the precedence relationships between the activities (or nodes). For example, Figure 14.2 shows that we cannot start laying the foundation (activity B) until the excavation (activity A) is complete. Similarly, the arcs leading into node H indicate that the sheetrock cannot be installed until the activities represented by nodes C, E, F, and G are *all* complete.

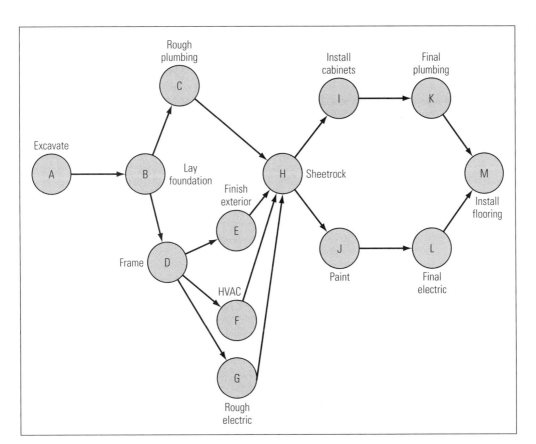

FIGURE 14.2

Activity-On-Node (AON) representation of the home-building project

In this type of network, activity A is called the **immediate predecessor** of activity B, and activities C and D are called the **immediate successors** of activity B. Throughout this chapter, we use the shortened terms **predecessor** and **successor** to mean immediate predecessor and immediate successor.

The second way to represent a project as a network is the **Activity-On-Arc** (AOA) design, in which the arcs represent the project's activities. Figure 14.3 shows an AOA network for our example problem.

The nodes in an AOA network represent the start and finish points (or milestones) for each activity. For example, in Figure 14.3, activity A starts at node 1 and ends at node 2. Activity B starts at node 2 and ends at node 3, and so on. Unfortunately, an AOA representation often produces a more complicated network when multiple activities start and end at common nodes. For example, because activity H (which begins at node 8) cannot begin until activities C, E, F, and G are complete, we might be inclined to draw the arcs for activities E, F, and G as starting at node 4 and finishing at node 8 (eliminating nodes 5, 6, and 7). However, an AOA network does not allow multiple arcs with common start and finish nodes. To get around this problem, we must include the "phantom" activities indicated by the dashed lines connecting nodes 5, 6, and 7 to node 8. AOA networks are mentioned here so that you will be aware of their existence (and shortcomings). In this chapter, we use only the AON network representation, which many believe to be superior.

FIGURE 14.3

Activity-On-Arc (AOA) representation of the home-building project

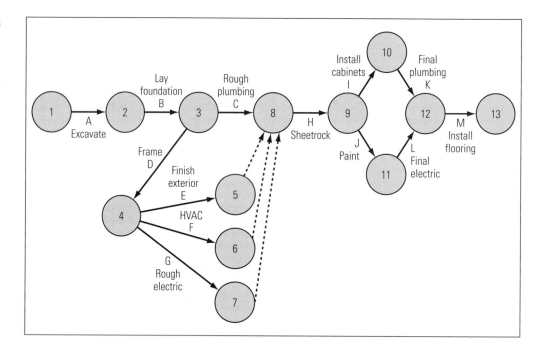

14.2.1 A NOTE ON START AND FINISH POINTS

The techniques discussed in this chapter require that all projects have one unique start activity and one unique finish activity. This requirement is met by our example project shown in Figure 14.2 in which activity A is the unique start point and activity M is the unique finish point. However, some projects involve multiple start and/or finish activities, as illustrated in Figure 14.4.

FIGURE 14.4

Using artificial start and finish activities to produce a network with unique start and finish points

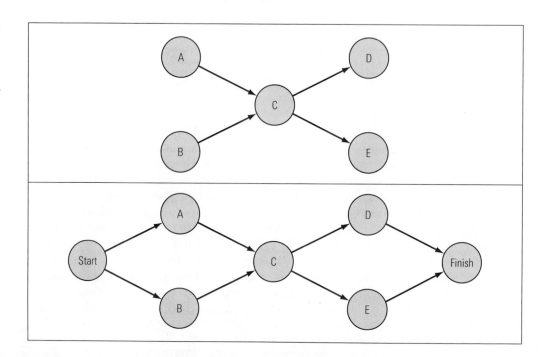

The first network shown in Figure 14.4 represents a project with five activities: A, B, C, D, and E. However, this project does not have a unique start or finish activity. In such cases, it is necessary to create artificial start and/or finish activities, as shown by the second network in Figure 14.4. Here, we created an artificial start activity that precedes activities A and B. Similarly, we inserted an artificial finish activity that follows the completion of activities D and E. These activities are artificial because they require no time to complete and merely serve to give a project a unique start and finish point. Thus, by using artificial start and finish activities, we can ensure that the network for any project has a unique start and finish point.

14.3 CPM: An Overview

After creating a network representation of a project, the next step in the CPM technique is to determine the earliest time that each activity in the network can start and finish. We determine these times by making what is called a **forward pass** through the network. Ultimately, this analysis determines the earliest time that the project itself can be completed. Next, we make a **backward pass** through the network to determine the latest time that each activity can start and finish without delaying the completion of the project.

One of the primary goals in CPM is to determine the critical path through the network. Figure 14.2 shows several paths that could be followed from the initial activity (node A) to the final activity (node M). For example, one path is given by the following set of activities: A→B→C→H→I→K→M. Another path through the network is given by: A→B→D→F→H→J→L→M. Figure 14.2 shows a total of eight paths through the network, each representing a set of activities that must be completed before the project is complete. Therefore, the earliest time that the project can be completed is the time required to complete the set of activities along the *longest* path through the network. The **critical path** is the longest path through a project network.

Any delays in the start or finish times of the activities on the critical path (also known as **critical activities**) delay the completion of the project. A project manager always should identify the critical activities in a project to focus attention on these activities and to avoid delays on these activities when possible.

In conducting the forward pass through the network, we will use the activity times to determine the earliest possible start time and the earliest possible finish time for each activity. The following notations represent these quantities:

$$t_i = \text{amount of time required to perform activity } i$$
$$\text{EST}_i = \text{earliest start time for activity } i$$
$$\text{EFT}_i = \text{earliest finish time for activity } i$$

During the backward pass, we will determine the latest time that each activity can be started and finished without delaying the project. These quantities are represented as:

$$\text{LST}_i = \text{latest start time for activity } i$$
$$\text{LFT}_i = \text{latest finish time for activity } i$$

We will record all the information about each project activity on the corresponding network node in the format shown in Figure 14.5.

FIGURE 14.5

Information recorded on the node for each project activity

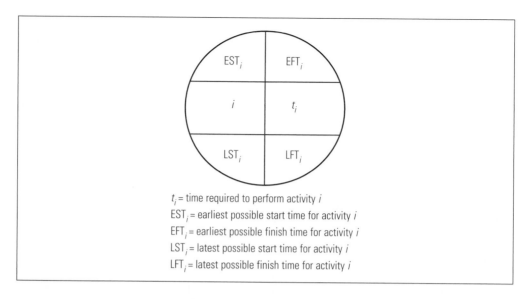

t_i = time required to perform activity i
EST_i = earliest possible start time for activity i
EFT_i = earliest possible finish time for activity i
LST_i = latest possible start time for activity i
LFT_i = latest possible finish time for activity i

14.4 The Forward Pass

The first step in the CPM technique (after constructing the project network) is to determine the earliest time at which each activity in the network can start and finish. The term **time zero** identifies the time period at which the first project activity begins—just as the time on a stopwatch starts from zero. Thus, in our example problem, the earliest time at which activity A (excavation) can begin is time zero, or $EST_A = 0$.

In general, the earliest time at which an activity can finish is the earliest time at which it can start plus the expected time required to perform the activity. That is, for any activity i:

$$EFT_i = EST_i + t_i$$

For activity A, $EFT_A = EST_A + t_A = 0 + 3 = 3$. The project network in Figure 14.6 shows the earliest start and finish times for activity A.

Now consider activity B. Because activity A must be completed before activity B can begin, the earliest start time for activity B equals the earliest finish time for activity A. That is, $EST_B = EFT_A = 3$. Activity B is expected to take four units of time; therefore, its earliest finish time is $EFT_B = EST_B + t_B = 3 + 4 = 7$.

Now consider activity C. Because activity B must be completed before activity C can begin, the earliest start time for activity C equals the earliest finish time for activity B. That is, $EST_C = EFT_B = 7$. Activity C is expected to take three units of time; therefore, its earliest finish time is $EFT_C = EST_C + t_C = 7 + 3 = 10$.

As you can see from these examples, calculating the earliest start and finish times for activities with a single predecessor activity is a simple process. We could apply this same logic to determine the earliest start and finish times for activities D, E, F, and G shown in Figure 14.6. You should verify the calculations for these activities on your own to make sure that you understand the process. Figure 14.7 provides details of all the forward pass calculations for this example.

Notice that the calculation of the earliest start time for activity H differs from the previous activities because it has *multiple* predecessors rather than a single predecessor. Activity H cannot begin until activities C, E, F, and G are *all* completed. Thus, if we consider the earliest finish times of activities C, E, F, and G, the latest of these times determines the earliest time at which activity H can start:

$$EST_H = MAX(EFT_C, EFT_E, EFT_F, EFT_G) = MAX(10, 25, 21, 23) = 25$$

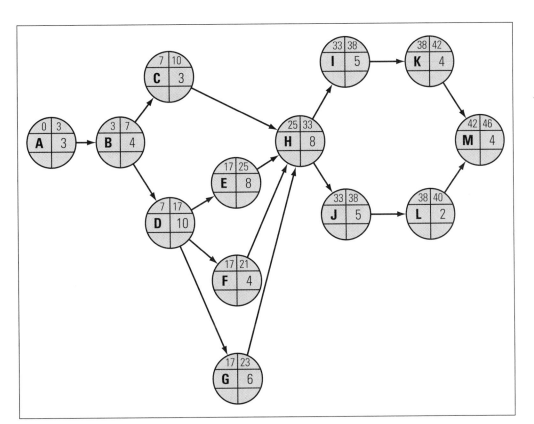

FIGURE 14.6

Results of forward pass calculation of earliest start and finish times

Earliest Start Times	Earliest Finish Times
$EST_A = 0$	$EFT_A = EST_A + t_A = 0 + 3 = 3$
$EST_B = EFT_A = 3$	$EFT_B = EST_B + t_B = 3 + 4 = 7$
$EST_C = EFT_B = 7$	$EFT_C = EST_C + t_C = 7 + 3 = 10$
$EST_D = EFT_B = 7$	$EFT_D = EST_D + t_D = 7 + 10 = 17$
$EST_E = EFT_D = 17$	$EFT_E = EST_E + t_E = 17 + 8 = 25$
$EST_F = EFT_D = 17$	$EFT_F = EST_F + t_F = 17 + 4 = 21$
$EST_G = EFT_D = 17$	$EFT_G = EST_G + t_G = 17 + 6 = 23$
$EST_H = MAX(EFT_C, EFT_E, EFT_F, EFT_G)$	$EFT_H = EST_H + t_H = 25 + 8 = 33$
$= MAX(10, 25, 21, 23) = 25$	
$EST_I = EFT_H = 33$	$EFT_I = EST_I + t_I = 33 + 5 = 38$
$EST_J = EFT_H = 33$	$EFT_J = EST_J + t_J = 33 + 5 = 38$
$EST_K = EFT_I = 38$	$EFT_K = EST_K + t_K = 38 + 4 = 42$
$EST_L = EFT_J = 38$	$EFT_L = EST_L + t_L = 38 + 2 = 40$
$EST_M = MAX(EFT_K, EFT_L)$	$EFT_M = EST_M + t_M = 42 + 4 = 46$
$= MAX(42, 40) = 42$	

FIGURE 14.7

Summary of forward pass calculations

The earliest start time of an activity is equal to the latest (or maximum) early finish time of the activities directly preceding it. This is true regardless of the number of predecessors an activity has.

The earliest start and finish times for the remaining activities are calculated using this same logic. Notice that the earliest start times for nodes I, J, K, and L are the earliest finish times of their respective predecessor activities. Because activity M has multiple predecessor activities, its earliest start time is the maximum of the earliest finish times of activities K and L.

Key Points: The Forward Pass

- The earliest start time for the initial activity in a project is time zero.
- The earliest start time of an activity is equal to the latest (or maximum) early finish time of the activities directly preceding it.
- The earliest finish time of an activity is equal to its earliest start time plus the time required to perform the activity.

At the end of our forward pass, we have determined the earliest possible start and finish times of each activity in the network. Note that the last activity in the project, activity M, can be completed no earlier than 46 time units (in this case, days) from the beginning of the project. Thus, the earliest the project can be completed is 46 days.

14.5 The Backward Pass

After completing the forward pass, the next step in the CPM technique is to make a **backward pass** to determine the *latest* times at which the project activities can start and finish without delaying the project. This process identifies those activities that *must* start and finish at their earliest possible times to complete the project in the minimum possible time identified by the forward pass. These activities constitute the critical path through the network.

The logic behind the backward pass is similar to that of the forward pass. Here, however, we start at the final activity in the network and work backwards through the network to determine the latest time at which each activity could be finished without delaying the project. Consider activity M. If the project can be completed within 46 days, the latest finish time for activity M is 46, or $LFT_M = 46$.

In general, the latest time at which an activity can start without delaying a project is the latest time by which it must be finished minus the time required to perform the activity. That is, for any activity i:

$$LST_i = LFT_i - t_i$$

For activity M, $LST_M = LFT_M - t_M = 46 - 4 = 42$. Figure 14.8 shows the latest start and finish times for activity M.

Now, let's consider activity L. Because activity L must be completed before activity M can begin, and activity M must begin no later than time period 42, activity L must be finished no later than time period 42. That is, $LFT_L = LST_M = 42$. Activity L is scheduled to take two units of time; therefore, the latest time at which this activity could start without delaying the project is $LST_L = LFT_L - t_L = 42 - 2 = 40$.

As another example, consider activity J. Because activity J must be completed before activity L can begin, and activity L must begin no later than time period 40, activity J must be finished no later than time period 40. That is, $LFT_J = LST_L = 40$. Activity J is scheduled to take five units of time; therefore, the latest time at which this activity could start without delaying the project is $LST_J = LFT_J - t_J = 40 - 5 = 35$.

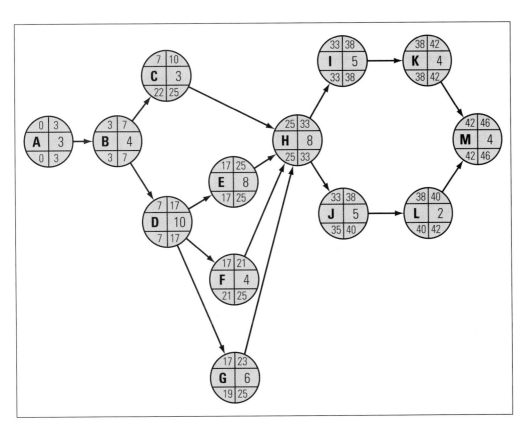

FIGURE 14.8

Results of backward pass calculation of latest start and finish times

Calculating the latest start and finish times for activities with a single successor activity is a simple process. We could apply this same logic to determine the earliest start and finish times for activities I and K, as shown in Figure 14.8. Again, you should verify the calculations for these activities on your own to make sure that you understand the process. Figure 14.9 provides the details of the backward pass calculations for this example.

Notice that the calculation of the latest finish time for activity H differs from the previous activities because it has *multiple* successors rather than a single successor. Activity H must be finished in time for activities I and J to begin by their latest start times. Thus, if we consider the latest start times for activities I and J, the earliest of these times determines the latest time by which activity H must be finished:

$$\text{LFT}_H = \text{MIN}(\text{LST}_I, \text{LST}_J) = \text{MIN}(33, 35) = 33$$

The latest finish time of an activity is equal to the earliest (or minimum) late start time of the activities directly following (or succeeding) it. This is true regardless of the number of successors an activity has.

The latest start and finish times for the remaining activities are calculated using this same logic. Notice that the latest finish times for nodes C, E, F, and G are the latest start times of their successor activities. Because activity D has multiple successor activities, its latest finish time is the minimum of the latest start times of activities E, F, and G. Similarly, because activity B has multiple successor activities, its latest finish time is the minimum of the latest start times of activities C and D. Finally, the latest finish time for activity A is the latest start time for activity B ($\text{LFT}_A = \text{LST}_B = 3$), and the latest start time for activity A is then determined by $\text{LST}_A = \text{LFT}_A - t_A = 0$.

FIGURE 14.9

Summary of backward pass calculations

Latest Finish Times	Latest Start Times
$LFT_M = EFT_M = 46$	$LST_M = LFT_M - t_M = 46 - 4 = 42$
$LFT_L = LST_M = 42$	$LST_L = LFT_L - t_L = 42 - 2 = 40$
$LFT_K = LST_M = 42$	$LST_K = LFT_K - t_K = 42 - 4 = 38$
$LFT_J = LST_L = 40$	$LST_J = LFT_J - t_J = 40 - 5 = 35$
$LFT_I = LST_K = 38$	$LST_I = LFT_I - t_I = 38 - 5 = 33$
$LFT_H = MIN(LST_I, LST_J)$	$LST_H = LFT_H - t_H = 33 - 8 = 25$
$\quad = MIN(33, 35) = 33$	
$LFT_G = LST_H = 25$	$LST_G = LFT_G - t_G = 25 - 6 = 19$
$LFT_F = LST_H = 25$	$LST_F = LFT_F - t_F = 25 - 4 = 21$
$LFT_E = LST_H = 25$	$LST_E = LFT_E - t_E = 25 - 8 = 17$
$LFT_D = MIN(LST_E, LST_F, LST_G)$	$LST_D = LFT_D - t_D = 17 - 10 = 7$
$\quad = MIN(17, 21, 19) = 17$	
$LFT_C = LST_H = 25$	$LST_C = LFT_C - t_C = 25 - 3 = 22$
$LFT_B = MIN(LST_C, LST_D)$	$LST_B = LFT_B - t_B = 7 - 4 = 3$
$\quad = MIN(22, 7) = 7$	
$LFT_A = LST_B = 3$	$LST_A = LFT_A - t_A = 3 - 3 = 0$

Key Points: The Backward Pass

- The latest finish time for the final activity in a project is equal to its earliest finish time as determined by the forward pass.
- The latest finish time for any other activity is equal to the earliest (or minimum) late start time of the activities directly following (or succeeding) it.
- The latest start time of an activity is equal to its latest finish time minus the time required to perform the activity.

14.6 Determining the Critical Path

As mentioned earlier, one of the key objectives of CPM is to determine the critical path through a project network. The critical path consists of the set of activities that, if delayed in any way, would cause a delay in the completion of the entire project. The activities on the critical path can be identified easily from the results of the forward pass and backward pass. Specifically, the activities whose latest start times equal their earliest start times make up the critical path (or, equivalently, whose latest finish times equal their earliest finish times). As shown by the heavier arcs in Figure 14.10, the critical path of activities in our example problem is:

$$A \rightarrow B \rightarrow D \rightarrow E \rightarrow H \rightarrow I \rightarrow K \rightarrow M.$$

If any of the activities in this path do not start by their earliest start time, the overall time required to complete the project will increase—unless management intervenes in some way. (Note that it is possible for an activity network to have more than one critical path, although this is not illustrated in our example.)

The noncritical activities in a project are distinguished by the presence of slack. **Slack** is the amount of time by which the start of an activity can be delayed without delaying

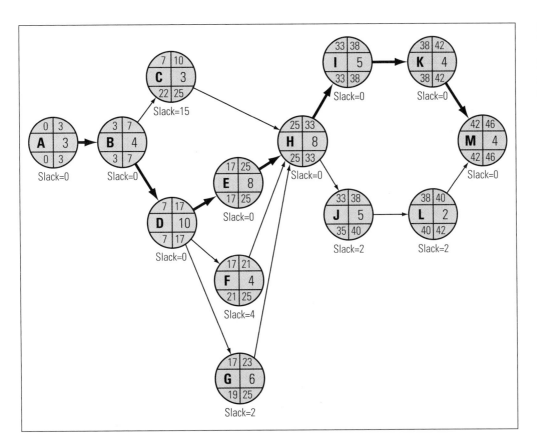

FIGURE 14.10

The critical path and slack conditions

the project. Critical activities have zero slack and noncritical activities have slack values that are strictly positive. The amount of slack for any activity i is defined as:

$$\text{Slack for activity } i = \text{LST}_i - \text{EST}_i$$

or, equivalently, as:

$$\text{Slack for activity } i = \text{LFT}_i - \text{EFT}_i$$

In our example, activities C, F, G, J, and L are noncritical. Thus, we compute the slack for activity C as:

$$\text{Slack for activity C} = \text{LST}_C - \text{EST}_C = 22 - 7 = 15$$

This indicates that activity C could be delayed up to 15 days beyond its earliest start time without delaying the project. The slack for activities F, G, J, and L are:

$$\text{Slack for activity F} = \text{LST}_F - \text{EST}_F = 21 - 17 = 4$$
$$\text{Slack for activity G} = \text{LST}_G - \text{EST}_G = 19 - 17 = 2$$
$$\text{Slack for activity J} = \text{LST}_J - \text{EST}_J = 35 - 33 = 2$$
$$\text{Slack for activity L} = \text{LST}_L - \text{EST}_L = 40 - 38 = 2$$

14.6.1 A NOTE ON SLACK

In Figure 14.10, note that activities J and L both appear to have 2 units of slack. Now suppose that the start of activity J is delayed for 2 time periods and does not start until time period 35. Because it takes 5 units of time to perform activity J, this activity should be complete at time period 40. Thus, activity L cannot start any sooner than time period 40. So does activity L still have 2 units of slack? The answer is *no*.

If the start of activity J is delayed by 2 time units, the start of activity L also is delayed by 2 time units. Delaying the start of activity J by 2 time units depletes the slack available not only for activity J but also for activity L. So, the amount of slack available at activity L depends on the amount of slack used at activity J.

You must be careful in interpreting how much slack is available for a given activity. To be precise, slack represents the amount of time by which the start of an activity can be delayed without delaying the entire project, *assuming that all predecessor activities start at their earliest start times*. If any activity on a noncritical path starts late, the slack available along the rest of the noncritical path is reduced. For this reason, it is safer to focus on the latest start times of each activity (rather than on slack) because if all activities start by their latest start times, the project should not be delayed.

Key Points: Determining the Critical Path

- Critical activities have zero slack and cannot be delayed without delaying the completion of the project.
- Noncritical activities have some positive amount of slack that represents the amount of time by which the start times of these activities can be delayed without delaying the completion of the entire project, assuming that all predecessor activities start at their earliest start times.

14.7 Project Management Using Spreadsheets

We can use a spreadsheet in several ways to manage a project. As shown in Figure 14.11 (and in the file Fig14-11.xls on your data disk), we can use a spreadsheet to perform all the calculations required to determine the earliest and latest start and finish times for the project activities in our example problem.

To create the spreadsheet in Figure 14.11, we first entered all the labels, predecessor relations, and the activity times shown in columns A through D. The earliest finish times in column F are calculated as the earliest start time for each activity plus the time required to perform the activity.

Formula for cell F5: $=E5+D5$

(Copy to cells F6 through F17)

The latest start times in column G are calculated as the latest finish time of each activity minus the time required to perform the activity.

Formula for cell G5: $=H5-D5$

(Copy to cells G6 through G17)

Calculating the earliest start times in column E and the latest finish times in column H is a bit tricky but can be accomplished easily using array formulas. An *array formula*

Key Cell Formulas

Cell	Formula	Copied to
E5	=MAX(IF(ISERR(FIND($A$5:$A$17,C5)),0,$F$5:$F$17)) (Press [Ctrl]+[Shift]+[Enter] to enter)	E6:E17
F5	=E5+D5	F6:F17
G5	=H5-D5	G6:G17
H5	=MIN(IF(ISERR(FIND(A5,$C$5:$C$17)),MAX($F$5:$F$17),$G$5:$G$17)) (Press [Ctrl]+[Shift]+[Enter] to enter)	H6:H17
I5	=H5-F5	I6:I17

can perform multiple calculations using a range of cells and then return either a single result or multiple results. You create array formulas in the same way that you create other formulas, except that you press [Ctrl]+[Shift]+[Enter] to enter the formula.

About Array Formulas...

Array formulas typically perform operations on one or more ranges of cells. To help you understand array formulas a little better, consider the following examples that show how various array formulas can be used to perform the same operations as standard Excel functions.

Standard Excel Function	Equivalent Array Formula
=SUMPRODUCT(E5:E17,F5:F17)	=SUM(E5:E17*F5:F17)
=SUMIF(E5:E17,">10",F5:F17)	=SUM(IF(E5:E17>10,F5:F17))

(Continued)

=COUNTIF(E5:E17,">0")   =SUM(IF(E5:E17>0,1))

=SUMXMY2(E5:E17,F5:F17)   =SUM((E5:E17-F5:F17)^2)

=VARP(E5:E17)   =AVERAGE
                             ((E5:E17-AVERAGE(E5:E17))^2)

As these examples illustrate, array formulas tend to be more obscure than their Excel function counterparts. However, when no standard Excel function exists to carry out a desired operation on a range of cells, array functions can be quite useful. For example, in Figure 14.11, suppose you want to find the maximum value in cells F5 through F17 where the corresponding value in cells E5 through E17 is less than 20. Your instincts may tell you to use the Excel MAXIF( ) function—but no such function currently exists! However, we can calculate the desired result using the array formula:

$$=MAX(IF(E5:E17<20,F5:F17))$$

Similarly, suppose you want to find the minimum value in cells F5 through F17 where the corresponding value in cells E5 through E17 is greater than 20. There is no MINIF( ) function in Excel, but we can calculate the desired result using the array formula:

$$=MIN(IF(E5:E17>20,F5:F17))$$

Remember that you must press [Ctrl]+[Shift]+[Enter] to enter array formulas. Also note that when you enter an array formula, Excel automatically inserts curly brackets (i.e., "{}") around the formula. You should not attempt to type the curly brackets as part of your array formula.

The array formulas used here create circular references in the workbook. A *circular reference* occurs when the value in a cell depends on the value in another cell that, in turn, is dependent on the value in the original cell. Usually, a circular reference in a workbook indicates that a formula contains an error—and Excel displays a dialog box telling you so! However, there are occasions when a circular reference is exactly what is needed to accomplish a particular task. This is such an occasion. So, to tell Excel that we intend to use circular references:

1. Click the Office button, Excel options, Formulas.
2. Select Enable Iterative Calculation.
3. Click OK.

Selecting the Iteration Option Automatically . . .

The file Fig4-11.xls on your data disk contains a macro that automatically selects the Iteration option. If you are familiar with macros in Excel and are curious, this macro may be found in the Workbook_Open event of the ThisWorkbook object in the VBA editor. The VBA editor was introduced at the end of Chapter 3 of this book.

Now, each cell in column E must implement the logic of the forward pass described earlier (and summarized in Figure 14.7) to calculate the earliest start times. For each activity, this involves determining the maximum earliest finish time (EFT) for the activities that precede it. This is accomplished by the following formula.

Array Formula for cell E5: =MAX(IF(ISERR(FIND($A$5:$A$17,C5)),0,$F$5:$F$17))

(Press [Ctrl]+[Shift]+[Enter] to enter, then copy to cells E6 through E17)

Be sure to enter this (and any) array formula using [Ctrl]+[Shift]+[Enter] or it will not work properly. Also note that when you enter an array formula, Excel automatically inserts curly brackets (*i.e.*, "{}") around the formula.

For the earliest start time for activity A, this formula for cell E5 first uses the FIND( ) function to look for activities in the range from A5 through A17 that appear in cell C5 as predecessors of activity A. Because activity A has no predecessors, the FIND( ) function returns an error value, the ISERR( ) function returns the value True, and the IF( ) function returns the value zero as activity A's EST value. When the formula is copied down the EST column, the relative reference to cell C5 changes accordingly to implement the correct forward pass logic for each of the remaining activities.

Note that when the FIND( ) function does find activities in the range from A5 through A17 that appear as predecessor activities in column C, this array formula returns the maximum of the corresponding EFT values from the range F5 through F17. For example, the array formula in cell E12 computes the EST for activity H as the maximum EFT of activities C, E, F, and G (*i.e.*, MAX(F7,F9,F10,F11) = 25). So for each activity, this array formula returns the maximum EFT for the activities that precede it, or the value zero if the activity has no predecessors.

Each cell in column H must implement the logic of the backward pass described earlier (and summarized in Figure 14.9) to calculate the latest finish times. For each activity, this involves determining the minimum latest start time (LST) for the activities that follow it. This is accomplished by the following formula.

Array Formula for cell H5:
=MIN(IF(ISERR(FIND(A5,$C$5:$C$17)),MAX($F$5:$F$17),$G$5:$G$17))

(Press [Ctrl]+[Shift]+[Enter] to enter, then copy to cells H6 through H17.)

Again, be sure to enter this formula using [Ctrl]+[Shift]+[Enter] or it will not work properly.

For the latest finish time for activity A, this formula for cell H5 first uses the FIND( ) function to locate activities that are successors of activity A. That is, the FIND( ) function looks for activities in the range from C5 through C17 where activity A (cell A5) appears as a predecessor. Because activity A is (only) found as a predecessor of activity B, the ISERR( ) function returns the value False, and the IF( ) function returns activity B's LST value of 3 (cell G6) as activity A's LFT value. When the formula is copied down the LFT column, the relative reference to cell A5 changes accordingly to implement the correct backward pass logic for each of the remaining activities.

Note that any activity in column A that does not appear as a predecessor activity in the range C5 through C17 must be a terminal node for the project. In this case, the FIND( ) function will not find the value from column A in the range C5 through C17, the ISERR( ) function returns the value True, and the IF( ) function returns the maximum of all the EFT values from the range F5 through F17. For example, the array formula in cell H17 computes the LFT for activity M (which has no successors) as the maximum EFT of all activities (*i.e.*, MAX(F5:F17) = 46). So for each activity, this array formula returns the minimum LST for the activities that succeed it, or the maximum of all EFTs if the activity has no successors.

Finally, the slack values in column I are calculated as the difference between the latest and earliest start times for each activity as follows:

Formula for cell I5:   =H5-F5

(Copy to cells I6 through I17.)

The final results in Figure 14.11 are identical to those we calculated manually and summarized earlier in Figure 14.10. More important if we need to change any of the predecessor relations in column C or the time estimates in column D, the spreadsheet in Figure 14.11 automatically adapts the project network and updates the results to reflect these changes. This spreadsheet also makes use of the conditional formatting capabilities of Excel to highlight critical and noncritical activities using red and blue font colors, respectively.

About Conditional Formatting...

Conditional formatting allows you to dynamically change the font, border, and pattern attributes of a range of cells depending on the value of the cell or a condition that you specify. You can explore the Conditional Formatting option under the Home, Styles command in Excel.

14.7.1 IMPORTANT IMPLEMENTATION ISSUE

The technique presented in Figure 14.11 relies on the (case-sensitive) FIND( ) function to identify immediate predecessor and successor activities when computing ESTs and LFTs for each activity. The function FIND(x, y) attempts to find the text string denoted by x within the text string denoted by y. As a result, it is critically important to use activity labels that are unique and do *not* appear as substrings within other activity labels.

For example, the 26 letters of the English alphabet may be used to uniquely identify up to 26 activities in a project. However, using the strings "A1" and "A11" as activity labels would not work in the technique presented in Figure 14.11 because the FIND( ) function would locate "A1" within "A11" (*i.e.*, FIND("A1","A11")=1), erroneously identifying activity A11 as a predecessor or successor of activity A1. Fortunately, use of the strings "A01" and "A11" as activity labels easily remedies this situation.

Similarly, if one wishes to use numbers rather than letters to identify activities, using the numbers 1, 2, 3, . . . , 9 as activity labels would create matching problems within activity labels 11, 12, 13, . . . , 19 (among others). However, this can be avoided easily by applying Excel's "Text" format to cells containing activity labels and immediate predecessors (*i.e.*, columns A and C in Figure 14.11) and using two-digit numbers for all activity labels (*e.g.*, 01, 02, 03, . . . , 09, 10, 11, 12, 13, . . . , 99). If more than 100 numeric activity labels are needed, three-digit numbers (formatted as text) should be used.

14.8 Gantt Charts

A **Gantt chart** is a popular technique for portraying the schedule of a project's activities over time. Figure 14.12 shows a Gantt chart that displays the earliest start and finish times and the slack for each activity in our example problem. (Click the Chart button in

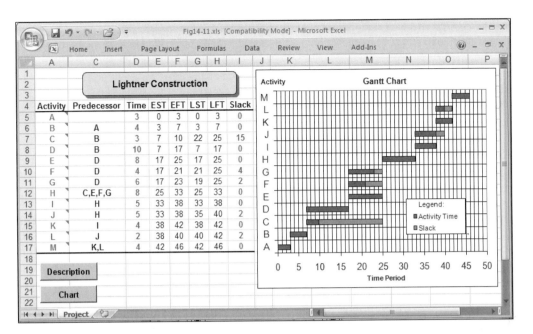

FIGURE 14.12

Gantt chart for the example problem

the worksheet to display this graph.) This type of chart helps a project manager see when activities can begin and end, and keep track of which activities are under way at any point in time.

Creating Gantt Charts in Excel

The Gantt chart in Figure 14.12 is a stacked horizontal bar chart that plots each activity's EST, activity time, and slack. However, the bars for the EST for each activity are formatted so that they do not appear on the graph—giving the illusion that only the activity times and slack are being graphed. To create a Gantt chart like the one shown in Figure 14.12:

1. Click cell A5. While pressing the left mouse button on cell A5, press and hold down the Ctrl key and select the ranges A5:A17, D5:E17, and I5:I17.
2. Click Insert, Bar.
3. Select the 2-D Stacked Bar chart.

Excel then displays an initial stacked bar chart on the screen. Next,

1. Right click the graph and choose Select Data.
2. Choose Series2 and click the up arrow icon.
3. Edit Series2 and change its name to Legend.
4. Edit Series1 and change its name to Activity Time.
5. Edit Series3 and change its name to Slack.
6. Click OK.

(Continued)

7. Right-click any of the bars labeled Legend (representing the EST of the activities) and select Format Data Series.
8. Click Fill and select the No Fill option.
9. Click Border Color and select the No Line option.
10. Click Close.

The basic Gantt chart is now complete. You can customize the chart by right-clicking any element and specifying options in the resulting dialog boxes.

A weakness of the Gantt chart shown in Figure 14.12 is that it does not show the precedence relationships between the activities in a project. For example, the Gantt chart shows that the painting and cabinetry activities both should end at time period 38, and that the final electrical and final plumbing activities should begin at that point. But what happens if the painting activity is delayed? Would this prevent both the final electrical *and* final plumbing activities from starting on time? To answer this question, we need to know if painting is a predecessor for both the final plumbing and final electrical activities. The Gantt chart does not provide this information. Thus, although the Gantt chart is a valuable monitoring tool, it does not tell the whole story about the precedence relationships among project activities.

As shown in Figure 14.13 (and the file Fig14-13.xls on your data disk), we can display the network structure of a project in a spreadsheet. Here, we used the relationships in Figures 14.7 and 14.9 to calculate the earliest and latest start and finish times for each activity. Then, we used the Excel drawing tool to draw arrows indicating the precedence relationships between activities. This approach is feasible for small projects but becomes cumbersome for larger projects.

FIGURE 14.13

Project network implemented in a spreadsheet

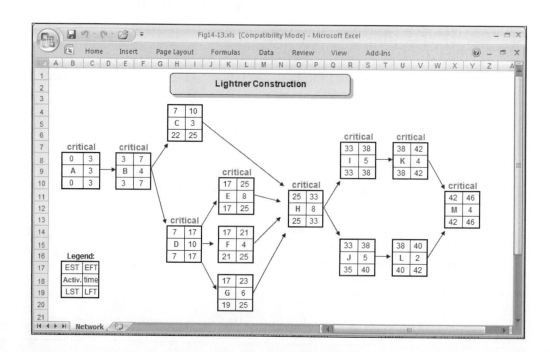

14.9 Project Crashing

With the CPM technique, we can use the times required to perform each activity to determine the least amount of time required to complete the entire project. However, the time required to complete an activity can often be shortened, or crashed. For example, suppose that the amount of time it takes to paint a house is *normally* five days. But, by hiring more painters or asking the existing painters to work overtime, it might be possible to paint the same house in two days. Thus, activities can have normal times and crash times.

The **normal time** of an activity represents the ordinary amount of time required to complete the activity with the usual amount of resources and effort. The **crash time** of an activity represents the least amount of time in which an activity can be accomplished if extra effort and resources are applied to the activity. The extra effort and resources required to crash certain activities usually increase the cost of performing these activities.

In managing projects, we often need to evaluate the trade-offs between the cost of crashing certain activities and the benefit of accomplishing these activities in less than normal time. For example, in our problem, we determined that it takes 46 working days to complete the construction of the house. But what if the buyer wants the house built in 35 days? We need some way to determine if this can be done and, if so, how much additional cost will be involved. Similarly, it is not unusual for some critical activities in a project to take more than their normal time. After all, projects are not immune to Murphy's Law, which states that if something can go wrong, it will go wrong. When a critical activity is delayed, the completion of the project will be delayed unless management chooses to crash some of the remaining critical activities.

Cashing in on a Project Crash

In early 1973, TRW (a large government defense contractor) was in trouble. TRW held a contract to develop software for several DEC PDP-10 computers to analyze the power needs of the Northwest region and control the amount of electricity generated by hydroelectric dams on the Columbia River. But the PDP-10 software was infested with bugs and the project soon fell behind schedule. If TRW could not get the bugs out quickly, it would have to pay substantial contract penalties—so it was time to crash the project. An urgent request from TRW's headquarters to DEC for bug-hunting experts led to a surprising suggestion—a high school senior named Bill Gates at Seattle's exclusive Lakeside prep school. Bill and his friend, Paul Allen, had debugged DEC software for Seattle's Computer Center Corporation in exchange for free time to "play" with the computers. But TRW offered to compensate Gates and Allen with real money—$165 per week. Gates and Allen took the job. Two years later, Bill Gates and Paul Allen teamed up again on a slightly more profitable software venture—the founding of the Microsoft Corporation.

Source: James Wallace and Jim Erickson, *HARDDRIVE*, HarperBusiness, 1992.

14.9.1 AN LP APPROACH TO CRASHING

We can use Solver to help determine the least costly way of crashing a project to meet certain deadlines. Although it is tempting to apply Solver directly to the spreadsheet

FIGURE 14.14

Summary of normal and crash times and costs for the home-building project

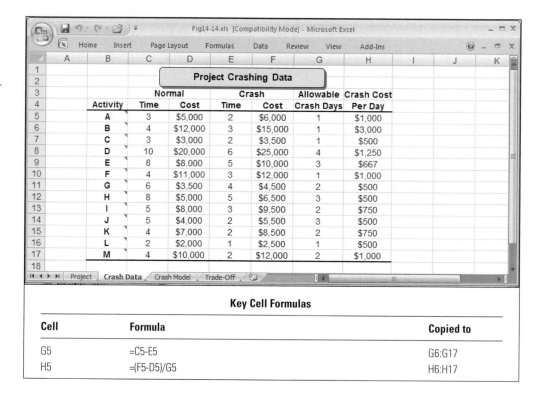

							Key Cell Formulas				

Key Cell Formulas

Cell	Formula	Copied to
G5	=C5-E5	G6:G17
H5	=(F5-D5)/G5	H6:H17

model shown in Figure 14.11, that model contains numerous nonlinearities that would force us to use Solver's evolutionary algorithm. Although this can work, the solution process is slow and the results might be local rather than global optimal solutions. As it turns out, we also can solve project crashing problems using an LP formulation that is easy for Solver to solve and guarantees that we obtain global optimal solutions.

We will illustrate the LP approach to crashing here. To do this, we first must determine the normal time, normal cost, crash time, and crash cost for each project activity. Suppose that Tom asked his subcontractors to estimate crash times and costs for activities involved in our example problem. This information is summarized in Figure 14.14 (and in the file Fig14-14.xls on your data disk), along with the normal times and normal costs that Tom originally estimated for each activity.

As shown in Figure 14.14, in his original plan, Tom estimated that the framing activity (activity D) would take 10 days and cost $20,000. However, the subcontractor indicated that if this activity were crashed by the maximum amount, it could be completed in only 6 days at a cost of $25,000. For planning purposes, Tom might assume that the time required to complete the framing activity can be reduced from its normal time of 10 days by no more than 4 days $(10 - 6 = 4)$. This value is indicated in Figure 14.14 in the Allowable Crash Days column. Tom might also assume that each day this activity is crashed will increase the cost of the activity by approximately $1,250 $(($25,000 - $20,000)/4 = $1,250)$. This value is shown for the framing activity in the Crash Cost Per Day column. The allowable number of crash days, and crash costs per day for the remaining activities, are determined in a similar way and are shown in Figure 14.14.

14.9.2 DETERMINING THE EARLIEST CRASH COMPLETION TIME

Tom might want to know the earliest possible date that the project could be completed and by what amount each activity would need to be crashed to achieve this date. An LP formulation of this problem is represented as:

MIN: $\quad T_M + t_m - C_M$

Subject to:
$$T_B - T_A \geq t_A - C_A$$
$$T_C - T_B \geq t_B - C_B$$
$$T_D - T_B \geq t_B - C_B$$
$$T_E - T_D \geq t_D - C_D$$
$$T_F - T_D \geq t_D - C_D$$
$$T_G - T_D \geq t_D - C_D$$
$$T_H - T_C \geq t_C - C_C$$
$$T_H - T_E \geq t_E - C_E$$
$$T_H - T_F \geq t_F - C_F$$
$$T_H - T_G \geq t_G - C_G$$
$$T_I - T_H \geq t_H - C_H$$
$$T_J - T_H \geq t_H - C_H$$
$$T_K - T_I \geq t_I - C_I$$
$$T_L - T_J \geq t_J - C_J$$
$$T_M - T_K \geq t_K - C_K$$
$$T_M - T_L \geq t_L - C_L$$
$$C_i \leq \text{allowable crash days for activity } i$$
$$T_i, C_i \geq 0, \text{ for all } i$$

where

T_i = the time at which activity i begins

t_i = the normal activity time of activity i

C_i = amount of time by which activity i is crashed

Each of the constraints in this LP model corresponds to one of the precedence relations in the project network. For example, the first time constraint ($T_B - T_A \geq t_A - C_A$) indicates that the difference between the start times of activities A and B must be greater than or equal to the normal time for activity A (t_A) minus the amount by which activity A is crashed (C_A). Equivalently, this constraint may be stated as $T_B \geq T_A + t_A - C_A$. That is, the start time for activity B must be greater than or equal to the start time for activity A plus the normal time for activity A minus the amount by which activity A is crashed.

The logic in the rest of the time constraints can be interpreted in a similar way. Also note that this model places appropriate upper limits on the amount of time by which each activity can be crashed. Finally, the objective function in this problem attempts to minimize the final completion time of the project (which is equal to the start time for activity M, plus its normal activity time, minus the amount by which this activity is crashed). Thus, the solution to this model should indicate the earliest possible time at which the project can be completed if activities are crashed.

Using LP to Identify Earliest and Latest Start Times

With minor modifications, the LP model used here for crashing projects also can be used to determine earliest start times and latest start times for all the activities in the project. To do this, first solve for the earliest start times by changing the objective to minimize the sum of all the activity start times (*i.e.*, MIN: ΣT_i) and do not allow crashing (*i.e.*, set all $C_i = 0$). Next, solve for the latest start times by changing the objective to maximize the sum of all the activity start times (*i.e.*, MAX: ΣT_i), force T_M to equal its earliest start time identified in the previous step (*i.e.*, set $T_M = 42$), and do not allow crashing (*i.e.*, set all $C_i = 0$).

14.9.3 IMPLEMENTING THE MODEL

One approach to implementing this model in a spreadsheet is shown on the Crash Model worksheet in Figure 14.15. In this spreadsheet, the values in column D represent the start time of each activity (the T_i) and the values in column E correspond to the amount by which each activity is crashed (the C_i).

The LHS formulas for the time constraints are implemented in column I in the same manner as described in the previous section. Specifically, cell I5 contains the following formula, which is copied to cells I6 through I20:

> Formula for cell I5:   =VLOOKUP(H5,$B$5:$D$17,3)−
> (Copy to I6 though I20)   VLOOKUP(G5,$B$5:$D$17,3)

The first VLOOKUP function in this formula corresponds to the value of T_B. The first VLOOKUP function takes the contents of cell H5 (the letter B) and looks for its match in the first column of the range $B$5:$D$17 (the match is in cell B6), then returns the value in the third column of the range—or the value in cell D6. Cell D6 corresponds to T_B. The second VLOOKUP function works in a similar way to return the appropriate value for T_A. The difference between the values of these two VLOOKUP functions represents the amount of time between the start of activities A and B.

The RHS values of the time constraints are implemented in column J as:

> Formula for cell J5:   =VLOOKUP(G5,$B$5:$C$17,2)−
> (Copy to J6 though J20)   VLOOKUP(G5,$B$5:$E$17,4)

This formula first finds the cell in column C corresponding to the normal time for activity A, then subtracts the cell in column E corresponding to the amount by which activity A will be crashed.

The objective function for this problem is implemented in cell E19 with the following formula:

> Formula for cell E19:   =D17+C17−E17

This value represents the time at which the project will be completed. Finally, for informational purposes (and future reference), in cell E21, we implement the following formula to calculate the total cost associated with crashing the project:

> Formula for cell E21:   =SUMPRODUCT(E5:E17,'Crash Data'!H5:H17)

This formula calculates the sum of products between the crash cost per day for each activity (calculated in cells H5 through H17 on the Crash Data sheet shown in Figure 14.14)

FIGURE
14.15

*Spreadsheet imple-
mentation of the
crashing model to
determine the
earliest possible
finish time*

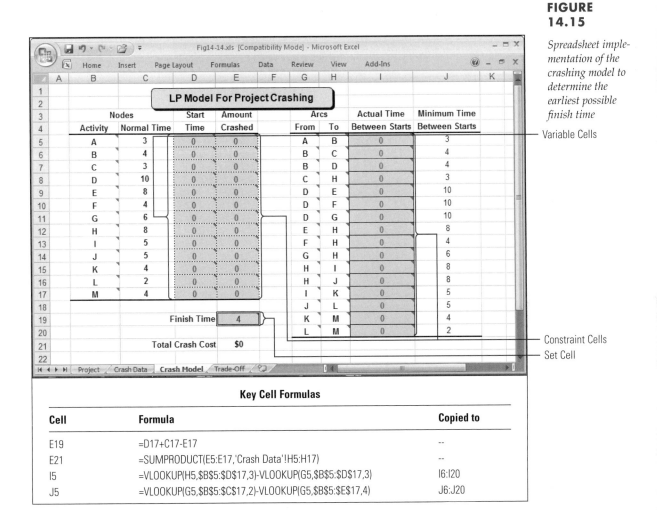

<table>
<tr><th colspan="3">Key Cell Formulas</th></tr>
<tr><th>Cell</th><th>Formula</th><th>Copied to</th></tr>
<tr><td>E19</td><td>=D17+C17-E17</td><td>--</td></tr>
<tr><td>E21</td><td>=SUMPRODUCT(E5:E17,'Crash Data'!H5:H17)</td><td>--</td></tr>
<tr><td>I5</td><td>=VLOOKUP(H5,$B$5:$D$17,3)-VLOOKUP(G5,$B$5:$D$17,3)</td><td>I6:I20</td></tr>
<tr><td>J5</td><td>=VLOOKUP(G5,$B$5:$C$17,2)-VLOOKUP(G5,$B$5:$E$17,4)</td><td>J6:J20</td></tr>
</table>

and the amount by which each activity is crashed (represented by cells E5 through E17 on the Crash Model sheet shown in Figure 14.15).

14.9.4 SOLVING THE MODEL

Figure 14.16 shows the Solver parameters and options used to solve this model. In defining the constraints for this problem, the values of cells E5 through E17 (the C_i) are required to be less than or equal to their maximum allowable values calculated earlier on the Crash Data sheet shown in Figure 14.4.

The optimal solution for this problem, shown in Figure 14.17, indicates that by crashing various activities, the project could be completed within 28 days rather than 46. However, the Total Crash Cost figure indicates this would raise the cost of the project by $19,000. (Note that in general, the total crash cost obtained when solving this type of model is not necessarily the minimum crash cost because the model minimizes completion time, not crash costs. Because other optimal solutions can occur, another crash schedule also might allow the project to be completed within 28 days but at a lower total crash cost. Thus, to verify that the minimum total crash cost is $19,000, we need to add

FIGURE 14.16

Solver parameters for the earliest possible finish times

FIGURE 14.17

Optimal solution for the earliest possible finish times

a constraint to hold the finish time at 28 days and attempt to minimize the total crash cost. In this case, the solution shown in Figure 14.17 is optimal and the minimum total crash cost is, in fact, $19,000.)

14.9.5 DETERMINING A LEAST COSTLY CRASH SCHEDULE

Another use of a crashing model is to determine the least costly way to complete a project at some time earlier than would be possible using normal activity times. For example, if the home buyer insists on the house being built within 35 days, we might want to determine the least costly way of crashing the schedule to meet this deadline.

We can solve this type of problem easily using the existing model. In this case, we simply would add a constraint to hold the project completion time at 35 days and attempt to minimize the total crash cost. The Solver parameters and options required to accomplish this are shown in Figure 14.18, and the optimal solution is shown in Figure 14.19.

FIGURE 14.18

Solver parameters for the least cost crash schedule to complete the project by time period 35

FIGURE 14.19

Optimal solution for the least cost crash schedule to complete the project by time period 35

The solution shown in Figure 14.19 indicates that it would cost an additional $8,500 to crash the project so that it could be completed within 35 days. The values in the Amount Crashed column indicate the amounts by which each activity must be crashed to implement this schedule.

14.9.6 CRASHING AS AN MOLP

As we have seen, two objectives can be pursued in our crashing model. On the one hand, we might want to minimize the finish time of the project. On the other hand, we might want to minimize the cost of crashing the project. These two objectives are in conflict with one another because reducing the completion time of the project increases the crash costs. Thus, we could use the techniques for MOLPs described in Chapter 7 if we want to study the cost/time trade-offs more formally in this type of problem.

Another way to study the cost/time trade-offs is to re-solve the problem several times to determine the minimum crash cost for each possible completion time. A graph showing the minimum crash cost for each possible completion time is useful in evaluating the trade-offs involved in crashing. Figure 14.20 shows such a graph for our example problem.

According to this graph, no crash costs will be incurred if the project is completed in its normal time of 46 days, but crash costs of $19,000 will be incurred if we complete the project in the least amount of time (28 days). Although it is relatively inexpensive to crash the project by a few days, the graph shows that it becomes increasingly expensive to crash the project by additional amounts. Note that a rather substantial increase in cost is incurred to complete the project in 28 days rather than 29. So, this type of graph gives us a clear picture of the cost/time trade-offs involved in crashing a project.

FIGURE 14.20

Graph of the relationship between crash time and completion time

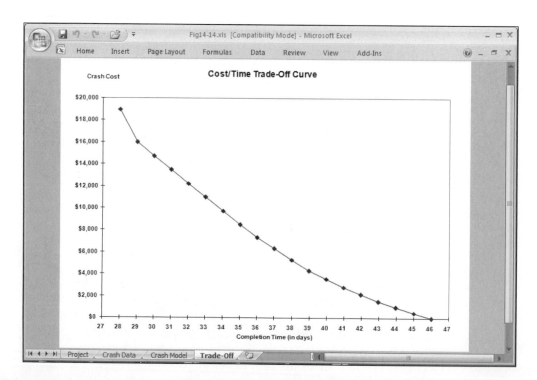

14.10 PERT: An Overview

Throughout our discussion of CPM, we assumed that the times required to complete project activities were known with certainty or could, at least, be estimated with a high degree of accuracy. This assumption does not hold for all projects. For example, consider the schedule of activities required to design and build the first space shuttle. Because no one had ever built a space shuttle before, no historical data were available for estimating how long it would take to perform many of the creative tasks required by this project. Even in projects in which the same or similar tasks have been performed before, the amount of time required to perform them might be different. PERT was developed as an attempt to deal with uncertainty in activity times.

In recent years, several problems have surfaced regarding the PERT technique, causing many to question the wisdom of using this technique at all. The following discussion of PERT focuses on illuminating these weaknesses. We will then briefly consider how to overcome some of these problems using the technique of simulation.

PERT differs from CPM in that it assumes that the times required to perform the project activities are *not* known with certainty. PERT assumes that the activity times are random variables that have some mean, or expected, value and some variance. However, rather than specifying a mean and variance for each activity, we must give three time estimates for each activity in the project. Specifically, for each activity, PERT requires estimates of:

a_i = estimate of the duration of activity i assuming the most favorable conditions

b_i = estimate of the duration of activity i assuming the least favorable conditions

m_i = estimate of the most likely duration of activity i

We can think of a_i, b_i, and m_i as representing, respectively, the best case, worst case, and most likely times required to perform activity i. PERT uses these values to calculate the expected duration of each activity as:

$$t_i = \frac{a_i + 4m_i + b_i}{6}$$

and estimates the variance of each activity's duration as:

$$v_i = \frac{(b_i - a_i)^2}{36}$$

The preceding formulas are based on the assumption that the times required to perform each activity are random variables that follow the beta probability distribution. An in-depth understanding of the beta distribution is not necessary for our purposes. The beta distribution can be used to describe a wide variety of random variables, and is a reasonable choice for describing the behavior of most activity times when their true distributions are unknown.

After calculating the expected times for each activity, the next step in PERT is to identify the critical path for the project. In most project networks, a variety of paths can be followed to get from the start activity to the finish activity. Each path represents a sequence of activities that must be performed to complete the project. Because PERT assumes that the times required to perform the activities along a path are random variables, the time required to complete a given path is also a random variable with some mean and variance.

The expected (or mean) time required to complete any path in the network is simply the sum of the expected times (the t_i) of the activities on the path. If we assume that the individual activity times in a project are independent of one another (as does PERT), we also may calculate the variance of the completion time for any path as the sum of the variances (the v_i) of the activities on the path. Because all the paths through a project network must be completed for the project to be completed, PERT deems the path with the largest expected completion time to be the most critical—the critical path.

The expected completion time and variance for the critical path are used in PERT to estimate the probability of completing the project by various dates and to assist in negotiating and setting deadlines for the project's completion. Many projects impose financial penalties for each day, week, or month a project is late; therefore, it is often important to identify a deadline for a project that management is confident will not be exceeded. Thus, in addition to identifying a critical path for management to scrutinize, PERT also claims to offer assistance in estimating and setting deadlines for a project.

14.10.1 THE PROBLEMS WITH PERT

The PERT technique presents a number of problems that should cause us to approach it with skepticism. First, as indicated previously, PERT assumes that the time required to perform project activities are random variables that are independent of one another. Although this assumption makes it easy to complete the calculations in PERT, it is probably not a realistic assumption. For example, if one activity along the critical path (or any other path) runs a bit over its expected time, a diligent project manager will make sure that one or more of the subsequent activities run a bit under their expected times to catch up on the schedule. To the extent that these over- and under-runs offset one another, the expected completion time of the project should not be affected seriously. However, the variance of the completion times of the paths through the network will be reduced as a result.

The more serious problem in PERT involves the identification of the critical path. As described earlier, PERT identifies the critical path as the path with the longest expected completion time. Thus, an unsuspecting project manager might focus on the activities on the critical path, believing that they are the activities most likely to delay the completion of the project. In reality, activities not on the critical path can pose a greater risk of delaying the project. Consider the activity network shown in Figure 14.21.

The network in Figure 14.21 represents a simple project consisting of only four activities. The three time estimates (a, b, and m) required by PERT are given for each activity. The expected time and variance (t and v) are calculated for each activity. Only two paths run through this network: A to B to D, and A to C to D. The expected times and variances for each path are calculated as shown in Figure 14.21. The path consisting of A-B-D has an expected time of 18 and variance of 1.0. The path consisting of A-C-D has an expected time of 17 and variance of 4.889. Thus, PERT would identify A-B-D as the critical path and use its expected value and variance to make estimates about when the project will be completed.

Earlier, we indicated that the time to complete any path in a PERT network is a random variable. We can view the time to complete path A-B-D and the time to complete path A-C-D as two separate random variables whose probability distributions are similar to those shown in Figure 14.22. Notice that the distribution of the critical A-B-D path is centered at its expected value of 18 and has a relatively small variance. The distribution of the noncritical A-C-D path is centered at its expected value of 17 and has a much larger variance.

If we focus only on the distribution of the critical path shown in Figure 14.22, it appears that almost no chance exists that completing this path will take more than 21 time periods. Thus, if we apply the PERT technique to this project, we would conclude that the project almost certainly can be completed within 21 time units. However, the distribution of times for path A-C-D indicates a fairly significant probability that this noncritical path will take more than 21 days. So, which path is really the critical path—the

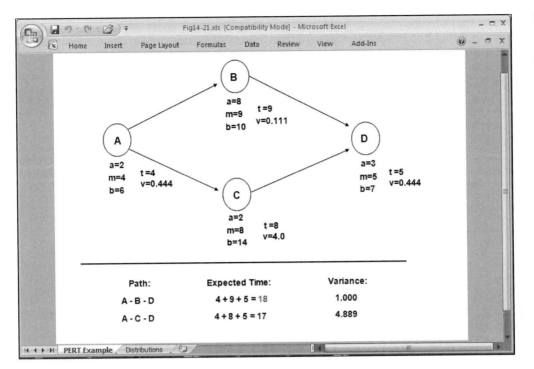

FIGURE 14.21

Example of a PERT network

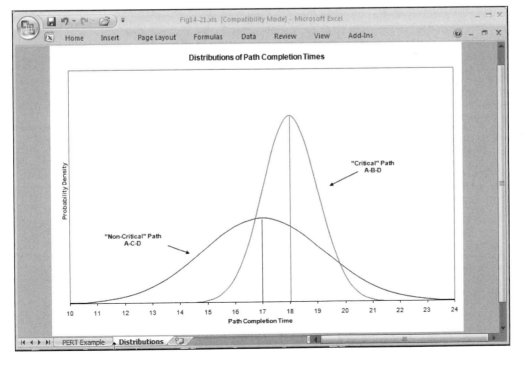

FIGURE 14.22

Graph of the distributions of completion times for each path through the PERT network one with the longest expected completion time or the one with the smallest probability of completion by the desired deadline? Furthermore, which activity in this project is really more critical—B or C? The fact that PERT causes us to ask such questions, and fails to answer them, should raise serious concerns about the wisdom of using this technique.

14.10.2 IMPLICATIONS

The preceding discussion makes it clear that activities not on PERT's critical path might, in fact, be more critical to the completion of a project than the activities that PERT identifies as critical. Indeed, *every* activity in a project has some probability of being critical. For some activities, this probability might be near 0; for others, it might be closer to 1. A project manager should focus on the activities with the highest probability of being critical—regardless of whether they fall on the critical path. Unfortunately, PERT does little to help us identify the project activities that truly are the most critical.

14.11 Simulating Project Networks

Although the PERT technique has serious drawbacks, it does highlight an important point—that activity times in a project are likely to be somewhat random. Although CPM ignores this point entirely, by calculating the earliest and latest start times for each activity, it at least shows which activities are likely to be critical if the actual activity times deviate from their expected values.

The best way to evaluate the impact of variability in activity times on the critical path and the completion time of a project involves the technique of simulation described previously. To simulate a project, we need to generate random times from appropriate probability distributions for each project activity. For the given set of random activity times, we can determine the critical path and the time required to complete the project. If we repeat this process many times, we can determine the frequency with which the project activities fall on the critical path. We also could analyze the resulting distribution project completion times to estimate more accurately the probability of completing the project within various time periods.

14.11.1 AN EXAMPLE

The following example, which is a modification of our earlier home-building example, illustrates the mechanics of simulating the duration of a project.

> Tom has asked the subcontractors for each activity in the home-building process to supply a best-case, most-likely-case, and worst-case estimate of the amount of time required to complete each activity. Figure 14.23 shows these time estimates.
>
> Tom wants to use these time estimates to conduct a simulation study of the project. In particular, he wants to determine how critical each activity is—that is, the probability of each activity falling on the critical path. He also wants to determine the number of days it will take to complete the entire project.

14.11.2 GENERATING RANDOM ACTIVITY TIMES

To simulate the duration of this project, we first must identify probability distributions that describe the behavior of the random activity times. Because the three time estimates for each activity correspond to the best-case, most-likely-case, and worst-case

Activity	Time Estimates		
	a Best Case	*m* Most Likely Case	*b* Worst Case
A	2	3	5
B	3	4	6
C	2	3	7
D	8	10	14
E	6	8	10
F	3	4	5
G	4	6	8
H	7	8	10
I	4	5	7
J	3	5	9
K	3	4	6
L	1	2	4
M	3	4	6

FIGURE 14.23

Summary of time estimates for activities in the home-building project

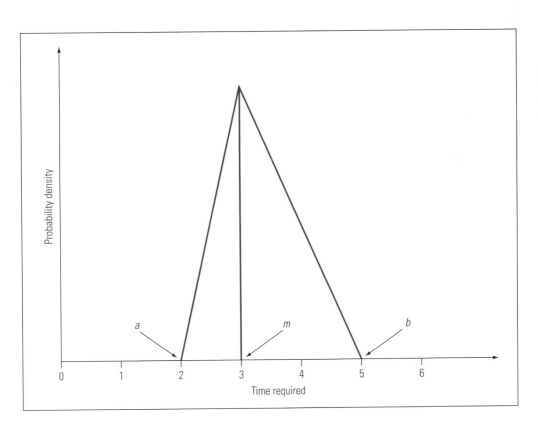

FIGURE 14.24

Example of a triangular distribution of activity times

scenarios for each activity, we might assume that the random behavior of the activity times can be approximated by a triangular probability distribution such as the one shown in Figure 14.24 for activity A. Notice that the shape of the triangular distribution varies depending on the parameters *a, m,* and *b,* which correspond (respectively) to the best-case, most-likely-case, and worst-case time estimates for a given activity.

**FIGURE
14.25**

*Spreadsheet model
for the home-
building project
with random
activity times*

Key Cell Formulas

Cell	Formula	Copied to
F6	=CB.Triangular(C6,D6,E6)	F7:F18

14.11.3 IMPLEMENTING THE MODEL

A spreadsheet model for this problem is shown in Figure 14.25 (and in the file Fig14-25.xls on your data disk).

The three times for each project activity are entered in columns C, D, and E. The formula to generate the random values representing the time required for activities in column A are implemented in column F as follows:

> Formula for cell F6:   =CB.Triangular(C6,D6,E6)
>
> (Copy to F7 through F18)

(Note: To use the CB.Triangular( ) function, the Crystal Ball add-in must be loaded as described previously.) Using the randomly generated activity times, we can create formulas to calculate the earliest and latest start and finish times and the amount of slack available for each activity. We would accomplish this in the same manner as described earlier with respect to Figure 14.11. The activities on the critical path are indicated by slack values of 0.

14.11.4 RUNNING THE SIMULATION

We can use the Data Table command to replicate this model repeatedly. To do so, we must identify the values in the model that we want to track. One objective in our problem is to

FIGURE 14.26

Simulation of the home-building project

Key Cell Formulas

Cell	Formula	Copied to
B3	=VLOOKUP(B2,Model!$A$6:$K$18,11)	C3:J3
K3	=Model!J18	--

determine how critical each activity is. Because critical activities are indicated by slack values of 0, we want to track the values in the Slack column for each activity in our model. However, because all paths go through activities A, B, H, and M, we know that these activities will always be critical, so there is no point in tracking their slack values. Thus, the slack value for activity C in the Model sheet in Figure 14.25 is repeated in cell B3 of the Simulation sheet shown in Figure 14.26 using the following formula:

Formula for cell B3:   = VLOOKUP(B2,Model!$A$6:$K$18,11)

(Copy to C3 through J3)

This formula is copied to cells C3 through J3 to provide the slack values for activities D, E, F, G, I, J, K, and L, respectively.

A second objective in our problem is to estimate the amount of time required to complete the project—or the finish time of activity M. This value is tracked in column K on the Simulation sheet shown in Figure 14.26 through the following formula in cell K3:

Formula for cell K3:   =Model!J18

The remainder of the spreadsheet shown in Figure 14.26 is completed using the Data Table command as follows:

1. Select the range A3 through K102.
2. Click Data, Data Tools, What-If Analysis, Data Table.

3. Specify a Column Input Cell of M1.
4. Click OK.

Each row in this table represents the amount of slack for the activities and the project completion times that were observed in each replication of our project activity model. The simulation shown in Figure 14.26 consists of 100 such replications.

Software Note

By default, Excel recalculates all Data Tables whenever a spreadsheet is recalculated. When using Data Tables for simulation purposes, it is desirable to freeze the values in a Data Table so this sample of observations can be analyzed without changes constantly occurring. To prevent a Data Table from recalculating, do the following:

1. Click Formulas, Calculation.
2. Click Calculate options.
3. Select "Automatic except for data tables."

This tells Excel to recalculate the data tables only when you manually recalculate the spreadsheet by pressing the F9 function key.

14.11.5 ANALYZING THE RESULTS

The Results sheet shown in Figure 14.27 provides the results of the simulation. In the top portion of this sheet, we used the AVERAGE( ) function to calculate the average amount of slack observed for each activity during the simulation. We also calculated the percentage of time that each activity was critical during the 100 replications performed on the model. For example, this sheet indicates that activity D was on the critical path (or had 0 slack) in 100% of the replications, activity E was critical in 96% of the replications, and so on. Thus, this sheet clearly shows which activities are most likely to be critical and warrant the most attention.

The average and variance of the finish times observed during the simulation are shown in cells F8 and F9, respectively. Assuming that the finish times are normally distributed, there is roughly a 50% chance that the actual project completion time will exceed 48.76 time periods. Thus, we might want to determine the amount of time within which it is virtually certain that the project will be completed. That is, we might want to determine the 99th percentile of the distribution of project completion times. This is calculated in cell F14 as:

Formula in cell F14:   =NORMINV(0.99,F8,SQRT(F9))

The result of this formula indicates a 99% chance that a normally distributed random variable with a mean of 48.76 and standard deviation of $\sqrt{4.75}$ will assume a value less than or equal to 53.83. Notice that this is consistent with the maximum finish time

FIGURE 14.27

Results of the simulation

Key Cell Formulas

Cell	Formula	Copied to
B3	=AVERAGE(Simulation!B3:B102)	C3:J3
B4	=COUNTIF(Simulation!B3:B102,"<.0001")/100	C4:J4
F8	=AVERAGE(Simulation!K3:K102)	--
F9	=VAR(Simulation!K3:K102)	--
F10	=MIN(Simulation!K3:K102)	--
F11	=MAX(Simulation!K3:K102)	--
F14	=NORMINV(0.99,F8,SQRT(F9))	--

(shown in cell F11) observed during the simulation. Thus, we could be reasonably confident that the project can be completed within 54 time periods.

14.12 Microsoft Project

Although spreadsheets can be used to track and manage projects, specialized project management software can greatly simplify much of this task. One of the most popular project management tools today is Microsoft Project (MS Project). A trial version of MS Project comes on the CD-ROM accompanying this book.

The first step to managing a project in MS Project is to enter the name and duration of each activity or task. This was done for the Lightner Construction project as shown in Figure 14.28 (and the file Fig14-28.mpp on your data disk). MS Project automatically inserts start and finish times for each task and draws a horizontal bar corresponding to the length of each task.

The next step is to indicate the precedence relations between the various tasks. This can be done in several ways. You can simply type numbers in the Predecessors column

**FIGURE
14.28**

*Listing of home
construction tasks
and durations in
Microsoft Project*

**FIGURE
14.29**

*Home construction
project with
precedence
relations*

that indicate the predecessors for each task. Alternatively, you can click on a task's horizontal bar and drag it to another bar to indicate the appropriate predecessor relations. Using either technique, the results for the Lightner Construction project (described in Figures 14.1 and 14.2) appear as shown in Figure 14.29. Note that the Gantt chart in Figure 14.29 is similar to the one shown earlier in Figure 14.12 except that the tasks are listed in reverse order, slack values for each activity are not shown, and the precedence relationships are explicitly shown on the graph via arrows.

After the tasks, durations, and precedence relations are entered, MS Project can easily create several different views of a project. For instance, you can select View, Network Diagram to create the chart shown in Figure 14.30. The Network Diagram shows details about each task and also indicates the critical path.

**FIGURE
14.30**

*PERT Chart view
of the project*

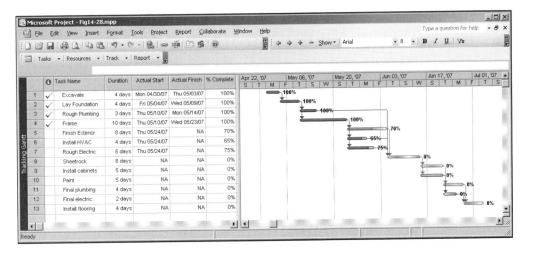

**FIGURE
14.31**

*The Tracking
Gantt view of the
project*

Another useful view of a project is obtained by selecting View, Tracking Gantt. The
resulting chart allows a project manager to keep track of when each task actually begins
and track its progress toward completion. Figure 14.31 shows an example of this type of
chart where hypothetical start and finish dates have been entered for several of the tasks.

MS Project offers many other features to assist with allocating and tracking costs and assigning resources to various activities in a project. A complete discussion of the capabilities of MS Project are beyond the intended scope of this book. However, this introduction should help you see that MS Project can be a very useful tool for project management.

14.13 Summary

This chapter presented a variety of techniques for managing projects by representing and analyzing a project in the form of a network. When the activity times in a project can be estimated with a reasonable amount of certainty, CPM can be applied to determine the earliest start and finish times for each activity and the earliest time for completing the entire project. CPM also can be used to determine the latest possible times that activities can start and finish without delaying the completion of the project. The slack in a project helps to distinguish between critical and noncritical activities. LP techniques can be used to analyze CPM networks and determine optimal crash schedules for projects that must be completed ahead of schedule.

When activity times cannot be estimated with certainty, they must be modeled as random variables. Although the PERT technique was designed to address these types of problems, it has some serious theoretical and practical shortcomings. However, simulation can be used to provide a more complete and accurate analysis of activity networks containing random activity times.

14.14 References

Gido, J. and J. Clements. *Successful Project Management with Microsoft® Project.* Cincinnati: South-Western, 1999.

Golenko, G. "On the Distribution of Activity Times in PERT." *Journal of the Operational Research Society,* vol. 39, August 1988.

Levy, F., A. Thompson, and S. Weist. "The ABCs of the Critical Path Method." *Harvard Business Review,* vol. 41, September–October 1963.

Meredith, J. and S. Mantel. *Project Management: A Managerial Approach.* New York: Wiley, 1985.

Phillips, C. and E. Davis. *Project Management with CPM, PERT, and Precedence Diagramming.* New York: Van Nostrand Reinhold, 1983.

Ragsdale, C. "The Current State of Network Simulation in Project Management Theory and Practice." *OMEGA,* vol. 17, no. 1, 1989.

Ragsdale, C. "A New Approach to Implementing Project Networks in Spreadsheets." *INFORMS Transactions on Education,* vol. 3, no. 3, 2003.

Schonberger, R. "Why Projects Are 'Always' Late: A Rationale Based on Manual Simulation of a PERT/CPM Network." *Interfaces,* vol. 11, no. 5, 1981.

THE WORLD OF MANAGEMENT SCIENCE

Food and Drug Administration Uses PERT to Control the Timeliness of Research and Development Projects

The National Center for Drug Analysis develops automated drug testing procedures for the U.S. Food and Drug Administration (FDA). The FDA uses these procedures to conduct production studies of drugs selected on the basis of therapeutic significance and how widely they are used.

(Continued)

To allocate personnel and facilities efficiently to drug testing studies, it is important to have a good estimate of when a new, automated testing procedure will be ready. If a method is not ready at the time samples are collected, either the samples must be analyzed manually or existing schedules must be reworked, causing serious disruptions.

The FDA chose PERT to manage methods of development projects because it treats activity completion times as random variables. This is appropriate for research and development activities, many of which are being done for the first time.

The PERT network for a development project consists of 24 nodes and 31 arcs. The network is updated weekly, giving management access to probabilities of completion times, activities on the critical path and second most critical path, slack times for noncritical activities, a list of completed activities, and so on. This information makes it easy to review and adjust personnel assignments and to control completion times. The PERT plans and reports are also useful to the individual chemists, providing a more comprehensive procedure for planning and organizing their work.

The director of the center successfully implemented the use of PERT by developing appropriate forms and computer programs, thoroughly training staff members on how to use PERT, and then incrementally introducing the procedure in a series of pilot tests. The pilot test results suggested some improvements, which were incorporated as the center proceeded with full implementation.

Source: N.K. Kwak and Lawrence Jones, "An Application of PERT to R&D Scheduling." *Information Processing and Management*, vol. 14, no. 2, 1978, pp. 121–131.

Questions and Problems

1. In this chapter, we stated that the longest path through an activity network is the critical path. Why isn't the completion time for a project defined by the shortest path through the network? Explain your answer.
2. Throughout this chapter, we assumed that a project manager identifies and organizes the activities in a project, estimates the time required for each activity, then determines how quickly the project can be completed. However, the deadlines for some projects are fixed before any planning begins. For example, consider the planning of a New Year's Eve celebration in the downtown area of a major city. Which, if any, of the techniques described in this chapter might be helpful in planning such an event?
3. In illustrating how to simulate an activity network, we used a triangular distribution based on three time estimates to generate random activity times. What problem might be encountered if we assume that activity times were normally distributed? (*Hint*: Consider the values that a normally distributed random variable with a mean of 5 and variance of 3 might assume.)
4. Consider the CPM network for the following set of activities:

Activity	Predecessor Activities
A	—
B	A
C	A, B

Is it necessary to draw an arc from the node for activity A to the node for activity C? Why or why not?

5. Consider the following set of activities:

Activity	Days Required	Predecessor Activities
A	3	—
B	2	A
C	5	A
D	8	B, C
E	4	B, C
F	2	D, E

a. Draw the CPM network for this problem.
b. Manually determine the earliest and latest start and finish times for each activity and the amount of slack for each activity.
c. What is the critical path?
d. How long should it take to complete the project?
e. Verify your answer to part c using Microsoft Project.

6. Consider the following set of activities:

Activity	Days Required	Predecessor Activities
A	3	—
B	2	—
C	5	A, B
D	8	A, B
E	4	D

a. Draw the CPM network for this problem. (Remember that a CPM network requires unique start and finish nodes.)
b. Manually determine the earliest and latest start and finish times for each activity and the amount of slack for each activity.
c. What is the critical path?
d. How long should it take to complete the project?
e. Verify your answer to part c using Microsoft Project.

7. Consider the following set of activities:

Activity	Time Required	Predecessor Activities
A	5	—
B	4	A
C	5	B
D	8	B
E	9	C
F	6	C, D
G	8	D
H	3	E, F, G

a. Draw the CPM network for this problem.
b. Identify each path through the network and its expected length.

c. What is the critical path?

d. Verify your answer to part c using Microsoft Project.

8. Consider the following set of activities:

Activity	Days Required	Predecessor Activities
A	3	—
B	4	A
C	4	A
D	3	A
E	3	D
F	4	B
G	6	B
H	5	F, C, E
I	6	G, H
J	4	F, C, E
K	2	D
L	6	I, J, K

a. Draw the CPM network for this problem.

b. Create a spreadsheet to calculate and summarize the earliest and latest start and finish times, the slack for each activity, and the critical activities.

c. What is the earliest time that the project can be completed?

d. Use Microsoft Project to verify the critical path for this project.

9. The following data summarizes the per-day cost of crashing the activities in the problem described in the previous question.

Activity	Crash Cost per Day	Maximum Crash Days
A	$50	2
B	60	3
C	57	1
D	45	2
E	25	2
F	30	2
G	65	5
H	55	2
I	28	4
J	33	3
K	40	1
L	37	2

a. Create an LP model to determine the least costly way of crashing the project to complete it within 20 days.

b. By how much should each activity be crashed, and what is the total crashing cost?

10. The Runabout Boat Company is considering the purchase of several units of an expensive new machine for its production facilities around the country. Before committing to this purchase, Runabout wants to set up a test facility to test the machine and make sure it lives up to its manufacturer's claims. The machine's manufacturer has agreed to loan Runabout a machine for this purpose. The activities required to carry out this testing are summarized in the following table.

Activity	Description	Predecessor Activities	Days Required
A	Prep test facility	None	4
B	Complete paperwork	None	4
C	Transport machine	A, B	8
D	Hire repairmen	A, B	7
E	Hire operators	A, B	6
F	Train repairmen	C, D	15
G	Install machine	C	9
H	Train operators	E, G	12
I	Testing	F, H	20

a. Draw the CPM network for this problem.
b. Create a spreadsheet to calculate and summarize the earliest and latest start and finish times, the slack for each activity, and the critical activities.
c. What is the earliest time that the project can be completed?
d. Use Microsoft Project to verify the critical path for this project.

11. Aerobatic, Inc. custom designs and manufactures light aircraft. The activities involved in this process are summarized in the following table.

Activity	Description	Weeks Required	Predecessor Activities
A	Design	4	—
B	Order and receive materials	5	A
C	Construct frame	8	B
D	Prepare engine	6	B
E	Prepare avionics	5	B
F	Cover frame	4	C
G	Install engine	2	E, F
H	Paint	2	F
I	Install avionics	2	D, G, H
J	Test	1	I

a. Draw the activity network for this problem.
b. Create a spreadsheet to calculate and summarize the earliest and latest start and finish times, the slack for each activity, and the critical activities.
c. What is the earliest this project can be finished?
d. Use Microsoft Project to verify the critical path for this project.

12. A software company is moving its helpdesk operations center from Newark, New Jersey to Plano, Texas. Some of its employees will be moved to Plano and others will be terminated and replaced by new workers in Texas. The activities that must be carried out to implement the move are summarized in the following table.

Activity	Description	Predecessors	Weeks
A	Revise organizational structure	—	5
B	Select new office location	—	3
C	Determine personnel requirements	A	3
D	Design new call center	B, C	4
E	Renovate office space	D	8
F	Select employees to move	C	2
G	Hire new employees	F	4
H	Set up new administrative systems	A	5
I	Move office equipment and records	F	2
J	Train new employees	E, G, H, I	3

a. Draw the CPM network for this problem.
b. Create a spreadsheet to calculate and summarize the earliest and latest start and finish times, the slack for each activity, and the critical activities.
c. What is the least amount of time required to complete the project?
d. Use Microsoft Project to verify the critical path for this project.

13. Linda Madison owns Creations, a business that provides hair and nail care services in a small college town. Recently, Linda has decided to expand her business to include tanning and massage services for her clients. To accommodate these new services and the additional clients Creations expects to attract, Linda is moving her business to a larger facility. However, the new location will require some renovation before she can relocate there. Linda has identified the following activities that must be performed before she can open at her new location.

Activity	Description	Days Required	Predecessor Activities
A	Install new plumbing	10	—
B	Order and receive furniture	20	—
C	Order and receive flooring	15	—
D	Construct partitions	5	—
E	Paint and wallpaper	5	A, D
F	Install furniture	3	E, B
G	Install flooring	4	E, C
H	Move inventory and records	2	F, G
I	Clean old shop	2	H

a. Draw the activity network for this problem.
b. Create a spreadsheet to calculate and summarize the earliest and latest start and finish times, the slack for each activity, and the critical activities.
c. What is the earliest this project can be finished?
d. Use Microsoft Project to verify the critical path for this project.

14. Refer to the previous question. Suppose that Linda's lease on her current facility expires in 20 days. The normal and crash times and costs for each activity in her moving project are summarized in the following table. By what amount should each activity be crashed in order for her to complete the move within 20 days?

Activity	Normal Time	Normal Cost	Crash Time	Crash Cost
A	10	$11,000	7	$15,000
B	20	5,000	18	6,000
C	15	3,000	12	3,500
D	5	1,500	3	2,000
E	5	750	2	1,200
F	3	600	1	1,200
G	4	1,000	2	1,500
H	2	250	1	450
I	2	200	1	300

15. The activities required to service a car at Zippy-Lube can be viewed as a mini-project as summarized in the following table.

Activity	Description	Predecessor Activity	Time Required		
			Min	Most Likely	Max
A	Drain oil	—	2	3.5	5
B	Replace filter	A	1	2	3
C	Refill oil	B, E	2	2.5	4
D	Check tires	—	2	3	4
E	Wash windows	D	2	3	5
F	Fill fluids	E	2	3	4
G	Final test	C, F	0.5	1	1.5

The variability in the time required to perform each activity is due to the different types, sizes, and condition of the cars to be serviced.

a. Draw the activity network for this problem.

b. Use PERT to identify the expected time and variance for each activity.

c. What is the critical path? What is the expected time and variance of the critical path?

16. Refer to the previous question. Create a spreadsheet model to simulate the completion times for servicing cars. Assume that activity times follow a triangular distribution, and perform 500 replications on the model.

a. Estimate the probability of each activity falling on the critical path.

b. On average, how long should it take to finish servicing a car?

c. Suppose that the manager of this business wants to guarantee that your car will be ready within 10 minutes or you will receive a coupon worth $5 off your next visit. What proportion of customers will receive the coupon?

17. Koene Technology is a rapidly growing nanotechnology firm. The company is moving into a new building that will allow it more research lab space and improved computing facilities. The lease on the new facility has already been signed and architectural renovations plans approved by the local municipality. The activities required to complete the move are summarized as follows:

Activity	Description	Predecessors	Days
A	Hire computer services manager	None	10
B	Structural renovation	None	19
C	Enlarge parking lot	None	13
D	Hire computer services staff	A	8
E	Purchase computing equipment	A	14
F	Electrical modifications	B	4
G	HVAC modifications	B	3
H	Plumbing modifications	B	5
I	Exterior painting/finishing	B	5
J	Computer network installation	E, F, G	4
K	Sheetrock	F, G, H	6
L	Computer staff training	D, J	8
M	Interior painting/finishing	K	9
N	Landscaping	C, I	7

a. Draw the activity network for this problem.

b. Create a spreadsheet to calculate and summarize the earliest and latest start and finish times, the slack for each activity, and the critical activities.

c. What is the earliest this project can be finished?

d. Use Microsoft Project to verify the critical path for this project.

18. Refer to the previous question. Suppose a partner in Koene Technology does not believe the time estimates for each activity can be specified with certainty. Instead, he prefers to specify a minimum, most likely, and maximum number of days for each activity. These estimates are given in the following table.

Activity	Minimum	Most Likely	Maximum
A	5	10	20
B	16	19	27
C	10	13	18
D	5	8	14
E	8	14	21
F	2	4	10
G	2	3	7
H	4	5	9
I	3	5	10
J	3	4	8
K	4	6	10
L	5	8	10
M	6	9	11
N	5	7	9

a. Use PERT to identify the expected time and variance for each activity.
b. What is the critical path? What is the expected time and variance for this path?
c. Assume that the distribution of the completion time for the critical path is normally distributed. What is the probability that it will take at least 40 days to complete the project?

19. Refer to the previous question. Create a spreadsheet model to simulate the completion times for Koene's move. Assume that activity times follow a triangular distribution and perform 500 replications on the model.
a. Estimate the probability of each activity falling on the critical path. Which activities are most critical?
b. On average, how long should it take to complete the project?
c. Based on your simulation results, estimate the probability that it will take at least 45 days to complete the project.

20. A national accounting firm has identified the following set of activities that must occur to carry out an audit for one of their major clients.

Activity	Days Required	Predecessor Activities	Activity	Days Required	Predecessor Activities
A	12	—	G	6	B, E
B	16	—	H	4	C, D, E
C	13	A	I	24	C, D, G
D	14	A	J	12	F, H
E	9	A	K	22	F, H
F	12	C	L	8	I, J

a. Draw the CPM network for this problem.
b. Create a spreadsheet to calculate and summarize the earliest and latest start and finish times, the slack for each activity, and the critical activities.
c. What is the earliest time the audit can be completed?
d. Use Microsoft Project to verify the critical path for this project.

21. Refer to the previous question. Suppose that each of the audit activities can be crashed by the amounts indicated in the following table.

Activity	Crash Days	Cost Per Day	Activity	Crash Days	Cost Per Day
A	2	$2,000	G	0	0
B	4	3,000	H	2	1,500
C	2	800	I	5	1,300
D	4	1,200	J	3	2,000
E	2	1,000	K	4	2,500
F	2	1,500	L	2	1,200

a. What is the earliest the audit could be completed and what is the incremental cost associated with this schedule?

b. How much incremental cost would be incurred if the client insisted that the audit be completed within 55 days?

c. Suppose the client wants the project completed within 55 days. Further suppose that it might be possible to crash activity G by one day. How much, if any, should the accounting firm be willing to pay to crash activity G by one day? Explain.

22. A partner in the national accounting firm mentioned in the previous questions does not believe that the time estimates for each activity can be specified with certainty. Instead, she prefers to specify a minimum, most likely, and maximum time estimate for each task. These estimates are given in the following table.

Activity	Predecessor Activities	Min	Most Likely	Max
A	—	9	12	15
B	—	12	16	18
C	A	11	13	15
D	A	10	14	20
E	A	7	9	15
F	C	9	12	14
G	B, E	4	6	7
H	C, D, E	3	4	5
I	C, D, G	20	24	26
J	F, H	10	12	15
K	F, H	18	22	30
L	I, J	6	8	12

a. Draw the activity network for this problem.

b. Use PERT to identify the expected time and variance for each activity.

c. What is the critical path? What is the expected time and variance for this path?

d. Assume that the distribution of the completion time for the critical path is normally distributed. What is the probability that it will take at least 67 days to complete the project?

23. Refer to the previous question. Create a spreadsheet model to simulate the completion times for the auditing project. Assume that activity times follow a triangular distribution and perform 500 replications on the model.

a. Estimate the probability of each activity falling on the critical path. Which activities are most critical?

b. On average, how long should it take to complete the project?

c. Based on your simulation results, estimate the probability that it will take at least 67 days to complete the project.

24. The activities summarized in the following table must be performed by the promoter of a country music concert in Dallas.

Activity	Description	Predecessor Activity	Days Required Min	Days Required Most Likely	Days Required Max
A	Find location	—	2	4	7
B	Hire opening act	A	3	6	10
C	Hire technicians	A	1	2	3
D	Set up radio ads	B	2	4	6
E	Distribute tickets	B	2	3	5
F	Rent sound and lights	B, C	3	4	6
G	Set up newspaper ads	B	1	2	4
H	Hire security	F	2	3	4
I	Conduct rehearsal	F, H	1	1.5	2
J	Final details	I	2	3	4

a. Draw the activity network for this problem.
b. According to PERT, what is the expected length of time required to accomplish these activities?
c. Assume that the durations of the activities are random variables that follow tri-angular distributions. Create a spreadsheet model of the project and use simula-tion to create 500 replications of the project. Rank the activities according to how critical they are.
d. When should the promoter begin working on the concert to have a 99% chance of completing the project by August 15? (Assume work is conducted seven days a week.)

25. A cosmetics company has identified a set of activities that must be performed to bring a new product to market. The activities, their precedence relations, and time estimates to complete each activity (in days) are shown in the following table.

Activity	Predecessors	Time Required Min	Time Required Most Likely	Time Required Max
A	—	0	0	0
B	A	10	15	20
C	B	15	20	22
D	C	21	26	30
E	C	15	18	23
F	E	13	15	17
G	D, F	30	38	45
H	G	20	25	30
I	G	10	15	20
J	G, O	11	18	22
K	H, I, J	23	30	45
L	K	22	28	39
M	A	120	140	180
N	M	13	18	22
O	N	15	20	25
P	O	10	15	20
Q	L, P	30	33	44
R	Q	5	8	11
S	R	10	15	25
T	R	13	17	19
U	S, T	20	25	40

a. Draw the activity network for this problem.
b. Assume that activity times follow a triangular distribution, and perform 500 replications on the model.
c. Estimate the probability of each activity falling on the critical path.
d. On average, how long should it take to finish the project?
e. Suppose a change can be made in activity J so that it no longer requires activity O to be completed before it begins. What effect would this have on the project completion time and the criticality of each activity?

26. Refer to the previous problem. Suppose that the maximum time listed for each activity is actually its normal completion time. Further assume that the maximum number of crash days per activity and cost per crash day are as follows.

	Maximum Crash Days	Crash Cost per Day
A	0	$0.0
B	10	8.4
C	7	3.3
D	9	24.4
E	8	17.0
F	4	31.3
G	15	13.5
H	10	3.0
I	10	10.4
J	11	6.3
K	22	4.5
L	17	13.1
M	60	18.5
N	9	8.9
O	10	10.9
P	10	2.0
Q	14	11.6
R	6	3.8
S	15	6.3
T	6	18.0
U	20	7.2

a. Create and solve an LP model to determine the earliest start time (with no crashing) for each activity.
b. Modify your LP model and solve it to determine the latest start time (with no crashing) for each activity.
c. Identify the EST, EFT, LST, LFT, and slack for each activity.
d. What is the critical path?
e. If crashing is allowed, how quickly could the project be completed? What is the optimal cost of completing the project in the least amount of time?
f. What is the optimal cost of completing the project in 320 days?

CASE 14.1   Project Management at a Crossroad

Cal Hampton is on the board of directors of Crossroad Academy, a private, parent-run, K-12 school in Shawsville, VA. In an effort to increase enrollment at this school in the coming year, several months ago Cal and other board members voted to give a 25%

tuition discount to any new students from families who had never been affiliated with Crossroad before. As it turned out, this offer worked so well that Crossroad's enrollment swelled by 30% and the school suddenly needed to build some new classrooms to accommodate this growth. And that's why Cal was in the town's building inspector's office on July 10th—where he was told that Crossroad's building plan for new classrooms were fine, but that no classes could be held at the school until a fire sprinkler and alarm system had been installed.

The school was planning to use volunteer labor to build the new classrooms before classes started on August 23rd. But installing a fire sprinkler and alarm system throughout the building is quite another matter. So Cal and his fellow board members quickly got busy contacting sprinkler contractors and getting price quotes on this job. They also got busy lining up other places they could conduct classes until their building situation was resolved.

Cal quickly learned more than he ever wanted to know about fire sprinkler systems. Because Crossroad's school building is a two-story wood-frame structure, a dry pipe system had to be installed in the attic of the building to protect the upper floor against fire. In a dry pipe system, the pipes are filled with pressurized air to avert the risk of freezing in unheated spaces. If a fire is detected, one or more sprinkler heads open, releasing the pressurized air which, in turn, allows water to flow through the pipes to the sprinkler heads. On the lower level of the building, a wet pipe system (where the pipes constantly hold water) would be more cost-effective.

A multitude of other details remain to be worked out: the wet and dry systems have to be designed and approved by the town, a new 6-inch water line has to be run to the building, new phone lines have to be installed to support the fire alarm monitoring service, various types of sprinkler heads have to be selected and ordered, and the whole thing needs to be installed and pass various tests required by the town and the local fire marshal.

Within a week, three different sprinkler contractors have visited the school and submitted proposals for completing the work at the school. One of the proposals is substantially more expensive than the other two and is immediately eliminated from further consideration. Now Cal and the rest of the board must decide on which of the other proposals to accept. One proposal is from a local company, Fire Protection Services (FPS), that has been in business for over 20 years. The other proposal is from Safety Technology Group (STG), a fairly new company located in a large city about 40 miles from Shawsville.

Although STG is a new company, the people working for STG have many years of experience in the fire safety industry. Their project manager, Ron Brag, supervised the largest sprinkler installation job in the commonwealth of Virginia while working for a different sprinkler company. Additionally, Ron has told Cal that while STG has a number of jobs in progress, he has a crew who is just finishing a project and could start on the Crossroads job immediately. In fact, Ron has told Cal he thinks there is a good chance his company could get the job done before the start of school and, in the worst case, by the end of August. One of the families at Crossroad used STG on another job and reported being pleased with their work.

FPS has held the service contract on the fire extinguishers at Crossroad for many years and always has done a good job. The project manager for FPS is a middle-aged man named Max Randall, a slow-talking country boy. He has supervised several sprinkler installations in the area (FPS typically does only one or two jobs at a time) and knows the town building inspector and fire marshal well. He knows that Crossroad is desperate to get this job done quickly, but he tells Cal, "Well, to get your business, I could lie to you and tell you we'll get this done before school starts. But the fact is, it will probably be the end of September before we or anyone else can get this done for you."

The bids from FPS and STG are both for turnkey systems and are within a few thousand dollars of each other. So now Cal and the rest of Crossroad's board members are trying to decide which bid to accept.

a. Describe how the various project management techniques covered in this chapter might be relevant to this problem. When and to whom might CPM be useful? When and to whom might PERT be useful? When and to whom might the crashing technique be useful?

b. If you were Cal and wanted to get the project done as quickly as possible, what aspects of this job might be of greatest concern to you? How would you manage these issues?

c. What are some of the worst case outcomes that might arise in this project?

d. What special clauses, if any, might you want included in the contract with whichever sprinkler company is selected? Would any of the techniques discussed in this chapter be useful in determining or negotiating these clauses?

CASE 14.2   # The World Trade Center Cleanup

In the aftermath of the September 11, 2001, terrorist attacks on the World Trade Center, the New York City Department of Design and Construction was put in charge of recovery and cleanup operations at the site. The attack killed 2,823 people, destroyed eight buildings, and crushed 1,300 feet of subway tunnel. Ultimately, the cleanup operations involved four construction firms, 3,000 workers, and 3.1 million man-hours. It took over 100,000 truckloads to carry the 1.8 million tons of debris from the site. Amazingly, no workers were killed or critically injured during the cleanup effort, which officially ended on May 30, 2002, at a cost of $650 million. (Source: www.pbs.org/americarebuilds)

Obviously, a project of this magnitude could not be completed successfully without careful planning and coordination of many, many activities. Indeed, many cleanup "activities" could be considered subprojects of the entire cleanup operation.

Imagine that you are the person in charge of the cleanup operations at the World Trade Center site. No one has ever faced this task before, so no one can give you a nice, neat list of things to do with precise time estimates for each activity. It is an enormous task requiring careful consideration of human emotion, dignity, and safety concerns in addition to the monumental logistics and financial issues. And the world is watching all you do.

Identify the key top-level activities you think would go into the cleanup project and prepare an AON project network summarizing the precedence relations among these activities. Also, describe how you would go about estimating the activity times and financial costs associated with these activities.

CASE 14.3   # The Imagination Toy Corporation

Amy White is the director of marketing for the Imagination Toy Corporation (ITC). She just received a phone call from her boss indicating that the company's board of directors gave final approval for the production and marketing of the Mighty Morphin' Monkeys—a new product line of action toys for ITC. Amy worked hard in developing the concept for this product line and is thrilled that her ideas will become reality. But this news also means that she must get busy developing the marketing and sales force training materials needed to launch this new product line successfully. Amy's boss wants to know how soon she can have the sales staff trained and equipped to handle the new line.

The development of marketing materials and training of the sales staff for the new product line constitute a project. Amy identifies ten specific project tasks that need to be accomplished before she can roll out the marketing program for this product line. First, Amy needs to collect information about the details of the decisions made by the board of directors. She can start this task (task A) immediately, and she estimates that it will take five days to determine exactly which items and accessories will be included in the first offering of the product line. After she completes this task, she will request prototypes of all items from the engineering department (task B), which she expects will take ten working days. While waiting for the prototypes, she can begin laying out the marketing program (task C). She expects this activity to take eight days. After the prototypes (task B) are available, Amy estimates that it will take seven days to prepare instructions (task D) on the operation and use of the items in the product line and nine days to design its packaging (task E). When the marketing program (task C) is finished, it must be approved (task F) by the president of the company. Amy expects this approval to take three days.

Amy plans to hold a two-day training course (task G) for the sales force once the operating instructions (task D) and the packaging design (task E) are completed. When the operating instructions (task D) are finished and the marketing plan is approved (task F), Amy will develop an information guide (task H) that the sales force can distribute to retailers. Amy expects to take eight days to complete the information guide. Also, as part of the marketing plan, Amy wants to hire a number of actors to portray Mighty Morphin' Monkeys (task I) at various promotional events around the country. Hiring and training these actors is expected to take eight days and can be done only after the marketing plan is approved (task F). Finally, after the marketing plan (task F) has been approved and the packaging for the product has been designed (task E), special point-of-sale display racks must be manufactured (task J). Amy expects this activity to take twelve working days.

a. Develop an AON network for this problem.
b. Create a spreadsheet to calculate and summarize the earliest and latest start and finish times, the slack for each activity, and the critical activities.
c. Identify the critical path.
d. If Amy starts working immediately, how long will it take her to complete this project?
e. Suppose that the engineering department can create the prototypes in only eight days if the engineers work overtime on this activity. Would this help reduce the length of time required to complete this project?